NOBEL PRIZE LIBRARY

———

KAWABATA

KIPLING

LEWIS

Nobel Prize Library

Yasunari Kawabata

Rudyard Kipling

Sinclair Lewis

ALEXIS GREGORY, *New York,* AND
GROLIER ENTERPRISES CORP., *Danbury, Connecticut*

Grolier Enterprises offers a varied selection of both adult and children's book racks. For details on ordering, please write:

Grolier Enterprises
Sherman Turnpike
Danbury, CT 06816
Attn: Premium Department

CONTENTS

Yasunari Kawabata

1968

"For his narrative mastery which

with great sensibility expresses

the essence of the Japanese mind"

Illustrated by LUCIEN DAVIGE

PRESENTATION ADDRESS

By *ANDERS ÖSTERLING*

PERMANENT SECRETARY

OF THE SWEDISH ACADEMY

THE RECIPIENT of this year's Nobel Prize for Literature, the Japanese Yasunari Kawabata, was born in 1899 in the big industrial town of Osaka, where his father was a highly cultured doctor with literary interests. At an early age, however, he was deprived of this favorable growing-up environment on the sudden death of his parents and, as an only child, was sent to his blind and ailing grandfather in a remote part of the country. These tragic losses, doubly significant in view of the Japanese people's intense feeling for blood ties, have undoubtedly affected Kawabata's whole outlook on life and been one of the reasons for his later study of Buddhist philosophy.

As a student at the imperial university in Tokyo he decided early on a writing career, and he is an example of the kind of restless absorption that is always a condition of the literary calling. In a youthful short story, which first drew attention to him at the age of twenty-seven, he tells of a student who, during lonely autumn walks on the peninsula of Izu, comes across a poor, despised dancing girl, with whom he has a touching love affair; she opens her pure heart and shows the young man a way to deep and genuine feeling. Like a sad refrain in a folksong the theme recurs with many variations in his following works.

He presents his own scale of values and with the years he has won renown far beyond the borders of Japan. True, of his production only three novels and a few short stories have so far been translated into different languages, evidently because translation in this case offers especially great difficulties and is apt to be far too coarse a filter, in which many finer shades of meaning in his richly expressive language must be lost. But the translated works do give us a sufficiently representative picture of his personality.

In common with his older countryman Tanizaki, now deceased, he has admittedly been influenced by modern Western realism, but at the same time he has, with greater fidelity, retained his footing in Japan's classical literature and therefore represents a clear tendency to cherish and preserve a genuinely national tradition of style. In Kawabata's narrative art it is still possible to find a sensitive poetry of situation which traces its origin back to Murasaki's vast canvas of life and manners in Japan about the year 1000.

Kawabata has been especially praised as a subtle psychologist of women. He has shown his mastery as such in the two short novels *Snow Country* and *Thousand Cranes*. In these we see a brilliant capacity to illuminate the erotic episode, an exquisite keenness of observation, a whole network of small, mysterious values, which often put the European narrative technique in the shade. Kawabata's writing is reminiscent of Japanese painting; he is a worshiper of the fragile beauty and melancholy picture language of existence in the life of nature and in man's destiny. If the transience of all outward action can be likened to drifting tufts of grass on the surface of the water, then it is the genuinely Japanese miniature art of haiku poetry which is reflected in Kawabata's prose style.

Even if we feel excluded, as it were, from his writing by a root-system, more or less foreign to us, of ancient Japanese ideas and instincts, we may find it tempting to notice in Kawabata certain similarities of temperament with European writers of our own time. Turgenev is the first to spring to mind; he too is a deeply sensitive storyteller and a broad-minded painter of the social scene, with pessimistically colored sympathies at a time of transition between old and new.

Kawabata's most recent work is also his most outstanding, the novel *Kyoto* completed six years ago and now available in translation. The story is about the young girl Chiëko, a foundling cast out by her poverty-stricken parents and adopted into the house of the merchant Takichiro, where she is brought up according to old Japanese principles. She is a sensitive, loyal being, who broods in secret on the riddle of her origin. Popular Japanese belief has it that an expelled child is afflicted with a lifelong curse, in addition to which the condition of being a twin, according to the strange Japanese viewpoint, bears the stigma of shame. One day it happens that she meets a pretty young working girl from a cedar forest near the city and finds that she is her twin sister. They are intimately united beyond the social pale of class—the robust, work-hardened Naëko and the delicate, anxiously guarded Chiëko, but their bewildering likeness soon gives rise to complications and confusion. The whole story is set against the background of the religious festival year in Kyoto, from the cherry-blossom spring to the now-glittering winter.

The city itself is really the leading character, the capital of the old kingdom, once the seat of the mikado and his court, still a romantic sanctuary after a thousand years, the home of the fine arts and elegant handicraft, nowadays exploited by tourism but still a beloved place of pilgrimage. With its Shinto and Buddhist temples, its old artisan quarters and botanical gardens, the place possesses a poetry which Kawabata expresses in a tender, courteous manner, with no sentimental overtones, but naturally, a moving appeal. He has experienced his country's crushing defeat and no doubt realizes what the future demands in the way of industrial go-ahead spirit, tempo, and vitality. But in the postwar wave of violent Americanization his novel is a gentle reminder of the necessity of trying to save something of the old Japan's beauty and individuality for the new. He describes the religious ceremonies in Kyoto with the same meticulous care as he does the textile trade's choice of patterns in the traditional sashes that are part of the women's dresses. These aspects of the novel may have their documentary worth, but the reader prefers to dwell on such a deeply characteristic passage as when the party of middle-class people from the city visits the botanical garden—which has been closed for a long time because the American occupation troops have had their barracks there—in order to see whether the lovely avenue of camphor trees is still intact and able to delight the connoisseur's eye.

With Kawabata, Japan enters the circle of literary Nobel Prizewinners for the first time. Essential to the forming of the decision is the fact that as a writer he imparts a moral-esthetic cultural awareness with unique artistry, thereby in his way contributing to the spiritual bridge-building between East and West.

ACCEPTANCE SPEECH

By *YASUNARI KAWABATA*

———

It is the great honor of my life to have been proposed by the Swedish Academy for the Nobel Prize for Literature for 1968 and to have received the award at Your Majesty's own hands.

The reason for the supreme brilliance of the history of this award is that it is also given to foreigners. It has, so to speak, the breadth of a world award. Two Japanese, Drs. Yukawa and Tomonaga, have in recent years become Nobel laureates in physics. Alfred Nobel wrote poetry and prose in several languages, and in that spirit the Prize for Literature has gone to writers in numbers of countries. It is now fifty-five years since it last went to an oriental, Rabindranath Tagore. In view of the complexities presented by differences in language, and in view of the fact that my works, no doubt more than those of others, have had to be perused in translation, I must indicate my deep and undying gratitude and respect for the resolve shown by Your Excellencies of the Academy. This first award to an oriental in fifty-five years has, I believe, made a deep impression upon Japan, and perhaps upon the other countries of Asia as well, and upon all countries whose languages are little known internationally. I do not look upon my happiness and good fortune in having received the award as mine alone. My emotions are yet deeper at the thought that it perhaps has a new and broad significance for the literature of the world.

Such are my feelings on this grand occasion when I have been so honored with my fellow laureates by Your Excellencies of the Nobel Foundation. Finally, I think we have here a symbol of understanding and friendship between East and West that will keep our literature moving from today into tomorrow. I thank you.

SNOW COUNTRY

By YASUNARI KAWABATA

Translated by Edward G. Seidensticker

PART ONE

The train came out of the long tunnel into the snow country. The earth lay white under the night sky. The train pulled up at a signal stop.

A girl who had been sitting on the other side of the car came over and opened the window in front of Shimamura. The snowy cold poured in. Leaning far out the window, the girl called to the station master as though he were a great distance away.

The station master walked slowly over the snow, a lantern in his hand. His face was buried to the nose in a muffler, and the flaps of his cap were turned down over his ears.

It's that cold, is it, thought Shimamura. Low, barracklike buildings that might have been railway dormitories were scattered here and there up the frozen slope of the mountain. The white of the snow fell away into the darkness some distance before it reached them.

"How are you?" the girl called out. "It's Yoko."

"Yoko, is it. On your way back? It's gotten cold again."

"I understand my brother has come to work here. Thank you for all you've done."

"It will be lonely, though. This is no place for a young boy."

"He's really no more than a child. You'll teach him what he needs to know, won't you?"

"Oh, but he's doing very well. We'll be busier from now on, with the snow and all. Last year we had so much that the trains were always being stopped by avalanches, and the whole town was kept busy cooking for them."

"But look at the warm clothes, would you. My brother said in his letter that he wasn't even wearing a sweater yet."

"I'm not warm unless I have on four layers, myself. The young ones start drinking when it gets cold, and the first thing you know they're over there in bed with colds." He waved his lantern toward the dormitories.

"Does my brother drink?"

"Not that I know of."

"You're on your way home now, are you?"

"I had a little accident. I've been going to the doctor."

"You must be more careful."

The station master, who had an overcoat on over his kimono, turned as if to cut the freezing conversation short. "Take care of yourself," he called over his shoulder.

"Is my brother here now?" Yoko looked out over the snow-covered platform. "See that he behaves himself." It was such a beautiful voice that it struck

[9]

one as sad. In all its high resonance it seemed to come echoing back across the snowy night.

The girl was still leaning out the window when the train pulled away from the station. "Tell my brother to come home when he has a holiday," she called out to the station master, who was walking along the tracks.

"I'll tell him," the man called back.

Yoko closed the window and pressed her hands to her red cheeks.

Three snowplows were waiting for the heavy snows here on the Border Range. There was an electric avalanche-warning system at the north and south entrances to the tunnel. Five thousand workers were ready to clear away the snow, and two thousand young men from the volunteer fire-departments could be mobilized if they were needed.

Yoko's brother would be working at this signal stop, so soon to be buried under the snow—somehow that fact made the girl more interesting to Shimamura.

"The girl"—something in her manner suggested the unmarried girl. Shimamura of course had no way of being sure what her relationship was to the man with her. They acted rather like a married couple. The man was clearly ill, however, and illness shortens the distance between a man and a woman. The more earnest the ministrations, the more the two come to seem like husband and wife. A girl taking care of a man far older than she, for all the world like a young mother, can from a distance be taken for his wife.

But Shimamura in his mind had cut the girl off from the man with her and decided from her general appearance and manner that she was unmarried. And then, because he had been looking at her from a strange angle for so long, emotions peculiarly his own had perhaps colored his judgment.

It had been three hours earlier. In his boredom, Shimamura stared at his left hand as the forefinger bent and unbent. Only this hand seemed to have a vital and immediate memory of the woman he was going to see. The more he tried to call up a clear picture of her, the more his memory failed him, the farther she faded away, leaving him nothing to catch and hold. In the midst of this uncertainty only the one hand, and in particular the forefinger, even now seemed damp from her touch, seemed to be pulling him back to her from afar. Taken with the strangeness of it, he brought the hand to his face, then quickly drew a line across the misted-over window. A woman's eye floated up before him. He almost called out in his astonishment. But he had been dreaming, and when he came to himself he saw that it was only the reflection in the window of the girl opposite. Outside it was growing dark, and the lights had been turned on in the train, transforming the window into a mirror. The mirror had been clouded over with steam until he drew that line across it.

The one eye by itself was strangely beautiful, but, feigning a traveler's weariness and putting his face to the window as if to look at the scenery outside, he cleared the steam from the rest of the glass.

The girl leaned attentively forward, looking down at the man before her. Shimamura could see from the way her strength was gathered in her shoulders that the suggestion of fierceness in her eyes was but a sign of an intentness that did not permit her to blink. The man lay with his head pillowed at the window and his legs bent so that his feet were on the seat facing, beside the girl. It was a third-class coach. The pair were not directly opposite Shimamura but rather one seat forward, and the man's head showed in the window-mirror only as far as the ear.

Since the girl was thus diagonally opposite him, Shimamura could as well have looked directly at her. When the two of them came on the train, however, something coolly piercing about her beauty had startled Shimamura, and as he hastily lowered his eyes he had seen the man's ashen fingers clutching at the girl's. Somehow it seemed wrong to look their way again.

The man's face in the mirror suggested the feeling of security and repose it gave him to be able to rest his eyes on the girl's breast. His very weakness lent a certain soft balance and harmony to the two figures. One end of his scarf served as a pillow, and the other end, pulled up tight over his mouth like a mask, rested on his cheek. Now and then it fell loose or slipped down over his nose, and almost before he had time to signal his annoyance the girl gently rearranged it. The process was repeated over and over, automatically, so often that Shimamura, watching them, almost found himself growing impatient. Occasionally the bottom of the overcoat in which the man's feet were wrapped would slip open and fall to the floor, and the girl would quickly pull it back together. It was all completely natural, as if the two of them, quite insensitive to space, meant to go on forever, farther and farther into the distance. For Shimamura there was none of the pain that the sight of something truly sad can bring. Rather it was as if he were watching a tableau in a dream—and that was no doubt the working of his strange mirror.

In the depths of the mirror the evening landscape moved by, the mirror and the reflected figures like motion pictures superimposed one on the other. The figures and the background were unrelated, and yet the figures, transparent and intangible, and the background, dim in the gathering darkness, melted together into a sort of symbolic world not of this world. Particularly when a light out in the mountains shone in the center of the girl's face, Shimamura felt his chest rise at the inexpressible beauty of it.

The mountain sky still carried traces of evening red. Individual shapes were clear far into the distance, but the monotonous mountain landscape, undistinguished for mile after mile, seemed all the more undistinguished for having lost its last traces of color. There was nothing in it to catch the eye, and it seemed to flow along in a wide, unformed emotion. That was of course because the girl's face was floating over it. Cut off by the face, the evening landscape moved steadily by around its outlines. The face too seemed transparent—but was it really transparent? Shimamura had the illusion that the evening landscape was actually passing over the face, and the flow did not stop to let him be sure it was not.

The light inside the train was not particularly strong, and the reflection was not as clear as it would have been in a mirror. Since there was no glare, Shimamura came to forget that it was a mirror he was looking at. The girl's face seemed to be out in the flow of the evening mountains.

It was then that a light shone in the face. The reflection in the mirror was not strong enough to blot out the light outside, nor was the light strong enough to dim the reflection. The light moved across the face, though not to light it up. It was a distant, cold light. As it sent its small ray through the pupil of the girl's eye, as the eye and the light were superimposed one on the other, the eye became a weirdly beautiful bit of phosphorescence on the sea of evening mountains.

There was no way for Yoko to know that she was being stared at. Her attention was concentrated on the sick man, and even had she looked toward Shimamura, she would probably not have seen her reflection, and she would have paid no attention to the man looking out the window.

It did not occur to Shimamura that it was improper to stare at the girl so long and stealthily. That too was no doubt because he was taken by the unreal, otherworldly power of his mirror in the evening landscape.

When, therefore, the girl called out to the station master, her manner again suggesting overearnestness, Shimamura perhaps saw her first of all as rather like a character out of an old, romantic tale.

The window was dark by the time they came to the signal stop. The charm of the mirror faded with the fading landscape. Yoko's face was still there, but for all the warmth of her ministrations, Shimamura had found in her a transparent coldness. He did not clear the window as it clouded over again.

He was startled, then, when a half-hour later Yoko and the man got off the train at the same station as he. He looked around as though he were about to be drawn into something, but the cold air on the platform made him suddenly ashamed of his rudeness on the train. He crossed the tracks in front of the locomotive without looking back again.

The man, clinging to Yoko's shoulder, was about to climb down to the tracks from the platform opposite when from this side a station attendant raised a hand to stop them.

A long freight train came out of the darkness to block them from sight.

The porter from the inn was so well-equipped for the cold that he suggested a fireman. He had on ear flaps and high rubber boots. The woman looking out over the tracks from the waiting-room wore a blue cape with the cowl pulled over her head.

Shimamura, still warm from the train, was not sure how cold it really was. This was his first taste of the snow-country winter, however, and he felt somewhat intimidated.

"Is it as cold as all that?"

"We're ready for the winter. It's always especially cold the night it clears after a snow. It must be below freezing tonight."

"This is below freezing, is it?" Shimamura looked up at the delicate icicles along the eaves as he climbed into the taxi. The white of the snow made the deep eaves look deeper still, as if everything had sunk quietly into the earth.

"The cold here is different, though, that's easy to see. It feels different when you touch something."

"Last year it went down to zero."

"How much snow?"

"Ordinarily seven or eight feet, sometimes as much as twelve or thirteen, I'd say."

"The heavy snows come from now on?"

"They're just beginning. We had about a foot, but it's melted down a good bit."

"It's been melting, has it?"

"We could have a heavy snow almost any time now, though."

It was the beginning of December.

Shimamura's nose had been stopped up by a stubborn cold, but it cleared to the middle of his head in the cold air, and began running as if the matter in it were washing cleanly away.

"Is the girl who lived with the music teacher still around?"

"She's still around. You didn't see her in the station? In the dark-blue cape?"

"So that's who it was. We can call her later, I suppose?"

"This evening?"

"This evening."

"I hear the music teacher's son came back on your train. She was at the station to meet him."

The sick man he had watched in that evening mirror, then, was the son of the music teacher in whose house the woman Shimamura had come to see was living.

He felt a current pass through him, and yet the coincidence did not seem especially remarkable. Indeed he was surprised at himself for being so little surprised.

Somewhere in his heart Shimamura saw a question, as clearly as if it were standing there before him: was there something, what would happen, between the woman his hand remembered and the woman in whose eye that mountain light had glowed? Or had he not yet shaken off the spell of the evening landscape in that mirror? He wondered whether the flowing landscape was not perhaps symbolic of the passage of time.

The hot-spring inn had its fewest guests in the weeks before the skiing season began, and by the time Shimamura had come up from the bath the place seemed to be asleep. The glass doors rattled slightly each time he took a step down the sagging corridor. At the end, where it turned past the office, he saw the tall figure of the woman, her skirts trailing coldly off across the dark floor.

He started back as he saw the long skirts—had she finally become a geisha? She did not come toward him, she did not bend in the slightest movement of recognition. From the distance he caught something intent and serious in the still form. He hurried up to her, but they said nothing even when he was beside her. She started to smile through the thick, white geisha's powder. Instead she melted into tears, and the two of them walked off silently toward his room.

In spite of what had passed between them, he had not written to her, or come to see her, or sent her the dance instructions he had promised. She was no doubt left to think that he had laughed at her and forgotten her. It should therefore

have been his part to begin with an apology or an excuse, but as they walked along, not looking at each other, he could tell that, far from blaming him, she had room in her heart only for the pleasure of regaining what had been lost. He knew that if he spoke he would only make himself seem the more wanting in seriousness. Overpowered by the woman, he walked along wrapped in a soft happiness. Abruptly, at the foot of the stairs, he shoved his left fist before her eyes, with only the forefinger extended.

"This remembered you best of all."

"Oh?" The woman took the finger in her hand and clung to it as though to lead him upstairs.

She let go his hand as they came to the *kotatsu** in his room, and suddenly she was red from her forehead to her throat. As if to conceal her confusion, she clutched at his hand again.

"This remembered me?"

"Not the right hand. This." He pushed his right hand into the *kotatsu* to warm it, and again gave her his left fist with the finger extended.

"I know." Her face carefully composed, she laughed softly. She opened his hand, and pressed her cheek against it. "This remembered me?"

"Cold! I don't think I've ever touched such cold hair."

"Is there snow in Tokyo yet?"

"You remember what you said then? But you were wrong. Why else would anyone come to such a place in December?"

"Then": the danger of avalanches was over, and the season for climbing mountains in the spring green had come.

---

* A charcoal brazier covered by a wooden frame and a quilt. Although it warms little more than the hands and feet, the *kotatsu* is the only heating device in the ordinary Japanese house.

Presently the new sprouts would be gone from the table.

Shimamura, who lived a life of idleness, found that he tended to lose his honesty with himself, and he frequently went out alone into the mountains to recover something of it. He had come down to the hot-spring village after seven days in the Border Range. He asked to have a geisha called. Unfortunately, however, there was a celebration that day in honor of the opening of a new road, the maid said, so lively a celebration that the town's combined cocoon-warehouse and theater had been taken over, and the twelve or thirteen geisha had more than enough to keep them busy. The girl who lived at the music teacher's might come, though. She sometimes helped at parties, but she would have gone home after no more than one or two dances. As Shimamura questioned her, the maid told him more about the girl at the music teacher's: the samisen and dancing teacher had living with her a girl who was not a geisha but who was sometimes asked to help at large parties. Since there were no young apprentice geisha in the town, and since most of the local geisha were at an age when they preferred not to have to dance, the services of the girl were much valued. She almost never came alone to entertain a guest at the inn, and yet she could not exactly be called an amateur—such in general was the maid's story.

An odd story, Shimamura said to himself, and dismissed the matter. An hour or so later, however, the woman from the music teacher's came in with the maid. Shimamura brought himself up straight. The maid started to leave but was called back by the woman.

The impression the woman gave was a wonderfully clean and fresh one. It seemed to Shimamura that she must be clean to the hollows under her toes. So clean indeed did she seem that he wondered whether his eyes, back from looking at early summer in the mountains, might not be deceiving him.

There was something about her manner of dress that suggested the geisha, but she did not have the trailing geisha skirts. On the contrary, she wore her soft, unlined summer kimono with an emphasis on careful propriety. The *obi** seemed expensive, out of keeping with the kimono, and struck him as a little sad.

The maid slipped out as they started talking about the mountains. The woman was not very sure of the names of the mountains that could be seen from the inn, and, since Shimamura did not feel the urge to drink that might have come to him in the company of an ordinary geisha, she began telling of her past in a surprisingly matter-of-fact way. She was born in this snow country, but she had been put under contract as a geisha in Tokyo. Presently she found a patron who paid her debts for her and proposed to set her up as a dancing teacher, but unfortunately a year and a half later he died. When it came to the story of what had happened since, the story of what was nearest to her, she was less quick to tell her secrets. She said she was nineteen. Shimamura had taken her to be twenty-one or twenty-two, and, since he assumed that she was not lying, the knowledge that she had aged beyond her years gave him for the first time a little of the ease he expected to feel with a geisha. When they began talking of the Kabuki, he found that she knew more about actors and styles than he did. She talked on feverishly, as though she had been starved for someone who would listen to her, and presently began to show an ease and abandon that revealed her to be at heart a woman of the pleasure quarters after all. And she seemed in general to

* The sash with which a kimono is tied. A woman's *obi* is wide and stiff, a man's narrower and usually softer.

know what there was to know about men. Shimamura, however, had labeled her an amateur and, after a week in the mountains during which he had spoken to almost no one, he found himself longing for a companion. It was therefore friendship more than anything else that he felt for the woman. His response to the mountains had extended itself to cover her.

On her way to the bath the next afternoon, she left her towel and soap in the hall and came in to talk to him.

She had barely taken a seat when he asked her to call him a geisha.

"Call you a geisha?"

"You know what I mean."

"I didn't come to be asked that." She stood up abruptly and went over to the window, her face reddening as she looked out at the mountains. "There are no women like that here."

"Don't be silly."

"It's the truth." She turned sharply to face him, and sat down on the window sill. "No one forces a geisha to do what she doesn't want to. It's entirely up to the geisha herself. That's one service the inn won't provide for you. Go ahead, try calling someone and talking to her yourself, if you want to."

"You call someone for me."

"Why do you expect me to do that?"

"I'm thinking of you as a friend. That's why I've behaved so well."

"And this is what you call being a friend?" Led on by his manner, she had become engagingly childlike. But a moment later she burst out: "Isn't it fine that you think you can ask me a thing like that!"

"What is there to be so excited about? I'm too healthy after a week in the mountains, that's all. I keep having the wrong ideas. I can't even sit here talking to you the way I would like to."

The woman was silent, her eyes on the floor. Shimamura had come to a point where he knew he was only parading his masculine shamelessness, and yet it seemed likely enough that the woman was familiar with the failing and need not be shocked by it. He looked at her. Perhaps it was the rich lashes of the downcast eyes that made her face seem warm and sensuous. She shook her head very slightly, and again a faint blush spread over her face.

"Call any geisha you like."

"But isn't that exactly what I'm asking you to do? I've never been here before, and I've no idea which geisha are the best-looking."

"What do you consider good-looking?"

"Someone young. You're less apt to make mistakes when they're young. And someone who doesn't talk too much. Clean, and not too quick. When I want someone to talk to, I can talk to you."

"I'll not come again."

"Don't be foolish."

"I said I'll not come again. Why should I come again?"

"But haven't I told you it's exactly because I want to be friends with you that I've behaved so well?"

"You've said enough."

"Suppose I were to go too far with you. Very probably from tomorrow I wouldn't want to talk to you. I couldn't stand the sight of you. I've had to come into the mountains to want to talk to people again, and I've left you alone so that I can talk to you. And what about yourself? You can't be too careful with travelers."

"That's true."

"Of course it is. Think of yourself. If it were a woman you objected to, you wouldn't want to see me afterwards. It would be much better for her to be a woman you picked out."

"I don't want to hear any more." She turned sharply away, but presently she added: "I suppose there's something in what you say."

"An affair of the moment, no more. Nothing beautiful about it. You know that—it couldn't last."

"That's true. It's that way with everyone who comes here. This is a hot spring and people are here for a day or two and gone." Her manner was remarkably open—the transition had been almost too abrupt. "The guests are mostly travelers. I'm still just a child myself, but I've listened to all the talk. The guest who doesn't say he's fond of you, and yet you somehow know is—he's the one you have pleasant memories of. You don't forget him, even long after he's left you, they say. And he's the one you get letters from."

She stood up from the window sill and took a seat on the mat below it. She seemed to be living in the past, and yet she seemed to be very near Shimamura.

Her voice carried such a note of immediate feeling that he felt a little guilty, as though he had deceived her too easily.

He had not been lying, though. To him this woman was an amateur. His desire for a woman was not of a sort to make him want this particular woman—it was something to be taken care of lightly and with no sense of guilt. This woman was too clean. From the moment he saw her, he had separated this woman and the other in his mind.

Then too, he had been trying to decide where he would go to escape the summer heat, and it occurred to him that he could bring his family to this mountain hot spring. The woman, being fortunately an amateur, would be a good companion for his wife. He might even have his wife take dancing lessons to keep from getting bored. He was quite serious about it. He said he felt only friendship for the woman, but he had his reasons for thus stepping into shallow water without taking the final plunge.

And something like that evening mirror was no doubt at work here too. He disliked the thought of drawn-out complications from an affair with a woman whose position was so ambiguous; but beyond that he saw her as somehow unreal, like the woman's face in that evening mirror.

His taste for the occidental dance had much the same air of unreality about it. He had grown up in the merchants' section of Tokyo, and he had been thoroughly familiar with the Kabuki theater from his childhood. As a student his interests had shifted to the Japanese dance and the dance-drama. Never satisfied until he learned everything about his subject, he had taken to searching through old documents and visiting the heads of various dance schools, and presently he had made friends with rising figures in the dance world and was writing what one might call research pieces and critical essays. It was but natural, then, that he should come to feel a keen dissatisfaction with the slumbering old tradition as well as with reformers who sought only to please themselves. Just as he had arrived at the conclusion that there was nothing for it but to throw himself actively into the dance movement, and as he was being persuaded to do so by certain of the younger figures in the dance world, he abruptly switched to the occidental dance. He stopped seeing the Japanese dance. He gathered pictures and descriptions of the occidental ballet, and began laboriously collecting programs and posters from abroad. This was more than simple fascination with the exotic and the unknown. The pleasure he found in his new hobby came in fact from his inability to see with his own eyes occidentals in occidental ballets. There was proof of this in his deliberate refusal to study the ballet as performed by Japanese. Nothing could be more comfortable than writing about the ballet from books. A ballet he had never seen was an art in another world. It was an unrivaled armchair reverie, a lyric from some paradise. He called his work research, but it was actually free, uncontrolled fantasy. He preferred not to savor the ballet in the flesh; rather he savored the phantasms of his own dancing imagination, called up by Western books and pictures. It was like being in love with someone he had never seen. But it was also true that Shimamura, with no real occupation, took some satisfaction from the fact that his occasional introductions to the occidental dance put him on the edge of the literary world—even while he was laughing at himself and his work.

It might be said that his knowledge was now for the first time in a very great while being put to use, since talk of the dance helped bring the woman nearer to him; and yet it was also possible that, hardly knowing it, he was treating the woman exactly as he treated the occidental dance.

He felt a little guilty, as though he had deceived her, when he saw how the frivolous words of the traveler who would be gone tomorrow seemed to have struck something deep and serious in the woman's life.

But he went on: "I can bring my family here, and we can all be friends."

"I understand that well enough." She smiled, her voice falling, and a touch of the geisha's playfulness came out. "I'd like that much better. It lasts longer if you're just friends."

"You'll call someone, then?"

"Now?"

"Now."

"But what can you say to a woman in broad daylight?"

"At night there's too much danger of getting the dregs no one else wants."

"You take this for a cheap hot-spring town like any other. I should think you could tell just from looking at the place." Her tone was sober again, as though she felt thoroughly degraded. She repeated with the same emphasis as before that there were no girls here of the sort he wanted. When Shimamura expressed his doubts, she flared up, then retreated a step. It was up to the geisha whether she would stay the night or not. If she stayed without permission from her house, it was her own responsibility. If she had permission the house took full responsibility, whatever happened. That was the difference.

"Full responsibility?"

"If there should happen to be a child, or some sort of disease."

Shimamura smiled wryly at the foolishness of his question. In a mountain village, though, the arrangements between a geisha and her keeper might indeed still be so easygoing. . . .

Perhaps with the idler's bent for protective coloring, Shimamura had an instinctive feeling for the spirit of the places he visited, and he had felt as he came down from the mountains that, for all its air of bare frugality, there was something comfortable and easy about the village. He heard at the inn that it was indeed one of the more comfortable villages in this harsh snow country. Until the railway was put through, only very recently, it had served mainly as a medicinal spring for farmers in the area. The house that kept geisha would generally have a faded shop curtain that advertised it as a restaurant or a tearoom, but a glance at the old-style sliding doors, their paper panels dark with age, made the passer-by suspect that guests were few. The shop that sold candy or everyday sundries might have its one geisha, and the owner would have his small farm besides the shop and the geisha. Perhaps because she lived with the music teacher, there seemed to be no resentment at the fact that a woman not yet licensed as a geisha was now and then helping at parties.

"How many are there in all?"

"How many geisha? Twelve or thirteen, I suppose."

"Which one do you recommend?" Shimamura stood up to ring for the maid.

"You won't mind if I leave now."

"I mind very much indeed."

"I can't stay." She spoke as if trying to shake off the humiliation. "I'm going. It's all right. I don't mind. I'll come again."

When the maid came in, however, she sat down as though nothing were amiss. The maid asked several times which geisha she should call, but the woman refused to mention a name.

One look at the seventeen- or eighteen-year-old geisha who was presently led in, and Shimamura felt his need for a woman fall dully away. Her arms, with their underlying darkness, had not yet filled out, and something about her suggested an unformed, good-natured young girl. Shimamura, at pains not to show that his interest had left him, faced her dutifully, but he could not keep himself from looking less at her than at the new green on the mountains behind her. It seemed almost too much of an effort to talk. She was the mountain geisha through and through. He lapsed into a glum silence. No doubt thinking to be tactful and adroit, the woman stood up and left the room, and the conversation became still heavier. Even so, he managed to pass perhaps an hour with the geisha. Looking for a pretext to be rid of her, he remembered that he had had money telegraphed from Tokyo. He had to go to the post office before it closed, he said, and the two of them left the room.

But at the door of the inn he was seduced by the mountain, strong with the smell of new leaves. He started climbing roughly up it.

He laughed on and on, not knowing himself what was funny.

When he was pleasantly tired, he turned sharply around and, tucking the skirts of his kimono into his *obi,* ran headlong back down the slope. Two yellow butterflies flew up at his feet.

The butterflies, weaving in and out, climbed higher than the line of the Border Range, their yellow turning to white in the distance.

"What happened?" The woman was standing in the shade of the cedar trees. "You must have been very happy, the way you were laughing."

"I gave it up." Shimamura felt the same senseless laugh rising again. "I gave it up."

"Oh?" She turned and walked slowly into the grove. Shimamura followed in silence.

It was a shrine grove. The woman sat down on a flat rock beside the moss-covered shrine dogs.

"It's always cool here. Even in the middle of the summer there's a cool wind."

"Are all the geisha like that?"

"They're all a little like her, I suppose. Some of the older ones are very attractive, if you had wanted one of them." Her eyes were on the ground, and she spoke coldly. The dusky green of the cedars seemed to reflect from her neck.

Shimamura looked up at the cedar branches. "It's all over. My strength left me—really, it seems very funny."

From behind the rock, the cedars threw up their trunks in perfectly straight lines, so high that he could see the tops only by arching his back. The dark needles blocked out the sky, and the stillness seemed to be singing quietly. The trunk against which Shimamura leaned was the oldest of all. For some reason all the branches on the north side had withered, and, their tips broken and fallen, they looked like stakes driven into the trunk with their sharp ends out, to make a terrible weapon for some god.

"I made a mistake. I saw you as soon as I came down from the mountains, and I let myself think that all the geisha here were like you," he laughed. It occurred to him now that the thought of washing away in such short order the vigor of seven days in the mountains had perhaps first come to him when he saw the cleanness of this woman.

She gazed down at the river, distant in the afternoon sun. Shimamura was a little unsure of himself.

"I forgot," she suddenly remarked, with forced lightness. "I brought your tobacco. I went back up to your room a little while ago and found that you had gone out. I wondered where you could be, and then I saw you running up the mountain for all you were worth. I watched from the window. You were very funny. But you forgot your tobacco. Here."

She took the tobacco from her kimono sleeve and lighted a match for him.

"I wasn't very nice to that poor girl."

"But it's up to the guest, after all, when he wants to let the geisha go."

Through the quiet, the sound of the rocky river came up to them with a rounded softness. Shadows were darkening in the mountain chasms on the other side of the valley, framed in the cedar branches.

"Unless she were as good as you, I'd feel cheated when I saw you afterwards."

"Don't talk to me about it. You're just unwilling to admit you lost, that's all." There was scorn in her voice, and yet an affection of quite a new sort flowed between them.

As it became clear to Shimamura that he had from the start wanted only this woman, and that he had taken his usual roundabout way of saying so, he began to see himself as rather repulsive and the woman as all the more beautiful. Something from that cool figure had swept through him after she called to him from under the cedars.

The high, thin nose was a little lonely, a little sad, but the bud of her lips opened and closed smoothly, like a beautiful little circle of leeches. Even when she was silent her lips seemed always to be moving. Had they had wrinkles or cracks, or had their color been less fresh, they would have struck one as unwholesome, but they were never anything but smooth and shining. The line of her eyelids neither rose nor fell. As if for some special reason, it drew its way straight across her face. There was something faintly comical about the effect, but the short, thick hair of her eyebrows sloped gently down to enfold the line discreetly. There was nothing remarkable about the outlines of her round, slightly aquiline face. With her skin like white porcelain coated over a faint pink, and her throat still girlish, not yet filled out, the impression she gave was above all one of cleanness, not quite one of real beauty.

Her breasts were rather full for a woman used to the high, binding *obi* of the geisha.

"The sand flies have come out," she said, standing up and brushing at the skirt of her kimono.

Alone in the quiet, they could think of little to say.

It was perhaps ten o'clock that night. The woman called loudly to Shimamura from the hall, and a moment later she fell into his room as if someone had thrown her. She collapsed in front of the table. Flailing with a drunken arm at everything that happened to be on it, she poured herself a glass of water and drank in great gulps.

She had gone out to meet some travelers down from the mountains that evening, men she had been friendly with during the skiing season the winter before. They had invited her to the inn, whereupon they had had a riotous party, complete with geisha, and had proceeded to get her drunk.

Her head waved uncertainly, and she seemed prepared to talk on forever. Presently she remembered herself. "I shouldn't be here. I'll come again. They'll be looking for me. I'll come again later." She staggered from the room.

An hour or so later, he heard uneven steps coming down the long hall. She was weaving from side to side, he could tell, running into a wall, stumbling to the floor.

"Shimamura, Shimamura," she called in a high voice. "I can't see. Shimamura!"

It was, with no attempt at covering itself, the naked heart of a woman calling out to her man. Shimamura was startled. That high, piercing voice must surely be echoing all through the inn. He got up hastily. Pushing her fingers through the paper panel, the woman clutched at the frame of the door, and fell heavily against him.

"You're here." Clinging to him, she sank to the floor. She leaned against him as she spoke. "I'm not drunk. Who says I'm drunk? Ah, it hurts, it hurts. It's just that it hurts. I know exactly what I'm doing. Give me water, I want water. I mixed my drinks, that was my mistake. That's what goes to your head. It hurts. They had a bottle of cheap whisky. How was I to know it was cheap?" She rubbed her forehead with her fists.

The sound of the rain outside was suddenly louder.

Each time he relaxed his embrace even a little, she threatened to collapse. His arm was around her neck so tight that her hair was rumpled against his cheek. He thrust a hand inside the neck of her kimono.

He added coaxing words, but she did not answer. She folded her arms like a bar over the breast he was asking for.

"What's the matter with you." She bit savagely at her arm, as though angered by its refusal to serve her. "Damn you, damn you. Lazy, useless. What's the matter with you."

Shimamura drew back startled. There were deep teeth-marks on her arm.

She no longer resisted, however. Giving herself up to his hands, she began writing something with the tip of her finger. She would tell him the people she liked, she said. After she had written the names of some twenty or thirty actors, she wrote "Shimamura, Shimamura," over and over again.

The delicious swelling under Shimamura's hand grew warmer.

"Everything is all right." His voice was serene. "Everything is all right again." He sensed something a little motherly in her.

But the headache came back. She writhed and twisted, and sank to the floor in a corner of the room.

"It won't do. It won't do. I'm going home. Going home."

"Do you think you can walk that far? And listen to the rain."

"I'll go home barefoot. I'll crawl home."

"You don't think that's a little dangerous? If you have to go, I'll take you."

The inn was on a hill, and the road was a steep one.

"Suppose you try loosening your clothes. Lie down for a little while and you'll feel well enough to go."

"No, no. This is the way. I'm used to it." She sat up straight and took a deep breath, but breathing was clearly painful. She felt a little nauseated, she said, and opened the window behind her, but she could not vomit. She seemed to be holding back the urge to fall down writhing on the floor. Now and then she came to herself. "I'm going home, I'm going home," she said again and again, and presently it was after two.

"Go on to bed. Go on to bed when a person tells you to."

"But what will you do?" Shimamura asked.

"I'll just sit here like this. When I feel a little better I'll go home. I'll go home before daylight." She crawled over on her knees and tugged at him. "Go on to sleep. Pay no attention to me, I tell you."

Shimamura went back to bed. The woman sprawled over the table and took another drink of water.

"Get up. Get up when a person tells you to."

"Which do you want me to do?"

"All right, go to sleep."

"You aren't making much sense, you know." He pulled her into bed after him.

Her face was turned half away, hidden from him, but after a time she thrust her lips violently toward him.

Then, as if in a delirium she were trying to tell of her pain, she repeated over and over, he did not know how many times: "No, no. Didn't you say you wanted to be friends?"

The almost too serious tone of it rather dulled his ardor, and as he saw her wrinkle her forehead in the effort to control herself, he thought of standing by the commitment he had made.

But then she said: "I won't have any regrets. I'll never have any regrets. But I'm not that sort of woman. It can't last. Didn't you say so yourself?"

She was still half numb from the liquor.

"It's not my fault. It's yours. You lost. You're the weak one. Not I." She ran on almost in a trance, and she bit at her sleeve as if to fight back the happiness.

She was quiet for a time, apparently drained of feeling. Then, as if the thought came to her from somewhere in her memory, she struck out: "You're laughing, aren't you? You're laughing at me."

"I am not."

"Deep in your heart you're laughing at me. Even if you aren't now, you will be later." She was choked with tears. Turning away from him, she buried her face in her hands.

But a moment later she was calm again. Soft and yielding as if she were offering herself up, she was suddenly very intimate, and she began telling him all about herself. She seemed quite to have forgotten the headache. She said not a word about what had just happened.

"But I've been so busy talking I haven't noticed how late it is." She smiled a little bashfully. She had to leave before daylight, she said. "It's still dark. But people here get up early." Time after time she got up to look out the window. "They won't be able to see my face yet. And it's raining. No one will be going out to the fields this morning."

She seemed reluctant to go even when the lines of the mountain and of the roofs on its slopes were floating out of the rain. Finally it was time for the hotel maids to be up and about. She retouched her hair and ran, almost fled from the room, brushing aside Shimamura's offer to see her to the door. Someone might catch a glimpse of the two of them together.

Shimamura went back to Tokyo that day.

.   .   .

"You remember what you said then? But you were wrong. Why else would anyone come to such a place in December? I wasn't laughing at you."

The woman raised her head. Her face where it had been pressed against Shimamura's hand was red under the thick powder, from the eye across the bridge of the nose. It made him think of the snow-country cold, and yet, because of the darkness of her hair, there was a certain warmth in it.

She smiled quietly, as though dazzled by a bright light. Perhaps, as she smiled, she thought of "then," and Shimamura's words gradually colored her whole body. When she bowed her head, a little stiffly, he could see that even her back under her kimono was flushed a deep red. Set off by the color of her hair, the moist sensuous skin was as if laid naked before him. Her hair could not really have been called thick. Stiff like a man's, and swept up into a high Japanese-style coiffure with not a hair out of place, it glowed like some heavy black stone.

Shimamura looked at the hair and wondered whether the coldness that had so startled him—he had never touched such cold hair, he said—might be less the cold of the snow-country winter than something in the hair itself. The woman began counting on her fingers. For some time she counted on.

"What are you counting?" he asked. Still the counting continued.

"It was the twenty-third of May."

"You're counting the days, are you? Don't forget that July and August are two long months in a row."

"It's the hundred-and-ninety-ninth day. It's exactly a hundred and ninety-nine days."

"How did you remember it was the twenty-third of May?"

"All I have to do is look in my diary."

"You keep a diary?"

"It's always fun to read an old diary. But I don't hide anything when I write in my diary, and sometimes I'm ashamed to look at it myself."

"When did you begin?"

"Just before I went to Tokyo as a geisha. I didn't have any money, and I bought a plain notebook for two or three sen and drew in lines. I must have had a very sharp pencil. The lines are all neat and close together, and every page is crammed from top to bottom. When I had enough money to buy a diary, it wasn't the same any more. I started taking things for granted. It's that way with my writing practice, too. I used to practice on newspapers before I even thought of trying good paper, but now I set it down on good paper from the start."

"And you've kept the diary all this time?"

"Yes. The year I was sixteen and this year have been the best. I write in my diary when I'm home from a party and ready for bed, and when I read it over I can see places where I've gone to sleep writing. . . . But I don't write every day. Some days I miss. Way off here in the mountains, every party's the same. This year I couldn't find anything except a diary with a new day on each page. It was a mistake. When I start writing, I want to write on and on."

But even more than at the diary, Shimamura was surprised at her statement that she had carefully catalogued every novel and short story she had read since she was fifteen or sixteen. The record already filled ten notebooks.

"You write down your criticisms, do you?"

"I could never do anything like that. I just write down the author and the characters and how they are related to each other. That is about all."

"But what good does it do?"

"None at all."

"A waste of effort."

"A complete waste of effort," she answered brightly, as though the admission meant little to her. She gazed solemnly at Shimamura, however.

A complete waste of effort. For some reason Shimamura wanted to stress the point. But, drawn to her at that moment, he felt a quiet like the voice of the rain flow over him. He knew well enough that for her it was in fact no waste of effort, but somehow the final determination that it was had the effect of distilling and purifying the woman's existence.

Her talk of novels seemed to have little to do with "literature" in the everyday sense of the word. The only friendly ties she had with the people of this village had come from exchanging women's magazines, and afterwards she had gone on with her reading by herself. She was quite indiscriminate and had little understanding of literature, and she borrowed even the novels and magazines she found lying in the guests' rooms at the inn. Not a few of the new novelists whose names came to her meant nothing to Shimamura. Her manner was as though she were talking of a distant foreign literature. There was something lonely, something sad in it, something that rather suggested a beggar who has lost all desire. It occurred to Shimamura that his own distant fantasy on the occidental ballet, built up from words and photographs in foreign books, was not in its way dissimilar.

She talked on happily too of movies and plays she had never seen. She had no doubt been starved all these months for someone who would listen to her. Had she forgotten that a hundred and ninety-nine days earlier exactly this sort of conversation had set off the impulse to throw herself at Shimamura? Again she lost herself in the talk, and again her words seemed to be warming her whole body.

But her longing for the city had become an undemanding dream, wrapped in simple resignation, and the note of wasted effort was much stronger in it than any suggestion of the exile's lofty dissatisfaction. She did not seem to find herself especially sad, but in Shimamura's eyes there was something strangely touching about her. Were he to give himself quite up to that consciousness of wasted effort, Shimamura felt, he would be drawn into a remote emotionalism that would make his own life a waste. But before him was the quick, live face of the woman, ruddy from the mountain air.

In any case, he had revised his view of her, and he had found, surprisingly, that her being a geisha made it even more difficult for him to be free and open with her.

Dead-drunk that night, she had savagely bitten her half-paralyzed arm in a fit of irritation at its recalcitrance. "What's the matter with you? Damn you, damn you. Lazy, worthless. What's the matter with you?"

And, unable to stand, she had rolled from side to side. "I'll never have any regrets. But I'm not that sort of woman. I'm not that sort of woman."

"The midnight for Tokyo." The woman seemed to sense his hesitation, and she spoke as if to push it away. At the sound of the train whistle she stood up. Roughly throwing open a paper-paneled door and the window behind it, she sat down on the sill with her body thrown back against the railing. The train moved off into the distance, its echo fading into a sound as of the night wind. Cold air flooded the room.

"Have you lost your mind?" Shimamura too went over to the window. The air was still, without a suggestion of wind.

It was a stern night landscape. The sound of the freezing of snow over the land seemed to roar deep into the earth. There was no moon. The stars, almost too many of them to be true, came forward so brightly that it was as if they were falling with the swiftness of the void. As the stars came nearer, the sky retreated deeper and deeper into the night color. The layers of the Border Range, indistinguishable one from another, cast their heaviness at the skirt of the starry sky in a blackness grave and somber enough to communicate their mass. The whole of the night scene came together in a clear, tranquil harmony.

As she sensed Shimamura's approach, the woman fell over with her breast against the railing. There was no hint of weakness in the pose. Rather, against the night, it was the strongest and most stubborn she could have taken. So we have to go through that again, thought Shimamura.

Black though the mountains were, they seemed at that moment brilliant with the color of the snow. They seemed to him somehow transparent, somehow lonely. The harmony between sky and mountains was lost.

Shimamura put his hand to the woman's throat. "You'll catch cold. See how cold it is." He tried to pull her back, but she clung to the railing.

"I'm going home." Her voice was choked.

"Go home, then."

"Let me stay like this a little longer."

"I'm going down for a bath."

"No, stay here with me."

"If you close the window."

"Let me stay here like this a little longer."

Half the village was hidden behind the cedars of the shrine grove. The light in the railway station, not ten minutes away by taxi, flickered on and off as if crackling in the cold.

The woman's hair, the glass of the window, the sleeve of his kimono— everything he touched was cold in a way Shimamura had never known before.

Even the straw mats under his feet seemed cold. He started down to the bath.

"Wait. I'll go with you." The woman followed meekly.

As she was rearranging the clothes he had thrown to the floor outside the bath, another guest, a man, came in. The woman crouched low in front of Shimamura and hid her face.

"Excuse me." The other guest started to back away.

"No, please," Shimamura said quickly. "We'll go next door." He scooped up his clothes and stepped over to the women's bath. The woman followed as if they were married. Shimamura plunged into the bath without looking back at her. He felt a high laugh mount to his lips now that he knew she was with him. He put his face to the hot-water tap and noisily rinsed his mouth.

Back in the room, she raised her head a little from the pillow and pushed her side hair up with her little finger.

"This makes me very sad." She said only that. Shimamura thought for a moment that her eyes were half open, but he saw that the thick eyelashes created the illusion.

The woman, always high-strung, did not sleep the whole night.

It was apparently the sound of the *obi* being tied that awakened Shimamura.

"I'm sorry. I should have let you sleep. It's still dark. Look—can you see me?" She turned off the light. "Can you see me? You can't?"

"I can't see you. It's still pitch dark."

"No, no. I want you to look close. Now. Can you see me?" She threw open the window. "It's no good. You can see me. I'm going."

Surprised anew at the morning cold, Shimamura raised his head from the pillow. The sky was still the color of night, but in the mountains it was already morning.

"But it's all right. The farmers aren't busy this time of the year, and no one will be out so early. But do you suppose someone might be going out into the mountains?" She talked on to herself, and she walked about trailing the end of the half-tied *obi*. "There were no guests on the five-o'clock from Tokyo. None of the inn people will be up for a long while yet."

Even when she had finished tying the

obi, she stood up and sat down and stood up again, and wandered about the room with her eye on the window. She seemed on edge, like some restless night beast that fears the approach of the morning. It was as though a strange, magical wildness had taken her.

Presently the room was so light that he could see the red of her cheeks. His eye was fastened on that extraordinarily bright red.

"Your cheeks are flaming. That's how cold it is."

"It's not from the cold. It's because I've taken off my powder. I only have to get into bed and in a minute I'm warm as an oven. All the way to my feet." She knelt at the mirror by the bed.

"It's daylight. I'm going home."

Shimamura glanced up at her, and immediately lowered his head. The white in the depths of the mirror was the snow, and floating in the middle of it were the woman's bright red cheeks. There was an indescribably fresh beauty in the contrast.

Was the sun already up? The brightness of the snow was more intense, it seemed to be burning icily. Against it, the woman's hair became a clearer black, touched with a purple sheen.

Probably to keep snow from piling up, the water from the baths was led around the walls of the inn by a makeshift ditch, and in front of the entrance it spread out like a shallow spring. A powerful black dog stood on the stones by the doorway lapping at the water. Skis for the hotel guests, probably brought out from a storeroom, were lined up to dry, and the faint smell of mildew was sweetened by the steam. The snow that had fallen from the cedar branches to the roof of the public bath was breaking down into something warm and shapeless.

By the end of the year, that road would be shut off from sight by the snowstorms. She would have to go to her parties in long rubber boots with baggy "mountain trousers" over her kimono, and she would have a cape pulled around her and a veil over her face. The snow would by then be ten feet deep—the woman had looked down on the steep road from the window of the inn, high on a hill, before daybreak this morning, and now Shimamura was walking down the same road. Diapers hung high beside the road to dry. Under them stretched the vista of the Border Range, the snow on its peaks glowing softly. The green onions in the garden patches were not yet buried in the snow.

Children of the village were skiing in the fields.

As he started into the part of the village that fronted on the highway, he heard a sound as of quiet rain.

Little icicles glistened daintily along the eaves.

"While you're at it, would you mind shoveling a little from ours?" Dazzled by the bright light, a woman on her way back from the bath wiped at her forehead with a damp towel as she looked up at a man shoveling snow from a roof. A waitress, probably, who had drifted into the village a little in advance of the skiing season. Next door was a cafe with a sagging roof, its painted window flaking with age.

Rows of stones held down the shingles with which most of the houses along the street were roofed. Only on the side exposed to the sun did the round stones show their black surfaces, less a moist black from the melting snow than an inkstone black, beaten away at by icy wind and storm. The houses were of a kind with the dark stones on their roofs. The low eaves hugging the ground seemed to have in them the very essence of the north country.

Children were breaking off chunks of ice from the drains and throwing them down in the middle of the road. It was no doubt the sparkle of the ice as it went flying off into bits that enchanted them so. Shimamura, standing in the sunlight, found it hard to believe that the ice could be so thick. He stopped for a moment to watch.

A girl of twelve or thirteen stood knitting apart from the rest, her back against a stone wall. Under the baggy "mountain trousers," her feet were bare but for sandals, and Shimamura could see that the soles were red and cracked from the cold. A girl of perhaps two stood on a bundle of firewood beside her patiently holding a ball of yarn. Even the faded, ashen line of reclaimed yarn from the younger girl to the older seemed warmly aglow.

He could hear a carpenter's plane in a ski shop seven or eight doors down the street. Five or six geisha were talking under the eaves opposite. Among them, he was sure, would be the woman, Komako —he had just that morning learned her geisha name from a maid at the inn. And indeed, there she was. She had apparently noticed him. The deadly serious expression on her face set her off from the others. She would of course flush scarlet, but if she could at least pretend that nothing had happened—before Shimamura had time to go further with his thoughts, he saw that she had flushed to the throat. She might better have looked away, but her head turned little by little to follow him, while her eyes were fixed on the ground in acute discomfort.

Shimamura's cheeks too were aflame. He walked briskly by, and immediately Komako came after him.

"You mustn't. You embarrass me, walking by at a time like this."

"I embarrass you—you think I'm not embarrassed myself, with all of you lined up to waylay me? I could hardly make myself walk past. Is it always this way?"

"Yes, I suppose so. In the afternoon."

"But I'd think you'd be even more embarrassed, turning bright red and then chasing after me."

"What difference does it make?" The words were clear and definite, but she was blushing again. She stopped and put her arm around a persimmon tree beside the road. "I ran after you because I thought I might ask you to come by my house."

"Is your house near here?"

"Very near."

"I'll come if you'll let me read your diary."

"I'm going to burn my diary before I die."

"But isn't there a sick man in your house?"

"How did you know?"

"You were at the station to meet him yesterday. You had on a dark-blue cape. I was sitting near him on the train. And there was a woman with him, looking after him, as gentle as she could be. His wife? Or someone who went from here to bring him home? Or someone from Tokyo? She was exactly like a mother. I was very much impressed."

"Why didn't you say so last night? Why were you so quiet?" Something had upset her.

"His wife?"

Komako did not answer. "Why didn't you say anything last night? What a strange person you are."

Shimamura did not like this sharpness. Nothing he had done and nothing that had happened seemed to call for it, and he wondered if something basic in the woman's nature might not be coming to the surface. Still, when she came at him the second time, he had to admit that he was being hit in a vulnerable spot. This morning, as he glanced at Komako in that mirror reflecting the mountain snow, he had of course thought of the girl in the evening train window. Why then had he said nothing?

"It doesn't matter if there is a sick man. No one ever comes to my room." Komako went in through an opening in a low stone wall.

To the right was a small field, and to the left persimmon trees stood along the wall that marked off the neighboring plot. There seemed to be a flower garden in front of the house, and red carp were swimming in the little lotus pond. The ice had been broken away and lay piled along the bank. The house was old and decayed, like the pitted trunk of a persimmon. There were patches of snow on the roof, the rafters of which sagged to draw a wavy line at the eaves.

The air in the earthen-floored hallway was still and cold. Shimamura was led up a ladder before his eyes had become accustomed to the darkness. It was a ladder in the truest sense of the word, and the room at the top was an attic.

"This is the room the silkworms used to live in. Are you surprised?"

"You're lucky you've never fallen downstairs, drinking the way you do."

"I have. But generally when I've had too much to drink I crawl into the *kotatsu* downstairs and go off to sleep." She pushed her hand tentatively into the *kotatsu*, then went below for charcoal. Shimamura looked around at the curious room. Although there was but one low window, opening to the south, the freshly changed paper on the door turned off the rays of the sun brightly. The walls had been industriously pasted over with rice paper, so that the effect was rather like the inside of an old-fashioned paper box; but overhead was only the bare roof sloping down toward the window, as if a dark loneliness had settled itself over the room. Wondering what might be on the other side of the wall, Shimamura had the uneasy feeling that he was suspended in a void. But the walls and the floor, for all their shabbiness, were spotlessly clean.

For a moment he was taken with the fancy that the light must pass through Komako, living in the silkworms' room, as it passed through the translucent silkworms.

The *kotatsu* was covered with a quilt of the same rough, striped cotton material as the standard "mountain trousers." The chest of drawers was old, but the grain of the wood was fine and straight— perhaps it was a relic of Komako's years in Tokyo. It was badly paired with a cheap dresser, while the vermilion sewing-box gave off the luxurious glow of good lacquer. The boxes stacked along the wall behind a thin woolen curtain apparently served as bookshelves.

The kimono of the evening before hung on the wall, open to show the brilliant red under-kimono.

Komako came spryly up the ladder with a supply of charcoal.

"It's from the sickroom. But you needn't worry. They say fire spreads no germs." Her newly dressed hair almost brushed the *kotatsu* as she stirred away at the coals. The music teacher's son had intestinal tuberculosis, she said, and had come home to die.

But it was not entirely accurate to say that he had "come home." He had as a matter of fact not been born here. This was his mother's home. His mother had taught dancing down on the coast even when she was no longer a geisha, but she had had a stroke while she was still in her forties, and had come back to this hot spring to recover. The son, fond of machinery since he was a child, had stayed behind to work in a watch-shop. Presently he moved to Tokyo and started going to night school, and the strain was evidently too much for him. He was only twenty-five.

All this Komako told him with no hesitation, but she said nothing about the girl who had brought the man home, and nothing about why she herself was in this house.

Shimamura felt most uncomfortable at what she did say, however. Suspended there in the void, she seemed to be broadcasting to the four directions.

As he stepped from the hallway, he saw something faintly white through the corner of his eye. It was a samisen box, and it struck him as larger and longer than it should be. He found it hard to imagine her carrying so unwieldy an object to parties. The darkened door inside the hallway slid open.

"Do you mind if I step over this, Komako?" It was that clear voice, so beautiful that it was almost sad. Shimamura waited for an echo to come back.

It was Yoko's voice, the voice that had called out over the snow to the station master the night before.

"No, please go ahead." Yoko stepped lightly over the samisen box, a glass chamber-pot in her hand.

It was clear, from the familiar way she had talked to the station master the evening before and from the way she wore "mountain trousers," that she was a native of this snow country, but the bold pattern of her *obi*, half visible over the trousers, made the rough russet and black stripes of the latter seem fresh and cheerful, and for the same reason the long sleeves of her woolen kimono took on a certain voluptuous charm. The trousers, split just below the knees, filled out toward the hips, and the heavy cotton, for all its natural stiffness, was somehow supple and gentle.

Yoko darted one quick, piercing glance at Shimamura and went silently out over the earthen floor.

Even when he had left the house, Shimamura was haunted by that glance, burning just in front of his forehead. It was cold as a very distant light, for the inexpressible beauty of it had made his heart rise when, the night before, that light off in the mountains had passed across the girl's face in the train window

and lighted her eye for a moment. The impression came back to Shimamura, and with it the memory of the mirror filled with snow, and Komako's red cheeks floating in the middle of it.

He walked faster. His legs were round and plump, but he was seized with a certain abandon as he walked along gazing at the mountains he was so fond of, and his pace quickened, though he hardly knew it. Always ready to give himself up to reverie, he could not believe that the mirror floating over the evening scenery and the other snowy mirror were really works of man. They were part of nature, and part of some distant world.

And the room he had only this moment left had become part of that same distant world.

Startled at himself, in need of something to cling to, he stopped a blind masseuse at the top of the hill.

"Could you give me a massage?"

"Let me see. What time will it be?" She tucked her cane under her arm and, taking a covered pocket watch from her *obi*, felt at the face with her left hand. "Two thirty-five. I have an appointment over beyond the station at three-thirty. But I suppose it won't matter if I'm a little late."

"You're very clever to be able to tell the time."

"It has no glass, and I can feel the hands."

"You can feel the figures?"

"Not the figures." She took the watch out again, a silver one, large for a woman, and flicked open the lid. She laid her fingers across the face with one at twelve and one at six, and a third halfway between at three. "I can tell the time fairly well. I may be a minute off one way or the other, but I never miss by as much as two minutes."

"You don't find the road a little slippery?"

"When it rains my daughter comes to

call for me. At night I take care of the people in the village, and never come up this far. The maids at the inn are always joking and saying it's because my husband won't let me go out at night."

"Your children are growing up?"

"The oldest girl is twelve." They had reached Shimamura's room, and they were silent for a time as the massaging began. The sound of a samisen came to them from the distance.

"Who would that be, I wonder."

"You can always tell which geisha it is by the tone?"

"I can tell some of them. Some I can't. You must not have to work. Feel how nice and soft you are."

"No stiff muscles on me."

"A little stiff here at the base of the neck. But you're just right, not too fat and not too thin. And you don't drink, do you?"

"You can tell that?"

"I have three other customers with physiques exactly like yours."

"A common sort of physique."

"But when you don't drink, you don't know what it is really to enjoy yourself— to forget everything that happens."

"Your husband drinks, does he?"

"Much too much."

"But whoever it is, she's not much of a musician."

"Very poor indeed."

"Do you play yourself?"

"I did when I was young. From the time I was eight till I was nineteen. I haven't played in fifteen years now. Not since I was married."

Did all blind people look younger than they were? Shimamura wondered.

"But if you learn when you're young, you never forget."

"My hands have changed from doing this sort of work, but my ear is still good. It makes me very impatient to hear them playing. But then I suppose I felt impatient at my own playing when I was

young." She listened for a time. "Fumi at the Izutsuya, maybe. The best ones and the worst are the easiest to tell."

"There are good ones?"

"Komako is very good. She's young, but she's improved a great deal lately."

"Really?"

"You know her, don't you? I say she's good, but you have to remember that our standards here in the mountains are not very high."

"I don't really know her. I was on the train with the music teacher's son last night, though."

"He's well again?"

"Apparently not."

"Oh? He's been sick for a long time in Tokyo, and they say it was to help pay the doctors' bills that Komako became a geisha last summer. I wonder if it did any good."

"Komako, you say?"

"They were only engaged. But I suppose you feel better afterwards if you've done everything you can."

"She was engaged to him?"

"So they say. I don't really know, but that's the rumor."

It was almost too ordinary a thing to hear gossip about geisha from the hot-spring masseuse, and that fact had the perverse effect of making the news the more startling; and Komako's having become a geisha to help her fiancé was so ordinary a bit of melodrama that he found himself almost refusing to accept it. Perhaps certain moral considerations —questions of the propriety of selling oneself as a geisha—helped the refusal.

Shimamura was beginning to think he would like to go deeper into the story, but the masseuse was silent.

If Komako was the man's fiancée, and Yoko was his new lover, and the man was going to die—the expression "wasted effort" again came into Shimamura's mind. For Komako thus to guard her promise to the end, for her even to sell herself to pay doctors' bills—what was it if not wasted effort?

He would accost her with this fact, he would drive it home, when he saw her again, he said to himself; and yet her existence seemed to have become purer and cleaner for this new bit of knowledge.

Aware of a shameful danger lurking in his numbed sense of the false and empty, he lay concentrating on it, trying to feel it, for some time after the masseuse left. He was chilled to the pit of his stomach —but someone had left the windows wide open.

The color of evening had already fallen on the mountain valley, early buried in shadows. Out of the dusk the distant mountains, still reflecting the light of the evening sun, seemed to have come much nearer.

Presently, as the mountain chasms were far and near, high and low, the shadows in them began to deepen, and the sky was red over the snowy mountains, bathed now in but a wan light.

Cedar groves stood out darkly by the river bank, at the ski ground, around the shrine.

Like a warm light, Komako poured in on the empty wretchedness that had assailed Shimamura.

There was a meeting at the inn to discuss plans for the ski season. She had been called in for the party afterwards. She put her hands into the *kotatsu*, then quickly reached up and stroked Shimamura's cheek.

"You're pale this evening. Very strange." She clutched at the soft flesh of his cheek as if to tear it away. "Aren't you the foolish one, though."

She already seemed a little drunk. When she came back from the party she collapsed before the mirror, and drunkenness came out on her face to almost comic effect. "I know nothing about it. Nothing. My head aches. I feel

terrible. Terrible. I want a drink. Give me water."

She pressed both hands to her face and tumbled over with little concern for her carefully dressed hair. Presently she brought herself up again and began cleaning away the thick powder with cold cream. The face underneath was a brilliant red. She was quite delighted with herself. To Shimamura it was astonishing that drunkenness could pass so quickly. Her shoulders were shaking from the cold.

All through August she had been near nervous collapse, she told him quietly.

"I thought I'd go mad. I kept brooding over something, and I didn't know myself what it was. It was terrifying. I couldn't sleep. I kept myself under control only when I went out to a party. I had all sorts of dreams, and I lost my appetite. I would sit there jabbing at the floor for hours on end, all through the hottest part of the day."

"When did you first go out as a geisha?"

"In June. I thought for a while I might go to Hamamatsu."

"Get married?"

She nodded. The man had been after her to marry him, but she couldn't like him. She had had great trouble deciding what to do.

"But if you didn't like him, what were you so undecided about?"

"It's not that simple."

"Marriage has so much charm?"

"Don't be nasty. It's more that I want to have everything around me tidy and in order."

Shimamura grunted.

"You're not a very satisfying person, you know."

"Was there something between you and the man from Hamamatsu?"

She flung out her answer: "If there had been, do you think I would have hesitated? But he said that as long as I stayed here, he wouldn't let me marry anyone else. He said he would do everything possible to stand in the way."

"But what could he do from as far away as Hamamatsu? You worried about that?"

Komako stretched out for a time, enjoying the warmth of her body. When she spoke again, her tone was quite casual. "I thought I was pregnant." She giggled. "It seems ridiculous when I look back on it now."

She curled up like a little child, and grabbed at the neck of his kimono with her two fists.

The rich eyelashes again made him think that her eyes were half open.

Her elbow against the brazier, Komako was scribbling something on the back of an old magazine when Shimamura awoke the next morning.

"I can't go home. I jumped up when the maid came to bring charcoal, but it was already broad daylight. The sun was shining in on the door. I was a little drunk last night, and slept too well."

"What time is it?"

"It's already eight."

"Let's go have a bath." Shimamura got out of bed.

"I can't. Someone might see me in the hall." She was completely tamed. When Shimamura came back from the bath, he found her industriously cleaning the room, a kerchief draped artistically over her head.

She had polished the legs of the table and the edge of the brazier almost too carefully, and she stirred up the charcoal with a practiced hand.

Shimamura sat idly smoking, his feet in the *kotatsu*. When the ashes dropped from his cigarette Komako took them up in a handkerchief and brought him an ashtray. He laughed, a bright morning laugh. Komako laughed too.

"If you had a husband, you'd spend all your time scolding him."

"I would not. But I'd be laughed at for folding up even my dirty clothes. I can't help it. That's the way I am."

"They say you can tell everything about a woman by looking inside her dresser drawers."

"What a beautiful day." They were having breakfast, and the morning sun flooded the room. "I should have gone home early to practice the samisen. The sound is different on a day like this." She looked up at the crystal-clear sky.

The snow on the distant mountains was soft and creamy, as if veiled in a faint smoke.

Shimamura, remembering what the masseuse had said, suggested that she practice here instead. Immediately she telephoned her house to ask for music and a change of clothes.

So the house he had seen the day before had a telephone, thought Shimamura. The eyes of the other girl, Yoko, floated into his mind.

"That girl will bring your music?"

"She might."

"You're engaged to the son, are you?"

"Well! When did you hear that?"

"Yesterday."

"Aren't you strange? If you heard it yesterday, why didn't you tell me?" But her tone showed none of the sharpness of the day before. Today there was only a clean smile on her face.

"That sort of thing would be easier to talk about if I had less respect for you."

"What are you really thinking, I wonder? That's why I don't like Tokyo people."

"You're trying to change the subject. You haven't answered my question, you know."

"I'm not trying to change the subject. You really believed it?"

"I did."

[31]

"You're lying again. You didn't really."

"I couldn't quite believe all of it, as a matter of fact. But they said you went to work as a geisha to help pay doctors' bills."

"It sounds like something out of a cheap magazine. But it's not true. I was never engaged to him. People seem to think I was, though. It wasn't to help anyone in particular that I became a geisha. But I owe a great deal to his mother, and I had to do what I could."

"You're talking in riddles."

"I'll tell you everything. Very clearly. There does seem to have been a time when his mother thought it would be a good idea for us to get married. But she only thought it. She never said a word. Both of us knew in a vague sort of way what was on her mind, but it went no farther. And that's all there is to tell."

"Childhood friends."

"That's right. But we've lived most of our lives apart. When they sent me to Tokyo to be a geisha, he was the only one who saw me off. I have that written down on the very first page of my very oldest diary."

"If the two of you had stayed together, you'd probably be married by now."

"I doubt it."

"You would be, though."

"You needn't worry about him. He'll be dead before long."

"But is it right for you to be spending your nights away from home?"

"It's not right for you to ask. How can a dying man keep me from doing as I like?"

Shimamura could think of no answer. Why was it that Komako said not a word about the girl Yoko? And Yoko, who had taken care of the sick man on the train, quite as his mother must have when he was very young—how would she feel coming to an inn with a change of kimono for Komako, who was something, Shimamura could not know what, to the man Yoko had come home with?

Shimamura found himself off in his usual distant fantasies.

"Komako, Komako." Yoko's beautiful voice was low but clear.

"Thank you very much." Komako went out to the dressing-room. "You brought it yourself, did you? It must have been heavy."

Yoko left immediately.

The top string snapped as Komako plucked tentatively at the samisen. Shimamura could tell even while she was changing the string and tuning the instrument that she had a firm, confident touch. She took up a bulky bundle and undid it on the *kotatsu*. Inside were an ordinary book of lyrics and some twenty scores. Shimamura glanced curiously at the latter.

"You practice from these?"

"I have to. There's no one here who can teach me."

"What about the woman you live with?"

"She's paralyzed."

"If she can talk she ought to be able to help you."

"But she can't talk. She can still use her left hand to correct mistakes in dancing, but it only annoys her to have to listen to the samisen and not be able to do anything about it."

"Can you really understand the music from only a score?"

"I understand it very well."

"The publishing gentleman would be happy if he knew he had a real geisha—not just an ordinary amateur—practicing from his scores way off here in the mountains."

"In Tokyo I was expected to dance, and they gave me dancing lessons. But I got only the faintest idea of how to play the samisen. If I were to lose that there would be no one here to teach me again. So I use scores."

"And singing?"

"I don't like to sing. I did learn a few songs from my dancing, and I manage to get through them, but newer things I've had to pick up from the radio. I've no idea how near right I am. My own private style—you'd laugh at it, I know. And then my voice gives out when I'm singing for someone I know well. It's always loud and brave for strangers." She looked a little bashful for a moment, then brought herself up and glanced at Shimamura as though signaling that she was ready for him to begin.

He was embarrassed. He was unfortunately no singer.

He was generally familiar with the Nagauta music of the Tokyo theater and dance, and he knew the words to most of the repertoire. He had had no formal training, however. Indeed he associated the Nagauta less with the parlor performance of the geisha than with the actor on the stage.

"The customer is being difficult." Giving her lower lip a quick little bite, Komako brought the samisen to her knee, and, as if that made her a different person, turned earnestly to the lyrics before her.

"I've been practicing this one since last fall."

A chill swept over Shimamura. The goose flesh seemed to rise even to his cheeks. The first notes opened a transparent emptiness deep in his entrails, and in the emptiness the sound of the samisen reverberated. He was startled—or, better, he fell back as under a well-aimed blow. Taken with a feeling almost of reverence, washed by waves of remorse, defenseless, quite deprived of strength—there was nothing for him to do but give himself up to the current, to the pleasure of being swept off wherever Komako would take him.

She was a mountain geisha, not yet twenty, and she could hardly be as good as all that, he told himself. And in spite of the fact that she was in a small room, was she not slamming away at the instrument as though she were on the stage? He was being carried away by his own mountain emotionalism. Komako purposely read the words in a monotone, now slowing down and now jumping over a passage that was too much trouble; but gradually she seemed to fall into a spell. As her voice rose higher, Shimamura began to feel a little frightened. How far would that strong, sure touch take him? He rolled over and pillowed his head on an arm, as if in bored indifference.

The end of the song released him. Ah, this woman is in love with me—but he was annoyed with himself for the thought.

Komako looked up at the clear sky over the snow. "The tone is different on a day like this." The tone had been as rich and vibrant as her remark suggested. The air was different. There were no theater walls, there was no audience, there was none of the city dust. The notes went out crystalline into the clean winter morning, to sound on the far, snowy peaks.

Practicing alone, not aware herself of what was happening, perhaps, but with all the wideness of nature in this mountain valley for her companion, she had come quite as a part of nature to take on this special power. Her very loneliness beat down sorrow and fostered a wild strength of will. There was no doubt that it had been a great victory of the will, even granted that she had had an amount of preparatory training, for her to learn complicated airs from only a score, and presently go through them from memory.

To Shimamura it was wasted effort,

this way of living. He sensed in it too a longing that called out to him for sympathy. But the life and way of living no doubt flowed thus grandly from the samisen with a new worth for Komako herself.

Shimamura, untrained in the niceties of samisen technique and conscious only of the emotion in the tone, was perhaps an ideal audience for Komako.

By the time she had begun her third song—the voluptuous softness of the music itself may have been responsible—the chill and the goose flesh had disappeared, and Shimamura, relaxed and warm, was gazing into Komako's face. A feeling of intense physical nearness came over him.

The high, thin nose was usually a little lonely, a little sad, but today, with the healthy, vital flush on her cheeks, it was rather whispering: I am here too. The smooth lips seemed to reflect back a dancing light even when they were drawn into a tight bud; and when for a moment they were stretched wide, as the singing demanded, they were quick to contract again into that engaging little bud. Their charm was exactly like the charm of her body itself. Her eyes, moist and shining, made her look like a very young girl. She wore no powder, and the polish of the city geisha had over it a layer of mountain color. Her skin, suggesting the newness of a freshly peeled onion or perhaps a lily bulb, was flushed faintly, even to the throat. More than anything, it was clean.

Seated rigidly upright, she seemed more demure and maidenly than usual.

This time using a score, she sang a song she had not yet finished memorizing. At the end she silently pushed the plectrum under the strings and let herself fall into an easier posture.

Her manner quickly took on a touch of the seductive and alluring.

Shimamura could think of nothing to

say. Komako did not seem to care particularly what he thought of her playing, however. She was quite unaffectedly pleased with herself.

"Can you always tell which geisha it is from the tone of the samisen?"

"That's easy. There aren't twenty of us all together. It depends a little on the style, though. The individual comes out more in some styles than in others."

She took up the samisen again and shifted her weight so that her feet were a little to one side and the instrument rested on the calf of one leg.

"This is the way you hold it when you're small." She leaned toward the samisen as though it were too large for her. "Da-a-ark hair. . . ." Her voice was deliberately childish and she picked out the notes uncertainly.

"'Dark Hair' was the first one you learned?"

"Uh-uh." She shook her head girlishly, as no doubt she did in the days when she was still too small to hold the samisen properly.

Komako no longer tried to leave before daybreak when she stayed the night.

"Komako," the two-year-old daughter of the innkeeper would call from far down the hall, her voice rising in the mountain-country lilt. The two of them would play happily in the *kotatsu* until nearly noon, when they would go for a bath.

Back from the bath, Komako was combing her hair. "Whenever the child sees a geisha, she calls out 'Komako' in that funny accent, and when she sees a picture of someone with her hair done in the old way, that's 'Komako' too. Children can tell when you like them. Come, Kimi. Let's go play at Komako's." She stood up to leave, then sat down lazily on the veranda. "Eager people from Tokyo already out skiing."

The room looked from high ground

directly south over the ski runs at the base of the mountain.

Shimamura glanced up from the *kotatsu*. There were patches of snow on the mountain, and five or six figures in black ski clothes were moving about in the terraced fields. It seemed a trifle silly. The slope was a gentle one, and the walls between the fields were not yet covered with snow.

"They look like students. Is today Sunday? Do you suppose that's fun?"

"They're good, though," Komako said, as if to herself. "Guests are always surprised when a geisha says hello to them on the ski grounds. They don't recognize her for the snow-burn. At night the powder hides it."

"You wear ski clothes?"

She wore "mountain trousers," she said. "But what a nuisance the ski season is. It's all coming again. You see them in the evening at the inn, and they say they'll see you again the next day skiing. Maybe I should give up skiing this year. Good-by. Come along, Kimi. We'll have snow this evening. It's always cold the night before it snows."

Shimamura went out to the veranda. Komako was leading Kimi down the steep road below the ski grounds.

The sky was clouding over. Mountains still in the sunlight stood out against shadowed mountains. The play of light and shade changed from moment to moment, sketching a chilly landscape. Presently the ski grounds too were in shadow. Below the window Shimamura could see little needles of frost like isinglass among the withered chrysanthemums, though water was still dripping from the snow on the roof.

It did not snow that evening. A hailstorm turned to rain.

Shimamura called Komako again the night before he was to leave. It was a clear, moonlit night. At eleven o'clock the air was bitterly cold, but Komako insisted on going for a walk. She pulled him roughly from the *kotatsu*.

The road was frozen. The village lay quiet under the cold sky. Komako hitched up the skirt of her kimono and tucked it into her *obi*. The moon shone like a blade frozen in blue ice.

"We'll go to the station," said Komako.

"You're insane. It's more than a mile each way."

"You'll be going back to Tokyo soon. We'll go look at the station."

Shimamura was numb from his shoulders to his thighs.

Back in his room, Komako sank disconsolately to the floor. Her head was bowed and her arms were deep in the *kotatsu*. Strangely, she refused to go with him to the bath.

Bedding had been laid out with the foot of the mattress inside the *kotatsu*. Komako was sitting forlornly beside it when Shimamura came back from the bath. She said nothing.

"What's the matter?"

"I'm going home."

"Don't be foolish."

"Go on to bed. Just let me sit here for a little while."

"Why do you want to go home?"

"I'm not going home. I'll sit here till morning."

"Don't be difficult."

"I'm not being difficult. I'm not being difficult."

"Then . . . ?"

"I . . . don't feel well."

"Is that all?" Shimamura laughed. "I'll leave you quite to yourself."

"No."

"And why did you have to go out and run all over town?"

"I'm going home."

"There's no need to go home."

"But it's not easy for me. Go on back to Tokyo. It's not easy for me." Her face was low over the *kotatsu*.

Was it sorrow at finding herself about to sink into too deep a relationship with a traveler? Or at having to keep herself under control at so dear a moment? She has come that far, then, Shimamura said to himself. He too was silent for a time.

"Please go back to Tokyo."

"As a matter of fact, I was thinking of going back tomorrow."

"No! Why are you going back?" She looked up, startled, as though aroused from sleep.

"What can I do for you, no matter how long I stay?"

She gazed at him for a moment, then burst out violently: "You don't have to say that. What reason have you to say that?" She stood up irritably, and threw herself at his neck. "It's wrong of you to say such things. Get up. Get up, I tell you." The words poured out deliriously, and she fell down beside him, quite forgetting in her derangement the physical difficulty she had spoken of earlier.

Some time later, she opened warm, moist eyes.

She picked up the hair ornament that had fallen to the floor.

"You really must go back tomorrow," she said quietly.

As Shimamura was changing clothes to leave on the three-o'clock train the next afternoon, the manager of the inn beckoned Komako into the hall. "Let's see. Suppose we make it about eleven hours," he could hear Komako's answer. They were evidently discussing the bill for her services as a geisha, and the manager perhaps thought it would be unreasonable to charge for the whole sixteen or seventeen hours.

The bill as a matter of fact was computed by the hour—"Left at five," or "Left at twelve"—without the usual charge for overnight services.

Komako, in an overcoat and a white scarf, saw him to the station.

Even when he had finished buying presents to take back to Tokyo, he had some twenty minutes to kill. Walking with Komako in the slightly raised station plaza, he thought what a narrow little valley it was, crowded in among the snowy mountains. Komako's too-black hair was a little touching, a little sad, in the loneliness of the shadowed mountain pocket.

The sun shone dimly on a spot in the mountains far down the river.

"It's melted a good deal since I came."

"Two days of snow, though, and we'll have six feet. Then it snows again, and before long the lights on those poles are out of sight. I'll walk along thinking of you, and I'll find myself strung up on a wire."

"The snow is that deep?"

"They say that in the next town up the line the schoolchildren jump naked from the second floor of the dormitory. They sink out of sight in the snow, and they move under it as though they were swimming. Look, a snowplow."

"I'd like to see it that deep. But I suppose the inn will be crowded. And there might be danger of slides along the way."

"With you it's not a question of money, is it? Have you always had so much to spend?" She turned to look up at his face. "Why don't you grow a mustache?"

"I've thought of it." Shimamura, freshly shaven, stroked the blue-black traces of his beard. A deep line from the corner of his mouth set off the softness of his cheek. Was that, he wondered, what Komako found attractive? "You always look a little as though you'd just shaved too when you take off that powder."

"Listen! The crows. That frightening way they sometimes have. Where are they, I wonder? And isn't it cold!" Komako hugged herself as she looked up at the sky.

"Shall we go in by the stove?"

A figure in "mountain trousers" came running up the wide road from the main highway into the station plaza. It was Yoko.

"Komako. Yukio— Komako," she panted, clinging to Komako like a child that has run frightened to its mother, "come home. Right away. Yukio's worse. Right away."

Komako closed her eyes, as if from the pain of the assault on her shoulder. Her face was white, but she shook her head with surprising firmness.

"I can't go home. I'm seeing off a guest."

Shimamura was startled. "You needn't see me off."

"It's not right to leave. How do I know you'll come again?"

"I'll come, I'll come."

Yoko seemed not to hear the exchange. "I just called the inn," she went on feverishly, "and they said you were at the station. So I came here. I ran all the way. Yukio is asking for you." She pulled at Komako, but Komako shook her off impatiently.

"Leave me alone."

It was Komako who reeled back, however. She retched violently, but nothing came from her mouth. The rims of her eyes were moist. There was goose flesh on her cheeks.

Yoko stood rigid, gazing at Komako. Her face, like a mask, wore an expression of such utter earnestness that it was impossible to tell whether she was angry or surprised or grieved. It seemed an extraordinarily pure and simple face to Shimamura.

She turned quickly and, without the slightest change of expression, clutched at Shimamura's hand. "I'm sorry, but would you let her go home?" A tense, high-pitched voice assailed him. "Let her go home."

"Of course I'll let her go home. Go on home," he called out to Komako. "Don't be a fool."

"And what say do you have in the matter?" Komako pushed Yoko roughly away from him.

Shimamura tried to signal the taxi waiting in front of the station. Yoko clutched at his arm so tightly that his fingers were numbed. "I'll send her home in a taxi," he said. "Why don't you go on ahead? People will be watching us."

Yoko nodded quickly, and turned away with almost unbelievable alacrity. Why was the girl always so earnest, so sober, Shimamura wondered. But such musings did not seem entirely in keeping with the occasion.

That voice, so beautiful it was almost lonely, lingered in Shimamura's ears as if it were echoing back from somewhere in the snowy mountains.

"Where are you going?" Komako pulled at Shimamura. He had signaled the taxi and was walking toward it. "I won't. I'm not going home."

For an instant Shimamura felt something very near physical revulsion.

"I don't know what there is among the three of you, but the man may be dying even now. She came for you, didn't she, because he wants to see you. Go home like a good girl. You'll regret it all your life if you don't. What if he dies even while you're standing here? Don't be stubborn. Forgive and forget."

"Forgive and forget? You don't understand. You don't understand at all."

"And when they sent you to Tokyo, he was the only one who saw you off, didn't you say? Do you think it's right not to say good-by to the man you yourself said was on the very first page of the very first volume of your diary? This is the very last page of his."

"But I don't want to. I don't want to see a man die."

It could have been the coldest heartlessness or too warm a passion—Shimamura did not know which.

"I'll not be able to write in my diary any more. I'll burn it," she said softly, almost to herself. Her cheeks were flushed. "You're a good, simple person at heart, aren't you? If you really are, I won't mind sending my whole diary to you. You won't laugh at me? You're a good, honest person at heart, I'm sure."

Shimamura was moved by a wave of feeling he could not define himself. He thought he must indeed be the plainest, most honest person in the world. He no longer worried about sending Komako home. She said nothing more.

A porter from the inn came to tell them that the gate to the tracks was open.

Four or five villagers in somber winter dress got on and off the train.

"I'll not go to the platform with you. Good-by." Komako stood inside the closed window of the waiting-room. From the train window it was as though one strange piece of fruit had been left behind in the grimy glass case of a shabby mountain grocery.

The window of the waiting-room was clear for an instant as the train started to move. Komako's face glowed forth, and as quickly disappeared. It was the bright red it had been in the mirror that snowy morning, and for Shimamura that color again seemed to be the point at which he parted with reality.

The train climbed the north slope of the Border Range into the long tunnel. On the far side it moved down a mountain valley. The color of evening was descending from chasms between the peaks. The dim brightness of the winter afternoon seemed to have been sucked into the earth, and the battered old train had shed its bright shell in the tunnel. There was no snow on the south slope.

Following a stream, the train came out on the plain. A mountain, cut at the top in curious notches and spires, fell off in a graceful sweep to the far skirts. Over it the moon was rising. The solid, integral shape of the mountain, taking up the whole of the evening landscape there at the end of the plain, was set off in a deep purple against the pale light of the sky. The moon was no longer an afternoon white, but, faintly colored, it had not yet taken on the clear coldness of the winter night. There was not a bird in the sky. Nothing broke the lines of the wide skirts to the right and the left. Where the mountain swept down to meet the river, a stark white building, a hydroelectric plant perhaps, stood out sharply from the withered scene the train window framed, one last spot saved from the night.

The window began to steam over. The landscape outside was dusky, and the figures of the passengers floated up half-transparent. It was the play of that evening mirror again. The train, probably no more than three or four worn-out, faded, old-fashioned coaches strung together, was not from the same world as the trains one finds on the main lines. The light inside was dim.

Shimamura abandoned himself to the fancy that he had stepped into some unreal conveyance, that he was being borne away in emptiness, cut off from time and place. The monotonous sound of the wheels became the woman's voice.

Her words, though short and broken, were a sign that she was alive in all her vital intensity, and he knew he had not forgotten her from the fact that listening was a trial. But to the Shimamura of that moment, moving away from the woman, the voice was already a distant one that could do no more than sharpen the poignancy of travel.

Would Yukio be breathing his last even now? Komako had for reasons of her own refused to go home; and had she then failed to reach his bedside in time?

[38]

There were so few passengers that Shimamura felt a little uneasy.

Besides Shimamura himself, there were only a man, probably in his fifties, and opposite him a red-faced girl. A black shawl was thrown over the full flesh of her shoulders, and her cheeks were a wonderful, fiery red. She leaned slightly forward to catch every word the man said, and she answered him happily. A pair off on a long journey together, Shimamura concluded.

As the train pulled into a station behind which rose the chimneys of spinning-factories, however, the man hastily got up, took a wicker trunk from the baggage rack, and threw it out the window to the platform. "Maybe we'll meet again sometime," he called back to the girl as he hurried from the train.

Shimamura suddenly wanted to weep. He had been caught quite off guard, and it struck him afresh that he had said good-by to the woman and was on his way home.

He had not considered the possibility that the two had simply met on the train. The man was perhaps a traveling salesman.

PART TWO

It was the egg-laying season for moths, Shimamura's wife told him as he left Tokyo, and he was not to leave his clothes hanging in the open. There were indeed moths at the inn. Five or six large corn-colored moths clung to the decorative lantern under the eaves, and in the little dressing-room was a moth whose body was large out of all proportion to its wings.

The windows were still screened from the summer. A moth so still that it might have been glued there clung to one of the screens. Its feelers stood out like delicate wool, the color of cedar bark, and its wings, the length of a woman's finger, were a pale, almost diaphanous green. The ranges of mountains beyond were already autumn-red in the evening sun. That one spot of pale green struck him as oddly like the color of death. The fore and after wings overlapped to make a deeper green, and the wings fluttered like thin pieces of paper in the autumn wind.

Wondering if the moth was alive, Shimamura went over to the window and rubbed his finger over the inside of the screen. The moth did not move. He struck at it with his fist, and it fell like a leaf from a tree, floating lightly up midway to the ground.

In front of the cedar grove opposite, dragonflies were bobbing about in countless swarms, like dandelion floss in the wind.

The river seemed to flow from the tips of the cedar branches.

He thought he would never tire of looking at the autumn flowers that spread a blanket of silver up the side of the mountain.

A White-Russian woman, a peddler, was sitting in the hallway when he came out of the bath. So you find them even in these mountains— He went for a closer look.

She appeared to be in her forties. Her face was wrinkled and dirty, but her skin, where it showed at the full throat and beyond, was a pure, glowing white.

"Where are you from?" Shimamura asked.

"Where am I from? Where am I from?" The woman seemed troubled for an answer. She began to put away her wares, the most ordinary Japanese cosmetics and hair ornaments.

Her skirt, like a dirty sheet wrapped around her, had quite lost the feel of occidental dress, and had taken on instead something of the air of Japan. She carried her wares on her back in a large

Japanese-style kerchief. But for all that, she still wore foreign shoes.

The innkeeper's wife stood beside Shimamura watching the Russian leave. The two of them went into the office, where a large woman was seated at the hearth with her back to them. She took her long skirts in her hand as she stood up to go. Her cloak was a formal black.

She was a geisha Shimamura remembered having seen with Komako in an advertising photograph, the two of them on skis with cotton "mountain trousers" pulled over party kimonos. She seemed to be well along in years, plump and to all appearances good-natured.

The innkeeper was warming thick, oblong cakes over the embers.

"Won't you have one?" he asked Shimamura. "You really must have one. The geisha you saw brought them to celebrate the end of her term."

"She's leaving, is she?"

"Yes."

"She looks like a good sort."

"She was very popular. Today she's going the rounds to say good-by."

Shimamura blew on the cake and bit into it. The hard crust, a little sour, gave off a musty smell.

Outside the window, the bright red of ripe persimmons was bathed in the evening sun. It seemed to send out a red glow even to the bamboo of the pothook over the hearth.

"See how long they are." Shimamura looked out in astonishment at the steep path, down which old women were trudging with bundles of autumn grass on their backs. The grass looked to be twice the height of the women, and the tassels were long and powerful.

"It's *kaya* grass."

"*Kaya*, is it?"

"The government railways built a sort of restroom, I suppose you would call it, for their hotspring exhibit, and they

thatched the teahouse with *kaya* from these mountains. Someone in Tokyo bought it exactly as it was."

"*Kaya*, is it," Shimamura repeated, half to himself. "It's *kaya* then on the mountain? I thought it must be a flower of some sort."

The first thing that had struck Shimamura's eye as he got off the train was that array of silver-white. High up the mountain, the *kaya* spread out silver in the sun, like the autumn sunlight itself pouring over the face of the mountain. Ah, I am here, something in Shimamura called out as he looked up at it.

But the great strands he saw here seemed quite different in nature from the grasses that had so moved him. The large bundles hid the women carrying them, and rustled against the rocks that flanked the path. And the plumes were long and powerful.

Under the dim light in the dressing-room, Shimamura could see that the large-bodied moth was laying eggs along the black lacquer of the clothes-frame. Moths were beating at the lantern under the eaves.

There was a steady humming of autumn insects, as there had been from before sundown.

Komako was a little late.

She gazed in at him from the hall.

"Why have you come here? Why have you come to a place like this?"

"I've come to see you."

"You don't mean that. I dislike people from Tokyo because they're always lying." She sat down, and her voice was softer. "I'm never going to see anyone off again. I can't describe how it felt to see you off."

"This time I'll go without telling you."

"No. I mean I won't go to the station again."

"What happened to him?"

"He died, of course."

"While you were seeing me off?"

"But that's not the reason. I had no idea I could hate so to see someone off."

Shimamura nodded.

"Where were you on the fourteenth of February? I was waiting for you. But I'll know better than to believe you next time."

The fourteenth of February was the "bird-chasing festival," a children's festival that had in it the spirit of this snow country. For ten days before the festival the children of the village tramped down the snow with straw boots, and presently, cutting the now boardlike snow into two-foot cubes, they built a snow palace some six yards square and more than ten feet high. Since the New Year was celebrated here early in February, the traditional straw ropes were still strung up over the village doorways. On the fourteenth the children gathered the ropes and burned them in a red bonfire before the snow palace. They pushed and jostled one another on the roof and sang the bird-chasing song, and afterwards, setting out lights, they spent the night in the palace. At dawn on the fifteenth they again climbed to the roof to sing the bird-chasing song.

It was then that the snow was deepest, and Shimamura had told Komako he would come for the festival.

"I was at home in February. I took a vacation. I was sure you would be here on the fourteenth, and I came back especially. I could have stayed to take care of her longer if I had known."

"Was someone ill?"

"The music teacher. She had pneumonia down on the coast. The telegram came when I was at home, and I went down to take care of her."

"Did she get better?"

"No."

"I'm sorry." Shimamura's words could have been either an expression of sympathy or an apology for the broken promise.

Komako shook her head mildly, and wiped at the table with her handkerchief. "The place is alive with insects." A swarm of tiny winged insects fell from the table to the floor. Several small moths were circling the light.

Moths, how many kinds he could not tell, dotted the screen, floating on the clear moonlight.

"My stomach aches." Komako thrust both hands tight inside her *obi*, and her head fell to Shimamura's knee. "My stomach aches."

Insects smaller than moths gathered on the thick white powder at her neck. Some of them died there as Shimamura watched.

The flesh on her neck and shoulders was richer than it had been the year before. She is just twenty, he told himself.

He felt something warm and damp on his knee.

" 'Komako, go on up and look in the Camellia Room,' they said in the office, very pleased with themselves. I don't like that way they have. I'd been to see Kikuyu off, and I was just ready for a good nap when someone said there had been a call from here. I didn't feel like coming. I had too much to drink last night at Kikuyu's farewell party. They only laughed down in the office and wouldn't tell me who was here. And it was you. It's been a whole year. You're the sort that comes only once a year?"

"I had one of the cakes she left."

"You did?" Komako sat up. Her face was red where it had been pressed against his knee. She seemed very young.

She had seen the old geisha Kikuyu to the second station down the line, she said.

"It's very sad. We used to be able to work things out together, but now it's every geisha for herself. The place has changed. New geisha come in and no one gets along with anyone else. I'll be lonesome without Kikuyu. She was at the center of everything. And she made more money than any of the rest of us. Her people took very good care of her."

Kikuyu had worked out her contract, and she was going home. Would she get married or would she open an inn or restaurant of her own? Shimamura asked.

"Kikuyu is a very sad case. She made a bad marriage, and she came here afterwards." Komako was silent for a time, evidently unsure how much she should tell. She looked out toward the slope below the terraced fields, bright in the moonlight. "You know the new house halfway up the hill?"

"The restaurant—the Kikumura, is it called?"

"That's the one. Kikuyu was supposed to manage the Kikumura, but at the last minute she had a change of heart. It caused all sorts of excitement. She had a patron build the place for her, and then, when she was all ready to move in, she threw it over. She found someone she liked and was going to marry him, but he ran off and left her. Is that what happens when you lose your head over a man? I wonder. She can't very well go back to her old work, and she can't take over the restaurant now that she's turned it down, and she's ashamed to stay here after all that's happened. There's nothing for her to do but start over somewhere else. It makes me very sad to think about Kikuyu. There were all sorts of people— but of course we don't really know the details."

"Men? How many? Five or so?"

"I wonder." Komako laughed softly and turned away. "Kikuyu was weak. A weakling."

"Maybe there was nothing else she could do."

"But isn't it so? You can't go losing your head over every man that likes you." Her eyes were on the floor, and she was stroking her hair meditatively with a hair ornament. "It wasn't easy, seeing her off."

"And what happened to the restaurant?"

"The wife of the man who built it has taken it over."

"An interesting situation. The wife managing the mistress's restaurant."

"But what else could they do? The place was ready to open, and the wife moved in with all her children."

"What about her own house?"

"They left the old woman to take care of it, I hear. The man's a farmer, but he likes to have his fun. He's a very interesting fellow."

"So it would seem. Is he well along in years?"

"He's young. No more than thirty-one or thirty-two."

"The mistress must be older than the wife, then."

"They're both twenty-six."

"The 'Kiku' of 'Kikumura' would be from 'Kikuyu.' And the wife took over the name even?"

"But they couldn't change the name once it was advertised."

Shimamura straightened the collar of his kimono. Komako got up to close the window.

"Kikuyu knew all about you. She told me today you were here."

"I saw her down in the office when she came to say good-by."

"Did she say anything to you?"

"Not a thing."

"Do you know how I feel?" Komako threw open the window she had just shut, and sat down on the sill as if she meant to throw herself out.

"The stars here are different from the stars in Tokyo," Shimamura said after a time. "They seem to float up from the sky."

"Not tonight, though. The moon is too bright. . . . The snow was dreadful this year."

"I understand there were times when the trains couldn't get through."

"I was almost afraid. The roads weren't open until May, a month later than usual. You know the shop up at the ski grounds? An avalanche went through the second floor of it. The people below heard a strange noise and thought the rats were tearing up the kitchen. There were no rats, though, and when they looked upstairs the place was full of snow and the shutters and all had been carried off. It was just a surface slide, but there was a great deal of talk on the radio. The skiers were frightened away. I said I wouldn't ski any more and I gave my skis away the end of last year, but I went out again after all. Twice, three times maybe. Have I changed?"

"What have you been doing since the music teacher died?"

"Don't you worry about other people's problems. I came back and I was waiting for you in February."

"But if you were down on the coast you could have written me a letter."

"I couldn't. I really couldn't. I couldn't possibly write the sort of letter your wife would see. I couldn't bring myself to. I don't tell lies just because people might be listening." The words came at him in a sudden torrent. He only nodded. "Why don't you turn out the light? You don't have to sit in this swarm of insects."

The moonlight, so bright that the furrows in the woman's ear were clearly shadowed, struck deep into the room and seemed to turn the mats on the floor a chilly green.

"No. Let me go home."

"I see you haven't changed." Shimamura raised his head. There was some-thing strange in her manner. He peered into the slightly aquiline face.

"People say I haven't changed since I came here. I was sixteen then. But life goes on the same, year after year."

Her cheeks still carried the ruddiness of her north-country girlhood. In the moonlight the fine geishalike skin took on the luster of a sea shell.

"But did you hear I'd moved?"

"Since the teacher died? You're not in the silkworms' room any more, then? This time it's a real geisha house?"

"A real geisha house? I suppose it is. They sell tobacco and candy in the shop, and I'm the only geisha they have. I have a real contract, and when I read late in the night I always use a candle to save electricity."

Shimamura let out a loud guffaw.

"The meter, you know. Shouldn't use too much electricity."

"I see, I see."

"But they're very good to me, so good that I sometimes find it hard to believe I'm really hired out as a geisha. When one of the children cries, the mother takes it outside so that I won't be bothered. I have nothing to complain about. Only sometimes the bedding is crooked. When I come home late at night, everything is laid out for me, but the mattresses aren't square one on the other, and the sheet is wrong. I hate it. After they've been so kind, though, I feel guilty making the bed over."

"You'd wear yourself out if you had a house of your own."

"So everyone says. There are four little children, and the place is a terrible clutter. I spend the whole day picking things up. I know everything will be thrown down again as soon as my back is turned, but somehow I can't help myself. I want to be as clean and neat as the place will let me. . . . Do you understand how I feel?"

"I understand."

"If you understand, then tell me. Tell me, if you see how I feel." Again that tense, urgent note came into her voice. "See, you can't. Lying again. You have plenty of money, and you're not much of a person. You don't understand at all." She lowered her voice. "I'm very lonely sometimes. But I'm a fool. Go back to Tokyo, tomorrow."

"It's very well for you to condemn me, but how can you expect me to tell you exactly what I mean?"

"Why can't you? It's wrong of you." Her voice was almost desperate. Then she closed her eyes, and began again as if she had asked herself whether Shimamura knew her, felt her for what she was, and had answered that he did. "Once a year is enough. You'll come once a year, won't you, while I'm here?"

Her contract was for four years, she said.

"When I was at home, I didn't dream I would ever be a geisha again. I even gave away my skis before I left. And so all I've accomplished, I suppose, has been to give up smoking."

"I remember how much you used to smoke, now that you mention it."

"When guests at parties give me cigarettes, I tuck them away in my sleeve, and I have a fine collection by the time I'm ready to go home."

"But four years—that's a long time."

"It will pass in a hurry."

"Aren't you warm, though." Shimamura took her in his arms as she came to him.

"I've always been warm."

"I suppose the nights will be getting chilly."

"It's five years now since I came here. At first I wondered how I could live in such a place—especially before the railroad came through. And it's going on two years since you first came."

He had come three times in less than

two years, and on each new visit he had found Komako's life changed.

Crickets were chirping outside in a noisy chorus.

"I wish they'd be a little quieter." Komako pulled away from Shimamura.

The moths at the window started up as the wind came from the north.

Shimamura knew well enough that the thick eyelashes made her eyes seem half open, and yet he found himself looking again to be sure.

"I'm fatter now that I've stopped smoking."

The fat on her abdomen was heavier, he had noticed.

They had long been apart, but what eluded his grasp when he was away from her was immediately near and familiar when he was beside her again.

"One is bigger than the other." She cupped her breasts lightly in her hands.

"I suppose that's a habit of his—one side only."

"What a nasty thing to say!" Here she was—this was it, he remembered.

"Next time tell him to treat them both alike."

"Alike? Shall I tell him to treat them both alike?" She brought her face gently toward his.

It was a second-floor room, but it seemed to be surrounded by croaking toads. Two or three of them were moving from spot to spot, remarkably long-winded croakers.

Back from the bath, Komako began talking of herself. Her voice was quiet and her manner was completely serene.

The first physical examination she had had here—she thought it would be as when she was an apprentice geisha, and she bared her chest for a tuberculosis check. The doctor laughed, and she burst into tears—such were the intimate details she went into. She talked on as Shimamura encouraged her with questions.

"I'm always exactly on the calendar.

Two days less than a month each time."

"I don't suppose it keeps you from your parties?"

"You understand such things, do you?"

Every day she had a bath in the hot spring, famous for its lingering warmth. She walked two miles and more between parties at the old spring and the new, and here in the mountains there were few parties that kept her up late. She was therefore healthy and full-bodied, though she did have a suggestion of the low, bunched-up hips so common with geisha, narrow from side to side and wide from front to back. To Shimamura there was something touching about the fact that such a woman could call him back from afar.

"I wonder if I can have children." And she wondered too if being generally faithful to one man was not the same thing as being married.

That was the first Shimamura had heard of the "one man" in Komako's life. She had known him since she was sixteen, she said. Shimamura thought he understood now the lack of caution that had at first so puzzled him.

She had never liked the man, Komako continued, and had never felt near him, perhaps because the affair had begun when she was down on the coast just after the death of the man who had paid her debts.

"But it's certainly better than average if it's lasted five years."

"I've had two chances to leave him. When I went to work as a geisha here, and when I moved after the music teacher died. But I've never had the will power to do it. I don't have much will power."

The man was still down on the coast. It had not been convenient to keep her there, and when the music teacher came back to these mountains he had left Komako with her. He had been very

kind, Komako said, and it made her sad to think that she could not give her whole self to him. He was considerably older than she, and he but rarely came to see her.

"I sometimes think it would be easiest to break away from him if I were to be really bad. I honestly think so sometimes."

"That would never do."

"But I wouldn't be up to it. It's not in my nature, I'm fond of this body I live in. If I tried, I could cut my four years down to two, but I don't strain myself. I take care of myself. Think of all the money I could make if I really tried. But it's enough if the man I have my contract with hasn't lost money at the end of four years. I know about how much it takes each month for an installment on the loan, and interest, and taxes, and my own keep, and I don't strain myself to make more. If it's a party that doesn't seem worth the trouble, I slip off and go home, and they don't call me late at night even from the inn unless an old guest has asked especially for me. If I wanted to be extravagant, I could go on and on, but I work as the mood takes me. That's enough. I've already paid back more than half the money, and it's not a year yet. But even so I manage to spend thirty yen or so on myself every month."

It was enough if she made a hundred yen a month, she said. The month before, the least busy of the year, she had made sixty yen. She had had some ninety parties, more than any other geisha. She received a fixed amount for herself from each party, and the larger number of parties therefore meant relatively more for her and less for the man to whom she was indentured. But she moved busily from one to another as the spirit took her. There was not a single geisha at this hot spring who lost money and had to extend her contract.

Komako was up early the next morning. "I dreamed I was cleaning house for the woman who teaches flower-arranging, and I woke up."

She had moved the little dresser over to the window. In the mirror the mountains were red with autumn leaves, and the autumn sun was bright.

This time it was not Yoko he heard, Yoko calling through the door in that voice so clear he found it a little sad. Komako's clothes were brought rather by the little daughter of the man with whom she had her contract.

"What happened to the girl?" Shimamura asked.

Komako darted a quick glance at him. "She spends all her time at the cemetery. Over there at the foot of the ski course. See the buckwheat field—the white flowers? And the cemetery to the left of it?"

Shimamura went for a walk in the village when Komako had left.

Before a white wall, shaded by eaves, a little girl in "mountain trousers" and an orange-red flannel kimono, clearly brand-new, was bouncing a rubber ball. For Shimamura, there was autumn in the little scene.

The houses were built in the style of the old regime. No doubt they were there when provincial lords passed down this north-country road. The eaves and the verandas were deep, while the latticed, paper-covered windows on the second floor were long and low, no more than a foot or so high. There were reed blinds hanging from the eaves.

Slender autumn grasses grew along the top of an earthen wall. The pale-yellow plumes were at their most graceful, and below each plume narrow leaves spread out in a delicate fountain.

Yoko knelt on a straw mat beside the road, flailing at beans spread out before her in the sunlight.

The beans jumped from their dry pods like little drops of light.

Perhaps she could not see him because of the scarf around her head. She knelt, flailing away at the beans, her knees spread apart in their "mountain trousers," and she sang in that voice so clear it was almost sad, the voice that seemed to be echoing back from somewhere.

"The butterfly, the dragonfly, the cricket. The pine cricket, bell cricket, horse cricket *Are singing in the hills."*

How large the crow is, starting up from the cedar in the evening breeze—so says the poet. Again there were swarms of dragonflies by the cedar grove Shimamura could see from his window. As the evening approached, they seemed to swim about faster, more restlessly.

Shimamura had bought a new guide to these mountains while he was waiting for his train in Tokyo. Thumbing through it, he learned that near the top of one of the Border Range peaks a path threaded its way through beautiful lakes and marshes, and in this watery belt Alpine plants grew in the wildest profusion. In the summer red dragonflies flew calmly about, lighting on a hat or a hand, or the rim of a pair of spectacles, as different from the persecuted city dragonfly as a cloud from a mud puddle.

But the dragonflies here before him seemed to be driven by something. It was as though they wanted desperately to avoid being pulled in with the cedar grove as it darkened before the sunset.

The western sun fell on distant mountains, and in the evening light he could see how the red leaves were working their way down from the summits.

"People are delicate, aren't they?" Komako had said that morning. "Broken into a pulp, they say, skull bones and all. And a bear could fall from a higher ledge and not be hurt in the least." There had been another accident up among the rocks, and she had pointed out the mountain on which it had happened.

If man had a tough, hairy hide like a bear, his world would be different indeed, Shimamura thought. It was through a thin, smooth skin that man loved. Looking out at the evening mountains, Shimamura felt a sentimental longing for the human skin.

"The butterfly, the dragonfly, the cricket." A geisha had been singing the song to a clumsy samisen accompaniment as he sat down to an early dinner.

The guidebook gave only the most essential information on routes, schedules, lodgings, costs, and left the rest to the imagination. Shimamura had come down from these mountains, as the new green was making its way through the last of the snow, to meet Komako for the first time; and now, in the autumn climbing season, he found himself drawn again to the mountains he had left his tracks in. Though he was an idler who might as well spend his time in the mountains as anywhere, he looked upon mountain climbing as almost a model of wasted effort. For that very reason it pulled at him with the attraction of the unreal.

When he was far away, he thought incessantly of Komako; but now that he was near her, this sighing for the human skin took on a dreamy quality like the spell of the mountains. Perhaps he felt a certain security, perhaps he was at the moment too intimate, too familiar with her body. She had stayed with him the night before. Sitting alone in the quiet, he could only wait for her. He was sure she would come without his calling. As he listened to the noisy chatter of a group of schoolgirls out on the hiking trip, however, he began to feel a little sleepy. He went to bed early.

Rain fell during the night, one of those quick showers that come in the autumn.

When he awoke the next morning, Komako was sitting primly beside the table, a book open before her. She wore an everyday kimono and cloak.

"Are you awake?" Her voice was soft as she turned to him.

"What are you doing here?"

"Are you awake?"

Shimamura glanced around the room, wondering if she had come in the night without his knowing it. He picked up the watch beside his pillow. It was only six-thirty.

"You're early."

"But the maid has already brought charcoal."

A morninglike steam was rising from the teakettle.

"It's time to get up." She sat beside his pillow, the picture of the proper housewife. Shimamura stretched and yawned. He took the hand on her knee and caressed the small fingers, callused from playing the samisen.

"But it's barely sunrise."

"Did you sleep well by yourself?"

"Very well."

"You didn't grow a mustache after all."

"You did tell me to grow a mustache, didn't you?"

"It's all right. I knew you wouldn't. You always shave yourself nice and blue."

"And you always look as if you'd just shaved when you wash away that powder."

"Isn't your face a little fatter, though? You were very funny asleep, all round and plump with your white skin and no mustache."

"Sweet and gentle?"

"But unreliable."

"You were staring at me, then? I'm not sure I like having people stare at me when I'm asleep."

Komako smiled and nodded. Then, like a glow that breaks into a flame, the smile became a laugh. There was strength in the fingers that took his.

"I hid in the closet. The maid didn't suspect a thing."

"When? How long were you hidden?"

"Just now, of course. When the maid came to bring charcoal." She laughed happily at the prank, and suddenly she was red to the ears. As if to hide her confusion, she began fanning herself with the edge of his quilt. "Get up. Get up, please."

"It's cold." Shimamura pulled the quilt away from her. "Are the inn people up yet?"

"I have no idea. I came in from the back."

"The back?"

"I fought my way up from the cedar grove."

"Is there a path in back?"

"No. But it's shorter."

Shimamura looked at her in surprise.

"No one knows I'm here. I heard someone in the kitchen, but the front door must still be locked."

"You seem to be an early riser."

"I couldn't sleep."

"Did you hear the rain?"

"It rained? That's why the underbrush was wet, then. I'm going home. Go on back to sleep."

But Shimamura jumped vigorously out of bed, the woman's hand still in his. He went over to the window and looked down at the hill she said she had come up.

Below the shrubbery, halfway down toward the cedar grove, dwarf bamboo was growing in a wild tangle. Directly below the window were rows of taro and sweet potatoes, onions and radishes. It was a most ordinary garden patch, and yet the varied colors of the leaves in the morning sun made him feel that he was seeing them for the first time.

The porter was throwing feed to the carp from the corridor that led to the bath.

"It's colder, and they aren't eating well," he said as Shimamura passed. Shimamura stood for a moment looking at the feed on the water, dried and crumbled silkworms.

Komako was waiting for him, clean and prim as before, when he came back from the bath.

"It would be good to work on my sewing in a quiet place like this," she said.

The room had evidently been cleaned, and the sun poured in on the deepest corners of the slightly worn matting.

"You sew, do you?"

"What an insulting question. I had to work harder than anyone else in the family. I see now, looking back, that the years when I was growing up were the worst ones of all." She spoke almost to herself, but her voice was tense as she continued: "The maid saw me. She gave me a strange look and asked when I had come. It was very embarrassing—but I couldn't go on hiding in the closet forever. I'm going home. I'm very busy. I couldn't sleep, and I thought I'd wash my hair. I have to wait for it to dry, and then go to the hairdresser's, and if I don't wash it early in the morning I'm never ready for an afternoon party. There's a party here too, but they only told me about it last night. I won't come. I've made other promises. And I won't be able to see you tonight—it's Saturday and I'll be very busy."

She showed no sign of leaving, however.

She decided not to wash her hair after all. She took Shimamura down to the back garden. Her damp sandals and stockings were hidden under the veranda where she had come in.

The dwarf bamboo she said she had fought her way through seemed impassable. Starting down along the garden path

[48]

toward the sound of the water, they came out on the high river bank. There were children's voices in the chestnut trees. A number of burrs lay in the grass at their feet. Komako stamped them open and took out the fruit. The kernels were small.

Kaya plumes waved on the steep slope of the mountain opposite, a dazzling silver in the morning sun. Dazzling, and yet rather like the fleeting translucence that moved across the autumn sky.

"Shall we cross over? We can see your fiancé's grave."

Komako brought herself to her full height and glared at him. A handful of chestnuts came at his face.

"You're making fun of me."

Shimamura had no time to dodge. The chestnuts lashed at his forehead.

"What possible reason could you have for going to the cemetery?"

"But there's no need to lose your temper."

"I was completely in earnest. I'm not like people who can do exactly as they want and think of no one else."

"And who can do that?" Shimamura muttered weakly.

"Why do you have to call him my fiancé? Didn't I tell you very carefully he wasn't? But you've forgotten, of course."

Shimamura had not forgotten. Indeed, the memory gave the man Yukio a certain weight in his thoughts.

Komako seemed to dislike talking about Yukio. She was not his fiancée, perhaps, but she had become a geisha to help pay doctors' bills. There was no doubt that she had been "completely in earnest."

Shimamura showed no anger even under the barrage of chestnuts. Komako looked curiously at him, and her resistance seemed to collapse. She took his arm. "You're a simple, honest person at heart, aren't you? Something must be making you sad."

"They're watching us from the trees."

"What of it? Tokyo people are complicated. They live in such noise and confusion that their feelings are broken to little bits."

"Everything is broken to little bits."

"Even life, before long. . . . Shall we go to the cemetery?"

"Well. . . ."

"See? You don't really want to go at all."

"But you made such an issue of it."

"Because I've never once gone to the cemetery. I really haven't gone once. I feel guilty sometimes, now that the teacher's buried there too. But I can't very well start going now. I'd only be pretending."

"You're more complicated than I am."

"Why? I'm never able to be completely open with living people, and I want at least to be honest with him now that he's dead."

They came out of the cedar grove, where the quiet seemed to fall in chilly drops. Following the railway along the foot of the ski grounds, they were soon at the cemetery. Some ten weathered old tombstones and a forlorn statue of Jizo, guardian of children, stood on a tiny island of high ground among the paddies. There were no flowers.

Quite without warning, Yoko's head and shoulders rose from the bushes behind the Jizo. Her face wore the usual solemn, masklike expression. She darted a burning glance at the two of them, and nodded a quick greeting to Shimamura. She said nothing.

"Aren't you early, though, Yoko? I thought of going to the hairdresser's. . . ." As Komako spoke, a black squall came upon them and threatened to sweep them from their feet.

A freight train roared past.

"Yoko, Yoko. . . ." A boy was waving his hat in the door of a black freight car.

"Saichiro, Saichiro," Yoko called back.

It was the voice that had called to the station master at the snowy signal stop, a voice so beautiful it was almost lonely, calling out as if to someone who could not hear, on a ship far away.

The train passed, and the buckwheat across the tracks emerged fresh and clean as the blind was lifted. The field of white flowers on red stems was quietness itself.

The two of them had been so startled at seeing Yoko that they had not noticed the approach of the freight train; but the first shock was dispelled by the train.

They seemed still to hear Yoko's voice, and not the dying rumble of the freight train. It seemed to come back like an echo of distilled love.

"My brother," said Yoko, looking after the train. "I wonder if I should go to the station."

"But the train won't wait for you at the station," Komako laughed.

"I suppose not."

"I didn't come to see Yukio's grave."

Yoko nodded. She seemed to hesitate a moment, then knelt down before the grave.

Komako watched stiffly.

Shimamura looked away, toward the Jizo. It had three long faces, and, besides the hands clasped at its breast, a pair each to the left and the right.

"I'm going to wash my hair," Komako said to Yoko. She turned and started back along a ridge between the paddies.

It was the practice in the snow country to string wooden or bamboo poles on a number of levels from tree trunk to tree trunk, and to hang rice sheaves head down from them to dry. At the height of the harvest the frames presented a solid screen of rice. Farmers were hanging out rice along the path Shimamura and Komako took back to the village.

A farm girl threw up a sheaf of rice with a twist of her trousered hips, and a man high above her caught it expertly and in one deft sweep of his hand spread it to hang from the frame. The unconscious, practiced motions were repeated over and over.

Komako took one of the dangling sheaves in her hand and shook it gently up and down, as though she were feeling the weight of a jewel.

"See how it's headed. And how nice it is to the touch. Entirely different from last year's rice." She half-closed her eyes from the pleasure. A disorderly flock of sparrows flew low over her head.

An old notice was pasted to a wall beside the road: "Pay for field hands. Ninety sen a day, meals included. Women forty per cent less."

There were rice frames in front of Yoko's house too, beyond the slightly depressed field that separated the house from the road. One set of frames was strung up high in a row of persimmon trees, along the white wall between the garden and the house next door, while another, at right angles to it, followed the line between the field and the garden. With an opening for a doorway at one end, the frames suggested a makeshift little theater covered not with the usual straw mats but with unthreshed rice. The taro in the field still sent out powerful stems and leaves, but the dahlias and roses beyond were withered. The lotus pond with its red carp was hidden behind the screen of rice, as was the window of the silkworm room, where Komako had lived.

Bowing her head sharply, almost angrily, Yoko went in through the opening in the headed rice.

"Does she live alone?" Shimamura asked, looking after the bowed figure.

"I imagine not." Komako's answer was a little tart. "But what a nuisance. I'll not go to the hairdresser's after all. You say things you have no business saying, and we ruin her visit to the cemetery."

"You're only being difficult—is it really so terrible to run into her at the cemetery?"

"You have no idea how I feel. . . . If I have time later, I'll stop by to wash my hair. I may be late, but I'll stop by."

It was three in the morning.

Shimamura was awakened by a slamming as though someone were knocking the doors loose. Komako lay stretched out on top of him.

"I said I would come and I've come. Haven't I? I said I'd come and I've come, haven't I?" Her chest, even her abdomen, rose and fell violently.

"You're dead-drunk."

"Haven't I? I said I'd come and I've come, haven't I?"

"You have indeed."

"Couldn't see a thing on the way. Not a thing. My head aches."

"How did you manage to get up the hill?"

"I have no idea. Not the slightest." She lay heavily across his chest. He found it a little oppressive, especially when she turned over and arched her back; but, too suddenly awakened, he fell back as he tried to get up. It was an astonishingly hot object that his head came to rest on.

"You're on fire."

"Oh? Fire for a pillow. See that you don't burn yourself."

"I might very well." He closed his eyes and the warmth sank into his head, bringing an immediate sense of life. Reality came through the violent breathing, and with it a sort of nostalgic remorse. He felt as though he were waiting tranquilly for some undefined revenge.

"I said I'd come, and I've come." She spoke with the utmost concentration. "I've come, and now I'm going home. I'm going to wash my hair."

She got to her knees and took a drink of water in great swallows.

"I can't let you go home like this."

"I'm going home. I have some people waiting. Where did I leave my towel?"

Shimamura got up and turned on the light. "Don't!" She hid her face in her hands, then buried it, hands and all, in the quilt.

She had on a bold informal kimono with a narrow undress *obi*, and under it a nightgown. Her under-kimono had slipped down out of sight. She was flushed from drink even to the soles of her bare feet, and there was something very engaging about the way she tried to tuck them out of sight.

Evidently she had thrown down her towel and bath utensils when she came in. Soap and combs were scattered over the floor.

"Cut. I brought scissors."

"What do you want me to cut?"

"This." She pointed at the strings that held her Japanese coiffure in place. "I tried to do it myself, but my hands wouldn't work. I thought maybe I could ask you."

Shimamura separated the hair and cut at the strings, and as he cut she shook the long hair loose. She was somewhat calmer.

"What time is it?"

"Three o'clock."

"Not really! You'll be careful not to cut the hair, won't you?"

"I've never seen so many strings."

The false hair that filled out the coiffure was hot where it touched her head.

"Is it really three o'clock? I must have fallen asleep when I got home. I promised to come for a bath with some people, and they stopped by to call me. They'll be wondering what's happened."

"They're waiting for you?"

"In the public bath. Three of them. There were six parties, but I only got to four. Next week we'll be very busy with people coming to see the maple leaves. Thanks very much." She raised her head to comb her hair, now long and flowing, and she laughed uncertainly. "Funny, isn't it." Unsure what to do with herself, she reached to pick up the false hair. "I have to go. It's not right to keep them waiting. I'll not come again tonight."

"Can you see your way home?"

"Yes."

But she tripped over the skirt of her kimono on the way out.

At seven and again at three in the morning—twice in one short day she had chosen unconventional hours to come calling. There was something far from ordinary in all this, Shimamura told himself.

Guests would soon be coming for the autumn leaves. The door of the inn was being decorated with maple branches to welcome them.

The porter who was somewhat arrogantly directing operations was fond of calling himself a "migrant bird." He and his kind worked the mountain resorts from spring through to the autumn leaves, and moved down to the coast for the winter. He did not much care whether or not he came to the same inn each year. Proud of his experience in the prosperous coast resorts, he had no praise for the way the inn treated its guests. He reminded one of a not-too-sincere beggar as he rubbed his hands together and hovered about prospective guests at the station.

"Have you ever tasted one of these?" he asked Shimamura, picking up a pomegranate-like akebi. "I can bring some in from the mountains if you like." Shimamura, back from a walk, watched him tie the akebi, stem and all, to a maple branch.

The freshly cut branches were so long that they brushed against the eaves. The hallway glowed a bright, fresh scarlet. The leaves were extraordinarily large.

As Shimamura took the cool akebi in his hand, he noticed that Yoko was sitting by the hearth in the office.

The innkeeper's wife was heating saké in a brass boiler. Yoko, seated opposite her, nodded quickly in answer to each remark. She was dressed informally, though she did not have on the everyday "mountain trousers." Her plain woolen kimono was freshly washed.

"That girl is working here?" Shimamura asked the porter nonchalantly.

"Yes, sir. Thanks to all of you, we've had to take on extra help."

"You, for instance."

"That's right. She's an unusual type, though, for a girl from these parts."

Yoko worked only in the kitchen, apparently. She was not yet serving at parties. As the inn filled, the voices of the maids in the kitchen became louder, but he did not remember having heard Yoko's clear voice among them. The maid who took care of his room said that Yoko liked to sing in the bath before she went to bed, but that, too, Shimamura had missed.

Now that he knew Yoko was in the house, he felt strangely reluctant to call Komako. He was conscious of an emptiness that made him see Komako's life as beautiful but wasted, even though he himself was the object of her love; and yet the woman's existence, her straining to live, came touching him like naked skin. He pitied her, and he pitied himself.

He was sure that Yoko's eyes, for all their innocence, could send a probing light to the heart of these matters, and he somehow felt drawn to her too.

Komako came often enough without being called.

When he went to see the maple leaves up the valley, he passed her house. Hearing the automobile and thinking it must be he, she ran out to look—and he did not even glance back, she complained. That was most unfeeling of him. She of course stopped by whenever she came to the inn, and she stopped by too on her way to the bath. When she was to go to a party, she came an hour or so early and waited in his room for the maid to call her. Often she would slip away from a party for a few minutes. After retouching her face in the mirror, she would stand up to leave. "Back to work. I'm all business. Business, business."

She was in the habit of forgetting something she had brought with her, a cloak, perhaps, or the cover to a samisen plectrum.

"Last night when I got home there was no hot water for tea. I hunted through the kitchen and found the left-overs from breakfast. Co-o-old. . . . They didn't call me this morning. When I woke up it was already ten-thirty. I meant to come see you at seven, but it was no good."

Such were the things she talked of. Or she told him of the inn she had gone to first, and the next and the next, and the parties she had been to at each.

"I'll come again later." She had a glass of water before she left. "Or maybe I won't. Thirty guests and only three of us. I'll be much too busy."

But almost immediately she was back. "It's hard work. Thirty of them and only three of us. And the other two are the very oldest and the very youngest in town, and that leaves all the hard work for me. Stingy people. A travel club of some sort, I suppose. With thirty guests you need at least six geisha. I'll go have a drink and pick a fight with them."

So it was every day. Komako must have wanted to crawl away and hide at the thought of where it was leading. But that indefinable air of loneliness only made her the more seductive.

"The floor always creaks when I come down the hall. I walk very softly, but

they hear me just the same. 'Off to the Camellia Room again, Komako?' they say as I go by the kitchen. I never thought I'd have to worry so about my reputation."

"The town's really too small."

"Everyone has heard about us, of course."

"That will never do."

"You begin to have a bad name, and you're ruined in a little place like this." But she looked up and smiled. "It makes no difference. My kind can find work anywhere."

That straightforward manner, so replete with direct, immediate feeling, was quite foreign to Shimamura, the idler who had inherited his money.

"It will be the same, wherever I go. There's nothing to be upset about."

But he caught an echo of the woman underneath the surface nonchalance.

"And I can't complain. After all, only women are able really to love." She flushed a little and looked at the floor.

Her kimono stood out from her neck, and her back and shoulders were like a white fan spread under it. There was something sad about the full flesh under that white powder. It suggested a woolen cloth, and again it suggested the pelt of some animal.

"In the world as it is," he murmured, chilled at the sterility of the words even as he spoke.

But Komako only replied: "As it always has been." She raised her head and added absentmindedly: "You didn't know that?"

The red under-kimono clinging to her skin disappeared as she looked up.

Shimamura was translating Valéry and Alain, and French treatises on the dance from the golden age of the Russian ballet. He meant to bring them out in a small luxury edition at his own expense. The book would in all likelihood contribute nothing to the Japanese dancing world. One could nonetheless say, if pressed, that it would bring aid and comfort to Shimamura. He pampered himself with the somewhat whimsical pleasure of sneering at himself through his work, and it may well have been from such a pleasure that his sad little dream world sprang. Off on a trip, he saw no need to hurry himself.

He spent much of his time watching insects in their death agonies.

Each day, as the autumn grew colder, insects died on the floor of his room. Stiff-winged insects fell on their backs and were unable to get to their feet again. A bee walked a little and collapsed, walked a little and collapsed. It was a quiet death that came with the change of seasons. Looking closely, however, Shimamura could see that the legs and feelers were trembling in the struggle to live. For such a tiny death, the empty eight-mat room* seemed enormous.

As he picked up a dead insect to throw it out, he sometimes thought for an instant of the children he had left in Tokyo.

A moth on the screen was still for a very long time. It too was dead, and it fell to the earth like a dead leaf. Occasionally a moth fell from the wall. Taking it up in his hand, Shimamura would wonder how to account for such beauty.

The screens were removed, and the singing of the insects was more subdued and lonely day by day.

The russet deepened on the Border Range. In the evening sun the mountains lighted up sharply, like a rather chilly stone. The inn was filled with maple-viewing guests.

"I don't think I'll come again tonight. Some people from the village are having a party." Komako left, and presently he heard a drum in the large banquet-room,

and strident women's voices. At the very height of the festivities he was startled by a clear voice almost at his elbow.

"May I come in?" It was Yoko. "Komako asked me to bring this."

She thrust her hand out like a postman. Then, remembering her manners, she knelt down awkwardly before him. Shimamura opened the knotted bit of paper, and Yoko was gone. He had not had time to speak to her.

"Having a fine, noisy time. And drinking." That was the whole of the message, written in a drunken hand on a paper napkin.

Not ten minutes later Komako staggered in.

"Did she bring something to you?"

"She did."

"Oh?" Komako cocked an eye at him in wonderfully high spirits. "I do feel good. I said I'd go order more saké, and I ran away. The porter caught me. But saké is wonderful. I don't care a bit if the floor creaks. I don't care if they scold me. As soon as I come here I start feeling drunk, though. Damn. Well, back to work."

"You're rosy down to the tips of your fingers."

"Business is waiting. Business, business. Did she say anything? Terribly jealous. Do you know how jealous?"

"Who?"

"Someone will be murdered one of these days."

"She's working here?"

"She brings saké, and then stands there staring in at us, with her eyes flashing. I suppose you like her sort of eyes."

"She probably thinks you're a disgrace."

"That's why I gave her a note to bring to you. I want water. Give me water. Who's a disgrace? Try seducing her too before you answer my question. Am I drunk?" She peered into the mirror, bracing both hands against the stand. A

_____
* About four yards square.

moment later, kicking aside the long skirts, she swept from the room.

The party was over. The inn was soon quiet, and Shimamura could hear a distant clatter of dishes. Komako must have been taken off by a guest to a second party, he concluded; but just then Yoko came in with another bit of paper.

"Decided not to go to Sampukan go from here to the Plum Room may stop by on way home good night."

Shimamura smiled wryly, a little uncomfortable before Yoko. "Thank you very much. You've come to help here?"

She darted a glance at him with those beautiful eyes, so bright that he felt impaled on them. His discomfort was growing.

The girl left a deep impression each time he saw her, and now she was sitting before him—a strange uneasiness swept over him. Her too-serious manner made her seem always at the very center of some remarkable occurrence.

"They're keeping you busy, I suppose."

"But there's very little I can do."

"It's strange how often I see you. The first time was when you were bringing that man home. You talked to the station master about your brother. Do you remember?"

"Yes."

"They say you sing in the bath before you go to bed."

"Really! They accuse me of having such bad manners?" The voice was astonishingly beautiful.

"I feel I know everything about you."

"Oh? And have you asked Komako, then?"

"She won't say a thing. She seems to dislike talking about you."

"I see." Yoko turned quickly away. "Komako is a fine person, but she's not been lucky. Be good to her." She spoke rapidly, and her voice trembled very slightly on the last words.

"But there's nothing I can do for her."

It seemed that the girl's whole body must soon be trembling. Shimamura looked away, fearful that a dangerous light would be breaking out on the too-earnest face.

He laughed. "I think I'd best go back to Tokyo soon."

"I'm going to Tokyo myself."

"When?"

"It doesn't matter."

"Shall I see you to Tokyo when I go back?"

"Please do." The seriousness was intense, and at the same time her tone suggested that the matter was after all trivial. Shimamura was startled.

"If it will be all right with your family."

"The brother who works on the railroad is all the family I have. I can decide for myself."

"Have you made arrangements in Tokyo?"

"No."

"Have you talked to Komako, then?"

"To Komako? I don't like Komako. I haven't talked to her."

She looked up at him with moist eyes—a sign perhaps that her defenses were breaking down—and he found in them an uncanny sort of beauty. But at that moment his affection for Komako welled up violently. To run off to Tokyo, as if eloping, with a nondescript woman would somehow be in the nature of an intense apology to Komako, and a penance for Shimamura himself.

"It doesn't frighten you to go off alone with a man?"

"Why should it?"

"It doesn't seem dangerous to go to Tokyo without at least deciding where you will stay and what you might want to do?"

"A woman by herself can always get by." There was a delicious lilt in her speech. Her eyes were fixed on his as she spoke again: "You won't hire me as a maid?"

"Really, now. Hire you as a maid?"

"But I don't want to be a maid."

"What were you in Tokyo before?"

"A nurse."

"You were in a hospital? Or in nursing school?"

"I just thought I'd like to be a nurse."

Shimamura smiled. This perhaps explained the earnestness with which she had taken care of the music teacher's son on the train.

"And you still want to be a nurse?"

"I won't be a nurse now."

"But you'll have to make up your mind. This indecisiveness will never do."

"Indecisiveness? It has nothing to do with indecisiveness." Her laugh threw back the accusation.

Her laugh, like her voice, was so high and clear that it was almost lonely. There was not a suggestion in it of the dull or the simple-minded; but it struck emptily at the shell of Shimamura's heart, and fell away in silence.

"What's funny?"

"But there has only been one man I could possibly nurse."

Again Shimamura was startled.

"I could never again."

"I see." His answer was quiet. He had been caught off guard. "They say you spend all your time at the cemetery."

"I do."

"And for the rest of your life you can never nurse anyone else, or visit anyone else's grave?"

"Never again."

"How can you leave the grave and go off to Tokyo, then?"

"I'm sorry. Do take me with you."

"Komako says you're frightfully jealous. Wasn't the man her fiancé?"

"Yukio? It's a lie. It's a lie."

"Why do you dislike Komako, then?"

"Komako." She spoke as if calling to someone in the same room, and she gazed hotly at Shimamura. "Be good to Komako."

"But I can do nothing for her."

There were tears in the corners of Yoko's eyes. She sniffled as she slapped at a small moth on the matting. "Komako says I'll go crazy." With that she slipped from the room.

Shimamura felt a chill come over him.

As he opened the window to throw out the moth, he caught a glimpse of the drunken Komako playing parlor games with a guest. She leaned forward half from her seat, as though to push her advantage home by force. The sky had clouded over. Shimamura went down for a bath.

In the women's bath next door, Yoko was bathing the innkeeper's little daughter.

Her voice was gentle as she undressed the child and bathed it—soothing and agreeable, like the voice of a young mother.

Presently she was singing in that same voice:

"See, out in back,
Three pears, three cedars,
Six trees in all.
Crows' nests below,
Sparrows' nests above.
And what is it they're singing?
'Hakamairi itchō, itchō, itchō ya.' "*

It was a song little girls sang as they bounced rubber balls. The quick, lively manner in which Yoko rolled off the nonsense-words made Shimamura wonder if he might not have seen the earlier Yoko in a dream.

She chattered on as she dressed the child and led it from the bath, and even

* In imitation of the birds. Literally: "To the cemetery, a hundred yards, a hundred yards, a hundred yards again."

when she was gone her voice seemed to echo on like a flute. On the worn floor of the hallway, polished to a dark glow, a geisha had left behind a samisen box, the very embodiment of quiet in the late autumn night. As Shimamura was looking for the owner's name, Komako came out from the direction of the clattering dishes.

"What are you looking at?"

"Is she staying the night?"

"Who? Oh, her. Don't be foolish. You think we carry these with us wherever we go, do you? Sometimes we leave them at an inn for days on end." She laughed, but almost immediately she was breathing painfully and her eyes were screwed tightly shut. Dropping her long skirts, she fell against Shimamura. "Take me home, please."

"You don't have to go, do you?"

"It's no good. I have to go. The rest went on to other parties and left me behind. No one will say anything if I don't stay too long—I had business here. But if they stop by my house on their way to the bath and find me away, they'll start talking."

Drunk though she was, she walked briskly down the steep hill.

"You made that girl weep."

"She does seem a trifle crazy."

"And do you enjoy making such remarks?"

"But didn't you say it yourself? She remembered how you said she would go crazy, and it was then that she broke down—mostly out of resentment, I suspect."

"Oh? It's all right, then."

"And not ten minutes later she was in the bath, singing in fine voice."

"She's always liked to sing in the bath."

"She said very seriously that I must be good to you."

"Isn't she foolish, though? But you didn't have to tell me."

"Tell you? Why is it that you always seem so touchy when that girl is mentioned?"

"Would you like to have her?"

"See? What call is there for a remark like that?"

"I'm not joking. Whenever I look at her, I feel as though I have a heavy load and can't get rid of it. Somehow I always feel that way. If you're really fond of her, take a good look at her. You'll see what I mean." She laid her hand on his shoulder and leaned toward him. Then, abruptly, she shook her head. "No, that's not what I want. If she were to fall into the hands of someone like you, she might not go crazy after all. Why don't you take my load for me?"

"You're going a little too far."

"You think I'm drunk and talking nonsense? I'm not. I would know she was being well taken care of, and I could go pleasantly to seed here in the mountains. It would be a fine, quiet feeling."

"That's enough."

"Just leave me alone." In her flight, she ran into the closed door of the house she lived in.

"They've decided you're not coming home."

"But I can open it." The door sounded old and dry as she lifted it from the groove and pushed it back.

"Come on in."

"But think of the hour."

"Everyone will be asleep."

Shimamura hesitated.

"I'll see you back to the inn, then."

"I can go by myself."

"But you haven't seen my room."

They stepped through the kitchen door, and the sleeping figures of the family lay sprawled before them. The thin mattresses on the floor were covered with cheap striped cloth, now faded, of the sort often used for "mountain trousers." The mother and father and five or six children, the oldest a girl perhaps

[57]

sixteen, lay under a scorched lampshade. Heads faced in every direction. There was drab poverty in the scene, and yet under it there lay an urgent, powerful vitality.

As if thrown back by the warm breath of all the sleepers, Shimamura started toward the door. Komako noisily closed it in his face, however, and went in through the kitchen. She made no attempt to soften her footsteps. Shimamura followed stealthily past the children's pillows, a strange thrill rising in his chest.

"Wait here. I'll turn on the light upstairs."

"It's all right." Shimamura climbed the stairs in the dark. As he looked back, he saw the candy shop beyond the homely sleeping faces.

The matting was worn in the four rustic rooms on the second floor.

"It's a little large, I have to admit, for just one person." The partitions between the rooms had been taken down, and Komako's bedding lay small and solitary inside the sliding doors, their paper panels yellowed with age, that separated the rooms from the skirting corridor. Old furniture and tools, evidently the property of the family she lived with, were piled in the far room. Party kimonos hung from pegs along the wall. The whole suggested a fox's or badger's lair to Shimamura.

Komako sat down solidly in the slightly raised alcove and offered him the only cushion.

"Bright red." She peered into the mirror. "Am I really so drunk?" She fumbled through the top drawer of the dresser. "Here. My diary."

"As long as this, is it?"

She took up a small figured-paper box filled to the top with assorted cigarettes.

"I push them up my sleeve or inside my *obi* when a guest gives them to me, and some of them are a little smashed.

They're clean, though. I make up for wrinkles by having every variety to offer." She stirred up the contents to demonstrate that he could have his choice.

"But I don't have a match. I don't need matches now that I've stopped smoking."

"It's all right. How is the sewing?"

"I try to work at it, but the guests for the maple leaves keep me busy." She turned to put away the sewing that lay in front of the dresser.

The fine-grained chest of drawers and the expensive vermilion-lacquered sewing-box, relics perhaps of her years in Tokyo, were as they had been in the attic that so resembled an old paper box; but they seemed sadly out of place in these dilapidated second-floor rooms.

A thin string ran from Komako's pillow to the ceiling.

"I turn the light out with this when I'm reading." She tugged at the string. Gentle and subdued, the proper housewife again, she was not quite able even so to hide her discomposure.

"Lonely as the fox's lady out at night, aren't you?"

"I really am."

"And do you mean to live here four years?"

"But it's going on a year already. It won't be long."

Shimamura was nervous. He thought he could hear the breathing of the family below, and he had run out of things to talk about. He stood up to leave.

Komako slid the door half shut behind him. She glanced up at the sky. "It's beginning to look like snow. The end of the maple leaves." She recited a line of poetry* as she stepped outside: "Here in our mountains, the snow falls even on the maple leaves."

_____
* The line is from a Kabuki play.

"Well, good night."

"Wait. I'll see you back to the hotel. As far as the door, no farther."

But she followed him inside.

"Go on to bed." She slipped away, and a few minutes later she was back with two glasses filled to the brim with *saké*.

"Drink," she ordered as she stepped into the room. "We're going to have a drink."

"But aren't they asleep? Where did you find it?"

"I know where they keep it." She had quite obviously had herself a drink as she poured from the vat. The earlier drunkenness had come back. With narrowed eyes, she watched the *saké* spill over on her hand. "It's no fun, though, swallowing the stuff down in the dark."

Shimamura drank meekly from the cup that was thrust at him.

It was not usual for him to get drunk on so little; but perhaps he was chilled from the walk. He began to feel sick. His head was whirling, and he could almost see himself going pale. He closed his eyes and fell back on the quilt. Komako put her arms around him in alarm. A child-like feeling of security came to him from the warmth of her body.

She seemed ill at ease, like a young woman, still childless, who takes a baby up in her arms. She raised her head and looked down, as at the sleeping child.

"You're a good girl."

"Why? Why am I good? What's good about me?"

"You're a good girl."

"Don't tease me. It's wrong of you." She looked aside, and she spoke in broken phrases, like little blows, as she rocked him back and forth.

She laughed softly to herself.

"I'm not good at all. It's not easy having you here. You'd best go home. Each time I come to see you I want to put on a new kimono, and now I have none left. This one is borrowed. So you see I'm not really good at all."

Shimamura did not answer.

"And what do you find good in me?" Her voice was a little husky. "The first day I met you I thought I had never seen anyone I disliked more. People just don't say the sort of things you said. I hated you."

Shimamura nodded.

"Oh? You understand then why I've not mentioned it before? When a woman has to say these things, she has gone as far as she can, you know."

"But it's all right."

"Is it?" They were silent for some moments. Komako seemed to be looking back on herself, and the awareness of a woman's being alive came to Shimamura in her warmth.

"You're a good woman."

"How am I good?"

"A good woman."

"What an odd person." Her face was hidden from him, as though she were rubbing her jaw against an itching shoulder. Then suddenly, Shimamura had no idea why, she raised herself angrily to an elbow.

"A good woman—what do you mean by that? What do you mean?"

He only stared at her.

"Admit it. That's why you came to see me. You were laughing at me. You were laughing at me after all."

She glared at him, scarlet with anger. Her shoulders were shaking. But the flush receded as quickly as it had come, and tears were falling over her blanched face.

"I hate you. How I hate you." She rolled out of bed and sat with her back to him.

Shimamura felt a stabbing in his chest as he saw what the mistake had been. He lay silent, his eyes closed.

"It makes me very sad," she murmured

to herself. Her head was on her knees, and her body was bent into a tight ball.

When she had wept herself out, she sat jabbing at the floor mat with a silver hair-ornament. Presently she slipped from the room.

Shimamura could not bring himself to follow her. She had reason to feel hurt.

But soon she was back, her bare feet quiet in the corridor. "Are you going for a bath?" she called from outside the door. It was a high, thin little voice.

"If you want."

"I'm sorry. I've reconsidered."

She showed no sign of coming in. Shimamura picked up his towel and stepped into the hall. She walked ahead of him with her eyes on the floor, like a criminal being led away. As the bath warmed her, however, she became strangely gay and winsome, and sleep was out of the question.

The next morning Shimamura awoke to a voice reciting a Nō play.

He lay for a time listening. Komako turned and smiled from the mirror.

"The guests in the Plum Room. I was called there after my first party. Remember?"

"A Nō club out on a trip?"

"Yes."

"It snowed?"

"Yes." She got up and threw open the sliding door in front of the window. "No more maple leaves."

From the gray sky, framed by the window, the snow floated toward them in great flakes, like white peonies. There was something quietly unreal about it. Shimamura stared with the vacantness that comes from lack of sleep.

The Nō reciters had taken out a drum.

He remembered the snowy morning toward the end of the year before, and glanced at the mirror. The cold peonies floated up yet larger, cutting a white outline around Komako. Her kimono was open at the neck, and she was wiping at her throat with a towel.

Her skin was as clean as if it had just been laundered. He had not dreamed that she was a woman who would find it necessary to take offense at such a trivial remark, and that very fact lent her an irresistible sadness.

The mountains, more distant each day as the russet of the autumn leaves had darkened, came brightly back to life with the snow.

The cedars, under a thin coating of snow, rose sheer from the white ground to the sky, each cut off sharply from the rest.

The thread was spun in the snow, and the cloth woven in the snow, washed in the snow, and bleached in the snow. Everything, from the first spinning of the thread to the last finishing touches, was done in the snow. "There is Chijimi linen because there is snow," someone wrote long ago. "Snow is the mother of Chijimi."

The Chijimi grass-linen of this snow country was the handwork of the mountain maiden through the long, snow-bound winters. Shimamura searched for the cloth in old-clothes shops to use for summer kimonos. Through acquaintances in the dance world, he had found a shop that specialized in old Nō robes, and he had a standing order that when a good piece of Chijimi came in he was to see it.

In the old days, it is said, the early Chijimi fair was held in the spring, when the snow had melted and the snow blinds were taken down from the houses. People came from far and near to buy Chijimi, even wholesalers from the great commercial cities, Edo, Nagoya, and Osaka; and the inns at which they stayed were fixed by tradition. Since the labors of half a year were on display, youths and maidens gathered from all the mountain villages. Sellers' booths and buyers' booths were lined up side by side, and the market took on the air of a festival. With prizes awarded for the best pieces of weaving, it came also to be sort of competition for husbands. The girls learned to weave as children, and they turned out their best work between the ages of perhaps fourteen and twenty-four. As they grew older they lost the touch that gave tone to the finest Chijimi. In their desire to be numbered among the few outstanding weavers, they put their whole labor and love into this product of the long snowbound months—the months of seclusion and boredom, between October, under the old lunar calendar, when the spinning began, and mid-February of the following year, when the last bleaching was finished.

There may have been among Shimamura's kimonos one or more woven by these mountain maidens toward the middle of the last century.

He still sent his kimonos back for "snow-bleaching." It was a great deal of trouble to return old kimonos—that had touched the skin of he could not know whom—for rebleaching each year to the country that had produced them; but when he considered the labors of those mountain maidens, he wanted the bleaching to be done properly in the country where the maidens had lived. The thought of the white linen, spread out on the deep snow, the cloth and the snow glowing scarlet in the rising sun, was enough to make him feel that the dirt of the summer had been washed away, even that he himself had been bleached clean. It must be added, however, that a Tokyo shop took care of the details for him, and he had no way of knowing that the bleaching had really been done in the old manner.

From ancient times there were houses that specialized in bleaching. The weavers for the most part did not do

their own. White Chijimi was spread out on the snow after it was woven, colored Chijimi bleached on frames while still in thread. The bleaching season came in January and February under the lunar calendar, and snow-covered fields and gardens were the bleaching grounds.

The cloth or thread was soaked overnight in ash water. The next morning it was washed over and over again, wrung, and put out to bleach. The process was repeated day after day, and the sight when, as the bleaching came to an end, the rays of the rising sun turned the white Chijimi blood-red was quite beyond description, Shimamura had read in an old book. It was something to be shown to natives of warmer provinces. And the end of the bleaching was a sign that spring was coming to the snow country.

The land of the Chijimi was very near this hot spring, just down the river, where the valley began to widen out. Indeed it must almost have been visible from Shimamura's window. All of the Chijimi market towns now had railway stations, and the region was still a well-known weaving center.

Since Shimamura had never come to the snow country in midsummer, when he wore Chijimi, or in the snowy season, when it was woven, he had never had occasion to talk of it to Komako; and she hardly seemed the person to ask about the fate of an old folk art.

When he heard the song Yoko sang in the bath, it had come to him that, had she been born long ago, she might have sung thus as she worked over her spools and looms, so exactly suited to the fancy was her voice.

The thread of the grass-linen, finer than animal hair, is difficult to work except in the humidity of the snow, it is said, and the dark, cold season is therefore ideal for weaving. The ancients used to add that the way this product of the cold has of feeling cool to the skin in the hottest weather is a play of the principles of light and darkness. This Komako too, who had so fastened herself to him, seemed at center cool, and the remarkable, concentrated warmth was for that fact all the more touching.

But this love would leave behind it nothing so definite as a piece of Chijimi. Though cloth to be worn is among the most short-lived of craftworks, a good piece of Chijimi, if it has been taken care of, can be worn quite unfaded a half-century and more after weaving. As Shimamura thought absently how human intimacies have not even so long a life, the image of Komako as the mother of another man's children suddenly floated into his mind. He looked around, startled. Possibly he was tired.

He had stayed so long that one might wonder whether he had forgotten his wife and children. He stayed not because he could not leave Komako nor because he did not want to. He had simply fallen into the habit of waiting for those frequent visits. And the more continuous the assault became, the more he began to wonder what was lacking in him, what kept him from living as completely. He stood gazing at his own coldness, so to speak. He could not understand how she had so lost herself. All of Komako came to him, but it seemed that nothing went out from him to her. He heard in his chest, like snow piling up, the sound of Komako, an echo beating against empty walls. And he knew that he could not go on pampering himself forever.

He leaned against the brazier, provided against the coming of the snowy season, and thought how unlikely it was that he would come again once he had left. The innkeeper had lent him an old Kyoto teakettle, skillfully inlaid in silver with flowers and birds, and from it came the sound of wind in the pines. He could make out two pine breezes, as a matter of fact, a near one and a far one. Just beyond the far breeze he heard faintly the tinkling of a bell. He put his ear to the kettle and listened. Far away, where the bell tinkled on, he suddenly saw Komako's feet, tripping in time with the bell. He drew back. The time had come to leave.

He thought of going to see the Chijimi country. That excursion might set him on his way toward breaking away from this hot spring.

He did not know at which of the towns downstream he should get off the train. Not interested in modern weaving centers, he chose a station that looked suitably lonesome and backward. After walking for a time he came out on what seemed to be the main street of an old post town.

The eaves pushing out far beyond the houses were supported by pillars along both sides of the street, and in their shade were passages for communication when the snow was deep, rather like the open lean-to the old Edo shopkeeper used for displaying his wares. With deep eaves on one side of each house, the passages stretched on down the street.

Since the houses were joined in a solid block, the snow from the roofs could only be thrown down into the street. One might more accurately say that at its deepest the snow was thrown not down but up, to a high bank of snow in the middle of the street. Tunnels were cut through for passage from one side to the other.

The houses in Komako's hot-spring village, for all of its being a part of this same snow country, were separated by open spaces, and this was therefore the first time Shimamura had seen the snow passages. He tried walking in one of them. The shade under the old eaves was dark, and the leaning pillars were beginning to rot at their bases. He walked along looking into the houses as into the gloom where generation after generation of his ancestors had endured the long snows.

He saw that the weaver maidens, giving themselves up to their work here under the snow, had lived lives far from as bright and fresh as the Chijimi they made. With an allusion to a Chinese poem, Shimamura's old book had pointed out that in harsh economic terms the making of Chijimi was quite impractical, so great was the expenditure of effort that went into even one piece. It followed that none of the Chijimi houses had been able to hire weavers from outside.

The nameless workers, so diligent while they lived, had presently died, and only the Chijimi remained, the plaything of men like Shimamura, cool and fresh against the skin in the summer. This rather unremarkable thought struck him as most remarkable. The labor into which a heart has poured its whole love —where will it have its say, to excite and inspire, and when?

Like the old post road that was its ancestor, the main street ran without a curve through the straggling village, and no doubt on through Komako's hot spring. The roofs, with rows of stones to weigh down their shingles, were very much like the ones he already knew.

The pillars supporting the deep eaves cast dim shadows across the ground. With his hardly having noticed, afternoon had drawn on toward evening.

There was nothing more to see. He took a train to another village, very much like the first. Again he walked about for a time. Feeling a little chilly, he stopped for a bowl of noodles.

The noodle shop stood beside a river, probably the river that flowed past the hot spring. Shaven-headed Buddhist nuns were crossing a bridge in twos and threes to the far side. All wore rough straw sandals, and some had dome-shaped straw hats tied to their backs. Evidently on their way from a service, they looked like crows hurrying home to their nests.

"Quite a procession of them," Shimamura said to the woman who kept the shop.

"There's a nunnery up in the hills. I suppose they're getting everything done now. It will be next to impossible for them to go out once the heavy snows begin."

The mountain beyond the bridge, growing dark in the twilight, was already covered with snow.

In this snow country, cold, cloudy days succeed one another as the leaves fall and the winds grow chilly. Snow is in the air. The high mountains near and far become white in what the people of the country call "the round of the peaks." Along the coast the sea roars, and inland the mountains roar—"the roaring at the center," like a distant clap of thunder. The round of the peaks and the roaring at the center announce that the snows are not far away. This too Shimamura had read in his old book.

The first snow had fallen the morning he lay in bed listening to the Nō recital. Had the roaring already been heard, then, in the sea and the mountains? Perhaps his senses were sharper, off on a trip with only the company of the woman Komako: even now he seemed to catch an echo of a distant roaring.

"They'll be snowbound too, will they? How many are there?"

"A great many."

"What do they do with themselves, do you suppose, shut up together through the snows? Maybe we could set them to making Chijimi."

The woman smiled vaguely at the inquisitive stranger.

Shimamura went back to the station and waited two hours for a train. The wintry sun set, and the air was so clear that it seemed to burnish the stars. Shimamura's feet were cold.

He arrived back at the hot spring not knowing what he had gone out looking for. The taxi crossed the tracks into the village as usual. A brightly lighted house stood before them as they skirted the cedar grove. Shimamura felt warm and safe again. It was the restaurant Kikumura, and three or four geisha were talking in the doorway.

Komako will be among them—but almost before he had time to frame the thought he saw only Komako.

The driver put on the brakes. Apparently he had heard rumors about the two.

Shimamura turned away from her to look out the rear window. In the light of the stars, the tracks were clear against the snow, surprisingly far into the distance.

Komako closed her eyes and jumped at the taxi. It moved slowly up the hill without stopping. She stood on the running-board, hunched over the door handle.

She had leaped at the car as if to devour it, but for Shimamura something warm had suddenly come near. The impulsive act struck him as neither rash nor unnatural. Komako raised one arm, half-embracing the closed window. Her kimono sleeve fell back from her wrist, and the warm red of the under-kimono, spilling through the thick glass, sank its way into the half-frozen Shimamura.

She pressed her forehead to the window. "Where have you been? Tell me where you've been," she called in a high voice.

"Don't be a fool. You'll get hurt," he shouted back, but they both knew it was only a gentle game.

She opened the door and fell inside the taxi. It had already stopped, however.

They were at the foot of the path up the mountain.

"Where have you been?"

"Well. . . ."

"Where?"

"Nowhere in particular."

He noticed with surprise that she had the geisha's way of arranging her skirts.

The driver waited silently. It was a bit odd, Shimamura had to admit, for them to be sitting in a taxi that had gone as far as it could.

"Let's get out." Komako put her hand on his. "Cold. See how cold. Why didn't you take me with you?"

"You think I should have?"

"What a strange person." She laughed happily as she hurried up the stone steps. "I saw you leave. About two . . . a little before three?"

"That's right."

"I ran out when I heard the car. I ran out in front. And you didn't look around."

"Look around?"

"You didn't. Why didn't you look around?"

Shimamura was a little surprised at this insistence.

"You didn't know I was seeing you off, did you?"

"I didn't."

"See?" Laughing happily to herself, she came very near him. "Why didn't you take me along? You leave me behind and you come back cold—I don't like it at all."

Suddenly a fire-alarm was ringing, with the special fury that told of an emergency.

They looked back.

"Fire, fire!"

"A fire!"

A column of sparks was rising in the village below.

Komako cried out two or three times, and clutched at Shimamura's hand.

A tongue of flames shot up intermittently in the spiral of smoke, dipping down to lick at the roofs about it.

"Where is it? Fairly near the music teacher's?"

"No."

"Where, then?"

"Farther up toward the station."

The tongue of flame sprang high over the roofs.

"It's the cocoon-warehouse. The warehouse. Look, look! The cocoon-warehouse is on fire." She pressed her face to his shoulder. "The warehouse, the warehouse!"

The fire blazed higher. From the mountain, however, it was as quiet under the starry sky as a little make-believe fire. Still the terror of it came across to them. They could almost hear the roar of the flames. Shimamura put his arm around Komako's shoulders.

"What is there to be afraid of?"

"No, no, no!" Komako shook her head and burst into tears. Her face seemed smaller than usual in Shimamura's hand. The hard forehead was trembling.

She had burst out weeping at the sight of the fire, and Shimamura held her to him without thinking to wonder what had so upset her.

She stopped weeping as quickly as she had begun, and pulled away from him.

"There's a movie in the warehouse. Tonight. The place will be full of people. . . . People will be hurt. People will burn to death."

They hurried up toward the inn. There was shouting above them. Guests stood on the second- and third-floor verandas, flooded with light from the open doors. At the edge of the garden, withering chrysanthemums were silhouetted against the light from the inn—or the starlight. For an instant he almost thought it was the light from the fire. Several figures stood beyond the chrysanthemums. The porter and two or three others came bounding down the steps.

"Is it the cocoon-warehouse?" Komako called after them.

"That's right."

"Is anyone hurt? Has anyone been hurt?"

"They're getting everyone out. The film caught fire, and in no time the whole place was on fire. Heard it over the telephone. Look!" The porter raised one arm as he ran off. "Throwing children over one after another from the balcony, they say."

"What shall we do?" Komako started off down the stairs after the porter. Several others overtook her, and she too broke into a run. Shimamura followed.

At the foot of the stairs, their uneasiness increased. Only the very tip of the flames showed over the roofs, and the fire-alarm was nearer and more urgent.

"Careful. It's frozen, and you might slip." She stopped as she turned to look back at him. "But it's all right. You don't need to go any farther. I ought to go on myself to see if anyone has been hurt."

There was indeed no reason for him to go on. His excitement fell away. He looked down at his feet and saw that they had come to the crossing.

"The Milky Way. Beautiful, isn't it," Komako murmured. She looked up at the sky as she ran off ahead of him.

The Milky Way. Shimamura too looked up, and he felt himself floating into the Milky Way. Its radiance was so near that it seemed to take him up into it. Was this the bright vastness the poet Bashō saw when he wrote of the Milky Way arched over a stormy sea? The Milky Way came down just over there, to wrap the night earth in its naked embrace. There was a terrible voluptuousness about it. Shimamura fancied that his own small shadow was being cast up against it from the earth. Each individual star stood apart from the rest, and even the particles of silver dust in the luminous clouds could be picked out, so clear was the night. The limitless depth of the Milky Way pulled his gaze up into it.

"Wait, wait," Shimamura called.

"Come on." Komako ran toward the dark mountain on which the Milky Way was falling.

She seemed to have her long skirts in her hands, and as her arms waved the skirts rose and fell a little. He could feel the red over the starlit snow.

He ran after her as fast as he could.

She slowed down and took his hand, and the long skirts fell to the ground. "You're going too?"

"Yes."

"Always looking for excitement." She clutched at her skirts, now trailing over the snow. "But people will laugh. Please go back."

"Just a little farther."

"But it's wrong. People won't like it if I take you to a fire."

He nodded and stopped. Her hand still rested lightly on his sleeve, however, as she walked on.

"Wait for me somewhere. I'll be right back. Where will you wait?"

"Wherever you say."

"Let's see. A little farther." She peered into his face, and abruptly shook her head. "No. I don't want you to."

She threw herself against him. He reeled back a step or two. A row of onions was growing in the thin snow beside the road.

"I hated it." That sudden torrent of words came at him again. "You said I was a good woman, didn't you? You're going away. Why did you have to say that to me?"

He could see her stabbing at the mat with that silver hair-ornament.

"I cried about it. I cried again after I got home. I'm afraid to leave you. But please go away. I won't forget that you made me cry."

A feeling of nagging, hopeless impotence came over Shimamura at the thought that a simple misunderstanding had worked its way so deep into the woman's being. But just then they heard shouts from the direction of the fire, and a new burst of flame sent up its column of sparks.

"Look. See how it's flaming up again."

They ran on, released.

Komako ran well. Her sandals skimmed the frozen snow, and her arms, close to her sides, seemed hardly to move. She was as one whose whole strength is concentrated in the breast—a strangely small figure, Shimamura thought. Too plump for running himself, he was exhausted the more quickly from watching her. But Komako too was soon out of breath. She fell against him.

"My eyes are watering," she said. "That's how cold it is."

Shimamura's eyes too were moist. His cheeks were flushed, and only his eyes were cold. He blinked, and the Milky Way came to fill them. He tried to keep the tears from spilling over.

"Is the Milky Way like this every night?"

"The Milky Way? Beautiful, isn't it? But it's not like this every night. It's not usually so clear."

The Milky Way flowed over them in the direction they were running, and seemed to bathe Komako's head in its light.

The shape of her slightly aquiline nose was not clear, and the color was gone from her small lips. Was it so dim, then, the light that cut across the sky and overflowed it? Shimamura found that hard to believe. The light was dimmer even than on the night of the new moon, and yet the Milky Way was brighter than the brightest full moon. In the faint light that left no shadows on the earth, Komako's face floated up like an old mask. It was strange that even in the mask there should be the scent of the woman.

He looked up, and again the Milky Way came down to wrap itself around the earth.

And the Milky Way, like a great aurora, flowed through his body to stand at the edges of the earth. There was a quiet, chilly loneliness in it, and a sort of voluptuous astonishment.

"If you leave, I'll lead an honest life," Komako said, walking on again. She put her hand to her disordered hair. When she had gone five or six steps she turned to look back at him. "What's the matter? You don't have to stand there, do you?"

But Shimamura stood looking at her.

"Oh? You'll wait, then? And afterwards you'll take me to your room with you."

She raised her left hand a little and ran off. Her retreating figure was drawn up into the mountain. The Milky Way spread its skirts to be broken by the waves of the mountain, and, fanning out again in all its brilliant vastness higher in the sky, it left the mountain in a deeper darkness.

Komako turned into the main street and disappeared. Shimamura started after her.

Several men were pulling a fire-pump down the street to a rhythmical chant. Floods of people poured after them. Shimamura joined the crowd from the side road he and Komako had taken.

Another pump came down the street. He let it pass, and fell in behind it.

It was an old wooden hand-pump, ridiculously small, with swarms of men at the long rope pulling it and other swarms to man it.

Komako too had stopped to let it pass. She spotted Shimamura and ran along beside him. All down the road people who had stood aside fell in again as if sucked up by the pump. The two of them were now no more than part of a mob running to a fire.

"So you came. Always looking for excitement."

"That's right. It's a sad little pump, though, isn't it. The better part of a hundred years old."

"At least. Careful you don't fall."

"It is slippery."

"Come sometime when we have a real blizzard, and the snow drives along the ground all night long. But you won't, of course. Rabbits and pheasants come running inside the house to get out of the storm." Komako's voice was bright and eager. She seemed to take her beat from the chanting voices and the tramping feet around her. Shimamura too was buoyed up by the crowd.

They could hear the sound of the flames now, and tongues of flame leaped up before them. Komako clutched at Shimamura's arm. The low, dark houses along the street seemed to be breathing as they floated up in the light of the fire and faded away again. Water from the pumps flowed along the street. They came against a wall of people. Mixed in with the smoke was a smell like boiling cocoons.

The same standard remarks were taken up in loud voices through the crowd: the fire had started at the projector; children had been thrown one after another from the balcony; no one was hurt; it was lucky there had been no rice or cocoons in the warehouse. And yet a sort of quiet unified the whole fiery scene, as though everyone were voiceless before the flames, as though the heart, the point of reference, had been torn away from each individual. Everyone seemed to be listening to the sound of the fire and the pumps.

Now and then a villager came running up late, and called out the name of a relative. There would be an answer, and the two would call happily back and forth. Only those voices seemed alive and present. The fire-alarm no longer sounded.

Afraid people would be watching, Shimamura slipped away from Komako and stood behind a group of children. The children moved back from the heat. The snow at their feet was melting, while farther on it had already turned to slush from the fire and water, a muddy confusion of footprints.

They were standing in the field beside the cocoon-warehouse. Most of the crowd on the main street had poured into that same open space.

The fire had apparently started near the entrance, and the walls and roof of half the building had burned away. The pillars and beams were still smoldering. It was a wide barn of a building, only shingles and boarded walls and floors, and the inside was fairly free of smoke. Though the roof, soaked from the pumps, did not seem to be burning, the fire continued to spread. A tongue would shoot up from a quite unexpected spot, the three pumps would turn hastily towards it, and a shower of sparks would fly up in a cloud of black smoke.

The sparks spread off into the Milky Way, and Shimamura was pulled up with them. As the smoke drifted away, the Milky Way seemed to dip and flow in the opposite direction. Occasionally a pump missed the roof, and the end of its line of water wavered and turned to a faint white mist, as though lighted by the Milky Way.

Komako had come up to him, he did not know when. She took his hand. He looked around at her, but said nothing. She gazed at the fire, the pulse of the fire beating on her intent, slightly flushed face. Shimamura felt a violent rising in his chest. Komako's hair was coming undone, and her throat was bare and arched. His fingers trembled from the urge to touch it. His hand was warm, but Komako's was still warmer. He did not know why he should feel that a separation was forcing itself upon them.

Flames shot up again from the pillars and beams at the entrance. A line of water was turned on them. Hissing clouds of steam arose as the framework began to give way.

The crowd gasped as one person. A woman's body had fallen through the flames.

The cocoon-warehouse had a balcony that was little more than a perfunctory recognition of its duties as an auditorium. Since it fell from the balcony, low for a second floor, the body could have taken but a fraction of a second to reach the ground; but the eye had somehow been able to trace its passage in detail. Perhaps the strange, puppetlike deadness of the fall was what made that fraction of a second seem so long. One knew immediately that the figure was unconscious. It made no noise as it struck the ground between the fire that had newly blazed up and the fire that still smoldered beyond. Water had collected inside the building, and no dust arose from the fall.

A line of water from one of the pumps arched down on the smoldering fire, and a woman's body suddenly floated up before it: such had been the fall. The body was quite horizontal as it passed through the air. Shimamura started back—not from fear, however. He saw the figure as a phantasm from an unreal world. That stiff figure, flung out into the air, became soft and pliant. With a doll-like passiveness, and the freedom of the lifeless, it seemed to hold both life and death in abeyance. If Shimamura felt even a flicker of uneasiness, it was lest the head drop, or a knee or a hip bend to disturb that perfectly horizontal line. Something of the sort must surely happen; but the body was still horizontal when it struck the ground.

Komako screamed and brought her hands to her eyes. Shimamura gazed at the still form.

When did he realize that it was Yoko? The gasp from the crowd and Komako's scream seemed to come at the same instant; and that instant too there was a suggestion of a spasm in the calf of Yoko's leg, stretched out on the ground.

The scream stabbed him through. At the spasm in Yoko's leg, a chill passed down his spine to his very feet. His heart was pounding in an indefinable anguish.

Yoko's leg moved very slightly, hardly enough to catch the eye.

Even before the spasm passed, Shimamura was looking at the face and the kimono, an arrow figure against a red ground. Yoko had fallen face up. The skirt of her kimono was pulled just over one knee. There was but that slight movement in her leg after she struck the earth. She lay unconscious. For some reason Shimamura did not see death in the still form. He felt rather that Yoko had undergone some shift, some metamorphosis.

Two or three beams from the collapsing balcony were burning over her head. The beautiful eyes that so pierced their object were closed. Her jaw was thrust slightly out, and her throat was arched. The fire flickered over the white face.

Shimamura felt a rising in his chest again as the memory came to him of the night he had been on his way to visit Komako, and he had seen that mountain light shine in Yoko's face. The years and months with Komako seemed to be lighted up in that instant; and there, he knew, was the anguish.

Komako put her hands to her eyes and screamed, and even as the crowd held its breath in that first gasp she broke away from Shimamura and ran toward the fire.

The long geisha's skirts trailing behind her, she staggered through the pools of water and the charred bits of wood that lay scattered over the ground. She turned and struggled back with Yoko at her breast. Her face was strained and desperate, and beneath it Yoko's face hung vacantly, as at the moment of the soul's flight. Komako struggled forward as if she bore her sacrifice, or her punishment.

The crowd found its various voices again. It surged forward to envelop the two.

"Keep back. Keep back, please." He heard Komako's cry. "This girl is insane. She's insane."

He tried to move toward that half-mad voice, but he was pushed aside by the men who had come up to take Yoko from her. As he caught his footing, his head fell back, and the Milky Way flowed down inside him with a roar.

THE LIFE AND WORKS OF
YASUNARI KAWABATA

By EDWARD G. SEIDENSTICKER

EVERYONE WHO WRITES about Yasunari Kawabata tells us, no doubt rightly, that the crucial events in his life happened very early: he was a child, in his own phrase, "without home or family," and, again as he himself has put it, he has had the mind of a wanderer ever since. He lost his parents in infancy, and his grandmother and his only sister, whom he never really knew, died not long afterward. He was fourteen when, in 1914, his grandfather died. From the following year he lived in a middle-school dormitory, and in 1917 he left his native Osaka to enter the First Higher School in Tokyo. Insofar as he has had a permanent abode since, it has been in eastern Japan.

He has spent much of his time on the Izu peninsula, south of Tokyo, during his years in Tokyo University (where in 1921 he took a degree in Japanese literature). In 1929, he settled in a part of Tokyo conveniently near the Asakusa entertainment district, and since 1936 he has lived in Kamakura. Though his life has been a quiet one, rather free of external incident, he was much honored in his own country before receiving the Nobel Prize in 1968. He became president of the Japan P.E.N. Center in 1948, and his duties in that capacity more than once

took him abroad. In 1953, he was elected a member of the Japan Academy. He has written very little about his native Osaka, although in recent years Kyoto has caught his fancy.

For some writers a sense of identity with place is essential. For others, homelessness is the big fact, the beginning of it all. Kawabata's writing practices suggest a positive longing for that condition. More than thirty years ago he remarked upon the fact that so much of his writing —more than half of it, he said—had been done at inns. As it is with the creator, so it is with the creations. Even when they have homes, as has Mrs. Ota of *Sembazuru* (*Thousand Cranes*) (1952), Kawabata characters are seldom seen in them. The most notable character of the early Kawabata is a wandering dancer on the Izu peninsula. The most notable recent characters are two old men. One of them, in *Nemureru Bijo* (*House of the Sleeping Beauties*) (1960–1961), is seen only at inns and apparently has mainly unpleasant memories of home; the other, in *Yama no Oto* (*The Sound of the Mountain*) (1949–1954), feels cut off from his nearest blood relatives, and dreams of two unattainable women, his daughter-in-law and his sister-in-law, the latter dead many years, in an

[71]

old home that Kawabata chooses not to take him back to.

During the years from 1928 to 1936, when Kawabata lived in and wrote of Tokyo, he described the places that most interested him as "islands in a distant sea." The novelist Mishima Yukio, in one of the most perceptive of critical essays on Kawabata, has called him "a perpetual traveler"—a sort of Japanese Flying Dutchman who enjoys and profits from the role.

Kawabata's earliest surviving work is called *Jūrokusai no Nikki* ("Diary of a Sixteen-year-old"). Though not published until 1925, it is, Kawabata has assured us, virtually unchanged from the form in which it was first written, in 1914, when, by the Western or "full" count, he was not yet fifteen. His diary for the weeks preceding his grandfather's death, it is an extraordinary work for a fourteen-year-old. The clear eye, the restraint, the curious mixture of pathos and coldness, of pity and loathing, have in them much of the mature Kawabata and suggest an extraordinary and disturbing precocity. This is not, one feels, the kind of boy one would like to have taking too close a look at one.

Kawabata's earliest important fiction, which appeared in the early twenties, is of a most unusual kind, collections of tiny short stories, or perhaps vignettes might be the more appropriate word, that are called in Japanese *tanagokoro shōsetsu*. Literally "palm-of-the-hand stories," the expression might be translated as "vest-pocket stories," and the form, which to my knowledge no one else had made such considerable use of as Kawabata has, might be called the prose equivalent of haiku. Sometimes these little fragments, the shortest of which could be translated into two or three hundred words of English and the longest of which would run to no more than perhaps fifteen hundred, are further fragmented into episodes no more than a sentence or two long, and call to mind less haiku than *renga* linked verse. A striking example is a little story called "Tsuki" ("The Moon"). It is about a young man who has trouble losing his virginity, and all the women who attempt to aid him in that endeavor.

One woman, standing beside his pillow, sank suddenly and roughly to her knees, and, throwing herself upon his head, breathed of his scent.

And another woman, washing his back in the bath, clutched at his shoulder with a hand that began to tremble violently.

And another woman, sitting with him in a winter room, suddenly jumped down into the garden, and, rolling over face up on the bench in the pergola, held her head tight between her two elbows.

And another woman, coming into his room with her sewing late at night, sat still as a rock while she waited for him to come back; and, red to the ears, in a hoarse voice that caught in her throat, she offered the strange lie that she was borrowing his electricity.

If this was Kawabata's point of departure, he has in many ways not departed far. We already have the Kawabata eroticism, chilling in its transience. We have the deftness of characterization, with these anonymous women, each allowed her one sentence and made to move on, floating up with remarkable vividness. We have, in each brief appearance which invites rejection, the Kawabata loneliness and refusal to believe in love, and the sense of emptiness that he himself has described as Buddhist in its origins. We have the emphasis on women, frequently overwrought women. We have the virtuosity of style. It will be noted how I had to strain the English to make the last little episode what it is in Japanese, a single sentence.

And, probably most important, we have the loose form, a stringing together of episodes with no clear beginning, middle, and end, which again calls to mind *renga,* and has been favored by Kawabata throughout his career. He has said that some scene or person, perhaps no more than a passer in the street, will catch his interest, and he will invent an incident to match it or him; and that incident may or may not call to mind a second incident, and the process may or may not be repeated indefinitely. It is a concept of fiction likely to seem less strange to someone reared in the tradition of the *renga* and the discursive essay than to someone used to the well-shaped Aristotelian poem; and yet it has its modern, even avant-garde, aspects too. Is this not essentially the shape of a "happening"?

Kawabata's reputation was really made by a long story, or novelette, *Izu no Odoriko* ("The Izu Dancer") of 1926, a partial translation of which is available in English. It tells of a high-school student who, going through the period of despondency that seems to be expected of high-school students, takes a walking trip down to Izu peninsula, and in the course of it encounters a party of strolling performers. He is greatly attracted to the little dancer of the title. At first the attraction is sexual, but then, in an exceedingly famous but untranslatable passage because of the subtle use it makes of onomatopoeia, he sees her naked and realizes that she has not yet reached adolescence. His relief and pleasure are boundless, and as he continues down the peninsula with her the despondency goes away. At Shimoda he leaves them, to return by boat to Tokyo.

The story is rather brighter than most Kawabata, strays nearer the borders of the sentimental, and comes closer to affirming the possibility of love. In other ways it is very representative. As is the way with Kawabata stories, it was long in gestating. Kawabata did walk down the Izu peninsula with a group of strolling players, but it was when he was a high-school student, eight years before the story was finished. In a sense it is unfinished, and so stands at the head of the impressive list of unfinished Kawabata stories. He has said that he meant to add passages of natural description but never got around to them. Given his way of moving from one episode to another by free association, it is sometimes not easy for Kawabata himself to say whether or not one of his stories is finished, and it is frequently impossible for the world to know whether or not he will suddenly add another episode to a story the world has long thought finished.

There has been much speculation as to why the very young virgin should play such an important part in Kawabata's writing. Mishima has offered the interesting theory that it is because she is the epitome of the unattainable. Once she is attained, she becomes, of course, something other than the object of the yearning. Kawabata's eroticism is of a curious kind, having in itself something of the preadolescent. Even when the union is consummated, as it is not in "The Izu Dancer," there is a standoffish quality about the male partner, as if he were not entering into the act but savoring it with a cold eye and hand.

Even in this brightest of Kawabata stories, the melancholy Kawabata themes are present: the loneliness, the homelessness, the unquenchable yearning. And there is the nothingness, the emptiness. "The lights went out," says the last paragraph of the story, "the smell of the sea and of the fish in the hold grew stronger. In the darkness, warmed by the boy beside me, I gave myself up to my tears. It was as though my head had turned to clear water, it was falling pleasantly away, and soon nothing would remain."

The translation, which is my own, is somewhat misleading. The word "nothing" is not really right, and the original has reference, in the last sentence, to "sweet feelings of pleasure, as of having nothing left behind." It seemed a touch too sweet in translation. Kawabata has insisted, most recently in his Nobel lecture, that the nothingness or emptiness of the East has little in common with the bleak nihilism of the West. Certainly there is an element of the positive in the sadness that so pervades Kawabata's writing, as if it were to be sought after, a sort of enlightenment, and not fled from. Kawabata himself traces its origins to Buddhism.

In the mid-twenties Kawabata was a member of a group to which was attached the label Shinkankaku-ha, usually translated Neosensualist School. Actually it was a very disparate group, scarcely to be called a school at all. Its members did have in common, however, an interest in European avant-garde movements, dadaism and surrealism and the rest. We are frequently told that the eccentric images, the sudden transitions, the obscurities of "Neosensualist" writing are to be traced to such sources. There are some Kawabata works of which this is clearly the case. The most conspicuous example is *Suishō Gensō* (*Crystal Vision*) (1931), an imitation of James Joyce. It is possible to see European influences in "The Izu Dancer" too, as for instance in the image of the leaky head which I have quoted; but when Kawabata is in good form, what seems new is also very venerable.

Another work, and a far better one, from the period of the unfortunate crystal adventure should be mentioned because it is one of Kawabata's major "at-home" novels, a novel about a city in which he was actually living. *Asakusa*

Kurenaiden (*The Scarlet Gang of Asakusa*), is yet another unfinished work, the merest introduction to its subject, Kawabata has said. It was published between 1929 and 1935. The material is flamboyant, having to do with Asakusa entertainers and thugs. The heroine, who lives on the periphery of the entertainment world, seeks revenge upon her sister's betrayer, and presently has it by transferring from her mouth to his a substance which the dictionaries tell us is arsenic. The two most striking things about the book are the fragmented, episodic structure and the sad, poignant lyricism. The characters in this at-home novel are wanderers too, and the roar of Asakusa becomes a muted call from one of those islands in a distant sea. And it is the Asakusa of the years after the earthquake. If specific incidents, other than his lonely boyhood, are to be held to account for the Kawabata sadness, the earthquake of 1923 and the defeat of 1945 must surely be among them.

In "My Life as a Writer," Kawabata has described how he went about gathering his material.

I passed whole nights, any number of them, in the park, but I only walked around. I did not make the acquaintance of any of the delinquents. I did not speak to the vagrants. I did not go into any of the cheap restaurants. I made the rounds of the thirty-odd shows and took notes, but always from the audience. I did not talk to the performers, and only at the Casino Folly did I go backstage. I did not go into any of the cheap inns around the park, I did not go into a bar.

The aloofness of the writer is in the book too.

From the same period comes what I think to be Kawabata's best short story, "Kinju" ("Of Birds and Beasts"), published in 1933. A year later Kawabata announced a great antipathy for the story, but now it would seem to have come back into his favor, for it is included in a lavish Nobel commemorative collection of his works, said to have been selected by Kawabata himself. It is about a man who rejects human attachments and keeps birds and dogs for companions. Scarcely a story at all in the Western sense of the term, it is a collection of little vignettes about the man's birds and beasts, interlarded with fragments about a dancer with whom he has had an affair and who has gone into a sad decline. Nowhere is Kawabata's refusal to believe in love more apparent, for the other side of the rejection of human affections is affection become cruelty, warping and torturing the birds and dogs in the quest for ever purer strains.

Formally, it is of great interest. If as a narrative it looks like an almost formless stringing together of small episodes, another Kawabata prose *renga,* on another level it is very tightly organized, perhaps the best illustration of the dexterity with which Kawabata manages time. It begins and ends at almost the same moment, and in between are flashbacks sometimes so complicated that the reader has to take out pencil and paper to decide whether everything is coming out all right. He may be assured that everything is.

Kawabata has said—the remark is reminiscent of what Faulkner said about *Sanctuary*—that in "Of Birds and Beasts" he set out to bring together the ugliest material he could think of. Ugliness there certainly is, and indeed a fascination with ugliness is an important feature of Kawabata's writing upon which I have not yet commented. "I am drawn to dirty beauty," he remarked in the 1934 essay in which he banished "Of Birds and Beasts" from the canon.

Yet there is another side, a note of affirmation that makes the sad and the ugly in Kawabata so paradoxical and so oriental. Near the end of the story, the hero, if so determinedly antihuman a figure can be called a hero, recalls an occasion on which he and the dancer thought to commit suicide together. The woman's figure as she lay with her hands together as if in supplication drove thoughts of suicide from his head. Here is Kawabata's description of what it was that so suddenly changed him: "He was struck, as by lightning, by the joy of emptiness." Here we have it again, emptiness become affirmation, something to be striven for.

I have written at some length elsewhere of *Yukigumi (Snow Country)*, which seems to me Kawabata's best work. A number of instalments that offered no real dénouement were published between 1935 and 1937. After an unsuccessful attempt at a conclusion, the work was brought to its present form in 1947. I have not changed my mind a great deal since I wrote the introduction to the English translation. The main points can be summarized as follows: in *Snow Country* and in its one truly vivid character, the geisha Komako, we feel most strongly the cold loneliness of Kawabata's world; his bold mating of superficially incongruous sensual impressions and his fragmentation put Kawabata "in a literary line that can be traced back to seventeenth-century haiku masters"; "the manner is notable for its terseness and austerity," making its points by extremely subtle changes in tone, as when the hero, Shimamura, angers Komako by first calling her "a good girl" and then unconsciously shifting to "a good woman"; and the novel, after moving past a moment that could have been a satisfactory ending ends with no ending at all. Today I might make some amendments and additions. I do not think that today I would be reminded so much of haiku by the book as of *renga*. It is quite obvious that Kawabata cannot have known where he was going when he started to write, any more than a group of poets know where they are going when they sit down to compose a *renga* sequence. The first chapter was intended to be a short story, and the last chapter is based on an actual event that had not yet happened when the writing was begun. I might also think of the *Tale of Genji*, both because of the sadness that pervades the novel and because of the structure. The *Genji* is so full of hesitations and new departures as to make it impossible to believe that Murasaki Shikibu had the whole work in her head when she started writing. And I might think of the *zuihitsu* lyrical essay. The narrative element in *Snow Country* is slight at best, having to do with an affair between a Tokyo dilettante and a hot-spring geisha, and at one point Kawabata breaks it off completely to give us an extended prose lyric about silk weaving.

I might be less inclined to describe the Kawabata style as terse than I was in 1956. In *Snow Country* it certainly is. In other works it can be repetitious, and somewhat too heavily loaded with adverbs and rhetorical questions and qualifications. I am of two minds about this last quality, however, because what can seem wordy can also seem incantatory, not decreasing but adding to the poetry. The terseness of *Snow Country* is to be accounted for by considerable cutting and rewording during the dozen years that were required to produce it. The original version began with reminiscences about Komako, the rustic geisha, and the present opening, with its evocation of the whiteness of the snow country, was buried some distance inside.

I might have wanted to add a few words about the curious nature of Kawabata's eroticism, and the way it has of intensifying loneliness and isolation by stopping at the surface. In *Snow Country* more than in earlier works one is aware of the remarkable part the sense of touch plays in Kawabata's writing. I am sure that if some computer were put to work counting up and classifying the sensual impressions, it would find a disproportionate number of them to be tactile. The most famous such impression comes very early in *Snow Country*, with the case of the remembering finger. Kawabata characters are particularly fond of the feel of a firm young breast. Perhaps psychologists can trace the proclivity to infantile deprival. I would but say that the way Kawabata characters have of pressing against each other and never achieving a union adds much to the sadness, the chilly lyricism, of the Kawabata world.

And, finally, I might have wanted to say a few words about the geisha Komako as the most Kawabata-like of Kawabata characters. Kawabata's successful characters are as curious as his eroticism. They constantly seem to be falling into and becoming part of the natural setting, as in the striking examples of Komako in the snowy mirror, and the eye of the other girl, Yoko, superimposed in a train window upon a light in the mountain darkness. Mishima has aptly likened the Kawabata character to ectoplasm, working its way to dissolution in the monochrome sadness of life. And yet how vivid they are, Komako and Yoko, as they appear in flickers and flashes. Kawabata somehow manages to endow ancient sadness and insubstantiality with modern assertiveness.

Although the composition of *Snow Country* spanned the war years, no new part of it was published during the war. Kawabata's principal wartime writing was of a battle far from the battlefields. In 1938 there occurred, over a period of six months, a *go* match between the great master, Honinbō Shūsai, and a younger challenger. Shūsai had never been defeated. He was old and ill, and this was to be his last match. He lost it. In 1940 he died. Kawabata covered the match for the *Tokyo Nichinichi* and the *Osaka Mainichi*. In 1942 he began to write of it with touches of fiction. He continued to do so down to 1954, when, we may perhaps assume, the work that bears the title *Meijin* (*The Master*), was finished. Kawabata has indicated particular affection for it among his works. It will probably never be much read outside Japan because of the complicated terminology, but it is an extraordinary work, evoking with remarkable power the harshness of battle, the absolute commitment of the fighter, and the loneliness of defeat.

Perhaps Kawabata's affection for *The Master* has to do with the fact that that same loneliness was very much with him in the years after the war. "Since the defeat," he wrote in 1947, "I have but been going back into the sadness that has always been with us in Japan. I have no faith in the appearances and the manners of the postwar world. Perhaps I do not believe in reality. It seems likely that I will move away from the realism that is the basis of the modern novel. Perhaps I have never been there." There has been a certain departure from realism in the most recent Kawabata. Yet the sadness is not a desperate throwing over of everything. It is rather an intensifying of something that has been present all along. Later in the same essay Kawabata says, quite in the spirit of "the master" himself: "The sadness of *Saturday Wife* [a novel by Oda Sakunosuke], the pathos of the *Genji*, are softened by a Japanese kind of consolation and succor. . . . I have never experienced pains and sorrows of the Western kind. I have not once seen in Japan emptiness and decay of the Western kind."

For some years, beginning in 1949, Kawabata was simultaneously at work on two of his major novels, *Thousand Cranes* and *The Sound of the Mountain*. The latter was at length, in 1954, brought to what Kawabata apparently now considers a conclusion. *Thousand Cranes* was brought to what seemed a suitable bleak conclusion in 1951, with the disappearance of all the women in the hero's life save the one he cannot stand. Then in 1953 Kawabata brought a couple of them back and apparently intended to produce *Thousand Cranes; Part the Second*. This last must be definitely put on his list of incomplete works. Perhaps he wishes the post-1951 chapters stricken from the record, for they are not included in his "collected works." It is the 1951 version that has been put into English.

Thousand Cranes is centered upon the tea ceremony and upon quasi-incest. The hero has an affair with a widow who was his father's mistress, and when she commits suicide his affections are transferred to her daughter. The latter flees him, and at the end of the 1951 version seems to have disappeared completely, only to come back in 1953. All the while a second mistress of the father, a mean and ugly woman, keeps intruding herself upon the scene, exuding venom and jealousy, trying to run people's lives and trying also to make money from the tea ceremony.

Kawabata objected in his Nobel lecture to the Western insistence upon reading *Thousand Cranes* as an anthem to the ageless beauty of the tea ceremony. It is rather, he said, a warning against the vulgarization into which the modern tea ceremony has fallen. Certainly there is more in it than ageless beauty; but surely too there is more in it than the didacticism suggested in the Nobel lecture.

It is possible to see the book as a parable upon the fragility and evanescence of makers of tea and the durability of the vessels with which they make and drink their tea. Life is brief, art is long. But if these vessels are a symbol of durable beauty, there is also in the book a symbol of durable ugliness. Much the most vivid character is Kurimoto Chikako, the second of the two mistresses. "And only Kurimoto is left," says Kikuji, the hero, at the end of the 1951 version. She, as much as Kawabata's beautiful women, is the eternal Japanese woman, taking one back to Lady Rokujo in the *Genji* and yet beyond, and reminding one of the morbid side of the Japanese aesthetic tradition, and of Kawabata's fascination with spoiled beauty, or, as he called it, dirty beauty. Chikako has an ugly birthmark on one of her breasts, a cancerlike object clutching at the heart of sensuality. One of Kikuji's most vivid childhood memories, and perhaps the most vivid detail in the novel, is of seeing her trimming the hair that grows from it. Of the three major Kawabata works available in the West, *Thousand Cranes* has received the least notice, possibly, because it disturbs people, reminding them that traditionalism is not a simple matter.

The workings of a morbid sensibility are to be seen all through *Thousand Cranes,* and the stimulus is strongly tactile. The novelist Ibuse Masuji has said that the feel of Shino pottery, which plays such an important part in the tea ceremony in *Thousand Cranes,* gave rise in Kawabata's mind to Mrs. Ota, the lady who commits suicide. Certainly it is Shino that reminds Kikuji most vividly of her after her death. "The very face of the Shino, glowing warmly cool, made him think of Mrs. Ota." The English translation is not really adequate to remind us once again of the subtleties and difficulties of the Kawabata style. The word translated "face" is "skin" in Japanese, suggesting much more immediately a caress, a hand wandering over a breast, than it does in English. Earlier we have been told, with a characteristic mixing of the senses, that as Kikuji kneels before the dead woman's ashes he cannot see her face but he can feel her touch, as of music. There is a coldness in this reduction to the tactile, making one feel that the poor woman has committed suicide because of a relationship that never really came into being. She has been destroyed by feelings of guilt for a love that was not there. Perhaps one can see in *Thousand Cranes,* a more difficult book than *Snow Country* to find the "meaning" of, the concrete expression of that disbelief in postwar manners and appearances.

The Sound of the Mountain is another "at-home" novel. It is set mostly in Kamakura, where Kawabata lives. The central figure is an old man, Ogata Shingo, who is far more strongly drawn to his daughter-in-law than to either of his own children. She is, once again, the object of a yearning that cannot be satisfied. There is another object: when he was young, back in his real home, Nagano Prefecture, he was drawn to his wife's sister, now dead, and married instead a woman about whom he seems to feel little except somewhat derisive amusement. The novel is a stringing together of brief episodes, tending toward the lyrical, in typical Kawabata fashion. The action, such as there is, has to do largely with the unhappy affairs of the younger generation and so reminds one of the last chapters of the *Genji.* The Ogata son has a mistress. In the course of the novel his wife has an abortion, her way of emphasizing the essential sterility of their marriage. The mistress becomes pregnant, and, refusing to have an abortion, goes off to the country, carrying with her testimony to another love that never arrived. The Ogata daughter packs up and comes home to mother, and her estranged husband attempts suicide. Shingo dreams of going back to Nagano to see the autumn leaves, which have deep associations with his dead sister-in-law; but the novel, which could have come to a stop almost anywhere along the way, comes to a quiet stop before even this fulfillment is allowed.

One scarcely needs to beat the drums to announce that this is very much in the main Kawabata line, in its form and in its content. It is another prose *renga,* and it is bathed in a classical sadness. And yet it is also a very modern book. The denial of romantic love is modern, and so, in a way, is the formlessness; and nowhere is Kawabata's skill at characterization, at giving the illusion of individual life, more beautifully in evidence. Characterization is an art in which the Japanese showed little interest from the eleventh century to the end of the nineteenth. Each of the five major characters in *The Sound of the Mountain* comes strongly to life, and this despite the fact that the dialogue is sparse and that the mode is strongly lyrical. One of the five, the mistress, has a single scene, but she is allowed to make supremely good use of it. It is often said that Kawabata is unable to depict male characters. Certainly it is true that most of his writing centers upon women, with men acting as foils. This probably has less to do with a want of skill, however, than with a want of interest, brought on by the obsessive Kawabata themes and preoccupations. Neither the father nor the son in *The Sound of the Mountain* can be described as anything but a successful venture in characterization.

Kawabata's best writing in the sixties sees the withdrawal from realism predicted shortly after the war. *House of the Sleeping Beauties,* a short novel serialized in 1960 and 1961, tells of an old man who spends four nights in the strange house of the title. It is a bordello with a difference, allowing him the company of young girls who have been drugged into a sleep from which they cannot be awakened. The rule of the house is that he can do anything with them except injure them or deflower them, and it is assumed in any event that he is past being capable of the latter offense. By the now-familiar method of free association, descriptions of how the girls look and feel and smell are mingled in among reminiscences, mostly of women, and short dialogues with the unpleasant woman who acts as procuress and housekeeper. Toward the end of the story we learn that another aged guest has died of heart failure in the course of a night with a sleeping beauty, and in a conclusion which Mishima, with his knack for the right word, has described as suffocating, one of the beauties dies and is dragged downstairs by the housekeeper.

In "Kata-ude" ("One Arm"), a short story which was serialized in 1963 and 1964, a man has converse with the detached but still living arm of a young girl.

A man incapable of acting as a man in bed with a girl who is incapable of responding, a man passing the night with the detached extremity of a girl; clearly we have eroticism as dehumanized as it can be, the Kawabata denial of love pushed as far as it can go. In *House of the Sleeping Beauties* especially, the eroticism becomes a quest for extinction, which again must be understood, or felt, in a Buddhist sense. The method of free association has never been used with more boldness and originality. One does not think of James Joyce, as in earlier Kawabata works, but of Kawabata himself, and extreme fragmentation takes one back to the earliest Kawabata. Some will perhaps have noticed and been mildly surprised by my description of "One Arm" as a serialized short story. The first installment, a very short story, was apparently intended to be complete in itself, for there was no indication at the end of it that it would be continued; and then several more very short stories were added, as in a collection of vest-pocket stories.

Yet Kawabata the modern writer is also in evidence, especially in the deftness of the characterization. The keeper of the house of the sleeping beauties appears in only the briefest bits of dialogue, but she is beautifully done, a new version of Chikako the eternal nasty woman. Even the five sleeping beauties and the detached arm have an abstract sort of individuality.

Something should be said of the third Kawabata novel that was available to the Swedish Academy. *Koto,* literally *Old Capital,* appeared in 1961 and 1962 and has been translated into German as *Kyōto.* I do not think it very good Kawabata. It is somewhat sugary and tells one that a touch of the morbid keeps the best Kawabata short of sentimentality. It is not wholly without interest, however. It contains some beautiful evocations of the evanescent, of what seems to be dying in Kyoto, and Kawabata's habit of feeling his way along and letting background create character and incident is very apparent. The two central figures, with whose romantic difficulties the main action of the novel is concerned, are twin sisters. When he started writing, Kawabata has told us, he did not know that there would be twins. It seems that he was strongly drawn to the Nishijin weaving district, where the action begins, and then to the cedar groves of the northern hills; and so he invented a northern-hill twin, estranged in infancy from the Nishijin twin.

Were I to try to summarize what I have said, I suppose the summary would come down to a listing of all the elements that make Kawabata such a unique mixture of the classical and the modern, so eminently qualified for the Nobel Prize. But I think I would rather let him talk about himself as he does so capably in the following selections from two justly

famous Kawabata essays: "Bungakuteki Jijoden" ("My Life as a Writer") (1934), and "Aishu" ("Sadness") (1947). He is also a very good essayist and critic.

Here he is in 1947, writing on what the classics mean to him:

During the war, on the train to and from Tokyo, and in bed during blackouts, I read the *Tale of Genji* in the *Kogetsusho* edition. . . .

I had reached the twenty-third book, about midway through the long romance, when Japan surrendered. It was a strange way to read the *Genji,* but it left a deep impression on me. It sometimes surprised me to see, there on the train, how completely absorbed I was in the *Genji.* I might well be surprised at the disharmony between me and the train, loaded with the baggage of refugees and victims of the bombings, making its way irregularly through the charred ruins, in terror of another bombing; but I was even more surprised at the harmony between me and a work a thousand years old.

And here is an earlier statement, from 1934:

I believe the oriental classics, and particularly the Buddhist scriptures, to be the greatest of the world's literature. I respect them not for their religious teachings but for their religious fantasies. For fifteen years now I have had in mind the plot for a story to be called "Song of the East." I have thought that I would like it to be my swan song. I will sing the classic Eastern fantasy after my fashion. I may die without having written it, but I wish to have it known that I wanted to write it. I have been baptized in and have tried my hand at imitating modern Western literature; but, at the foundation an oriental, I have not once lost my direction these last fifteen years. I have thus far told no one of this fact. It has been the happy secret formula of the house of Kawabata. Among the great Western realists, there have been some who, approaching death after great trials and agonies, have finally caught sight of the distant East; and perhaps I am playing there with a children's song in my heart.

Here he is again in 1934, on the chilly, aloof nature of his eroticism:

Hayashi Fusao [the novelist and critic] has remarked upon the strangeness of the fact that the author of "Chirinuru wo" [a short story published in 1933, translated "They Fall"] has a boy's longing for the female body; precisely by virtue of the fact that it seemed so strange, I thought that the remark struck home. . . . I have not, like the proletarian writers, a happy ideal, I have no children, I cannot become a miser, I know the emptiness of fame; and love is more than anything my bond with life. But I do not think I have ever held a woman's hand in a manner that falls within the meaning of love. . . . But is it not more than women that I have not held hands with? Is not life also thus for me? It is not thus with reality? And

perhaps with literature too? Am I a sadly fortunate man?

Here in 1934 is the homelessness:

I do not wish to visit the West. I wish rather to visit the lost countries of the East. Probably I am a citizen of a lost country. No other people have so moved me as those endless lines, as if going into exile, of refugees from the fires after the earthquake. I have quite lost myself in Dostoevsky, and I have not taken to Tolstoi. Perhaps because I was a child without a home and without family, melancholy wandering thoughts never leave me.

Here, in 1947, the paradox, the strange fact that the homelessness itself brings one home:

In those days it was with me the reverse of the usual: I received not a few letters of consolation from soldiers in foreign countries. Some were from people I did not know, but most of them were the same. The writer had chanced to come upon my works, and had been filled with thoughts of home, and wanted to offer his thanks and best wishes. My writing seemed to make people think of Japan. Perhaps the *Genji* brought me a similar homesickness.

Edward G. Seidensticker, a close friend and the English translator of Kawabata, was winner of the 1971 National Book Award.

THE 1968 PRIZE

By KJELL STRÖMBERG

THE FIRST Japanese proposed for the Nobel Prize for Literature (by Pearl Buck, in 1958) was Tanizaki Junichiro. Tanizaki was the unchallenged master of the modern novel in Japan, and from 1958 until his death in 1965, his name was repeatedly submitted by various European and Japanese sources.

In the early sixties, three other Japanese writers became serious contenders: Nishiwaki Junzaburo, a subtle poet and the translator of T. S. Eliot, proposed by the Japanese Academy of Letters; Yasunari Kawabata, proposed by the Japanese P.E.N. Center, which he had served as a highly popular president since 1948; and Mishima Yukio, novelist and playwright, much younger and more Westernized than the first two, but already substantially more than just a promising writer. Through translations Kawabata and Mishima were beginning to achieve a certain fame abroad and to rival Tanizaki.

Finally, it was Yasunari Kawabata who won the first Nobel Prize for Literature to be awarded to a Far Eastern writer, "for his narrative art, which expresses with a sensitivity charged with finesse the Japanese soul in its most characteristic verity." His closest rival among the eighty-three candidates that year was apparently Samuel Beckett, the Irish playwright, father of the Theater of the Absurd, and a candidate proposed

and passionately defended by the bustling Swedish avant-garde. (Beckett won his award the following year.)

The first examination of Kawabata's works submitted for the Academy's consideration dates from 1961. It was written by a young critic named Per-Erik Wahlund, who has been interested in the Far East since he first visited that part of the world. He regretted that he was obliged to base his judgment on only two or three novels in English, French, or German translations. These included *Snow Country*, which he himself translated into Swedish from an English version by Edward Seidensticker; *Thousand Cranes*, which had sold very well, especially in France, since its publication in translation in 1952; and "Envy, or The Spot of Wine," a short story which he had found in the comprehensive anthology, *Modern Japanese Literature*. Like most critics who have examined Kawabata's works, Wahlund stressed the writer's remarkable talent as an interpreter of femininity in its subtlest manifestations and as a highly refined painter of the Japanese landscape through all seasons of the year. He concluded by characterizing Kawabata as a writer of extraordinary sensitivity and originality.

The judgment of this official reporter of the Nobel Prize Committee was widely confirmed and supported by foreign experts subsequently approached for consultation. Howard S. Hibbett, professor of Japanese language and literature at Cambridge University, observed that as novelists both Tanizaki and Kawabata belong to world literature as much as to Japanese literature. Professor Donald Keene of Columbia University hesitated between Kawabata and Mishima, but finally chose the former because of his greater age, while expressing his hope that the latter might win the award at some later date. Finally, a Japanese scholar, Sei Ito, declared flatly that after the death of Tanizaki, Kawabata was the only writer worthy of representing modern Japanese literature at Stockholm.

The world press approved the choice enthusiastically. In France, *Le Monde* printed a long article by Lucien Dumont, essentially a conscientious analysis of the translated novels, saying, "Each of Kawabata's books shows how, even in the worst deprivation, man preserves his obsession with crystalline beauty." *Figaro* gave a factual account of the life and works, but critically held its observations to noting that once again, as so often in recent years, the Swedish Academy had remained faithful to the principle of honoring a nation rather than an outstandingly meritorious person. "We sense that there may have been a certain hesitation in the Academy on the application of this principle this time, but if it was necessary at all costs to honor a Japanese, the choice of the veteran Kawabata could not raise any objection."

In the United States, the award of the prize to a writer from the recently occupied Land of the Rising Sun attracted the most attention and elicited the warmest approval. The *New York Times Book Review* honored Kawabata and his work in a number of well-documented articles. One recalled that the year before Kawabata had been one of four Japanese writers to raise a ringing protest against

the "cultural revolution" in China, characterized as "a massacre of art and the freedom of education." Professor Keene wrote a substantial analysis not only of Kawabata's books but also of modern Japanese literature in general. He noted with surprise that of all the contemporary Japanese writers who are most imbued with old traditions of their country, it should have been Kawabata who attracted so many fervent readers in the West, because his books, with their highly refined style and frequent archaisms, offer certain difficulties even to the Japanese. But he rejoiced that Kawabata was the first Japanese to be so honored, not only because his books are of great intrinsic interest but also because the award of the Nobel Prize marked the assimilation of the great Japanese narrative tradition, the most ancient on earth, into the mainstream of world literature.

In Japan, the news of Kawabata's victory was greeted with almost delirious enthusiasm. Emperor Hirohito, through a high dignitary of his court, and Sato, the prime minister, called to congratulate him. The Japanese had previously had the satisfaction of seeing two Nobel Prizes for the sciences awarded in 1949 and 1965 to Hideki Yukawa and Shinichiro Tomonaga, but Japanese literature had remained practically unknown in the West until the last ten or twenty years and was consequently ignored by committees voting on literary awards. To the many Japanese and foreign journalists who went to interview him in his country house at Kamakura, near Tokyo, the new laureate declared simply, "I was lucky. I owe my Prize first of all to Japanese literature itself, then to my translators. I should like to think that the flavor of the Japanese literary tradition which people find in my books has been understood by the West."

Kawabata's statements to the press in Stockholm revealed great modesty. "We shall not know for another thirty or fifty years whether the Nobel Prize has fallen into worthy hands this year!" he said. Someone asked him whether European writers had played an important role in the development of his art. He admitted that they had, then politely explained that he owed much to two or three great Western writers—Turgenev, Dostoevsky, and Strindberg. If he had been interviewed in France he could doubtless have cited Flaubert and, perhaps even above all others, Proust.

At the ceremony in the Concert Palace on December 10, 1968, Kawabata wore the Japanese national costume—a full-length black silk tunic with purple embroidery and white slippers. The opera singer Birgit Nilsson sang the musical interludes which precede the entrance of each Prizewinner. Österling made the presentation. King Gustav Adolphus clasped Kawabata's hands in a long embrace, and Kawabata drew his hands up close to his heart as he bowed deeply before taking his place again on the flower-banked platform to thank those present for his warm welcome.

Later, at the dinner in the great gilded banquet room of the Town Hall, Kawabata expressed his thanks briefly in Japanese. His words were translated into English by his interpreter and inseparable companion, Edward Seidensticker. Kawabata noted that a good fifty-five years had gone by since an oriental—Rabindranath Tagore—had received the Nobel Prize for Literature. That award had made a deep impression on the Japanese, he declared, and doubtless in the other countries of Asia as well. Kawabata declined to consider the Nobel Prize a personal distinction and declared that his emotion at that moment would be even deeper if he could think that the Prize might take on a new and broader significance for the whole world. Thus, the Prize would become a token of understanding and friendship between East and West, nourishing not only the literature of today but that of tomorrow as well.

Translated by Dale McAdoo.

Rudyard Kipling

1907

"In consideration of the power of observation, originality of imagination, virility of ideas, and remarkable talent for narration which characterize the creations of this world-famous author"

Illustrated by GÉRARD ÉCONOMOS

PRESENTATION ADDRESS

By C. D. af WIRSÉN

PERMANENT SECRETARY
OF THE SWEDISH ACADEMY

———

THE SUGGESTIONS FOR NAMES of suitable recipients of this year's Nobel Prize for Literature have been numerous, and there has been no dearth of exceedingly well-qualified candidates for this honorable and coveted distinction.

From these candidates, the Swedish Academy has selected for this occasion a writer who belongs to Great Britain. For centuries past the literature of England has flourished and blossomed with marvelous luxuriance. When Tennyson's immortal lyre was silenced forever, the cry which is so customary at the passing of literary giants was raised. With him the glorious reign of poetry is over; there is none to take up the mantle. Similar despairing notes were struck in this country on the demise of Tegnér, but it is not so with the fair goddess, Poetry. She does not perish, is not deposed from her high estate; she but arrays herself in a fresh garb to suit the altered tastes of a new age.

In the works of Tennyson idealism is so pervasive that it meets the eye in a very palpable and direct form. Traits of idealism, however, may be traced in the conceptions and gifts of writers who differ widely from him, writers who seem primarily concerned with mere externals and who have won renown especially for their vivid word-painting of the various phases of the strenuous, pulsating life of our own times, that life which is often checkered and fretted by the painful struggle for existence and by all its concomitant worries and embarrassments. This description applies to Rudyard Kipling, to whom the Swedish Academy has awarded the Nobel Prize for Literature this year. Of him a French author, who has devoted much time and study to English literature, wrote more than six years ago: "He, Kipling, is undoubtedly the most noteworthy figure that has appeared within recent years in the domain of English literature."

Kipling was born in Bombay on December 30, 1865. At the age of six he was placed in the care of some relatives in England, but he returned to India on reaching the age of seventeen. He obtained a position on the staff of *The Civil and Military Gazette*, published at Lahore, and in his early twenties edited *The Pioneer* at Allahabad. In his capacity as a journalist, and for his own purposes, he traveled extensively throughout India. On those journeys he acquired a thorough insight into Hindu conceptions and sentiments and became intimately acquainted with the different Hindu groups, with their varying customs and institutions, and with the special features of English military life in India. This firm grasp of the true inwardness of all things Indian is abundantly reflected in Kipling's writings, so much so that it has even been said that they have brought India nearer home to the English nation than has the construction of the Suez Canal. Of his early works the satirical *Departmental Ditties* (1886) attracted notice by the audacity of the allusions it contained, and by the originality of its tone. Also among the early productions are *Plain Tales from the Hills* (1888) and *Soldiers Three* (1888), collections of stories famous among other things for the three lovingly drawn soldier types: Mulvaney, Ortheris, and Learoyd. Other works in the same category are, for instance, *The Story of the Gadsbys* (1888), *In Black and White* (1888), and *Under the Deodars* (1889), all of which are concerned with society life in Simla. The series entitled *Life's Handicap*, embracing some stories of serious import, appeared in 1891. The same year saw the publication of *The Light that Failed*, a novel somewhat harsh in style but containing some strongly colored descriptive passages of excellent effect.

As a poet Kipling was already full-fledged at the appearance of *Barrack-Room Ballads* (1892), magnificent soldier-songs brimming over with virile humor and depicting realistically Tommy Atkins in all his phases, valiantly marching onward to encounter dangers and misery wherever it pleases "the Widow of Windsor," or her successor on the throne, to dispatch him. In Kipling the British army has found a minstrel to interpret in a new, original, and tragi-comical manner the toils and deprivations through which it has to pass, and to depict its life and work with abundant acknowledgment of the great qualities it displays, but without the least trace of meretricious embellishment. In his verses descriptive of soldiers and sailors he so happily expresses their own thoughts, often in the very language they themselves employ, that they appreciate him deeply and, as we are told, sing his song whenever they have a pause in the day's occupations. Surely, there is hardly any greater mark of honor that can be given to a poet than to be beloved by the lower orders.

In the cycle entitled *The Seven Seas* (1896) Kipling reveals himself as an imperialist, a citizen of a worldwide empire. He has undoubtedly done more than any other writer of pure literature to draw tighter the bonds of union between England and her colonies.

In Sweden, as elsewhere, the *Jungle Books* by Kipling, the first of which appeared in 1894, are much admired and beloved. A primordial type of imaginative power inspired the creator of these mythlike tales of the animals in whose midst Mowgli waxed in strength: Bagheera the Black Panther, Baloo the Bear, Kaa the cunning and mighty Rock Python, Nag the White Cobra, and the chattering, foolish Monkeys. Some of the scenes are simply sublime; for instance, the one where Mowgli is resting in the "living armchair" Kaa, while the latter, who has witnessed so many generations of trees and animals, dreams of bygone ages; or again when Mowgli causes Hathi the Elephant to "let in the jungle" to take over the fields of men. These descriptions display an instinctive feeling for a poetry of nature which is quite phenomenal, and Kipling is far more in his true element in the primeval grandeur of these jungle stories than, for instance, in "The Ship that Found Herself" (in *The Day's Work,* 1898), an interesting though eccentric personification of mechanical inventions. The *Jungle Book* tales have made Kipling a favorite author among children in many countries. Adults share the delight experienced by the young and relive their childhood while perusing these marvelously delightful, wonderfully imaginative fables of animals.

Among the large number of Kipling's creations, *Kim* (1901) deserves special notice, for in the delineation of the Buddhist priest, who goes on a pilgrimage along the banks of the stream that purifies sinners, there is an elevated diction as well as a tenderness and charm which are otherwise unusual traits in this dashing writer's style. There is, too, in the figure of the little rascal Kim, the priest's chela, a thorough type of good-humored roguishness.

The accusation has occasionally been made against Kipling that his language is at times somewhat coarse and that his use of soldier's slang in some of the broadest of his songs and ballads verges on the vulgar. Though there may be some truth in such remarks, their importance is offset by the invigorating directness and ethical drive of Kipling. He has won immense popularity, not only in the Anglo-Indian world, which possesses in him a great literary master, but also far beyond the limits of the vast British Empire. During his serious illness in America in 1899, the American newspapers issued daily bulletins regarding his condition, and the German Emperor dispatched a telegram to his wife to express his earnest sympathy.

What is then the cause of this worldwide popularity that Kipling enjoys? Or, rather: In what way has Kipling shown himself to deserve it? How is it, too, that he has been deemed worthy of the Nobel Prize for Literature, for which a writer must especially show an idealism in his conceptions and in his art? The answer follows.

Kipling may not be eminent essentially for the profundity of his thought or for the surpassing wisdom of his meditations, yet even the most cursory observer sees immediately his absolutely unique power of observation, capable of reproducing with astounding accuracy the minutest detail from real life. However, the gift of observation alone, be it ever so closely true to nature, would not suffice as a qualification in this instance. There is something else by which his poetical gifts are revealed. His marvelous power of imagination enables him to give us not only copies from nature but also visions out of his own inner consciousness. His landscapes appear to the inner vision as sudden apparitions do to the eye. In sketching a personality he makes clear, almost in his first words, the peculiar traits of that person's character and temper. Creativeness which does not rest content with merely photographing the temporary phases of things but desires to penetrate to their inmost kernel and soul, is the basis of his literary activity, as Kipling himself says: "He draws the thing as he sees it for the God of things as they are." In these weighty words lies a real appreciation of the poet's responsibility in the exercise of his calling.

Rudyard Kipling's manly, at times brusque, energy does not preclude tenderness and delicacy of touch, though these qualities never clamor for recognition in his works. The simple "Story of Muhammad Din" is imbued with the poetry of genuine heartfelt emotion, and who can ever forget the little drummer boys in "The Taking of Lungtumpen" (in *Plain Tales*)?

In the innermost being of this indefatigable observer of life and human nature vibrate strings attuned to a lofty note. His poem "To the True Romance" reveals that yearning for a patiently sought, never to be attained ideal that resides in living form in the breast of every true poet, from where the scenes and impressions of the sensuous world can never dislodge it:

> *Enough for me in dreams to see*
> *And touch thy garment's hem:*
> *Thy feet have trod so near to God*
> *I may not follow them!*

This writer's philosophy of life is diffused with a piety characteristic of the Old Testament, or rather perhaps of Puritan times, wholly devoid of pretentiousness or wordiness, based upon a conviction that "the fear of the Lord is the beginning of wisdom" and that there exists a

> *God of our fathers, known of old,*
> *Beneath whose awful Hand we hold*
> *Dominion . . .*

If Kipling is an idealist from an aesthetic point of view by reason of poetical intuition, he is so, too, from an ethical-religious standpoint by virtue of his sense of duty, which has its inspiration in a faith firmly rooted in conviction. He is acutely conscious of the truth that even the mightiest states would perish unless they rested upon the sure foundation in the citizens' hearts of a loyal observance of the law and a reasoned self-restraint. For Kipling, God is first and foremost Almighty Providence, termed in *Life's Handicap* a "Great Overseer." The English as a nation can well appreciate these conceptions, and Kipling has become the nation's poet, owing not only to his numerous highly prized soldier-songs, but perhaps quite as much to the brief lines of the hymn ("Recessional") which he composed on the occasion of Queen Victoria's Diamond Jubilee in 1897. Especially striking are these words expressing genuine and humble religious feelings:

The tumult and the shouting dies;
The Captains and the Kings depart:
Still stands Thine ancient sacrifice,
An humble and a contrite heart.

The recessional hymn voices the spirit of national pride, yet it also conveys a warning against the dangers of presumptuous pride.

Quite naturally, during the Boer War Kipling sided with his own nation, the English. He has, however, done full justice to the heroic courage of the Boers, for his imperialism is not of the uncompromising type that pays no regard to the sentiments of others.

Many and varied are the movements that have had their vogue in English literature, a literature unparalleled for wealth of output and adorned to surpass all others by the immortal figure of Shakespeare. In Kipling may be traced perhaps more of Swift and Defoe than of Spenser, Keats, Shelley, or Tennyson. Clearly, however, imagination is as strong in him as empirical observation. Though he does not possess the refined and sensuously beautiful style of Swinburne, yet he escapes, on the other hand, all tendency toward a pagan worship of pleasure for pleasure's sake. He avoids all morbid sentimentality in matter and Alexandrian superflorescence in form.

Kipling favors concreteness and concentration; empty abstractions and circumlocutionary descriptions are wholly absent from his works. He has a knack for finding the telling phrase, the characteristic epithet, with swift accuracy and certainty. He has been compared now to Bret Harte, now to Pierre Loti, now to Dickens; he is, however, always original, and it would seem that his powers of invention are inexhaustible. Nevertheless, the apostle of the imagination is likewise, as stated above, the standard-bearer of law-abidingness and discipline. The laws of the jungle are the laws of the universe; if we ask what their chief purport is, we shall receive the brief answer: "Struggle, duty, obedience." Kipling thus advocates courage, self-sacrifice, and loyalty; unmanliness and lack of self-discipline are abominations to him, and in the world order he perceives a nemesis before which presumption is constrained to surrender.

If Kipling is quite independent as a writer, it does not follow that he has learned nothing from others; even the greatest masters have done so. With Bret Harte, Kipling shares his appreciation of the picturesqueness of vagabond life, and with Defoe his accuracy in depicting every detail and his sense of the values of exactness in the use of terms and phrases. Like Dickens he feels a keen sympathy with those of low degree in the community, and like him he can perceive humor in trifling traits and acts. But his style is distinctively original and personal. It accomplishes its ends by suggestion rather than by description. It is not quite uniformly brilliant but it is always eminently expressive and picturesque. The series *From Sea to Sea* (1899) is a veritable model of graphic description, whether the scene is laid in the Elephant City governed by the Grand Divinity of Laziness, in Palm Island, or in Singapore, or whether the story deals with manners and customs of Japan. Kipling has at his command a large fund of irony—sometimes highly pungent—but he has abundant resources of sympathy, too, sympathy for the most part extended to those soldiers and sailors who have upheld the honor of England in far-distant lands. He has every right and reason to tell them: "I have eaten your bread and your salt, I have drunk your water and wine, I have lived your life, I have watched o'er your beds of death."

He attained fame and success as a very young man, but he has continued to develop ever since. One of his biographers has stated that there are three "notes" to be traced in his authorship. The satirical note is found in *Departmental Ditties, Plain Tales from the Hills, The Story of the Gadsbys,* with its amusing commendation of single blessedness, and in the much-debated novel, *The Light that Failed.* The second, the note of sympathy and human kindness, is most clearly marked in "The Story of Muhammad Din" and in "Without Benefit of Clergy" (in *Life's Handicap*), a gem of heartfelt emotion. The third, the ethical note, is clearly traceable in *Life's Handicap.* Whether there be much value or not in this classification which, as is usually the case in such matters, cannot be consistently applied to the whole of his production, one thing is certain: Kipling has written and sung of faithful labor, fulfilment of duty, and love of one's country. Love of one's country with Kipling does not mean solely devotion to the island kingdom of England, but rather an enthusiastic affection for the British Empire. The closer uniting of that Empire's separate members is a long and fervently cherished aspiration of the poet's. That is surely clear from his exclamation: "What should they know of England who only England know?"

Kipling has given us descriptions in vivid colors of many different countries. But the picturesque surface of things has not been the principal matter with him; he has always, in all places, had a manly ideal before him: ever to be "ready, aye ready at the call of duty" and then, when the appointed time comes, to "go to God like a soldier."

The Swedish Academy, in awarding the Nobel Prize for Literature this year to Rudyard Kipling, desires to pay a tribute of homage to the literature of England, so rich in manifold glories, and to the greatest genius in the realm of narrative that that country has produced in our times.

There was no banquet because of the death of King Oscar II of Sweden on December 8, 1907, and consequently no acceptance speech.

POEMS

By RUDYARD KIPLING

DANNY DEEVER

"What are the bugles blowin' for?" said Files-on-Parade.
"To turn you out, to turn you out," the Colour-Sergeant said.
"What makes you look so white, so white?" said Files-on-Parade.
"I'm dreadin' what I've got to watch," the Colour-Sergeant said.
  For they're hangin' Danny Deever, you can hear the Dead March play,
  The regiment's in 'ollow square—they're hangin' him to-day;
  They've taken of his buttons off an' cut his stripes away,
  An' they're hangin' Danny Deever in the mornin'.
"What makes the rear-rank breathe so 'ard?" said Files-on-Parade.
"It's bitter cold, it's bitter cold," the Colour-Sergeant said.
"What makes that front-rank man fall down?" said Files-on-Parade.
"A touch o' sun, a touch o' sun," the Colour-Sergeant said.
  They are hangin' Danny Deever, they are marchin' of 'im round,
  They 'ave 'alted Danny Deever by 'is coffin on the ground;
  An' 'e'll swing in 'arf a minute for a sneakin' shootin' hound—
  O they're hangin' Danny Deever in the mornin'!

" 'Is cot was right-'and cot to mine," said Files-on-Parade.
" 'E's sleepin' out an' far to-night," the Colour-Sergeant said.
"I've drunk 'is beer a score o' times," said Files-on-Parade.
" 'E's drinkin' bitter beer alone," the Colour-Sergeant said.
  They are hangin' Danny Deever, you must mark 'im to 'is place,
  For 'e shot a comrade sleepin'—you must look 'im in the face;
  Nine 'undred of 'is county an' the Regiment's disgrace,
  While they're hangin' Danny Deever in the mornin'.

"What's that so black agin the sun?" said Files-on-Parade.
"It's Danny fightin' 'ard for life," the Colour-Sergeant said.
"What's that that whimpers over'ead?" said Files-on-Parade.
"It's Danny's soul that's passin' now," the Colour-Sergeant said.
    For they're done with Danny Deever, you can 'ear the quickstep play,
    The regiment's in column, an' they're marchin' us away;
    Ho! the young recruits are shakin', an' they'll want their beer to-day,
    After hangin' Danny Deever in the mornin'!

GUNGA DIN

    You may talk o' gin and beer
    When you're quartered safe out 'ere,
    An' you're sent to penny-fights an' Aldershot it;
    But when it comes to slaughter
    You will do your work on water,
    An' you'll lick the bloomin' boots of 'im that's got it.
    Now in Injia's sunny clime,
    Where I used to spend my time
    A-servin' of 'Er Majesty the Queen,
    Of all them blackfaced crew
    The finest man I knew
    Was our regimental bhisti, Gunga Din.
            He was "Din! Din! Din!
      "You limpin' lump o' brick-dust, Gunga Din!
          "Hi! Slippy *hitherao!*
          "Water, get it! *Panee lao*[1]
      "You squidgy-nosed old idol, Gunga Din."

---

[1] Bring water swiftly.

The uniform 'e wore
Was nothin' much before,
An' rather less than 'arf o' that be'ind,
For a piece o' twisty rag
An' a goatskin water-bag
Was all the field-equipment 'e could find.
When the sweatin' troop-train lay
In a sidin' through the day,
Where the 'eat would make your bloomin' eyebrows crawl,
We shouted "Harry By!"[2]
Till our throats were bricky-dry,
Then we wopped 'im 'cause 'e couldn't serve us all.
   It was "Din! Din! Din!
  "You 'eathen, where the mischief 'ave you been?
   "You put some *juldee*[3] in it
   "Or I'll *marrow*[4] you this minute
  "If you don't fill up my helmet, Gunga Din!"

'E would dot an' carry one
Till the longest day was done;
An' 'e didn't seem to know the use o' fear.
If we charged or broke or cut,
You could bet your bloomin' nut,
'E'd be waitin' fifty paces right flank rear.
With 'is mussick[5] on 'is back,
'E would skip with our attack,
An' watch us till the bugles made "Retire"
An' for all 'is dirty 'ide
'E was white, clear white, inside
When 'e went to tend the wounded under fire!
   It was "Din! Din! Din!"
  With the bullets kickin' dust-spots on the green
   When the cartridges ran out,
   You could hear the front-ranks shout,
  "Hi! ammunition-mules an' Gunga Din!"

---

2 O brother. 3 Be quick. 4 Hit you. 5 Water-skin.

I sha'n't forgit the night
When I dropped be'ind the fight
With a bullet where my belt-plate should 'a' been.
I was chokin' mad with thirst,
An' the man that spied me first
Was our good old grinnin', gruntin' Gunga Din.
'E lifted up my 'ead,
An' he plugged me where I bled,
An' 'e guv me 'arf-a-pint o' water green.
It was crawlin' and it stunk,
But of all the drinks I've drunk,
I'm gratefullest to one from Gunga Din.
   It was "Din! Din! Din!
 " 'Ere's a beggar with a bullet through 'is spleen;
  " 'E's chawin' up the ground,
  "An' 'e's kickin' all around:
 "For Gawd's sake git the water, Gunga Din!"

'E carried me away
To where a dooli lay,
An' a bullet come an' drilled the beggar clean.
'E put me safe inside,
An' just before 'e died,
"I 'ope you liked your drink," sez Gunga Din.
So I'll meet 'im later on
At the place where 'e is gone—
Where it's always double drill and no canteen.
'E'll be squattin' on the coals
Givin' drink to poor damned souls,
An' I'll get a swig in hell from Gunga Din!
   Yes, Din! Din! Din!
 You Lazarushian-leather Gunga Din!
   Though I've belted you and flayed you,
   By the livin' Gawd that made you,
 You're a better man than I am, Gunga Din!

THE BALLAD OF EAST AND WEST

Oh, East is East, and West is West, and never the twain shall meet,
Till Earth and Sky stand presently at God's great Judgment Seat;
But there is neither East nor West, Border, nor Breed, nor Birth,
When two strong men stand face to face, though they come from the ends of
*   the earth!*

Kamal is out with twenty men to raise the Border side,
And he has lifted the Colonel's mare that is the Colonel's pride.
He has lifted her out of the stable-door between the dawn and the day.
And turned the calkins upon her feet, and ridden her far away.
Then up and spoke the Colonel's son that led a troop of the Guides:
"Is there never a man of all my men can say where Kamal hides?"
Then up and spoke Mohammed Khan, the son of the Ressaldar:
"If ye know the track of the morning-mist, ye know where his pickets are.
"At dusk he harries the Abazai—at dawn he is into Bonair,
"But he must go by Fort Bukloh to his own place to fare.
"So if ye gallop to Fort Bukloh as fast as a bird can fly,
"By the favour of God ye may cut him off ere he win to the Tongue of Jagai.
"But if he be past the Tongue of Jagai, right swiftly turn ye then,
"For the length and the breadth of that grisly plain is sown with Kamal's men.
"There is rock to the left, and rock to the right, and low lean thorn between,
"And ye may hear a breech-bolt snick where never a man is seen."
The Colonel's son has taken a horse, and a raw rough dun was he,
With the mouth of a bell and the heart of Hell and the head of a gallows-tree.
The Colonel's son to the Fort has won, they bid him stay to eat—
Who rides at the tail of a Border thief, he sits not long at his meat.
He's up and away from Fort Bukloh as fast as he can fly,
Till he was aware of his father's mare in the gut of the Tongue of Jagai,
Till he was aware of his father's mare with Kamal upon her back,
And when he could spy the white of her eye, he made the pistol crack.
He has fired once, he has fired twice, but the whistling ball went wide.

"Ye shoot like a soldier," Kamal said. "Show now if ye can ride!"
It's up and over the Tongue of Jagai, as blown dust-devils go,
The dun he fled like a stag of ten, but the mare like a barren doe.
The dun he leaned against the bit and slugged his head above,
But the red mare played with the snaffle-bars, as a maiden plays with a glove.
There was rock to the left and rock to the right, and low lean thorn between,
And thrice he heard a breech-bolt snick tho' never a man was seen.
They have ridden the low moon out of the sky, their hoofs drum up the dawn,
The dun he went like a wounded bull, but the mare like a new-roused fawn.
The dun he fell at a water-course—in a woeful heap fell he,
And Kamal has turned the red mare back, and pulled the rider free.
He has knocked the pistol out of his hand—small room was there to strive,
" 'T was only by favour of mine," quoth he, "ye rode so long alive:
"There was not a rock for twenty mile, there was not a clump of tree,
"But covered a man of my own men with his rifle cocked on his knee.
"If I had raised my bridle-hand, as I have held it low,
"The little jackals that flee so fast were feasting all in a row.
"If I had bowed my head on my breast, as I have held it high,
"The kite that whistles above us now were gorged till she could not fly."
Lightly answered the Colonel's son: "Do good to bird and beast,
"But count who come for the broken meats before thou makest a feast.
"If there should follow a thousand swords to carry my bones away,
"Belike the price of a jackal's meal were more than a thief could pay.
"They will feed their horse on the standing crop, their men on the garnered
      grain,
"The thatch of the byres will serve their fires when all the cattle are slain.
"But if thou thinkest the price be fair,—thy brethren wait to sup,
"The hound is kin to the jackal-spawn,—howl, dog, and call them up!
"And if thou thinkest the price be high, in steer and gear and stack,
"Give me my father's mare again, and I'll fight my own way back!"
Kamal has gripped him by the hand and set him upon his feet.
"No talk shall be of dogs," said he, "when wolf and grey wolf meet.
"May I eat dirt if thou hast hurt of me in deed or breath;
"What dam of lances brought thee forth to jest at the dawn with Death?"
Lightly answered the Colonel's son: "I hold by the blood of my clan:
"Take up the mare for my father's gift—by God, she has carried a man!"
The red mare ran to the Colonel's son, and nuzzled against his breast;

"We be two strong men," said Kamal then, "but she loveth the younger best.
"So she shall go with a lifter's dower, my turquoise-studded rein,
"My 'broidered saddle and saddle-cloth, and silver stirrups twain."
The Colonel's son a pistol drew, and held it muzzle-end,
"Ye have taken the one from a foe," said he; "Will ye take the mate from a
    friend?"
"A gift for a gift," said Kamal straight; "a limb for the risk of a limb.
"Thy father has sent his son to me, I'll send my son to him!"
With that he whistled his only son, that dropped from a mountain-crest—
He trod the ling like a buck in spring, and he looked like a lance in rest.
"Now here is thy master," Kamal said, "who leads a troop of the Guides,
"And thou must ride at his left side as shield on shoulder rides.
"Till Death or I cut loose the tie, at camp and board and bed,
"Thy life is his—thy fate it is to guard him with thy head.
"So, thou must eat the White Queen's meat, and all her foes are thine,
"And thou must harry thy father's hold for the peace of the Border-line.
"And thou must make a trooper tough and hack thy way to power—
"Belike they will raise thee to Ressaldar when I am hanged in Peshawur."

They have looked each other between the eyes, and there they found no fault,
They have taken the Oath of the Brother-in-Blood on leavened bread and salt:
They have taken the Oath of the Brother-in-Blood on fire and fresh-cut sod,
On the hilt and the haft of the Khyber knife, and the Wondrous Names of God.
The Colonel's son he rides the mare and Kamal's boy the dun,
And two have come back to Fort Bukloh where there went forth but one.
And when they drew to the Quarter-Guard, full twenty swords flew clear—
There was not a man but carried his feud with the blood of the mountaineer.
"Ha' done! ha' done!" said the Colonel's son. "Put up the steel at your sides!
"Last night ye had struck at a Border thief—to-night 't is a man of the Guides!"

Oh, East is East, and West is West, and never the twain shall meet,
Till Earth and Sky stand presently at God's great Judgment Seat;
But there is neither East nor West, Border, nor Breed, nor Birth,
When two strong men stand face to face, though they come from the ends of
    the earth!

RECESSIONAL

God of our fathers, known of old,
    Lord of our far-flung battle-line,
Beneath whose awful Hand we hold
    Dominion over palm and pine—
Lord God of Hosts, be with us yet,
Lest we forget—lest we forget!

The tumult and the shouting dies;
    The Captains and the Kings depart:
Still stands Thine ancient sacrifice,
    An humble and a contrite heart.
Lord God of Hosts, be with us yet,
Lest we forget—lest we forget!

Far-called, our navies melt away;
    On dune and headland sinks the fire:
Lo, all our pomp of yesterday
    Is one with Nineveh and Tyre!
Judge of the Nations, spare us yet,
Lest we forget—lest we forget!

If, drunk with sight of power, we loose
    Wild tongues that have not Thee in awe,
Such boastings as the Gentiles use,
    Or lesser breeds without the Law—
Lord God of Hosts, be with us yet,
Lest we forget—lest we forget!

For heathen heart that puts her trust
    In reeking tube and iron shard,
All valiant dust that builds on dust,
    And guarding, calls not Thee to guard,
For frantic boast and foolish word—
Thy mercy on Thy People, Lord!

THE LIGHT THAT FAILED

By RUDYARD KIPLING

CHAPTER 1

So we settled it all when the storm was done
  As comf'y as comf'y could be;
And I was to wait in the barn, my dears,
  Because I was only three,
And Teddy would run to the rainbow's foot,
  Because he was five and a man.
And that's how it all began, my dears,
  And that's how it all began.

Big Barn Stories

'What do you think she'd do if she caught us? We oughtn't to have it, you know,' said Maisie.

'Beat me, and lock you up in your bedroom,' Dick answered, without hesitation. 'Have you got the cartridges?'

'Yes; they're in my pocket, but they are joggling horribly. Do pin-fire cartridges go off of their own accord?'

'Don't know. Take the revolver, if you are afraid, and let me carry them.'

'I'm not afraid.' Maisie strode forward swiftly, a hand in her pocket and her chin in the air. Dick followed with a small pin-fire revolver.

The children had discovered that their lives would be unendurable without pistol-practice. After much forethought and self-denial, Dick had saved seven shillings and sixpence, the price of a badly-constructed Belgian revolver. Maisie could only contribute half a crown to the syndicate for the purchase of a hundred cartridges. 'You can save better than I can, Dick,' she explained; 'I like nice things to eat, and it doesn't matter to you. Besides, boys ought to do these things.'

Dick grumbled a little at the arrangement, but went out and made the purchases, which the children were then on their way to test. Revolvers did not lie in the scheme of their daily life as decreed for them by the guardian who was incorrectly supposed to stand in the place of a mother to these two orphans. Dick had been under her care for six years, during which time she had made her profit of the allowances supposed to be expended on his clothes, and, partly through thoughtlessness, partly through a natural desire to pain,—she was a widow of some years anxious to marry again,—had made his days burdensome on his young shoulders. Where he had looked for love, she gave him first aversion and then hate. Where he growing older had sought a little sympathy, she gave him ridicule. The many hours that she could spare from the ordering of her small house she devoted to what she called the home-training of Dick Heldar. Her religion, manufactured in the main by her own intelligence and a keen study of the Scriptures, was an aid to her in this matter. At such times as she herself was not personally displeased with Dick, she left him to

[105]

understand that he had a heavy account to settle with his Creator; wherefore Dick learned to loathe his God as intensely as he loathed Mrs. Jennett; and this is not a wholesome frame of mind for the young. Since she chose to regard him as a hopeless liar, when dread of pain drove him to his first untruth, he naturally developed into a liar, but an economical and self-contained one, never throwing away the least unnecessary fib, and never hesitating at the blackest, were it only plausible, that might make his life a little easier. The treatment taught him at least the power of living alone,—a power that was of service to him when he went to a public school and the boys laughed at his clothes, which were poor in quality and much mended. In the holidays he returned to the teachings of Mrs. Jennett, and, that the chain of discipline might not be weakened by association with the world, was generally beaten, on one count or another, before he had been twelve hours under her roof.

The autumn of one year brought him a companion in bondage, a long-haired, gray-eyed little atom, as self-contained as himself, who moved about the house silently, and for the first few weeks spoke only to the goat that was her chiefest friend on earth and lived in the back-garden. Mrs. Jennett objected to the goat on the grounds that he was un-Christian,—which he certainly was. 'Then,' said the atom, choosing her words very deliberately, 'I shall write to my lawyer-people and tell them that you are a very bad woman. Amomma is mine, mine, mine!" Mrs. Jennett made a movement to the hall, where certain umbrellas and canes stood in a rack. The atom understood as clearly as Dick what this meant. 'I have been beaten before,' she said, still in the same passionless voice; 'I have been beaten worse than you can ever beat me. If you beat me I shall write to

my lawyer-people and tell them that you do not give me enough to eat. I am not afraid of you.' Mrs. Jennett did not go into the hall, and the atom, after a pause to assure herself that all danger of war was past, went out, to weep bitterly on Amomma's neck.

Dick learned to know her as Maisie, and at first mistrusted her profoundly, for he feared that she might interfere with the small liberty of action left to him. She did not, however; and she volunteered no friendliness until Dick had taken the first steps. Long before the holidays were over, the stress of punishment shared in common drove the children together, if it were only to play into each other's hands as they prepared lies for Mrs. Jennett's use. When Dick returned to school, Maisie whispered, 'Now I shall be all alone to take care of myself; but,' and she nodded her head bravely, 'I can do it. You promised to send Amomma a grass collar. Send it soon.' A week later she asked for that collar by return of post, and was not pleased when she learned that it took time to make. When at last Dick forwarded the gift she forgot to thank him for it.

Many holidays had come and gone since that day, and Dick had grown into a lanky hobbledehoy more than ever conscious of his bad clothes. Not for a moment had Mrs. Jennett relaxed her tender care of him, but the average canings of a public school—Dick fell under punishment about three times a month—filled him with contempt for her powers. 'She doesn't hurt,' he explained to Maisie, who urged him to rebellion, 'and she is kinder to you after she has whacked me.' Dick shambled through the days unkept in body and savage in soul, as the smaller boys of the school learned to know, for when the spirit moved him he would hit them, cunningly and with science. The same spirit made him more than once try to tease Maisie, but the girl refused to be made unhappy. 'We are both miserable as it is,' said she. 'What is the use of trying to make things worse? Let's find things to do, and forget things.'

The pistol was the outcome of that search. It could only be used on the muddiest foreshore of the beach, far away from bathing-machines and pier-heads, below the grassy slopes of Fort Keeling. The tide ran out nearly two miles on that coast, and the many-coloured mud-banks, touched by the sun, sent up a lamentable smell of dead weed. It was late in the afternoon when Dick and Maisie arrived on their ground, Amomma trotting patiently behind them.

'Mf!' said Maisie, sniffing the air. 'I wonder what makes the sea so smelly. I don't like it.'

'You never like anything that isn't made just for you,' said Dick bluntly. 'Give me the cartridges, and I'll try first shot. How far does one of these little revolvers carry?'

'Oh, half a mile,' said Maisie promptly. 'At least it makes an awful noise. Be careful with the cartridges; I don't like those jagged stick-up things on the rim. Dick, do be careful.'

'All right. I know how to load. I'll fire at the breakwater out there.'

He fired, and Amomma ran away bleating. The bullet threw up a spurt of mud to the right of the weed-wreathed piles.

'Throws high and to the right. You try, Maisie. Mind, it's loaded all round.'

Maisie took the pistol and stepped delicately to the verge of the mud, her hand firmly closed on the butt, her mouth and left eye screwed up. Dick sat down on a tuft of bank and laughed. Amomma returned very cautiously. He was accustomed to strange experiences in his afternoon walks, and, finding the car-tridge-box unguarded, made investiga-

tions with his nose. Maisie fired, but could not see where the bullet went.

'I think it hit the post,' she said, shading her eyes and looking out across the sailless sea.

'I know it has gone out to the Marazion Bell Buoy,' said Dick, with a chuckle. 'Fire low and to the left; then perhaps you'll get it. Oh, look at Amomma!—he's eating the cartridges!'

Maisie turned, the revolver in her hand, just in time to see Amomma scampering away from the pebbles Dick threw after him. Nothing is sacred to a billy-goat. Being well fed and the adored of his mistress, Amomma had naturally swallowed two loaded pin-fire cartridges. Maisie hurried up to assure herself that Dick had not miscounted the tale.

'Yes, he's eaten two.'

'Horrid little beast! Then they'll joggle about inside him and blow up, and serve him right. . . . Oh, Dick! have I killed you?'

Revolvers are tricky things for young hands to deal with. Maisie could not explain how it had happened, but a veil of reeking smoke separated her from Dick, and she was quite certain that the pistol had gone off in his face. Then she heard him sputter, and dropped on her knees beside him, crying, 'Dick, you aren't hurt, are you? I didn't mean it.'

'Of course you didn't,' said Dick, coming out of the smoke and wiping his cheek. 'But you nearly blinded me. That powder stuff stings awfully.' A neat little splash of gray lead on a stone showed where the bullet had gone. Maisie began to whimper.

'Don't,' said Dick, jumping to his feet and shaking himself. 'I'm not a bit hurt.'

'No, but I might have killed you,' protested Maisie, the corners of her mouth drooping. 'What should I have done then?'

'Gone home and told Mrs. Jennett.'

Dick grinned at the thought; then, softening, 'Please don't worry about it. Besides, we are wasting time. We've got to get back to tea. I'll take the revolver for a bit.'

Maisie would have wept on the least encouragement, but Dick's indifference, albeit his hand was shaking as he picked up the pistol, restrained her. She lay panting on the beach while Dick methodically bombarded the breakwater. 'Got it at last!' he exclaimed, as a lock of weed flew from the wood.

'Let me try,' said Maisie imperiously. 'I'm all right now.'

They fired in turns till the rickety little revolver nearly shook itself to pieces, and Amomma the outcast—because he might blow up at any moment—browsed in the background and wondered why stones were thrown at him. Then they found a balk of timber floating in a pool which was commanded by the seaward slope of Fort Keeling, and they sat down together before this new target.

'Next holidays,' said Dick, as the now thoroughly fouled revolver kicked wildly in his hand, 'we'll get another pistol,—central fire,—that will carry farther.'

'There won't be any next holidays for me,' said Maisie. 'I'm going away.'

'Where to?'

'I don't know. My lawyers have written to Mrs. Jennett, and I've got to be educated somewhere,—in France, perhaps,—I don't know where; but I shall be glad to go away.'

'I shan't like it a bit. I suppose I shall be left. Look here, Maisie, is it really true you're going? Then these holidays will be the last I shall see anything of you; and I go back to school next week. I wish—'

The young blood turned his cheeks scarlet. Maisie was picking grass-tufts and throwing them down the slope at a yellow sea-poppy nodding all by itself to the illimitable levels of the mud-flats and the milk-white sea beyond.

'I wish,' she said, after a pause, 'that I could see you again some time. You wish that too?'

'Yes, but it would have been better if—if—you had—shot straight over there—down by the breakwater.'

Maisie looked with large eyes for a moment. And this was the boy who only ten days before had decorated Amomma's horns with cut-paper ham-frills and turned him out, a bearded derision, among the public ways! Then she dropped her eyes: this was not the boy.

'Don't be stupid,' she said reprovingly, and with swift instinct attacked the side-issue. 'How selfish you are! Just think what I should have felt if that horrid thing had killed you! I'm quite miserable enough already.'

'Why? Because you're going away from Mrs. Jennett?'

'No.'

'From me, then?'

No answer for a long time. Dick dared not look at her. He felt, though he did not know, all that the past four years had been to him, and this the more acutely since he had no knowledge to put his feelings in words.

'I don't know,' she said. 'I suppose it is.'

'Maisie, you must know. I'm not supposing.'

'Let's go home,' said Maisie weakly.

But Dick was not minded to retreat.

'I can't say things,' he pleaded, 'and I'm awfully sorry for teasing you about Amomma the other day. It's all different now, Maisie, can't you see? And you might have told me that you were going, instead of leaving me to find out.'

'You didn't. I did tell. Oh, Dick, what's the use of worrying?'

'There isn't any; but we've been together years and years, and I didn't know how much I cared.'

'I don't believe you ever did care.'

'No, I didn't; but I do,—I care awfully

now. Maisie,' he gulped,—'Maisie, darling, say you care too, please.'

'I do; indeed I do; but it won't be any use.'

'Why?'

'Because I am going away.'

'Yes, but if you promise before you go. Only say—will you?' A second 'darling' came to his lips more easily than the first. There were few endearments in Dick's home or school life; he had to find them by instinct. Dick caught the little hand blackened with the escaped gas of the revolver.

'I promise,' she said solemnly; 'but if I care there is no need for promising.'

'And you do care?' For the first time in the past few minutes their eyes met and spoke for them who had no skill in speech. . . .

'Oh, Dick, don't! please don't! It was all right when we said good-morning; but now it's all different!' Amomma looked on from afar. He had seen his property quarrel frequently, but he had never seen kisses exchanged before. The yellow sea-poppy was wiser, and nodded its head approvingly. Considered as a kiss, that was a failure, but since it was the first, other than those demanded by duty, in all the world that either had ever given or taken, it opened to them new worlds, and every one of them glorious, so that they were lifted above the consideration of any worlds at all, especially those in which tea is necessary, and sat still, holding each other's hands and saying not a word.

'You can't forget now,' said Dick at last. There was that on his cheek that stung more than gunpowder.

'I shouldn't have forgotten anyhow,' said Maisie, and they looked at each other and saw that each was changed from the companion of an hour ago to a wonder and a mystery they could not understand. The sun began to set, and a night-wind thrashed along the bents of the foreshore.

'We shall be awfully late for tea,' said Maisie. 'Let's go home.'

'Let's use the rest of the cartridges first,' said Dick; and he helped Maisie down the slope of the fort to the sea,—a descent that she was quite capable of covering at full speed. Equally gravely Maisie took the grimy hand. Dick bent forward clumsily; Maisie drew the hand away, and Dick blushed.

'It's very pretty,' he said.

'Pooh!' said Maisie, with a little laugh of gratified vanity. She stood close to Dick as he loaded the revolver for the last time and fired over the sea, with a vague notion at the back of his head that he was protecting Maisie from all the evils in the world. A puddle far across the mud caught the last rays of the sun and turned into a wrathful red disc. The light held Dick's attention for a moment, and as he raised his revolver there fell upon him a renewed sense of the miraculous, in that he was standing by Maisie who had promised to care for him for an indefinite length of time till such date as— A gust of the growing wind drove the girl's long black hair across his face as she stood with her hand on his shoulder calling Amomma 'a little beast,' and for a moment he was in the dark,—a darkness that stung. The bullet went singing out to the empty sea.

'Spoilt my aim,' said he, shaking his head. 'There aren't any more cartridges; we shall have to run home.' But they did not run. They walked very slowly, arm in arm. And it was a matter of indifference to them whether the neglected Amomma with two pin-fire cartridges in his inside blew up or trotted beside them; for they had come into a golden heritage and were disposing of it with all the wisdom of all their years.

'And I shall be—' quoth Dick valiantly. Then he checked himself: 'I don't know what I shall be. I don't seem to be able to pass any exams, but I can make awful caricatures of the masters. Ho! ho!'

'Be an artist, then,' said Maisie. 'You're always laughing at my trying to draw; and it will do you good.'

'I'll never laugh at anything you do,' he answered. 'I'll be an artist, and I'll do things.'

'Artists always want money, don't they?'

'I've got a hundred and twenty pounds a year of my own. My guardians tell me I'm to have it when I come of age. That will be enough to begin with.'

'Ah, I'm rich,' said Maisie. 'I've got three hundred a year all my own when I'm twenty-one. That's why Mrs. Jennett is kinder to me than she is to you. I wish, though, that I had somebody that belonged to me,—just a father or a mother.'

'You belong to me,' said Dick, 'for ever and ever.'

'Yes, we belong—for ever. It's very nice.' She squeezed his arm. The kindly darkness hid them both, and, emboldened because he could only just see the profile of Maisie's cheek with the long lashes veiling the gray eyes, Dick at the front door delivered himself of the words he had been boggling over for the last two hours.

'And I—love you, Maisie,' he said, in a whisper that seemed to him to ring across the world,—the world that he would to-morrow or the next day set out to conquer.

There was a scene, not, for the sake of discipline, to be reported, when Mrs. Jennett would have fallen upon him, first for disgraceful unpunctuality, and secondly, for nearly killing himself with a forbidden weapon.

'I was playing with it, and it went off by itself,' said Dick, when the powder-pocked cheek could no longer be hidden,

'but if you think you're going to lick me you're wrong. You are never going to touch me again. Sit down and give me my tea. You can't cheat us out of that, anyhow.'

Mrs. Jennett gasped and became livid. Maisie said nothing, but encouraged Dick with her eyes, and he behaved abominably all that evening. Mrs. Jennett prophesied an immediate judgment of Providence and a descent into Tophet later, but Dick walked in Paradise and would not hear. Only when he was going to bed Mrs. Jennett recovered and asserted herself. He had bidden Maisie good-night with down-dropped eyes and from a distance.

'If you aren't a gentleman you might try to behave like one,' said Mrs. Jennett spitefully. 'You've been quarrelling with Maisie again.'

This meant that the usual good-night kiss had been omitted. Maisie, white to the lips, thrust her cheek forward with a fine air of indifference, and was duly pecked by Dick, who tramped out of the room red as fire. That night he dreamed a wild dream. He had won all the world and brought it to Maisie in a cartridge-box, but she turned it over with her foot, and, instead of saying, 'Thank you,' cried—

'Where is the grass collar you promised for Amomma? Oh, how selfish you are!'

CHAPTER 2

Then we brought the lances down, then the
        bugles blew
When we went to Kandahar, ridin' two an'
        two,
    Ridin', ridin', ridin' two an' two,
        Ta-ra-ra-ra-ra-ra-ra,
All the way to Kandahar, ridin' two an' two.
                    Barrack-Room Ballad

'I'm not angry with the British public, but I wish we had a few thousand of them scattered among these rocks. They wouldn't be in such a hurry to get at their morning papers then. Can't you imagine the regulation householder—Lover of Justice, Constant Reader, Paterfamilias, and all that lot—frizzling on hot gravel?'

'With a blue veil over his head, and his clothes in strips. Has any man here a needle? I've got a piece of sugarsack.'

'I'll lend you a packing-needle for six square inches of it then. Both my knees are worn through.'

'Why not six square acres, while you're about it? But lend me the needle, and I'll see what I can do with the selvage. I don't think there's enough to protect my royal body from the cold blast as it is. What are you doing with that everlasting sketch-book of yours, Dick?'

'Study of our Special Correspondent repairing his wardrobe,' said Dick gravely, as the other man kicked off a pair of sorely-worn riding-breeches and began to fit a square of coarse canvas over the most obvious open space. He grunted disconsolately as the vastness of the void developed itself.

'Sugar-bags, indeed! Hi! you pilot-man there! lend me all the sails of that whale-boat.'

A fez-crowned head bobbed up in the stern-sheets, divided itself into exact halves with one flashing grin, and bobbed down again. The man of the tattered breeches, clad only in a Norfolk jacket and a gray flannel shirt, went on with his clumsy sewing, while Dick chuckled over the sketch.

Some twenty whale-boats were nuzzling a sand-bank which was dotted with English soldiery of half a dozen corps, bathing or washing their clothes. A heap of boat-rollers, commissariat-boxes, sugar-bags, and flour- and small-arm-ammunition-cases showed where one of the whale-boats had been compelled to unload hastily; and a regimental carpenter was swearing aloud as he tried, on a wholly insufficient allowance of white lead, to plaster up the sun-parched gaping seams of the boat herself.

'First the bloomin' rudder snaps,' said he to the world in general; 'then the mast goes; an' then, s' 'elp me, when she can't do nothin' else, she opens 'erself out like a cock-eyed Chinese lotus.'

'Exactly the case with my breeches, whoever you are,' said the tailor, without looking up. 'Dick, I wonder when I shall see a decent shop again.'

There was no answer, save the incessant angry murmur of the Nile as it raced round a basalt-walled bend and foamed across a rock-ridge half a mile upstream. It was as though the brown weight of the river would drive the white men back to their own country. The indescribable scent of Nile mud in the air told that the stream was falling and that the next few miles would be no light thing for the whale-boats to overpass. The desert ran down almost to the banks, where, among gray, red, and black hillocks, a camel-corps was encamped. No man dared even for a day lose touch of the slow-moving boats; there had been no fighting for weeks past, and throughout all that time the Nile had never spared them. Rapid had followed rapid, rock rock, and island-group island-group, till the rank and file had long since lost all count of direction and very nearly of time. They were moving somewhere, they did not know why, to do something, they did not know what. Before them lay the Nile, and at the other end of it was one Gordon, fighting for the dear life, in a town called Khartoum. There were columns of British troops in the desert, or in one of the many deserts; there were columns on the river; there were yet more columns waiting to embark on the river; there were fresh drafts waiting at Assioot and Assuan; there were lies and rumours running over the face of the hopeless land from Suakin to the Sixth Cataract, and men supposed generally that there must be some one in authority to direct the general scheme of the many movements. The duty of that particular river-column was to keep the whale-boats afloat in the water, to avoid trampling on the villagers' crops when the gangs 'tracked' the boats with lines thrown from midstream, to get as much sleep and food as was possible, and, above all, to press on without delay in the teeth of the churning Nile.

With the soldiers sweated and toiled the correspondents of the newspapers, and they were almost as ignorant as their companions. But it was above all things necessary that England at breakfast should be amused and thrilled and interested, whether Gordon lived or died, or half the British army went to pieces in the sands. The Soudan campaign was a picturesque one, and lent itself to vivid word-painting. Now and again a 'Special' managed to get slain,—which was not altogether a disadvantage to the paper that employed him,—and more often the hand-to-hand nature of the fighting allowed of miraculous escapes which were worth telegraphing home at eighteenpence the word. There were many correspondents with many corps and columns, —from the veterans who had followed on the heels of the cavalry that occupied Cairo in '82, what time Arabi Pasha called himself king, who had seen the first miserable work round Suakin when the sentries were cut up nightly and the scrub swarmed with spears, to youngsters jerked into the business at the end of a telegraph-wire to take the place of their betters killed or invalided.

Among the seniors—those who knew every shift and change in the perplexing postal arrangements, the value of the seediest, weediest Egyptian garron

offered for sale in Cairo or Alexandria, who could talk a telegraph clerk into amiability and soothe the ruffled vanity of a newly-appointed staff-officer when press regulations became burdensome— was the man in the flannel shirt, the black-browed Torpenhow. He represented the Central Southern Syndicate in the campaign, as he had represented it in the Egyptian war, and elsewhere. The syndicate did not concern itself greatly with criticisms of attack and the like. It supplied the masses, and all it demanded was picturesqueness and abundance of detail; for there is more joy in England over a soldier who insubordinately steps out of square to rescue a comrade than over twenty generals slaving even to baldness at the gross details of transport and commissariat.

He had met at Suakin a young man, sitting on the edge of a recently-abandoned redoubt about the size of a hat-box, sketching a clump of shell-torn bodies on the gravel plain.

'What are you for?' said Torpenhow. The greeting of the correspondent is that of the commercial traveller on the road.

'My own hand,' said the young man, without looking up. 'Have you any tobacco?'

Torpenhow waited till the sketch was finished, and when he had looked at it said, 'What's your business here?'

'Nothing; there was a row, so I came. I'm supposed to be doing something down at the painting-slips among the boats, or else I'm in charge of the condenser on one of the water-ships. I've forgotten which.'

'You've cheek enough to build a redoubt with,' said Torpenhow, and took stock of the new acquaintance. 'Do you always draw like that?'

The young man produced more sketches. 'Row on a Chinese pig-boat,' said he sententiously, showing them one after another.—'Chief mate dirked by a comprador.—Junk ashore off Hako-date.—Somali muleteer being flogged.—Star-shell bursting over camp at Berbera.—Slave-dhow being chased round Tajur-rah Bay.—Soldier lying dead in the moonlight outside Suakin,—throat cut by Fuzzies.'

'H'm!' said Torpenhow, 'can't say I care for Verest-chagin-and-water myself, but there's no accounting for tastes. Do-ing anything now, are you?'

'No. I'm amusing myself here.'

Torpenhow looked at the aching deso-lation of the place. ' 'Faith, you've queer notions of amusement. 'Got any money?'

'Enough to go on with. Look here: do you want me to do war-work?'

'I don't. My syndicate may, though. You can draw more than a little, and I don't suppose you care much what you get, do you?'

'Not this time. I want my chance first.'

Torpenhow looked at the sketches again, and nodded. 'Yes, you're right to take your first chance when you can get it.'

He rode away swiftly through the Gate of the Two War-Ships, rattled across the causeway into the town, and wired to his syndicate, 'Got man here, picture-work. Good and cheap. Shall I arrange? Will do letterpress with sketches.'

The man on the redoubt sat swinging his legs and murmuring, 'I knew the chance would come, sooner or later. By Gad, they'll have to sweat for it if I come through this business alive!'

In the evening Torpenhow was able to announce to his friend that the Central Southern Agency was willing to take him on trial, paying expenses for three months. 'And, by the way, what's your name?' said Torpenhow.

'Heldar. Do they give me a free hand?'

'They've taken you on chance. You must justify the choice. You'd better stick to me. I'm going up country with a column, and I'll do what I can for you.

Give me some of your sketches taken here, and I'll send 'em along.' To himself he said, 'That's the best bargain the Cen-tral Southern has ever made; and they got me cheaply enough.'

So it came to pass that, after some purchase of horse-flesh and arrangements financial and political, Dick was made free of the New and Honourable Frater-nity of war correspondents, who all pos-sess the inalienable right of doing as much work as they can and getting as much for it as Providence and their owners shall please. To these things are added in time, if the brother be worthy, the power of glib speech that neither man nor woman can resist when a meal or a bed is in question, the eye of a horse-coper, the skill of a cook, the constitu-tion of a bullock, the digestion of an ostrich, and an infinite adaptability to all circumstances. But many die before they attain to this degree, and the past-masters in the craft appear for the most part in dress-clothes when they are in England, and thus their glory is hidden from the multitude.

Dick followed Torpenhow wherever the latter's fancy chose to lead him, and between the two they managed to accom-plish some work that almost satisfied themselves. It was not an easy life in any way, and under its influence the two were drawn very closely together, for they ate from the same dish, they shared the same water-bottle, and, most binding tie of all, their mails went off together. It was Dick who managed to make gloriously drunk a telegraph-clerk in a palm hut far beyond the Second Cataract, and, while the man lay in bliss on the floor, possessed himself of some laboriously acquired exclusive information, forwarded by a confiding correspondent of an opposition syndi-cate, made a careful duplicate of the matter, and brought the result to Torpen-how, who said that all was fair in love or war correspondence, and built an excellent descriptive article from his rival's riotous waste of words. It was Torpenhow who—but the tale of their adventures, together and apart, from Philæ to the waste wilderness of Herawi and Muella, would fill many books. They had been penned into a square side by side, in deadly fear of being shot by overexcited soldiers; they had fought with baggage-camels in the chill dawn; they had jogged along in silence under blinding sun on indefatigable little Egyptian horses; and they had floundered on the shallows of the Nile when the whale-boat in which they had found a berth chose to hit a hidden rock and rip out half her bottom-planks.

Now they were sitting on the sand-bank, and the whale-boats were bringing up the remainder of the column.

'Yes,' said Torpenhow, as he put the last rude stitches into his over-long-neglected gear, 'it has been a beautiful business.'

'The patch or the campaign?' said Dick. 'Don't think much of either myself.'

'You want the "Eurylas" brought up above the Third Cataract, don't you? and eighty-one-ton guns at Jakdul? Now, I'm quite satisfied with my breeches.' He turned round gravely to exhibit himself, after the manner of a clown.

'It's very pretty. Specially the lettering on the sack. G. B. T. Government Bullock Train. That's a sack from India.'

'It's my initials,—Gilbert Belling Torpenhow. I stole the cloth on purpose. What the mischief are the camel-corps doing yonder?' Torpenhow shaded his eyes and looked across the scrub-strewn gravel.

A bugle blew furiously, and the men on the bank hurried to their arms and accoutrements.

' "Pisan soldiery surprised while bathing," ' remarked Dick calmly. 'D'you remember the picture? It's by Michael Angelo. All beginners copy it. That scrub's alive with enemy.'

The camel-corps on the bank yelled to the infantry to come to them, and a hoarse shouting down the river showed that the remainder of the column had wind of the trouble and was hastening to take share in it. As swiftly as a reach of still water is crisped by the wind, the rock-strewn ridges and scrub-topped hills were troubled and alive with armed men. Mercifully, it occurred to these to stand far off for a time, to shout and gesticulate joyously. One man even delivered himself of a long story. The camel-corps did not fire. They were only too glad of a little breathing-space, until some sort of square could be formed. The men on the sandbank ran to their side; and the whale-boats, as they toiled up within shouting distance, were thrust into the nearest bank and emptied of all save the sick and a few men to guard them. The Arab orator ceased his outcries, and his friends howled.

'They look like the Mahdi's men,' said Torpenhow, elbowing himself into the crush of the square; 'but what thousands of 'em there are! The tribes hereabout aren't against us, I know.'

'Then the Mahdi's taken another town,' said Dick, 'and set all these yelping devils free to chaw us up. Lend us your glass.'

'Our scouts should have told us of this. We've been trapped,' said a subaltern. 'Aren't the camel-guns ever going to begin? Hurry up, you men!'

There was no need for any order. The men flung themselves panting against the sides of the square, for they had good reason to know that whoso was left outside when the fighting began would very probably die in an extremely unpleasant fashion. The little hundred-and-fifty pound camel-guns posted at one corner of the square opened the ball as the square moved forward by its right to get possession of a knoll of rising ground. All had fought in this manner many times before, and there was no novelty in the entertainment: always the same hot and stifling formation, the smell of dust and leather, the same boltlike rush of the enemy, the same pressure on the weakest side of the square, the few minutes of desperate hand-to-hand scuffle, and then the silence of the desert, broken only by the yells of those whom the handful of cavalry attempted to pursue. They had grown careless. The camel-guns spoke at intervals, and the square slouched forward amid the protests of the camels. Then came the attack of three thousand men who had not learned from books that it is impossible for troops in close order to attack against breech-loading fire. A few dropping shots heralded their approach, and a few horsemen led, but the bulk of the force was naked humanity, mad with rage, and armed with the spear and the sword. The instinct of the desert, where there is always much war, told them that the right flank of the square was the weakest, for they swung clear of the front. The camel-guns shelled them as they passed, and opened for an instant lanes through their midst, most like those quick-closing vistas in a Kentish hop-garden seen when the train races by at full speed; and the infantry fire, held till the opportune moment, dropped them in close-packed hundreds. No civilised troops in the world could have endured the hell through which they came, the living leaping high to avoid the dying who clutched at their heels, the wounded cursing and staggering forward, till they fell—a torrent black as the sliding water above a mill-dam—full on the right flank of the square. Then the line of the dusty troops and the faint blue desert sky overhead went out in rolling smoke, and the little stones on the heated ground and the tinder-dry clumps of scrub became matters of surpassing interest, for

men measured their agonised retreat and recovery by these things, counting mechanically and hewing their way back to chosen pebble and branch. There was no semblance of any concerted fighting. For aught the men knew, the enemy might be attempting all four sides of the square at once. Their business was to destroy what lay in front of them, to bayonet in the back those who passed over them, and, dying, to drag down the slayer till he could be knocked on the head by some avenging gun-butt. Dick waited quietly with Torpenhow and a young doctor till the stress became unendurable. There was no hope of attending to the wounded till the attack was repulsed, so the three moved forward gingerly towards the weakest side. There was a rush from without, the short 'hough-hough' of the stabbing spears, and a man on a horse, followed by thirty or forty others, dashed through, yelling and hacking. The right flank of the square sucked in after them, and the other sides sent help. The wounded, who knew that they had but a few hours more to live, caught at the enemy's feet and brought them down, or, staggering to a discarded rifle, fired blindly into the scuffle that raged in the centre of the square. Dick was conscious that somebody had cut him violently across his helmet, that he had fired his revolver into a black, foam-flecked face which forthwith ceased to bear any resemblance to a face, and that Torpenhow had gone down under an Arab whom he had tried to 'collar low,' and was turning over and over with his captive, feeling for the man's eyes. The doctor was jabbing at a venture with a bayonet, and a helmetless soldier was firing over Dick's shoulder: the flying grains of powder stung his cheek. It was to Torpenhow that Dick turned by instinct. The representative of the Central Southern Syndicate had shaken himself clear of his enemy, and rose, wiping his thumb on his trousers. The Arab, both hands to his forehead, screamed aloud, then snatched up his spear and rushed at Torpenhow, who was panting under shelter of Dick's revolver. Dick fired twice, and the man dropped limply. His upturned face lacked one eye. The musketry-fire redoubled, but cheers mingled with it. The rush had failed, and the enemy were flying. If the heart of the square were shambles, the ground beyond was a butcher's shop. Dick thrust his way forward between the maddened men. The remnant of the enemy were retiring, as the few—the very few—English cavalry rode down the laggards.

Beyond the lines of the dead, a broad blood-stained Arab spear cast aside in the retreat lay across a stump of scrub, and beyond this again the illimitable dark levels of the desert. The sun caught the steel and turned it into a savage red disc. Some one behind him was saying, 'Ah, get away, you brute!' Dick raised his revolver and pointed towards the desert. His eye was held by the red splash in the distance, and the clamour about him seemed to die down to a very far-away whisper, like the whisper of a level sea. There was the revolver and the red light, . . . and the voice of some one scaring something away, exactly as had fallen somewhere before,—probably in a past life. Dick waited for what should happen afterwards. Something seemed to crack inside his head, and for an instant he stood in the dark,—a darkness that stung. He fired at random, and the bullet went out across the desert as he muttered, 'Spoilt my aim. There aren't any more cartridges. We shall have to run home.' He put his hand to his head and brought it away covered with blood.

'Old man, you're cut rather badly,' said Torpenhow. 'I owe you something for this business. Thanks. Stand up! I say, you can't be ill here.'

Dick had fallen stiffly on Torpenhow's

shoulder, and was muttering something about aiming low and to the left. Then he sank to the ground and was silent. Torpenhow dragged him off to a doctor and sat down to work out an account of what he was pleased to call 'a sanguinary battle, in which our arms had acquitted themselves,' etc.

All that night, when the troops were encamped by the whale-boats, a black figure danced in the strong moonlight on the sand-bar and shouted that Gordon the accursed one was dead,—was dead, —was dead,—that two steamers were rock-staked on the Nile outside the city, and that of all their crews there remained not one; and Gordon was dead,—was dead,—was dead!

But Torpenhow took no heed. He was watching Dick, who was calling aloud to the restless Nile for Maisie,—and again Maisie!

'Behold a phenomenon,' said Torpenhow, rearranging the blanket. 'Here is a man, presumably human, who mentions the name of one woman only. And I've seen a good deal of delirium, too.—Dick, here's some fizzy drink.'

'Thank you, Maisie,' said Dick.

CHAPTER 3

So he thinks he shall take to the sea again
    For one more cruise with his buccaneers,
To singe the beard of the King of Spain,
And capture another Dean of Jaen
    And sell him in Algiers.
                          A Dutch Picture

The Soudan campaign and Dick's broken head had been some months ended and mended, and the Central Southern Syndicate had paid Dick a certain sum on account for work done, which work they were careful to assure him was not altogether up to their standard. Dick heaved the letter into the Nile at Cairo, cashed the draft in the same town, and bade a warm farewell to Torpenhow at the station.

'I am going to lie up for a while and rest,' said Torpenhow. 'I don't know where I shall live in London, but if God brings us to meet, we shall meet. Are you staying here on the off-chance of another row? There will be none till the Southern Soudan is reoccupied by our troops. Mark that. Good-bye; bless you; come back when your money's spent; and give me your address.'

Dick loitered in Cairo, Alexandria, Ismailia, and Port Said,—especially Port Said. There is iniquity in many parts of the world, and vice in all, but the concentrated essence of all the iniquities and all the vices in all the continents finds itself at Port Said. And through the heart of that sand-bordered hell, where the mirage flickers day long above the Bitter Lakes, move, if you will only wait, most of the men and women you have known in this life. Dick established himself in quarters more riotous than respectable. He spent his evenings on the quay, and boarded many ships, and saw very many friends,—gracious Englishwomen with whom he had talked not too wisely in the veranda of Shepheard's Hotel, hurrying war correspondents, skippers of the contract troop-ships employed in the campaign, army officers by the score, and others of less reputable trades. He had choice of all the races of the East and West for studies, and the advantage of seeing his subjects under the influence of strong excitement at the gaming-tables, saloons, dancing-hells, and elsewhere. For recreation there was the straight vista of the Canal, the blazing sands, the procession of shipping, and the white hospitals where the English soldiers lay. He strove to set down in black and white and colour all that Providence sent him, and when that supply was ended sought about for fresh material. It was a fasci-

nating employment, but it ran away with his money, and he had drawn in advance the hundred and twenty pounds to which he was entitled yearly. 'Now I shall have to work and starve!' thought he, and was addressing himself to this new fate when a mysterious telegram arrived from Torpenhow in England, which said, 'Come back, quick: you have caught on. Come.'

A large smile overspread his face. 'So soon! that's good hearing,' said he to himself. 'There will be an orgie to-night. I'll stand or fall by my luck. 'Faith, it's time it came!' He deposited half of his funds in the hands of his well-known friends Monsieur and Madame Binat, and ordered himself a Zanzibar dance of the finest. Monsieur Binat was shaking with drink, but Madame smiled sympathetically—

'Monsieur needs a chair, of course, and of course Monsieur will sketch: Monsieur amuses himself strangely.'

Binat raised a blue-white face from a cot in the inner room. 'I understand,' he quavered. 'We all know Monsieur. Monsieur is an artist, as I have been.' Dick nodded. 'In the end,' said Binat, with gravity, 'Monsier will descend alive into hell, as I have descended.' And he laughed.

'You must come to the dance, too,' said Dick; 'I shall want you.'

'For my face? I knew it would be so. For my face? My God! and for my degradation so tremendous! I will not. Take him away. He is a devil. Or at least do thou. Celeste, demand of him more.' The excellent Binat began to kick and scream.

'All things are for sale in Port Said,' said Madame. 'If my husband comes it will be so much more. Eh, 'ow you call— 'alf a sovereign.'

The money was paid, and the mad dance was held at night in a walled courtyard at the back of Madame Binat's house. The lady herself, in faded mauve silk always about to slide from her yellow shoulders, played the piano, and to the tin-pot music of a Western waltz the naked Zanzibari girls danced furiously by the light of kerosene lamps. Binat sat upon a chair and stared with eyes that saw nothing, till the whirl of the dance and the clang of the rattling piano stole into the drink that took the place of blood in his veins, and his face glistened. Dick took him by the chin brutally and turned that face to the light. Madame Binat looked over her shoulder and smiled with many teeth. Dick leaned against the wall and sketched for an hour, till the kerosene lamps began to smell, and the girls threw themselves panting on the hard-beaten ground. Then he shut his book with a snap and moved away, Binat plucking feebly at his elbow. 'Show me,' he whimpered. 'I too was once an artist, even I!' Dick showed him the rough sketch. 'Am I that?' he screamed. 'Will you take that away with you and show all the world that it is I,—Binat?' He moaned and wept.

'Monsieur has paid for all,' said Madame. 'To the pleasure of seeing Monsieur again.'

The courtyard gate shut, and Dick hurried up the sandy street to the nearest gambling-hell, where he was well known. 'If the luck holds, it's an omen; if I lose, I must stay here.' He placed his money picturesquely about the board, hardly daring to look at what he did. The luck held. Three turns of the wheel left him richer by twenty pounds, and he went down to the shipping to make friends with the captain of a decayed cargo-steamer, who landed him in London with fewer pounds in his pocket than he cared to think about.

A thin gray fog hung over the city, and the streets were very cold; for summer was in England.

'It's a cheerful wilderness, and it hasn't the knack of altering much,' Dick thought, as he tramped from the Docks westward. 'Now, what must I do?'

The packed houses gave no answer. Dick looked down the long lightless streets and at the appalling rush of traffic. 'Oh, you rabbit-hutches!' said he, addressing a row of highly respectable semi-detached residences. 'Do you know what you've got to do later on? You have to supply me with men-servants and maid-servants,'—here he smacked his lips,—'and the peculiar treasure of kings. Meantime I'll get clothes and boots, and presently I will return and trample on you.' He stepped forward energetically; he saw that one of his shoes was burst at the side. As he stooped to make investigations, a man jostled him into the gutter. 'All right,' he said. 'That's another nick in the score. I'll jostle you later on.'

Good clothes and boots are not cheap, and Dick left his last shop with the certainty that he would be respectably arrayed for a time, but with only fifty shillings in his pocket. He returned to streets by the Docks, and lodged himself in one room, where the sheets on the bed were almost audibly marked in case of theft, and where nobody seemed to go to bed at all. When his clothes arrived he sought the Central Southern Syndicate for Torpenhow's address, and got it, with the intimation that there was still some money owing to him.

'How much?' said Dick, as one who habitually dealt in millions.

'Between thirty and forty pounds. If it would be any convenience to you, of course we could let you have it at once; but we usually settle accounts monthly.'

'If I show that I want anything now, I'm lost,' he said to himself. 'All I need I'll take later on.' Then, aloud, 'It's hardly worth while; and I'm going into the country for a month, too. Wait till I come back, and I'll see about it.'

'But we trust, Mr. Heldar, that you do not intend to sever your connection with us?'

Dick's business in life was the study of faces, and he watched the speaker keenly. 'That man means something,' he said. 'I'll do no business till I've seen Torpenhow. There's a big deal coming.' So he departed, making no promises, to his one little room by the Docks. And that day was the seventh of the month, and that month, he reckoned with awful distinctness, had thirty-one days in it!

It is not easy for a man of catholic tastes and healthy appetites to exist for twenty-four days on fifty shillings. Nor is it cheering to begin the experiment alone in all the loneliness of London. Dick paid seven shillings a week for his lodging, which left him rather less than a shilling a day for food and drink. Naturally, his first purchase was of the materials of his craft; he had been without them too long. Half a day's investigation and comparison brought him to the conclusion that sausages and mashed potatoes, twopence a plate, were the best food. Now, sausages once or twice a week for breakfast are not unpleasant. As lunch, even, with mashed potatoes, they become monotonous. As dinner they are impertinent. At the end of three days Dick loathed sausages, and, going forth, pawned his watch to revel on sheep's head, which is not as cheap as it looks, owing to the bones and the gravy. Then he returned to sausages and mashed potatoes. Then he confined himself entirely to mashed potatoes for a day, and was unhappy because of pain in his inside. Then he pawned his waistcoat and his tie, and thought regretfully of money thrown away in times past. There are few things more edifying unto Art than the actual belly-pinch of hunger, and Dick in his few walks abroad—he did not care for exercise, it raised desires that could not be satisfied—found himself dividing mankind into two classes,—those who looked as if they might give him something to eat, and those who looked otherwise. 'I never knew what I had to learn about the human face before,' he thought; and, as a reward for his humility, Providence caused a cab-driver at a sausage-shop where Dick fed that night to leave half eaten a great chunk of bread. Dick took it,—would have fought all the world for its possession,—and it cheered him.

The month dragged through at last, and, nearly prancing with impatience, he went to draw his money. Then he hastened to Torpenhow's address and smelt the smell of cooking meats all along the corridors of the chambers. Torpenhow was on the top floor, and Dick burst into his room, to be received with a hug which nearly cracked his ribs, as Torpenhow dragged him to the light and spoke of twenty different things in the same breath.

'But you're looking tucked up,' he concluded.

'Got anything to eat?' said Dick, his eye roaming round the room.

'I shall be having breakfast in a minute. What do you say to sausages?'

'No, anything but sausages! Torp, I've been starving on that accursed horse-flesh for thirty days and thirty nights.'

'Now, what lunacy has been your latest?'

Dick spoke of the last few weeks with unbridled speech. Then he opened his coat; there was no waistcoat below. 'I ran it fine, awfully fine, but I've just scraped through.'

'You haven't much sense, but you've got a backbone anyhow. Eat, and talk afterwards.' Dick fell upon eggs and bacon and gorged till he could gorge no more. Torpenhow handed him a filled pipe, and he smoked as men smoke who for three weeks have been deprived of good tobacco.

'Ouf!' said he. 'That's heavenly! Well?'

'Why in the world didn't you come to me?'

'Couldn't; I owe you too much already, old man. Besides, I had a sort of superstition that this temporary starvation—that's what it was, and it hurt—would bring me more luck later. It's over and done with now, and none of the Syndicate know how hard up I was. Fire away. What's the exact state of affairs as regards myself?'

'You had my wire? You've caught on here. People like your work immensely. I don't know why, but they do. They say you have a fresh touch and a new way of drawing things. And, because they're chiefly homebred English, they say you have insight. You're wanted by half a dozen papers; you're wanted to illustrate books.'

Dick grunted scornfully.

'You're wanted to work up your smaller sketches and sell them to the dealers. They seem to think the money sunk in you is a good investment. Good Lord! who can account for the fathomless folly of the public?'

'They're a remarkably sensible people.'

'They are subject to fits, if that's what you mean; and you happen to be the object of the latest fit among those who are interested in what they call Art. Just now you're a fashion, a phenomenon, or whatever you please. I appeared to be the only person who knew anything about you here, and I have been showing the most useful men a few of the sketches you gave me from time to time. Those coming after your work on the Central Southern Syndicate appear to have done your business. You're in luck.'

'Huh! call it luck! Do call it luck, when a man has been kicking about the world like a dog, waiting for it to come! I'll luck 'em later on. I want a place to work in first.'

'Come here,' said Torpenhow, crossing the landing. 'This place is a big box room really, but it will do for you. There's your skylight, or your north light, or whatever window you call it, and plenty of room to thrash about in, and a bedroom beyond. What more do you need?'

'Good enough,' said Dick, looking round the large room that took up a third of a top story in the rickety chambers overlooking the Thames. A pale yellow sun shone through the skylight and showed the much dirt of the place. Three steps led from the door to the landing, and three more to Torpenhow's room. The well of the staircase disappeared into darkness, pricked by tiny gas-jets, and there were sounds of men talking, and doors slamming seven flights below, in the warm gloom.

'Do they give you a free hand here?' said Dick cautiously. He was Ishmael enough to know the value of liberty.

'Anything you like: latch-keys and license unlimited. We are permanent tenants for the most part here. 'Tisn't a place I would recommend for a Young Men's Christian Association, but it will serve. I took these rooms for you when I wired.'

'You're a great deal too kind, old man.'

'You didn't suppose you were going away from me, did you?' Torpenhow put his hand on Dick's shoulder, and the two walked up and down the room, henceforward to be called the studio, in sweet and silent communion. They heard rapping at Torpenhow's door. 'That's some ruffian come up for a drink,' said Torpenhow; and he raised his voice cheerily. There entered no one more ruffianly than a portly middle-aged gentleman in a satin-faced frockcoat. His lips were parted and pale, and there were deep pouches under the eyes.

'Weak heart,' said Dick to himself, and, as he shook hands, 'very weak heart. His pulse is shaking his fingers.'

The man introduced himslf as the head of the Central Southern Syndicate and 'one of the most ardent admirers of your work, Mr. Heldar. I assure you, in the name of the syndicate, that we are immensely indebted to you; and I trust, Mr. Heldar, you won't forget that we were largely instrumental in bringing you before the public.' He panted because of the seven flights of stairs.

Dick glanced at Torpenhow, whose left eyelid lay for a moment dead on his cheek.

'I shan't forget,' said Dick, every instinct of defence roused in him. 'You've paid me so well that I couldn't, you know. By the way, when I am settled in this place I should like to send and get my sketches. There must be nearly a hundred and fifty of them with you.'

'That is er—is what I came to speak about. I fear we can't allow it exactly, Mr. Heldar. In the absence of any specified agreement the sketches are our property, of course.'

'Do you mean to say that you are going to keep them?'

'Yes; and we hope to have your help, on your own terms, Mr. Heldar, to assist us in arranging a little exhibition, which, backed by our name and the influence we naturally command among the press, should be of material service to you. Sketches such as yours—'

'Belong to me. You engaged me by wire, you paid me the lowest rates you dared. You can't mean to keep them! Good God alive, man, they're all I've got in the world!'

Torpenhow watched Dick's face and whistled.

Dick walked up and down, thinking. He saw the whole of his little stock in trade, the first weapon of his equipment, annexed at the outset of his campaign by an elderly gentleman whose name Dick had not caught aright, who said that he represented a syndicate, which was a

thing for which Dick had not the least reverence. The injustice of the proceedings did not much move him; he had seen the strong hand prevail too often in other places to be squeamish over the moral aspects of right and wrong. But he ardently desired the blood of the gentleman in the frockcoat, and when he spoke again it was with a strained sweetness that Torpenhow knew well for the beginning of strife.

'Forgive me, sir, but you have no—no younger man who can arrange this business with me?'

'I speak for the syndicate. I see no reason for a third party to—'

'You will in a minute. Be good enough to give back my sketches.'

The man stared blankly at Dick, and then at Torpenhow, who was leaning against the wall. He was not used to ex-employees who ordered him to be good enough to do things.

'Yes, it is rather a cold-blooded steal,' said Torpenhow critically; 'but I'm afraid, I am very much afraid, you've struck the wrong man. Be careful, Dick: remember, this isn't the Soudan.'

'Considering what services the syndicate have done you in putting your name before the world—'

This was not a fortunate remark; it reminded Dick of certain vagrant years lived out in loneliness and strife and unsatisfied desires. The memory did not contrast well with the prosperous gentleman who proposed to enjoy the fruit of those years.

'I don't know quite what to do with you,' began Dick meditatively. 'Of course, you're a thief, and you ought to be half killed, but in your case you'd probably die. I don't want you dead on this floor, and, besides, it's unlucky just as one's moving in. Don't hit, sir; you'll only excite yourself.' He put one hand on the man's forearm and ran the other down the plump body beneath the coat.

'My goodness!' said he to Torpenhow, 'and this gray beast dares to be a thief! I have seen an Esneh camel-driver have the black hide taken off his body in strips for stealing half a pound of wet dates, and he was as tough as whipcord. This thing's soft all over—like a woman.'

There are few things more poignantly humiliating than being handled by a man who does not intend to strike. The head of the syndicate began to breathe heavily. Dick walked round him, pawing him, as a cat paws a soft hearth-rug. Then he traced with his forefinger the leaden pouches underneath the eyes, and shook his head. 'You were going to steal my things,—mine, mine, mine!—you, who don't know when you may die. Write a note to your office,—you say you're the head of it,—and order them to give Torpenhow my sketches,—every one of them. Wait a minute: your hand's shaking. Now!' He thrust a pocket-book before him. The note was written. Torpenhow took it and departed without a word, while Dick walked round and round the spellbound captive, giving him such advice as he conceived best for the welfare of his soul. When Torpenhow returned with a gigantic portfolio, he heard Dick say, almost soothingly, 'Now, I hope this will be a lesson to you; and if you worry me when I have settled down to work with any nonsense about actions for assault, believe me, I'll catch you and manhandle you, and you'll die. You haven't very long to live, anyhow. Go! Imshi! Bootsak!—Get out!' The man departed, staggering and dazed. Dick drew a long breath: 'Phew! what a lawless lot these people are! The first thing a poor orphan meets is gang robbery, organised burglary! Think of the hideous blackness of that man's mind! Are my sketches all right, Torp?'

'Yes; one hundred and forty-seven of them. Well, I must say, Dick, you've begun well.'

'He was interfering with me. It only meant a few pounds to him, but it was everything to me. I don't think he'll bring an action. I gave him some medical advice gratis about the state of his body. It was cheap at the little flurry it cost him. Now, let's look at my things.'

Two minutes later Dick had thrown himself down on the floor and was deep in the portfolio, chuckling lovingly as he turned the drawings over and thought of the price at which they had been bought.

The afternoon was well advanced when Torpenhow came to the door and saw Dick dancing a wild saraband under the skylight.

'I built better than I knew, Torp,' he said, without stopping the dance. 'They're good! They're damned good! They'll go like flame! I shall have an exhibition of them on my own brazen hook. And that man would have cheated me out of it! Do you know that I'm sorry now that I didn't actually hit him?'

'Go out,' said Torpenhow,—'go out and pray to be delivered from the sin of arrogance, which you never will be. Bring your things up from whatever place you're staying in, and we'll try to make this barn a little more shipshape.'

'And then—oh, then,' said Dick, still capering, 'we will spoil the Egyptians!'

CHAPTER 4

The wolf-cub at even lay hid in the corn,
   When the smoke of, the cooking hung gray:
He knew where the doe made a couch for her fawn,
   And he looked to his strength for his prey.
But the moon swept the smoke-wreaths away.
And he turned from his meal in the villager's close,
And he bayed to the moon as she rose.

In Seonee

'Well, and how does success taste?' said Torpenhow, some three months later. He had just returned to chambers after a holiday in the country.

'Good,' said Dick, as he sat licking his lips before the easel in the studio. 'I want more,—heaps more. The lean years have passed, and I approve of these fat ones.'

'Be careful, old man. That way lies bad work.'

Torpenhow was sprawling in a long chair with a small fox-terrier asleep on his chest, while Dick was preparing a canvas. A dais, a background, and a lay-figure were the only fixed objects in the place. They rose from a wreck of oddments that began with felt-covered water-bottles, belts, and regimental badges, and ended with a small bale of second-hand uniforms and a stand of mixed arms. The mark of muddy feet on the dais showed that a military model had just gone away. The watery autumn sunlight was failing, and shadows sat in the corners of the studio.

'Yes,' said Dick deliberately, 'I like the power; I like the fun; I like the fuss; and above all I like the money. I almost like the people who make the fuss and pay the money. Almost. But they're a queer gang,—an amazingly queer gang!'

'They have been good enough to you, at any rate. That tin-pot exhibition of your sketches must have paid. Did you see that the papers called it the "Wild Work Show"?'

'Never mind. I sold every shred of canvas I wanted to; and, on my word, I believe it was because they believed I was a self-taught flagstone artist. I should have got better prices if I had worked my things on wool or scratched them on camel-bone instead of using mere black and white and colour. They are a queer gang, these people. Limited isn't the word to describe 'em. I met a fellow the other day who told me that it was impossible that shadows on white sand should be blue,—ultramarine,—which they are. I found out, later, that that man had been as far as Brighton beach; but he knew all about Art, confound him. He gave me a lecture on it, and recommended me to go to school to learn technique. I wonder what old Kami would have said to that.'

'When were you under Kami, man of extraordinary beginnings?'

'I studied with him for two years in Paris. He taught by personal magnetism. All he ever said was, "Continuez, mes enfants," and you had to make the best you could of that. He had a divine touch, and he knew something about colour. Kami used to dream colour. I swear he could never have seen the genuine article; but he evolved it, and it was good.'

'Recollect some of those views in the Soudan?' said Torpenhow, with a provoking drawl.

Dick squirmed in his place. 'Don't! It makes me want to get out there again. What colour that was! Opal and umber and amber and claret and brick-red and sulphur—cockatoo-crest sulphur—against brown, with a nigger-black rock sticking up in the middle of it all, and a decorative frieze of camels festooning in front of a pure pale turquoise sky.' He began to walk up and down. 'And yet, you know, if you try to give these people the thing as God gave it keyed down to their comprehension and according to the powers He has given you—'

'Modest man! Go on.'

'Half a dozen epicene young pagans who haven't even been to Algiers will tell you, first, that your notion is borrowed, and, secondly, that it isn't Art.'

'This comes of my leaving town for a month. Dickie, you've been promenading among the toy-shops and hearing people talk.'

'I couldn't help it,' said Dick penitently. 'You weren't here, and it was lonely these long evenings. A man can't work for ever.'

'A man might have gone to a pub, and got decently drunk.'

'I wish I had; but I forgathered with some men of sorts. They said they were artists, and I knew some of them could draw,—but they wouldn't draw. They gave me tea,—tea at five in the afternoon!—and talked about Art and the state of their souls. As if their souls mattered. I've heard more about Art and seen less of her in the last six months than in the whole of my life. Do you remember Cassavetti, who worked for some continental syndicate, out with the desert column? He was a regular Christmas-tree of contraptions when he took the field in full fig, with his water-bottle, lanyard, revolver, writing-case, housewife, gig-lamps, and the Lord knows what all. He used to fiddle about with 'em and show us how they worked; but he never seemed to do much except fudge his reports from the Nilghai. See?'

'Dear old Nilghai! He's in town, fatter than ever. He ought to be up here this evening. I see the comparison perfectly. You should have kept clear of all that man-millinery. Serves you right; and I hope it will unsettle your mind.'

'It won't. It has taught me what Art—holy sacred Art—means.'

'You've learnt something while I've been away. What is Art?'

'Give 'em what they know, and when you've done it once do it again.' Dick dragged forward a canvas laid face to the wall. 'Here's a sample of real Art. It's going to be a facsimile reproduction for a weekly. I called it "His Last Shot." It's worked up from the little water-colour I made outside El Maghrib. Well, I lured my model, a beautiful rifleman, up here with drink. I drored him, and I redrored him, and I tredrored him, and I made him a flushed, dishevelled, bedevilled scallawag, with his helmet at the back of his head, and the living fear of death in his eye, and the blood oozing out of a cut over his ankle-bone. He wasn't pretty, but he was all soldier and very much man.'

'Once more, modest child!'

Dick laughed. 'Well, it's only to you I'm talking. I did him just as well as I knew how, making allowance for the slickness of oils. Then the art-manager of that abandoned paper said that his subscribers wouldn't like it. It was brutal and coarse and violent,—man being naturally gentle when he's fighting for his life. They wanted something more restful, with a little more colour. I could have said a good deal, but you might as well talk to a sheep as an art-manager. I took my "Last Shot" back. Behold the result! I put him into a lovely red coat without a speck on it. That is Art. I polished his boots,—observe the high light on the toe. That is Art. I cleaned his rifle,—rifles are always clean on service, —because that is Art. I pipeclayed his helmet,—pipeclay is always used on active service, and is indispensable to Art. I shaved his chin, I washed his hands, and gave him an air of fatted peace. Result, military tailor's pattern-plate. Price, thank Heaven, twice as much as for the first sketch, which was moderately decent.'

'And do you suppose you're going to give that thing out as your work?'

'Why not? I did it. Alone I did it, in the interests of sacred, home-bred Art and "Dickenson's Weekly." '

Torpenhow smoked in silence for a while. Then came the verdict, delivered from rolling clouds: 'If you were only a mass of blathering vanity, Dick, I wouldn't mind,—I'd let you go to the deuce on your own mahl-stick; but when I consider what you are to me, and when I find that to vanity you add the twopenny-halfpenny pique of a twelve-year-old girl, then I bestir myself in your behalf. Thus!'

The canvas ripped as Torpenhow's

booted foot shot through it, and the terrier jumped down, thinking rats were about.

'If you have any bad language to use, use it. You have not. I continue. You are an idiot, because no man born of woman is strong enough to take liberties with his public, even though they be—which they ain't—all you say they are.'

'But they don't know any better. What can you expect from creatures born and bred in this light?' Dick pointed to the yellow fog. 'If they want furniture-polish, let them have furniture-polish, so long as they pay for it. They are only men and women. You talk as though they were gods.'

'That sounds very fine, but it has nothing to do with the case. They are the people you have to work for, whether you like it or not. They are your masters. Don't be deceived, Dickie; you aren't strong enough to trifle with them,—or with yourself, which is more important. Moreover,—Come back, Binkie: that red daub isn't going anywhere,—unless you take precious good care you will fall under the damnation of the cheque-book, and that's worse than death. You will get drunk—you're half drunk already—on easily-acquired money. For that money and your own infernal vanity you are willing to deliberately turn out bad work. You'll do quite enough bad work without knowing it. And, Dickie, as I love you and as I know you love me, I am not going to let you cut off your nose to spite your face for all the gold in England. That's settled. Now swear.'

'Don't know,' said Dick. 'I've been trying to make myself angry, but I can't, you're so abominably reasonable. There will be a row on "Dickenson's Weekly," I fancy.'

'Why the Dickenson do you want to work on a weekly paper? It's slow bleeding of power.'

'It brings in the very desirable dollars,' said Dick, his hands in his pockets.

Torpenhow watched him with large contempt. 'Why, I thought it was a man!' he said. 'It's a child.'

'No, it isn't,' said Dick, wheeling quickly. 'You've no notion what the certainty of cash means to a man who has always wanted it badly. Nothing will pay me for some of my life's joys; on that Chinese pig-boat, for instance, when we ate bread and jam for every meal, because Ho-Wang wouldn't allow us anything better, and it all tasted of pig,—Chinese pig. I've worked for this, I've sweated and I've starved for this, line on line and month after month. And now I've got it I am going to make the most of it while it lasts. Let them pay—they've no knowledge.'

'What does Your Majesty please to want? You can't smoke more than you do; you won't drink; you're a gross feeder; and you dress in the dark, by the look of you. You wouldn't keep a horse the other day when I suggested, because, you said, it might fall lame, and whenever you cross the street you take a hansom. Even you are not foolish enough to suppose that theatres and all the live things you can buy thereabouts mean Life. What earthly need have you for money?'

'It's there, bless its golden heart,' said Dick. 'It's there all the time. Providence has sent me nuts while I have teeth to crack 'em with. I haven't yet found the nut I wish to crack, but I'm keeping my teeth filed. Perhaps some day you and I will go for a walk round the wide earth.'

'With no work to do, nobody to worry us, and nobody to compete with? You would be unfit to speak to in a week. Besides, I shouldn't go. I don't care to profit by the price of a man's soul,—for that's what it would mean. Dick, it's no use arguing. You're a fool.'

'Don't see it. When I was on that Chinese pig-boat our captain got enormous credit for saving about twenty-five thousand very sea-sick little pigs, when our old tramp of a steamer fell foul of a timber-junk. Now, taking those pigs as a parallel—'

'Oh, confound your parallels! Whenever I try to improve your soul you always drag in some irrelevant anecdote from your shady past. Pigs aren't the British public; credit on the high seas isn't credit here; and self-respect is self-respect all the world over. Go out for a walk and try to catch some self-respect. And I say, if the Nilghai comes up this evening can I show him your diggings?'

'Surely. You'll be asking whether you must knock at my door, next.' And Dick departed, to take counsel with himself in the rapidly-gathering London fog.

Half an hour after he had left the Nilghai laboured up the staircase. He was the chiefest, as he was the hugest, of the war correspondents, and his experiences dated from the birth of the needle-gun. Saving only his ally, Keneu the Great War Eagle, there was no man mightier in the craft than he, and he always opened his conversation with the news that there would be trouble in the Balkans in the spring. Torpenhow laughed as he entered.

'Never mind the trouble in the Balkans. Those little states are always screeching. You've heard about Dick's luck?'

'Yes; he has been called up to notoriety, hasn't he? I hope you keep him properly humble. He wants suppressing from time to time.'

'He does. He's beginning to take liberties with what he thinks is his reputation.'

'Already! By Jove, he has cheek! I don't know about his reputation, but he'll come a cropper if he tries that sort of thing.'

'So I told him. I don't think he believes it.'

'They never do when they first start off. What's that wreck on the ground there?'

'Specimen of his latest impertinence.' Torpenhow thrust the torn edges of the canvas together and showed the well-groomed picture to the Nilghai, who looked at it for a moment and whistled.

'It's a chromo,' said he,—'a chromo-litholeo-margarine fake! What possessed him to do it? And yet how thoroughly he has caught the note that catches a public who think with their boots and read with their elbows! The cold-blooded insolence of the work almost saves it; but he mustn't go on with this. Hasn't he been praised and cockered up too much? You know these people here have no sense of proportion. They'll call him a second Detaille and a third-hand Meissonier while his fashion lasts. It's windy diet for a colt.'

'I don't think it affects Dick much. You might as well call a young wolf a lion and expect him to take the compliment in exchange for a shin-bone. Dick's soul is in the bank. He's working for cash.'

'Now he has thrown up war work, I suppose he doesn't see that the obligations of the service are just the same, only the proprietors are changed.'

'How should he know? He thinks he is his own master.'

'Does he? I could undeceive him for his good if there's any virtue in print. He wants the whip-lash.'

'Lay it on with science, then. I'd flay him myself, but I like him too much.'

'I've no scruples. He had the audacity to try to cut me out with a woman at Cairo once. I forgot that, but I remember now.'

'Did he cut you out?'

'You'll see when I have dealt with him. But, after all, what's the good? Leave him alone and he'll come home, if he has any stuff in him, dragging or wagging his tail behind him. There's more in a week of life than in a lively weekly. None the less I'll slate him. I'll slate him ponderously in the "Cataclysm." '

'Good luck to you; but I fancy nothing short of a crowbar would make Dick wince. His soul seems to have been fired before we came across him. He's intensely suspicious and utterly lawless.'

'Matter of temper,' said the Nilghai. 'It's the same with horses. Some you wallop and they work, some you wallop and they jib, and some you wallop and they go out for a walk with their hands in their pockets.'

'That's exactly what Dick has done,' said Torpenhow. 'Wait till he comes back. In the meantime you can begin your slating here. I'll show you some of his last and worst work in his studio.'

Dick had instinctively sought running water for a comfort to his mood of mind. He was leaning over the Embankment wall, watching the rush of the Thames, through the arches of Westminster Bridge. He began by thinking of Torpenhow's advice, but, as of custom, lost himself in the study of the faces flocking past. Some had death written on their features, and Dick marvelled that they could laugh. Others, clumsy and coarse-built for the most part, were alight with love; others were merely drawn and lined with work; but there was something, Dick knew, to be made out of them all. The poor at least should suffer that he might learn, and the rich should pay for the output of his learning. Thus his credit in the world and his cash balance at the bank would be increased. So much the better for him. He had suffered. Now he would take toll of the ills of others.

The fog was driven apart for a moment, and the sun shone, a blood-red wafer, on the water. Dick watched the spot till he heard the voice of the tide between the piers die down like the wash of the sea at low tide. A girl hard pressed by her lover shouted shamelessly, 'Ah, get away, you beast!' and a shift of the same wind that had opened the fog drove across Dick's face the black smoke of a river-steamer at her berth below the wall. He was blinded for the moment, then spun round and found himself face to face with—Maisie.

There was no mistaking. The years had turned the child to a woman, but they had not altered the dark-gray eyes, the thin scarlet lips, or the firmly-modelled mouth and chin; and, that all should be as it was of old, she wore a closely-fitting gray dress.

Since the human soul is finite and not in the least under its own command, Dick, advancing, said, 'Halloo!' after the manner of schoolboys, and Maisie answered, 'Oh, Dick, is that you?' Then against his will, and before the brain, newly released from considerations of the cash balance, had time to dictate to the nerves, every pulse of Dick's body throbbed furiously and his palate dried in his mouth. The fog shut down again, and Maisie's face was pearl-white through it. No word was spoken, but Dick fell into step at her side, and the two paced the Embankment together, keeping the step as perfectly as in their afternoon excursions to the mud-flats. Then Dick, a little hoarsely—

'What has happened to Amomma?'

'He died, Dick. Not cartridges; overeating. He was always greedy. Isn't it funny?'

'Yes. No. Do you mean Amomma?'

'Ye—es. No. This. Where have you come from?'

'Over there.' He pointed eastward through the fog. 'And you?'

'Oh, I'm in the north,—the black north, across all the Park. I am very busy.'

'What do you do?'

'I paint a great deal. That's all I have to do.'

'Why, what's happened? You had three hundred a year.'

'I have that still. I am painting; that's all.'

'Are you alone, then?'

'There's a girl living with me. Don't walk so fast. Dick; you're out of step.'

'Then you noticed it too?'

'Of course I did. You're always out of step.'

'So I am. I'm sorry. You went on with the painting?'

'Of course. I said I should. I was at the Slade, then at Merton's in St. John's Wood, the big studio, then I pepper-potted,—I mean I went to the National, —and now I'm working under Kami.'

'But Kami is in Paris surely?'

'No; he has his teaching studio at Vitry-sur-Marne. I work with him in the summer, and I live in London in the winter. I'm a householder.'

'Do you sell much?'

'Now and again, but not often. There is my 'bus, I must take it or lose half an hour. Good-bye, Dick.' 'Good-bye, Maisie. Won't you tell me where you live? I must see you again; and perhaps I could help you. I—I paint a little myself.'

'I may be in the Park to-morrow if there is no working light. I walk from the Marble Arch down and back again; that is my little excursion. But of course I shall see you again.' She stepped into the omnibus and was swallowed up by the fog.

'Well—I—am—damned!' exclaimed Dick, and returned to the chambers.

Torpenhow and the Nilghai found him sitting on the steps to the studio door, repeating the phrase with an awful gravity.

'You'll be more damned when I've done with you,' said the Nilghai, upheaving his bulk from behind Torpenhow's

shoulder and waving a sheaf of half-dry manuscript. 'Dick, it is of common report that you are suffering from swelled head.'

'Halloo, Nilghai. Back again? How are the Balkans and all the little Balkans? One side of your face is out of drawing, as usual.'

'Never mind that. I am commissioned to smite you in print. Torpenhow refuses from false delicacy. I've been overhauling the pot-boilers in your studio. They are simply disgraceful.'

'Oho! that's it, is it? If you think you can slate me, you're wrong. You can only describe, and you need as much room to turn in, on paper, as a P. and O. cargo-boat. But continue, and be swift. I'm going to bed.'

'H'm! h'm! h'm! The first part only deals with your pictures. Here's the peroration: "For work done without conviction, for power wasted on trivialities, for labour expended with levity for the deliberate purpose of winning the easy applause of a fashion-driven public—" '

'That's "His Last Shot," second edition. Go on.'

'—"public, there remains but one end,—the oblivion that is preceded by toleration and cenotaphed with contempt. From that fate Mr. Heldar has yet to prove himself out of danger." '

'Wow—wow—wow—wow—wow!' said Dick profanely. 'It's a clumsy ending and vile journalese, but it's quite true. And yet,' he sprang to his feet and snatched at the manuscript,—'you scarred, deboshed, battered old gladiator! you're sent out when a war begins, to minister to the blind, brutal, British public's bestial thirst for blood. They have no arenas now, but they must have special correspondents. You're a fat gladiator who comes up through a trap-door and talks of what he's seen. You stand on precisely the same level as an energetic bishop, an affable actress, a devastating cyclone, or—mine own sweet self. And you presume to lecture me about my work! Nilghai, if it were worth while I'd caricature you in four papers!'

The Nilghai winced. He had not thought of this.

'As it is, I shall take this stuff and tear it small—so!' The manuscript fluttered in slips down the dark well of the staircase. 'Go home, Nilghai,' said Dick; 'go home to your lonely little bed, and leave me in peace. I am about to turn in till to-morrow.'

'Why, it isn't seven yet!' said Torpenhow, with amazement.

'It shall be two in the morning, if I choose,' said Dick, backing to the studio door. 'I go to grapple with a serious crisis, and I shan't want any dinner.'

The door shut and was locked.

'What can you do with a man like that?' said the Nilghai.

'Leave him alone. He's as mad as a hatter.'

At eleven there was kicking on the studio door. 'Is the Nilghai with you still?' said a voice from within. 'Then tell him he might have condensed the whole of his lumbering nonsense into an epigram: "Only the free are bond, and only the bond are free." Tell him he's one idiot, Torp, and tell him I'm another.'

'All right. Come out and have supper. You're smoking on an empty stomach.'

There was no answer.

CHAPTER 5

'I have a thousand men,' said he,
 'To wait upon my will,
And towers nine upon the Tyne,
 And three upon the Till.'

'And what care I for your men,' said she,
 'Or towers from Tyne to Till,

Sith you must go with me,' she said,
 'To wait upon my will?'
                    Sir Hoggie and the Fairies

Next morning Torpenhow found Dick sunk in deepest repose of tobacco.

'Well, madman, how d'you feel?'

'I don't know. I'm trying to find out.'

'You had much better do some work.'

'Maybe; but I'm in no hurry. I've made a discovery. Torp, there's too much Ego in my Cosmos.'

'Not really! Is this revelation due to my lectures, or the Nilghai's?'

'It came to me suddenly, all on my own account. Much too much Ego; and now I'm going to work.'

He turned over a few half-finished sketches, drummed on a new canvas, cleaned three brushes, set Binkie to bite the toes of the lay-figure, rattled through his collection of arms and accoutrements, and then went out abruptly, declaring that he had done enough for the day.

'This is positively indecent,' said Torpenhow, 'and the first time that Dick has ever broken up a light morning. Perhaps he has found out that he has a soul, or an artistic temperament, or something equally valuable. That comes of leaving him alone for a month. Perhaps he has been going out of evenings. I must look to this.' He rang for the bald-headed old housekeeper, whom nothing could astonish or annoy.

'Beeton, did Mr. Heldar dine out at all while I was out of town?'

'Never laid 'is dress-clothes out once, sir, all the time. Mostly 'e dined in; but 'e brought some most remarkable fancy young gentlemen up 'er after theatres once or twice. Remarkable fancy they was. You gentlemen on the top floor does very much as you likes, but it do seem to me, sir, droppin' a walkin'-stick down five flights o' stairs an' then goin' down four abreast to pick it up again at half-past two in the mornin', singin', "Bring back the whisky, Willie darlin',"—not once or twice, but scores o' times,—isn't charity to the other tenants. What I say is, "Do as you would be done by." That's my motto.'

'Of course! of course! I'm afraid the top floor isn't the quietest in the house.'

'I make no complaints, sir. I have spoke to Mr. Heldar friendly, an' he laughed, an' did me a picture of the missis that is as good as a coloured print. It 'asn't the 'igh shine of a photograph, but what I say is, "Never look a gift-horse in the mouth." Mr. Heldar's dress-clothes 'aven't been on him for weeks.'

'Then it's all right,' said Torpenhow to himself. 'Orgies are healthy, and Dick has a head of his own, but when it comes to women making eyes I'm not so certain.—Binkie, never you be a man, little dorglums. They're contrary brutes, and they do things without any reason.'

Dick had turned northward across the Park, but he was walking in the spirit of the mud-flats with Maisie. He laughed aloud as he remembered the day when he had decked Amomma's horns with the ham-frills, and Maisie, white with rage, had cuffed him. How long those four years seemed in review, and how closely Maisie was connected with every hour of them! Storm across the sea, and Maisie in a gray dress on the beach, sweeping her drenched hair out of her eyes and laughing at the homeward race of the fishing-smacks; hot sunshine on the mud-flats, and Maisie sniffing scornfully, with her chin in the air; Maisie flying before the wind that threshed the foreshore and drove the sand like small shot about her ears; Maisie, very composed and independent, telling lies to Mrs. Jennett while Dick supported her with coarser perjuries; Maisie picking her way delicately from stone to stone, a pistol in her hand and her teeth firm-set; and Maisie in a

gray dress sitting on the grass between the mouth of a cannon and a nodding yellow sea-poppy. The pictures passed before him one by one, and the last stayed the longest. Dick was perfectly happy with a quiet peace that was as new to his mind as it was foreign to his experience. It never occurred to him that there might be other calls upon his time than loafing across the Park in the forenoon.

'There's a good working light now,' he said, watching his shadow placidly. 'Some poor devil ought to be grateful for this. And there's Maisie!'

She was walking towards him from the Marble Arch, and he saw that no mannerism of her gait had been changed. It was good to find her still Maisie, and, so to speak, his next-door neighbour. No greeting passed between them, because there had been none in the old days.

'What are you doing out of your studio at this hour?' said Dick, as one who was entitled to ask.

'Idling. Just idling. I got angry with a chin and scraped it out. Then I left it in a little heap of paint-chips and came away.'

'I know what palette-knifing means. What was the piccy?'

'A fancy head that wouldn't come right,—horrid thing!'

'I don't like working over scraped paint when I'm doing flesh. The grain comes up woolly as the paint dries.'

'Not if you scrape properly.' Maisie waved her hand to illustrate her methods. There was a dab of paint on the white cuff. Dick laughed.

'You're as untidy as ever.'

'That comes well from you. Look at your own cuff.'

'By Jove, yes! It's worse than yours. I don't think we've much altered in anything. Let's see, though.' He looked at Maisie critically. The pale blue haze of an autumn day crept between the tree-trunks of the Park and made a background for the gray dress, the black velvet toque above the black hair, and the resolute profile.

'No, there's nothing changed. How good it is! D'you remember when I fastened your hair into the snap of a handbag?'

Maisie nodded, with a twinkle in her eyes, and turned her full face to Dick.

'Wait a minute,' said he. 'That mouth is down at the corners a little. Who's been worrying you, Maisie?'

'No one but myself. I never seem to get on with my work, and yet I try hard enough, and Kami says—'

' "Continuez, mesdemoiselles. Continuez toujours, mes enfants." Kami is depressing. I beg your pardon.'

'Yes, that's what he says. He told me last summer that I was doing better and he'd let me exhibit this year.'

'Not in this place, surely?'

'Of course not. The Salon.'

'You fly high.'

'I've been beating my wings long enough. Where do you exhibit, Dick?'

'I don't exhibit. I sell.'

'What is your line, then?'

'Haven't you heard?' Dick's eyes opened. Was this thing possible? He cast about for some means of conviction. They were not far from the Marble Arch. 'Come up Oxford Street a little and I'll show you.'

A small knot of people stood round a print-shop that Dick knew well. 'Some reproduction of my work inside,' he said, with suppressed triumph. Never before had success tasted so sweet upon the tongue. 'You see the sort of things I paint. D'you like it?'

Maisie looked at the wild whirling rush of a field-battery going into action under fire. Two artillerymen stood behind her in the crowd.

'They've chucked the off lead-'orse,' said one to the other. ' 'E's tore up awful, but they're makin' good time with the others. That lead-driver drives better nor you, Tom. See 'ow cunnin' 'e's nursin' 'is 'orse.'

'Number Three'll be off the limber, next jolt,' was the answer.

'No, 'e won't. See 'ow 'is foot's braced against the iron? 'E's all right.'

Dick watched Maisie's face and swelled with joy—fine, rank, vulgar triumph. She was more interested in the little crowd than in the picture. That was something that she could understand.

'And I wanted it so! Oh, I did want it so!' she said at last, under her breath.

'Me,—all me!' said Dick placidly. 'Look at their faces. It hits 'em. They don't know what makes their eyes and mouths open; but I know. And I know my work's right.'

'Yes. I see. Oh, what a thing to have come to one!'

'Come to one, indeed! I had to go out and look for it. What do you think?'

'I call it success. Tell me how you got it.'

They returned to the Park, and Dick delivered himself of the saga of his own doings, with all the arrogance of a young man speaking to a woman. From the beginning he told the tale, the I—I—I's flashing through the records as telegraph-poles fly past the traveller. Maisie listened and nodded her head. The histories of strife and privation did not move her a hair's-breadth. At the end of each canto he would conclude, 'And that gave me some notion of handling colour,' or light, or whatever it might be that he had set out to pursue and understand. He led her breathless across half the world, speaking as he had never spoken in his life before. And in the flood-tide of his exaltation there came upon him a great desire to pick up this maiden who nodded her head and said, 'I understand.

Go on,'—to pick her up and to carry her away with him, because she was Maisie, and because she understood, and because she was his right, and a woman to be desired above all women.

Then he checked himself abruptly. 'And so I took all I wanted,' he said, 'and I had to fight for it. Now you tell.'

Maisie's tale was almost as gray as her dress. It covered years of patient toil backed by savage pride that would not be broken though dealers laughed, and fogs delayed work, and Kami was unkind and even sarcastic, and girls in other studios were painfully polite. It had a few bright spots, in pictures accepted at provincial exhibitions, but it would up with the oft-repeated wail, 'And so you see, Dick, I had no success, though I worked so hard.'

Then pity filled Dick. Even thus had Maisie spoken when she could not hit the breakwater, half an hour before she had kissed him. And that had happened yesterday.

'Never mind,' he said. 'I'll tell you something, if you'll believe it.' The words were shaping themselves of their own accord. 'The whole thing, lock, stock, and barrel, isn't worth one big yellow sea-poppy below Fort Keeling.'

Maisie flushed a little. 'It's all very well for you to talk, but you've had the success and I haven't.'

'Let me talk, then. I know you'll understand. Maisie, dear, it sounds a bit absurd, but those ten years never existed, and I've come back again. It really is just the same. Can't you see? You're alone now and I'm alone. What's the use of worrying? Come to me instead, darling.'

Maisie poked the gravel with her parasol. They were sitting on a bench. 'I understand,' she said slowly. 'But I've got my work to do, and I must do it.'

'Do it with me, then, dear. I won't interrupt.'

'No, I couldn't. It's my work,—

mine,—mine,—mine! I've been alone all my life in myself, and I'm not going to belong to anybody except myself. I remember things as well as you do, but that doesn't count. We were babies then, and we didn't know what was before us. Dick, don't be selfish. I think I see my way to a little success next year. Don't take it away from me.'

'I beg your pardon, darling. It's my fault for speaking stupidly. I can't expect you to throw up all your life just because I'm back. I'll go to my own place and wait a little.'

'But, Dick, I don't want you to—go—out of—my life, now you've just come back.'

'I'm at your orders; forgive me.' Dick devoured the troubled little face with his eyes. There was triumph in them, because he could not conceive that Maisie should refuse sooner or later to love him, since he loved her.

'It's wrong of me,' said Maisie, more slowly than before; 'it's wrong and selfish; but, oh, I've been so lonely! No, you misunderstand. Now I've seen you again,—it's absurd, but I want to keep you in my life.'

'Naturally. We belong.'

'We don't; but you always understood me, and there is so much in my work that you could help me in. You know things and the ways of doing things. You must.'

'I do, I fancy, or else I don't know myself. Then I suppose you won't care to lose sight of me altogether, and you want me to help you in your work?'

'Yes; but remember, Dick, nothing will ever come of it. That's why I feel so selfish. Let things stay as they are. I do want your help.'

'You shall have it. But let's consider. I must see your pics first, and overhaul your sketches, and find out about your tendencies. You should see what the papers say about my tendencies! Then I'll give you good advice, and you shall paint according. Isn't that it, Maisie?'

Again there was unholy triumph in Dick's eye.

'It's too good of you,—much too good. Because you are consoling yourself with what will never happen, and I know that, and yet I wish to keep you. Don't blame me later, please.'

'I'm going into the matter with my eyes open. Moreover, the queen can do no wrong. It isn't your selfishness that impresses me. It's your audacity in proposing to make use of me.'

'Pooh! You're only Dick,—and a print-shop.'

'Very good: that's all I am. But, Maisie, you believe, don't you, that I love you? I don't want you to have any false notions about brothers and sisters.'

Maisie looked up for a moment and dropped her eyes.

'It's absurd, but—I believe. I wish I could send you away before you get angry with me. But—but the girl that lives with me is red-haired, and an impressionist, and all our notions clash.'

'So do ours, I think. Never mind. Three months from to-day we shall be laughing at this together.'

Maisie shook her head mournfully. 'I knew you wouldn't understand, and it will only hurt you more when you find out. Look at my face, Dick, and tell me what you see.'

They stood up and faced each other for a moment. The fog was gathering, and it stifled the roar of the traffic of London beyond the railings. Dick brought all his painfully-acquired knowledge of faces to bear on the eyes, mouth, and chin underneath the black velvet toque.

'It's the same Maisie, and it's the same me,' he said. 'We've both nice little wills of our own, and one or other of us has to be broken. Now about the future. I must come and see your pictures some day,—I

suppose when the red-haired girl is on the premises.'

'Sundays are my best times. You must come on Sundays. There are such heaps of things I want to talk about and ask your advice about. Now I must get back to work.'

'Try to find out before next Sunday what I am,' said Dick. 'Don't take my word for anything I've told you. Good-bye, darling, and bless you.'

Maisie stole away like a little gray mouse. Dick watched her till she was out of sight, but he did not hear her say to herself, very soberly, 'I'm a wretch,—a horrid, selfish wretch. But it's Dick, and Dick will understand.'

No one has yet explained what actually happens when an irresistible force meets the immovable post, though many have thought deeply, even as Dick thought. He tried to assure himself that Maisie would be led in a few weeks by his mere presence and discourse to a better way of thinking. Then he remembered much too distinctly her face and all that was written on it.

'If I know anything of heads,' he said, 'there's everything in that face but love. I shall have to put that in myself; and that chin and mouth won't be won for nothing. But she's right. She knows what she wants, and she's going to get it. What insolence! Me! Of all the people in the wide world, to use me! But then she's Maisie. There's no getting over that fact; and it's good to see her again. This business must have been simmering at the back of my head for years. . . . She'll use me as I used Binat at Port Said. She's quite right. It will hurt a little. I shall have to see her every Sunday,— like a young man courting a housemaid. She's sure to come round; and yet—that mouth isn't a yielding mouth. I shall be wanting to kiss her all the time, and I shall have to look at her pictures,—I don't even know what sort of work she does yet,—and I shall have to talk about Art,—Woman's Art! Therefore, particularly and perpetually, damn all varieties of Art! It did me a good turn once, and now it's in my way. I'll go home and do some Art.'

Half-way to the studio Dick was smitten with a terrible thought. The figure of a solitary woman in the fog suggested it.

'She's all alone in London, with a red-haired impressionist girl, who probably has the digestion of an ostrich. Most red-haired people have. Maisie's a bilious little body. They'll eat like lone women,—meals at all hours and tea with all meals. I remember how the students in Paris used to pig along. She may fall ill at any minute, and I shan't be able to help. Whew! This is ten times worse than owning a wife.'

Torpenhow came into the studio at dusk, and looked at Dick with his eyes full of the austere love that springs up between men who have tugged at the same oar together and are yoked by custom and use and the intimacies of toil. This is a good love, and, since it allows, and even encourages, strife, recrimination, and the most brutal sincerity, does not die, but increases, and is proof against any absence and evil conduct.

Dick was silent after he handed Torpenhow the filled pipe of council. He thought of Maisie and her possible needs. It was a new thing to think of anybody but Torpenhow, who could think for himself. Here at last was an outlet for that cash balance. He could adorn Maisie barbarically with jewelry,—a thick gold necklace round that little neck, bracelets upon the rounded arms, and rings of price upon her hands,—the cool, temperate, ringless hands that he had taken between his own. It was an absurd thought, for Maisie would not even allow him to put one ring on one finger, and she would laugh at golden trappings. It

would be better to sit with her quietly in the dusk, his arm round her neck and her face on his shoulder, as befitted husband and wife. Torpenhow's boots creaked that night, and his strong voice jarred. Dick's brows contracted and he murmured an evil word because he had taken all his success as a right and part payment for past discomfort, and now he was checked in his stride by a woman who admitted all the success and did not instantly care for him.

'I say, old man,' said Torpenhow, who had made one or two vain attempts at conversation, 'I haven't put your back up by anything I've said lately, have I?'

'You! No. How could you?'

' 'Liver out of order?'

'The truly healthy man doesn't know he has a liver. I'm only a bit worried about things in general. I suppose it's my soul.'

'The truly healthy man doesn't know he has a soul. What business have you with luxuries of that kind?'

'It came of itself. Who's the man that says that we're all islands shouting lies to each other across seas of misunderstanding?'

'He's right, whoever he is,—except about the misunderstanding. I don't think we could misunderstand each other.'

The blue smoke curled back from the ceiling in clouds. Then Torpenhow, insinuatingly—

'Dick, is it a woman?'

'Be hanged if it's anything remotely resembling a woman; and if you begin to talk like that, I'll hire a red-brick studio with white paint trimmings and begonias and petunias and blue Hungarias to play among three-and-sixpenny pot-palms, and I'll mount all my pics in aniline-dye plush plasters, and I'll invite every woman who yelps and maunders and moans over what her guidebooks tell her is Art, and you shall receive 'em, Torp,— in a snuff-brown velvet coat with yellow trousers and an orange tie. You'll like that.'

'Too thin, Dick. A better man than you denied with cursing and swearing on a memorable occasion. You've overdone it, just as he did. It's no business of mine, of course, but it's comforting to think that somewhere under the stars there's saving up for you a tremendous thrashing. Whether it'll come from heaven or earth I don't know, but it's bound to come and break you up a little. You want hammering.'

Dick shivered. 'All right,' said he. 'When this island is disintegrated it will call for you.'

'I shall come round the corner and help to disintegrate it some more. We're talking nonsense. Come along to a theatre.'

CHAPTER 6

'And you may lead a thousand men,
  Nor ever draw the rein,
But ere ye lead the Faery Queen
'Twill burst your heart in twain.'

He has slipped his foot from the stirrup-bar,
  The bridle from his hand,
And he is bound by hand and foot
  To the Queen o' Faery-land.
                    Sir Hoggie and the Fairies

Some weeks later, on a very foggy Sunday, Dick was returning across the Park to his studio. 'This,' he said, 'is evidently the thrashing that Torp meant. It hurts more than I expected; but the queen can do no wrong. And she certainly has some notion of drawing.'

He had just finished a Sunday visit to Maisie,—always under the green eyes of the red-haired impressionist girl, whom he learned to hate at sight,—and was tingling with a keen sense of shame. Sunday after Sunday, putting on his best clothes, he had walked over to the untidy

house north of the Park, first to see Maisie's pictures, and then to criticise and advise upon them as he realised that they were productions on which advice would not be wasted. Sunday after Sunday, and his love grew with each visit, he had been compelled to cram his heart back from between his lips when it prompted him to kiss Maisie several times and very much indeed. Sunday after Sunday, the head above the heart had warned him that Maisie was not yet attainable, and that it would be better to talk as connectedly as possible upon the mysteries of the craft that was all in all to her. Therefore it was his fate to endure weekly torture in the studio built out over the clammy back-garden of a frail stuffy little villa where nothing was ever in its right place and nobody ever called,—to endure and to watch Maisie moving to and fro with the teacups. He abhorred tea, but, since it gave him a little longer time in her presence, he drank it devoutly, and the red-haired girl sat in an untidy heap and eyed him without speaking. She was always watching him. Once, and only once, when she had left the studio Maisie showed him an album that held a few poor cuttings from provincial papers,—the briefest of hurried notes on some of her pictures sent to outlying exhibitions. Dick stooped and kissed the paint-smudged thumb on the open page. 'Oh, my love, my love,' he muttered, 'do you value these things? Chuck 'em into the waste-paper basket!'

'Not till I get something better,' said Maisie, shutting the book.

Then Dick, moved by no respect for his public and a very deep regard for the maiden, did deliberately propose, in order to secure more of these coveted cuttings, that he should paint a picture which Maisie should sign.

'That's childish,' said Maisie, 'and I didn't think it of you. It must be my work. Mine,—mine,—mine!'

'Go and design decorative medallions for rich brewers' houses. You are thoroughly good at that.' Dick was sick and savage.

'Better things than medallions, Dick,' was the answer in tones that recalled a gray-eyed atom's fearless speech to Mrs. Jennett. Dick would have abased himself utterly, but that the other girl trailed in.

Next Sunday, he laid at Maisie's feet small gifts of pencils that could almost draw of themselves and colours in whose permanence he believed, and he was ostentatiously attentive to the work in hand. It demanded, among other things, an exposition of the faith that was in him. Torpenhow's hair would have stood on end had he heard the fluency with which Dick preached his own gospel of Art.

A month before, Dick would have been equally astonished; but it was Maisie's will and pleasure, and he dragged his words together to make plain to her comprehension all that had been hidden to himself of the whys and wherefores of work. There is not the least difficulty in doing a thing if you only know how to do it; the trouble is to explain your method.

'I could put this right if I had a brush in my hand,' said Dick despairingly, over the modelling of a chin that Maisie complained would not 'look flesh,'—it was the same chin that she had scraped out with the palette-knife,—'but I find it almost impossible to teach you. There's a queer grim Dutch touch about your painting that I like; but I've a notion that you're weak in drawing. You foreshorten as though you never used the model, and you've caught Kami's pasty way of dealing with flesh in shadow. Then, again, though you don't know it yourself, you shirk hard work. Suppose you spend some of your time on line alone. Line doesn't allow of shirking. Oils do, and three square inches of flashy, tricky stuff in the corner of a pic some-times carry a bad thing off,—as I know. That's immoral. Do line-work for a little while, and then I can tell more about your powers, as old Kami used to say.'

Maisie protested: she did not care for the pure line.

'I know,' said Dick. 'You want to do your fancy heads with a bunch of flowers at the base of the neck to hide bad modelling.' The red-haired girl laughed a little. 'You want to do landscapes with cattle knee-deep in grass to hide bad drawing. You want to do a great deal more than you can do. You have sense of colour, but you want form. Colour's a gift,—put it aside and think no more about it,—but form you can be drilled into. Now, all your fancy heads—and some of them are very good—will keep you exactly where you are. With line you must go forward or backward, and it will show up all your weaknesses.'

'But other people—' began Maisie.

'You mustn't mind what other people do. If their souls were your soul it would be different. You stand and fall by your own work, remember, and it is waste of time to think of any one else in this battle.'

Dick paused, and the longing that had been so resolutely put away came back into his eyes. He looked at Maisie, and the look asked as plainly as words, Was it not time to leave all this barren wilderness of canvas and counsel and join hands with Life and Love?

Maisie assented to the new programme of schooling so adorably that Dick could hardly restrain himself from picking her up then and there and carrying her off to the nearest registrar's office. It was the implicit obedience to the spoken word and the blank indifference to the unspoken desire that baffled and buffeted his soul. He held authority in that house,—authority limited, indeed, to one-half of one afternoon in seven, but very real while it lasted. Maisie had learned to appeal to him on many subjects, from the proper packing of pictures to the condition of a smoky chimney. The red-haired girl never consulted him about anything. On the other hand she accepted his appearances without protest, and watched him always. He discovered that the meals of the establishment were irregular and fragmentary. They depended chiefly on tea, pickles, and biscuit, as he had suspected from the beginning. The girls were supposed to market week and week about, but they lived, with the help of a charwoman, as casually as the young ravens. Maisie spent most of her income on models, and the other girl revelled in apparatus as refined as her work was rough. Armed with knowledge dear-bought from the Docks, Dick warned Maisie that the end of semi-starvation meant the crippling of power to work, which was considerably worse than death. Maisie took the warning, and gave more thought to what she ate and drank. When this trouble returned upon him, as it generally did in the long winter twilights, the remembrance of that little act of domestic authority and his coercion with a hearth-brush of the smoky drawing-room chimney stung Dick like a whip-lash.

He conceived that this memory would be the extreme of his sufferings, till, one Sunday, the red-haired girl announced that she would make a study of Dick's head, and that he would be good enough to sit still, and—quite as an afterthought —look at Maisie. He sat, because he could not well refuse, and for the space of half an hour he reflected on all the people in the past whom he had laid open for the purposes of his own craft. He remembered Binat most distinctly,—that Binat who had once been an artist and talked about degradation.

It was the merest monochrome roughing-in of a head, but it presented the dumb waiting, the longing, and, above all, the hopeless enslavement of the man, in a spirit of bitter mockery.

'I'll buy it,' said Dick promptly, 'at your own price.'

'My price is too high, but I daresay you'll be as grateful if—' The wet sketch fluttered from the girl's hand and fell into the ashes of the studio stove. When she picked it up it was hopelessly smudged.

'Oh, it's all spoiled!' said Maisie. 'And I never saw it. Was it like?'

'Thank you,' said Dick under his breath to the red-haired girl, and he removed himself swiftly.

'How that man hates me!' said the girl. 'And how he loves you, Maisie!'

'What nonsense! I know Dick's very fond of me, but he has his work to do, and I have mine.'

'Yes, he is fond of you, and I think he knows there is something in impressionism, after all. Maisie, can't you see?'

'See? See what?'

'Nothing; only, I know that if I could get any man to look at me as that man looks at you, I'd—I don't know what I'd do! But he hates me. Oh, how he hates me!'

She was not altogether correct. Dick's hatred was tempered with gratitude for a few moments, and then he forgot the girl entirely. Only the sense of shame remained, and he was nursing it across the Park in the fog. 'There'll be an explosion one of these days,' he said wrathfully. 'But it isn't Maisie's fault; she's right, quite right, as far as she knows, and I can't blame her. This business has been going on for three months nearly. Three months!—and it cost me ten years' knocking about to get at the notion, the merest raw notion, of my work. That's true; but then I didn't have pins, drawing-pins and palette-knives, stuck into me every Sunday. Oh, my little darling, if ever I break you, somebody will have a very bad time of it. No, she won't. I'd be as big a fool about her as I am now. I'll poison that red-haired girl on my wedding-day,—she's unwholesome,—and now I'll pass on these present bad times to Torp.'

Torpenhow had been moved to lecture Dick more than once lately on the sin of levity, and Dick had listened and replied not a word. In the weeks between the first few Sundays of his discipline he had flung himself savagely into his work, resolved that Maisie should at least know the full stretch of his powers. Then he had taught Maisie that she must not pay the least attention to any work outside her own, and Maisie had obeyed him all too well. She took his counsels, but was not interested in his pictures.

'Your things smell of tobacco and blood,' she said once. 'Can't you do anything except soldiers?'

'I could do a head of you that would startle you,' thought Dick,—this was before the red-haired girl had brought him under the guillotine,—but he only said, 'I am very sorry,' and harrowed Torpenhow's soul that evening with blasphemies against Art. Later, insensibly and to a large extent against his own will, he ceased to interest himself in his own work. For Maisie's sake, and to soothe the self-respect that it seemed to him he lost each Sunday, he would not consciously turn out bad stuff, but, since Maisie did not care even for his best, it were better not to do anything at all save wait and mark time between Sunday and Sunday. Torpenhow was disgusted as the weeks went by fruitless, and then attacked him one Sunday evening when Dick felt utterly exhausted after three hours' biting self-restraint in Maisie's presence. There was Language, and Torpenhow withdrew to consult the Nilghai, who had come in to talk continental politics.

'Bone-idle, is he? Careless, and touched in the temper?' said the Nilghai. 'It isn't worth worrying over. Dick is

probably playing the fool with a woman.'

'Isn't that bad enough?'

'No. She may throw him out of gear and knock his work to pieces for a while. She may even turn up here some day and make a scene on the staircase: one never knows. But until Dick speaks of his own accord you had better not touch him. He is no easy-tempered man to handle.'

'No; I wish he were. He is such an aggressive, cocksure, you-be-damned fellow.'

'He'll get that knocked out of him in time. He must learn that he can't storm up and down the world with a box of moist tubes and a slick brush. You're fond of him?'

'I'd take any punishment that's in store for him if I could; but the worst of it is, no man can save his brother.'

'No, and the worser of it is, there is no discharge in this war. Dick must learn his lesson like the rest of us. Talking of war, there'll be trouble in the Balkans in the spring.'

'That trouble is long coming. I wonder if we could drag Dick out there when it comes off?'

Dick entered the room soon afterwards, and the question was put to him. 'Not good enough,' he said shortly. 'I'm too comf'y where I am.'

'Surely you aren't taking all the stuff in the papers seriously?' said the Nilghai. 'Your vogue will be ended in less than six months,—the public will know your touch and go on to something new,—and where will you be then?'

'Here, in England.'

'When you might be doing decent work among us out there? Nonsense! I shall go, The Keneu will be there, Torp will be there, Cassavetti will be there, and the whole lot of us will be there, and we shall have as much as ever we can do, with unlimited fighting and the chance for you of seeing things that would make the reputation of three Verestchagins.'

'Um!' said Dick, pulling at his pipe.

'You prefer to stay here and imagine that all the world is gaping at your pictures? Just think how full an average man's life is of his own pursuits and pleasures. When twenty thousand of him find time to look up between mouthfuls and grunt something about something they aren't the least interested in, the net result is called fame, reputation, or notoriety, according to the taste and fancy of the speller my lord.'

'I know that as well as you do. Give me credit for a little gumption.'

'Be hanged if I do!'

'Be hanged, then; you probably will be,—for a spy, by excited Turks. Heighho! I'm weary, dead weary, and virtue has gone out of me.' Dick dropped into a chair, and was fast asleep in a minute.

'That's a bad sign,' said the Nilghai, in an undertone.

Torpenhow picked the pipe from the waistcoat where it was beginning to burn, and put a pillow behind the head. 'We can't help; we can't help,' he said. 'It's a good ugly sort of old cocoa-nut, and I'm fond of it. There's the scar of the wipe he got when he was cut over in the square.'

'Shouldn't wonder if that has made him a trifle mad.'

'I should. He's a most businesslike madman.'

Then Dick began to snore furiously.

'Oh, here, no affection can stand this sort of thing. Wake up, Dick, and go and sleep somewhere else, if you intend to make a noise about it.'

'When a cat has been out on the tiles all night,' said the Nilghai in his beard, 'I notice that she usually sleeps all day. This is natural history.'

Dick staggered away rubbing his eyes and yawning. In the night-watches he was overtaken with an idea, so simple and so luminous that he wondered he had never conceived it before. It was full of craft. He would seek Maisie on a week-

day,—would suggest an excursion, and would take her by train to Fort Keeling, over the very ground that they two had trodden together ten years ago.

'As a general rule,' he explained to his chin-lathered reflection in the morning, 'it isn't safe to cross an old trail twice. Things remind one of things, and a cold wind gets up, and you feel sad; but this is an exception to every rule that ever was. I'll go to Maisie at once.'

Fortunately, the red-haired girl was out shopping when he arrived, and Maisie in a paint-spattered blouse was warring with her canvas. She was not pleased to see him; for week-day visits were a stretch of the bond; and it needed all his courage to explain his errand.

'I know you've been working too hard,' he concluded, with an air of authority. 'If you do that you'll break down. You had much better come.'

'Where to?' said Maisie wearily. She had been standing before her easel too long, and was very tired.

'Anywhere you please. We'll take a train to-morrow and see where it stops. We'll have lunch somewhere, and I'll bring you back in the evening.'

'If there's a good working light to-morrow I lose a day.' Maisie balanced the heavy white chestnut palette irresolutely.

Dick bit back an oath that was hurrying to his lips. He had not yet learned patience with the maiden to whom her work was all in all.

'You'll lose ever so many more, dear, if you use every hour of working light. Overwork's only murderous idleness. Don't be unreasonable. I'll call for you to-morrow after breakfast early.'

'But surely you are going to ask—'

'No, I am not. I want you and nobody else. Besides, she hates me as much as I hate her. She won't care to come. To-morrow, then; and pray that we get sunshine.'

Dick went away delighted, and by consequence did no work whatever. He strangled a wild desire to order a special train, but bought a great gray kangaroo cloak lined with glossy black marten, and then retired into himself to consider things.

'I'm going out for the day to-morrow with Dick,' said Maisie to the red-haired girl when the latter returned, tired, from marketing in the Edgware Road.

'He deserves it. I shall have the studio floor thoroughly scrubbed while you're away. It's very dirty.'

Maisie had enjoyed no sort of holiday for months, and looked forward to the little excitement, but not without misgivings.

'There's nobody nicer than Dick when he talks sensibly,' she thought, 'but I'm sure he'll be silly and worry me, and I'm sure I can't tell him anything he'd like to hear. If he'd only be sensible I should like him so much better.'

Dick's eyes were full of joy when he made his appearance next morning and saw Maisie, gray-ulstered and black-velvet-hatted, standing in the hall-way. Palaces of marble, and not sordid imitations of grained wood, were surely the fittest background for such a divinity. The red-haired girl drew her into the studio for a moment and kissed her hurriedly. Maisie's eyebrows climbed to the top of her forehead; she was altogether unused to these demonstrations. 'Mind my hat,' she said, hurrying away, and ran down the steps to Dick waiting by the hansom.

'Are you quite warm enough? Are you sure you wouldn't like some more breakfast? Put this cloak over your knees.'

'I'm quite comf'y, thanks. Where are we going, Dick? Oh, do stop singing like that. People will think we're mad.'

'Let 'em think,—if the exertion doesn't kill them. They don't know who we are,

and I'm sure I don't care who they are. My faith, Maisie, you're looking lovely!"

Maisie stared directly in front of her and did not reply. The wind of a keen, clear winter morning had put colour into her cheeks. Overhead, the creamy-yellow smoke-clouds were thinning away one by one against a pale-blue sky, and the improvident sparrows broke off from water-spout committees and cab-rank cabals to clamour of the coming of spring.

'It will be lovely weather in the country,' said Dick.

'But where are we going?'

'Wait and see.'

They stopped at Victoria, and Dick sought tickets. For less than half the fraction of an instant it occurred to Maisie, comfortably settled by the waiting-room fire, that it was much more pleasant to send a man to the booking-office than to elbow one's way through the crowd. Dick put her into a Pullman, —solely on account of the warmth there; and she regarded the extravagance with grave scandalised eyes as the train moved out into the country.

'I wish I knew where we are going,' she repeated for the twentieth time. The name of a well-remembered station flashed by, towards the end of the run, and Maisie was enlightened.

'Oh, Dick, you villain!'

'Well, I thought you might like to see the place again. You haven't been here since old times, have you?'

'No. I never cared to see Mrs. Jennett again; and she was all that was ever there.'

'Not quite. Look out a minute. There's the windmill above the potato-fields; they haven't built villas there yet; d'you remember when I shut you up in it?'

'Yes. How she beat you for it! I never told it was you.'

'She guessed. I jammed a stick under the door and told you that I was burying

Amomma alive in the potatoes, and you believed me. You had a trusting nature in those days.'

They laughed and leaned to look out, identifying ancient landmarks with many reminiscences. Dick fixed his weather eye on the curve of Maisie's cheek, very near his own, and watched the blood rise under the clear skin. He congratulated himself upon his cunning, and looked that the evening would bring him a great reward.

When the train stopped they went out to look at an old town with new eyes. First, but from a distance, they regarded the house of Mrs. Jennett.

'Suppose she should come out now, what would you do?' said Dick, with mock terror.

'I should make a face.'

'Show then,' said Dick, dropping into the speech of childhood.

Maisie made that face in the direction of the mean little villa, and Dick laughed aloud.

' "This is disgraceful," ' said Maisie, mimicking Mrs Jennett's tone. ' "Maisie, you run in at once, and learn the collect, gospel, and epistle for the next three Sundays. After all I've taught you, too, and three helps every Sunday at dinner! Dick's always leading you into mischief. If you aren't a gentleman, Dick, you might at least—" '

The sentence ended abruptly. Maisie remembered when it had last been used.

' "Try to behave like one," ' said Dick promptly. 'Quite right. Now we'll get some lunch and go on to Fort Keeling,— unless you'd rather drive there?'

'We must walk, out of respect to the place. How little changed it all is!'

They turned in the direction of the sea through unaltered streets, and the influence of old things lay upon them. Presently they passed a confectioner's shop much considered in the days when their joint pocket-money amounted to a shilling a week.

'Dick, have you any pennies?' said Maisie, half to herself.

'Only three; and if you think you're going to have two of 'em to buy peppermints with, you're wrong. She says peppermints aren't ladylike.'

Again they laughed, and again the colour came into Maisie's cheeks as the blood boiled through Dick's heart. After a large lunch they went down to the beach and to Fort Keeling across the waste, wind-bitten land that no builder had thought it worth his while to•defile. The winter breeze came in from the sea and sang about their ears.

'Maisie,' said Dick, 'your nose is getting a crude Prussian blue at the tip. I'll race you as far as you please for as much as you please.'

She looked round cautiously, and with a laugh set off, swiftly as the ulster allowed, till she was out of breath.

'We used to run miles,' she panted. 'It's absurd that we can't run now.'

'Old age, dear. This it is to get fat and sleek in town. When I wished to pull your hair you generally ran for three miles, shrieking at the top of your voice. I ought to know, because those shrieks were meant to call up Mrs. Jennett with a cane and—'

'Dick, I never got you a beating on purpose in my life.'

'No, of course you never did. Good Heavens! look at the sea.'

'Why, it's the same as ever!' said Maisie.

Torpenhow had gathered from Mr. Beeton that Dick, properly dressed and shaved, had left the house at half-past eight in the morning with a travelling-rug over his arm. The Nilghai rolled in at mid-day for chess and polite conversation.

'It's worse than anything I imagined,' said Torpenhow.

'Oh, the everlasting Dick, I suppose! You fuss over him like a hen with one chick. Let him run riot if he thinks it'll amuse him. You can whip a young pup off feather, but you can't whip a young man.'

'It isn't a woman. It's one woman; and it's a girl.'

'Where's your proof?'

'He got up and went out at eight this morning,—got up in the middle of the night, by Jove! a thing he never does except when he's on service. Even then, remember, we had to kick him out of his blankets before the fight began at El-Maghrib. It's disgusting.'

'It looks odd; but maybe he's decided to buy a horse at last. He might get up for that, mightn't he?'

'Buy a blazing wheelbarrow! He'd have told us if there was a horse in the wind. It's a girl.'

'Don't be certain. Perhaps it's only a married woman.'

'Dick has some sense of humour, if you haven't. Who gets up in the gray dawn to call on another man's wife? It's a girl.'

'Let it be a girl, then. She may teach him that there's somebody else in the world besides himself.'

'She'll spoil his hand. She'll waste his time, and she'll marry him, and ruin his work for ever. He'll be a respectable married man before we can stop him, and—he'll never go on the long trail again.'

'All quite possible, but the earth won't spin the other way when it happens. . . . Ho! ho! I'd give something to see Dick "go wooing with the boys." Don't worry about it. These things be with Allah, and we can only look on. Get the chessmen.'

The red-haired girl was lying down in her own room, staring at the ceiling. The footsteps of people on the pavement sounded, as they grew indistinct in the distance, like a many-times-repeated kiss that was all one long kiss. Her hands were by her side, and they opened and shut savagely from time to time.

The charwoman in charge of the scrubbing of the studio knocked at her door: 'Beg y' pardon, miss, but in cleanin' of a floor there's two, not to say three, kind of soap, which is yaller, an' mottled, an' disinfectink. Now, jist before I took my pail into the passage I thought it would be pre'aps jest as well if I was to come up 'ere an ask you what sort of soap you was wishful that I should use on them boards. The yaller soap, miss—'

There was nothing in the speech to have caused the paroxysm of fury that drove the red-haired girl into the middle of the room, almost shouting—

'Do you suppose I care what you use? Any kind will do!—any kind.'

The woman fled, and the red-haired girl looked at her own reflection in the glass for an instant and covered her face with her hands. It was as though she had shouted some shameless secret aloud.

CHAPTER 7

Roses red and roses white
Plucked I for my love's delight.
She would none of all my posies,—
Bade me gather her blue roses.

Half the world I wandered through,
Seeking where such flowers grew;
Half the world unto my quest
Answered but with laugh and jest.

It may be beyond the grave
She shall find what she would have.
Mine was but an idle quest.—
Roses white and red are best!
                        Blue Roses

Indeed the sea had not changed. Its waters were low on the mud-banks, and the

Marazion bell-buoy clanked and swung in the tide-way. On the white beach-sand dried stumps of sea-poppy shivered and chattered together.

'I don't see the old breakwater,' said Maisie under her breath.

'Let's be thankful that we have as much as we have. I don't believe they've mounted a single new gun on the fort since we were here. Come and look.'

They came to the glacis of Fort Keeling, and sat down in a nook sheltered from the wind under the tarred throat of a forty-pounder cannon.

'Now, if Amomma were only here!' said Maisie.

For a long time both were silent. Then Dick took Maisie's hand and called her by her name.

She shook her head and looked out to sea.

'Maisie, darling, doesn't it make any difference?'

'No!' between clenched teeth. 'I'd—I'd tell you if it did; but it doesn't. Oh, Dick, please be sensible.'

'Don't you think that it ever will?'

'No, I'm sure it won't.'

'Why?'

Maisie rested her chin on her hand, and, still regarding the sea, spoke hurriedly—

'I know what you want perfectly well, but I can't give it you, Dick. It isn't my fault; indeed it isn't. If I felt that I could care for any one— But I don't feel that I care. I simply don't understand what the feeling means.'

'Is that true, dear?'

'You've been very good to me, Dickie; and the only way I can pay you back is by speaking the truth. I daren't tell a fib. I despise myself quite enough as it is.'

'What in the world for?'

'Because—because I take everything that you give me and I give you nothing in return. It's mean and selfish of me, and whenever I think of it it worries me.'

'Understand once for all, then, that I can manage my own affairs, and if I choose to do anything you aren't to blame. You haven't a single thing to reproach yourself with, darling.'

'Yes, I have, and talking only makes it worse.'

'Then don't talk about it.'

'How can I help myself? If you find me alone for a minute you are always talking about it; and when you aren't you look it. You don't know how I despise myself sometimes.'

'Great goodness!' said Dick, nearly jumping to his feet. 'Speak the truth now, Maisie, if you never speak it again! Do I—does this worrying bore you?'

'No. It does not.'

'You'd tell me if it did?'

'I should let you know, I think.'

'Thank you. The other thing is fatal. But you must learn to forgive a man when he's in love. He's always a nuisance. You must have known that?'

Maisie did not consider the last question worth answering, and Dick was forced to repeat it.

'There were other men, of course. They always worried just when I was in the middle of my work, and wanted me to listen to them.'

'Did you listen?'

'At first; and they couldn't understand why I didn't care. And they used to praise my pictures; and I thought they meant it. I used to be proud of the praise, and tell Kami, and—I shall never forget—once Kami laughed at me.'

'You don't like being laughed at, Maisie, do you?'

'I hate it. I never laugh at other people unless—unless they do bad work. Dick, tell me honestly what you think of my pictures generally—of everything of mine that you've seen.'

' "Honest, honest, and honest over!" ' quoted Dick from a catchword of long ago. 'Tell me what Kami always says.'

Maisie hesitated. 'He—he says that there is feeling in them.'

'How dare you tell me a fib like that? Remember, I was under Kami for two years. I know exactly what he says.'

'It isn't a fib.'

'It's worse; it's a half-truth. Kami says, when he puts his head on one side,— so,—"Il y a du sentiment, mais il n'y a pas de parti pris."' He rolled the 'r' threateningly, as Kami used to do.

'Yes, that is what he says; and I'm beginning to think that he is right.'

'Certainly he is.' Dick admitted that two people in the world could do and say no wrong. Kami was the man.

'And now you say the same thing. It's so disheartening.'

'I'm sorry, but you asked me to speak the truth. Besides, I love you too much to pretend about your work. It's strong, it's patient sometimes,—not always,—and sometimes there's power in it, but there's no special reason why it should be done at all. At least, that's how it strikes me.'

'There's no special reason why anything in the world should ever be done. You know that as well as I do. I only want success.'

'You're going the wrong way to get it, then. Hasn't Kami ever told you so?'

'Don't quote Kami to me. I want to know what you think. My work's bad, to begin with.'

'I didn't say that, and I don't think it.'

'It's amateurish, then.'

'That it most certainly is not. You're a workwoman, darling, to your boot-heels, and I respect you for that.'

'You don't laugh at me behind my back?'

'No, dear. You see, you are more to me than any one else. Put this cloak thing round you, or you'll get chilled.'

Maisie wrapped herself in the soft marten skins, turning the gray kangaroo fur to the outside.

'This is delicious,' she said, rubbing her chin thoughtfully along the fur. 'Well? Why am I wrong in trying to get a little success?'

'Just because you try. Don't you understand, darling? Good work has nothing to do with—doesn't belong to—the person who does it. It's put into him or her from outside.'

'But how does that affect—'

'Wait a minute. All we can do is to learn how to do our work, to be masters of our materials instead of servants, and never to be afraid of anything.'

'I understand that.'

'Everything else comes from outside ourselves. Very good. If we sit down quietly to work out notions that are sent to us, we may or we may not do something that isn't bad. A great deal depends on being master of the bricks and mortar of the trade. But the instant we begin to think about success and the effect of our work—to play with one eye on the gallery—we lose power and touch and everything else. At least that's how I have found it. Instead of being quiet and giving every power you possess to your work, you're fretting over something which you can neither help nor hinder by a minute. See?'

'It's so easy for you to talk in that way. People like what you do. Don't you ever think about the gallery?'

'Much too often; but I'm always punished for it by loss of power. It's as simple as the Rule of Three. If we make light of our work by using it for our own ends, our work will make light of us, and, as we're the weaker, we shall suffer.'

'I don't treat my work lightly. You know that it's everything to me.'

'Of course; but, whether you realise it or not, you give two strokes for yourself to one for your work. It isn't your fault, darling. I do exactly the same thing, and know that I'm doing it. Most of the French schools, and all the schools here, drive the students to work for their own credit, and for the sake of their pride. I was told that all the world was interested in my work, and everybody at Kami's talked turpentine, and I honestly believed that the world needed elevating and influencing and all manner of impertinences, by my brushes. By Jove, I actually believed that! When my little head was bursting with a notion that I couldn't handle because I hadn't sufficient knowledge of my craft, I used to run about wondering at my own magnificence and getting ready to astonish the world.'

'But surely one can do that sometimes?'

'Very seldom with malice aforethought, darling. And when it's done it's such a tiny thing, and the world's so big, and all but a millionth part of it doesn't care. Maisie, come with me and I'll show you something of the size of the world. One can no more avoid working than eating,—that goes on by itself,—but try to see what you are working for. I know such little heavens that I could take you to,—islands tucked away under the Line. You sight them after weeks of crashing through water as black as black marble because it's so deep, and you sit in the fore-chains day after day and see the sun rise almost afraid because the sea's so lonely.'

'Who is afraid?—you, or the sun?'

'The sun, of course. And there are noises under the sea, and sounds overhead in a clear sky. Then you find your island alive with hot moist orchids that make mouths at you, and can do everything except talk. There's a waterfall in it three hundred feet high, just like a sliver of green jade laced with silver; and millions of wild bees live up in the rocks; and you can hear the fat cocoa-nuts falling from the palms; and you order an ivory-white servant to sling you a long yellow hammock with tassels on it like ripe maize, and you put up your feet and

hear the bees hum and the water fall till you go to sleep.'

'Can one work there?'

'Certainly. One must do something always. You hang your canvas up in a palm-tree and let the parrots criticise. When they scuffle you heave a ripe custard-apple at them, and it bursts in a lather of cream. There are hundreds of places. Come and see them.'

'I don't quite like that place. It sounds lazy. Tell me another.'

'What do you think of a big, red, dead city built of red sandstone, with raw green aloes growing between the stones, lying out neglected on honey-coloured sands? There are forty dead kings there, Maisie, each in a gorgeous tomb finer than all the others. You look at the palaces and streets and shops and tanks, and think that men must live there, till you find a wee gray squirrel rubbing its nose all alone in the market-place, and a jewelled peacock struts out of a carved doorway and spreads its tail against a marble screen as fine pierced as point-lace. Then a monkey—a little black monkey—walks through the main square to get a drink from a tank forty feet deep. He slides down the creepers to the water's edge, and a friend holds him by the tail in case he should fall in.'

'Is all that true?'

'I've been there and seen. Then evening comes, and the lights change till it's just as though you stood in the heart of a king-opal. A little before sundown, as punctually as clockwork, a big bristly wild boar, with all his family following, trots through the city gate, churning the foam on his tusks. You climb on the shoulder of a blind black stone god and watch that pig choose himself a palace for the night and stump in wagging his tail. Then the night-wind gets up, and the sands move, and you hear the desert outside the city singing, "Now I lay me down to sleep," and everything is dark till the moon rises. Maisie, darling, come with me and see what the world is really like. It's very lovely, and it's very horrible,—but I won't let you see anything horrid,—and it doesn't care your life or mine for pictures or anything else except doing its own work and making love. Come and I'll show you how to brew sangaree, and sling a hammock, and— oh, thousands of things, and you'll see for yourself what colour means, and we'll find out together what love means, and then, maybe, we shall be allowed to do some good work. Come away!'

'Why?' said Maisie.

'How can you do anything until you have seen everything, or as much as you can? And besides, darling, I love you. Come along with me. You have no business here; you don't belong to this place; you're half a gipsy,—your face tells that; and I—even the smell of open water makes me restless. Come across the sea and be happy!'

He had risen to his feet, and stood in the shadow of the gun, looking down at the girl. The very short winter afternoon had worn away, and, before they knew, the winter moon was walking the untroubled sea. Long ruled lines of silver showed where a ripple of the rising tide was turning over the mud-banks. The wind had dropped, and in the intense stillness they could hear a donkey cropping the frosty grass many yards away. A faint beating like that of a muffled drum came out of the moon-haze.

'What's that?' said Maisie quickly. 'It sounds like a heart beating. Where is it?'

Dick was so angry at this sudden wrench to his pleadings that he could not trust himself to speak, and in this silence caught the sound. Maisie from her seat under the gun watched him with a certain amount of fear. She wished so much that he would be sensible and cease to worry her with over-sea emotion that she

both could and could not understand. She was not prepared, however, for the change in his face as he listened.

'It's a steamer,' he said,—'a twin-screw steamer, by the beat. I can't make her out, but she must be standing very close in-shore. Ah!' as the red of a rocket streaked the haze, 'she's standing into signal before she clears the Channel.'

'Is it a wreck?' said Maisie, to whom these words were as Greek.

Dick's eyes were turned to the sea. 'Wreck! What nonsense! She's only reporting herself. Red rocket forward— there's a green light aft now, and two red rockets from the bridge.'

'What does that mean?'

'It's the signal of the Cross Keys Line running to Australia. I wonder which steamer it is.' The note of his voice had changed; he seemed to be talking to himself, and Maisie did not approve of it. The moonlight broke the haze for a moment, touching the black sides of a long steamer working down Channel. 'Four masts and three funnels—she's in deep draught, too. That must be the "Barralong," or the "Bhutia." No, the "Bhutia" has a clipper bow. It's the "Barralong," to Australia. She'll lift the Southern Cross in a week,—lucky old tub! —oh, lucky old tub!'

He stared intently, and moved up the slope of the fort to get a better view, but the mist on the sea thickened again, and the beating of the screws grew fainter. Maisie called to him a little angrily, and he returned, still keeping his eyes to seaward. 'Have you ever seen the Southern Cross blazing right over your head?' he asked. 'It's superb!'

'No,' she said shortly, 'and I don't want to. If you think it's so lovely why don't you go and see it yourself?'

She raised her face from the soft blackness of the marten skins about her throat, and her eyes shone like diamonds. The moonlight on the gray kangaroo fur turned it to frosted silver of the coldest.

'By Jove, Maisie, you look like a little heathen idol tucked up there.' The eyes showed that they did not appreciate the compliment. 'I'm sorry,' he continued. 'The Southern Cross isn't worth looking at unless some one helps you to see. That steamer's out of hearing.'

'Dick,' she said quietly, 'suppose I were to come to you now,—be quiet a minute,—just as I am, and caring for you just as much as I do.'

'Not as a brother, though? You said you didn't—in the Park.'

'I never had a brother. Suppose I said, "Take me to those places, and in time, perhaps, I might really care for you," what would you do?'

'Send you straight back to where you came from, in a cab. No, I wouldn't; I'd let you walk. But you couldn't do it, dear. And I wouldn't run the risk. You're worth waiting for till you can come without reservation.'

'Do you honestly believe that?'

'I have a hazy sort of idea that I do. Has it never struck you in that light?'

'Ye—es. I feel so wicked about it.'

'Wickeder than usual?'

'You don't know all I think. It's almost too awful to tell.'

'Never mind. You promised to tell me the truth—at least.'

'It's so ungrateful of me, but—but, though I know you care for me, and I like to have you with me, I'd—I'd even sacrifice you, if that would bring me what I want.'

'My poor little darling! I know that state of mind. It doesn't lead to good work.'

'You aren't angry? Remember, I do despise myself.'

'I'm not exactly flattered,—I had guessed as much before,—but I'm not angry. I'm sorry for you. Surely you ought to have left a littleness like that behind you years ago.'

'You've no right to patronise me! I only want what I have worked for so long. It came to you without any trouble, and—and I don't think it's fair.'

'What can I do? I'd give ten years of my life to get you what you want. But I can't help you; even I can't help.'

A murmur of dissent from Maisie. He went on—

'And I know by what you have just said that you're on the wrong road to success. It isn't got at by sacrificing other people,—I've had that much knocked into me; you must sacrifice yourself, and live under orders, and never think for yourself, and never have real satisfaction in your work except just at the beginning, when you're reaching out after a notion.'

'How can you believe all that?'

'There's no question of belief or disbelief. That's the law, and you take it or refuse it as you please. I try to obey, but I can't, and then my work turns bad on my hands. Under any circumstances, remember, four-fifths of everybody's work must be bad. But the remnant is worth the trouble for its own sake.'

'Isn't it nice to get credit even for bad work?'

'It's much too nice. But— May I tell you something? It isn't a pretty tale, but you're so like a man that I forget when I'm talking to you.'

'Tell me.'

'Once when I was out in the Soudan I went over some ground that we had been fighting on for three days. There were twelve hundred dead; and we hadn't time to bury them.'

'How ghastly!'

'I had been at work on a big double-sheet sketch, and I was wondering what people would think of it at home. The sight of that field taught me a good deal. It looked just like a bed of horrible toadstools in all colours, and—I'd never seen men in bulk go back to their beginnings before. So I began to understand that men and women were only material to work with, and that what they said or did was of no consequence. See? Strictly speaking, you might just as well put your ear down to the palette to catch what your colours are saying.'

'Dick, that's disgraceful!'

'Wait a minute. I said strictly speaking. Unfortunately, everybody must be either a man or a woman.'

'I'm glad you allow that much.'

'In your case I don't. You aren't a woman. But ordinary people, Maisie, must behave and work as such. That's what makes me so savage.' He hurled a pebble towards the sea as he spoke. 'I know that it is outside my business to care what people say; I can see that it spoils my output if I listen to 'em; and yet, confound it all,'—another pebble flew seaward,—'I can't help purring when I'm rubbed the right way. Even when I can see on a man's forehead that he is lying his way through a clump of pretty speeches, those lies make me happy and play the mischief with my hand.'

'And when he doesn't say pretty things?'

'Then, belovedest,'—Dick grinned,—'I forget that I am the steward of these gifts, and I want to make that man love and appreciate my work with a thick stick. It's too humiliating altogether; but I suppose even if one were an angel and painted humans altogether from outside, one would lose in touch what one gained in grip.'

Maisie laughed at the idea of Dick as an angel.

'But you seem to think,' she said, 'that everything nice spoils your hand.'

'I don't think. It's the law,—just the same as it was at Mrs. Jennett's. Everything that is nice does spoil your hand. I'm glad you see so clearly.'

'I don't like the view.'

'Nor I. But—have got orders: what can do? Are you strong enough to face it alone?'

'I suppose I must.'

'Let me help, darling. We can hold each other very tight and try to walk straight. We shall blunder horribly, but it will be better than stumbling apart. Maisie, can't you see reason?'

'I don't think we should get on together. We should be two of a trade, so we should never agree.'

'How I should like to meet the man who made that proverb! He lived in a cave and ate raw bear, I fancy. I'd make him chew his own arrow-heads. Well?'

'I should be only half married to you. I should worry and fuss about my work as I do now. Four days out of the seven I'm not fit to speak to.'

'You talk as if no one else in the world had ever used a brush. D'you suppose that I don't know the feeling of worry and bother and can't-get-at-ness? You're lucky if you only have it four days out of the seven. What difference would that make?'

'A great deal—if you had it too.'

'Yes, but I could respect it. Another man might not. He might laugh at you. But there's no use talking about it. If you can think in that way you can't care for me—yet.'

The tide had nearly covered the mud-banks, and twenty little ripples broke on the beach before Maisie chose to speak.

'Dick,' she said slowly, 'I believe very much that you are better than I am.'

'This doesn't seem to bear on the argument—but in what way?'

'I don't quite know, but in what you said about work and things; and then you're so patient. Yes, you're better than I am.'

Dick considered rapidly the murkiness of an average man's life. There was nothing in the review to fill him with a sense of virtue. He lifted the hem of the cloak to his lips.

'Why,' said Maisie, making as though she had not noticed, 'can you see things that I can't? I don't believe what you believe; but you're right, I believe.'

'If I've seen anything, God knows I couldn't have seen it but for you, and I know that I couldn't have said it except to you. You seemed to make everything clear for a minute; but I don't practise what I preach. You would help me. . . . There are only us two in the world for all purposes, and—and you like to have me with you?'

'Of course I do. I wonder if you can realise how utterly lonely I am!'

'Darling, I think I can.'

'Two years ago, when I first took the little house, I used to walk up and down the back-garden trying to cry. I never can cry. Can you?'

'It's some time since I tried. What was the trouble? Overwork?'

'I don't know; but I used to dream that I had broken down, and had no money, and was starving in London. I thought about it all day, and it frightened me—oh, how it frightened me!'

'I know that fear. It's the most terrible of all. It wakes me up in the night sometimes. You oughtn't to know anything about it.'

'How do you know?'

'Never mind. Is your three hundred a year safe?'

'It's in Consols.'

'Very well. If any one comes to you and recommends a better investment,—even if I should come to you,—don't you listen. Never shift the money for a minute, and never lend a penny of it,—even to the red-haired girl.'

'Don't scold me so! I'm not likely to be foolish.'

'The earth is full of men who'd sell their souls for three hundred a year; and women come and talk, and borrow a five-pound note here and a ten-pound note there; and a woman has no conscience in a money debt. Stick to your money, Maisie; for there's nothing more ghastly in the world than poverty in London. It's scared me. By Jove, it put the fear into me! And one oughtn't to be afraid of anything.'

To each man is appointed his particular dread,—the terror that, if he does not fight against it, must cow him even to the loss of his manhood. Dick's experience of the sordid misery of want had entered into the deeps of him, and, lest he might find virtue too easy, that memory stood behind him, tempting to shame, when dealers came to buy his wares. As the Nilghai quaked against his will at the still green water of a lake or a mill-dam, as Torpenhow flinched before any white arm that could cut or stab and loathed himself for flinching, Dick feared the poverty he had once tasted half in jest. His burden was heavier than the burdens of his companions.

Maisie watched the face working in the moonlight.

'You've plenty of pennies now,' she said soothingly.

'I shall never get enough,' he began, with vicious emphasis. Then laughing, 'I shall always be threepence short in my accounts.'

'Why threepence?'

'I carried a man's bag once from Liverpool Street Station to Blackfriars Bridge. It was a sixpenny job,—you needn't laugh; indeed it was,—and I wanted the money desperately. He only gave me threepence; and he hadn't even the decency to pay in silver. Whatever money I make I shall never get that odd threepence out of the world.'

This was not language befitting the man who had preached of the sanctity of work. It jarred on Maisie, who preferred her payment in applause, which, since all men desire it, must be of the right. She hunted for her little purse and gravely took out a threepenny bit.

'There it is,' she said. 'I'll pay you, Dickie; and don't worry any more; it isn't worth while. Are you paid?'

'I am,' said the very human apostle of fair craft, taking the coin. 'I'm paid a thousand times, and we'll close that account. It shall live on my watch-chain; and you're an angel, Maisie.'

'I'm very cramped, and I'm feeling a little cold. Good gracious! the cloak is all white, and so is your moustache! I never knew it was so chilly.'

A light frost lay white on the shoulder of Dick's ulster. He, too, had forgotten the state of the weather. They laughed together, and with that laugh ended all serious discourse.

They ran inland across the waste to warm themselves, then turned to look at the glory of the full tide under the moonlight and the intense black shadows of the furze-bushes. It was an additional joy to Dick that Maisie could see colour even as he saw it,—could see the blue in the white of the mist, the violet that is in gray palings, and all things else as they are,—not of one hue, but a thousand. And the moonlight came into Maisie's soul, so that she, usually reserved, chattered of herself and of the things she took interest in,—of Kami, wisest of teachers, and of the girls in the studio,—of the Poles, who will kill themselves with overwork if they are not checked; of the French, who talk at great length of much more than they will ever accomplish; of the slovenly English, who toil hopelessly and cannot understand that inclination does not imply power; of the Americans, whose rasping voices in the hush of a hot afternoon strain tense-drawn nerves to breaking-point, and

whose suppers lead to indigestion; of tempestuous Russians, neither to hold nor to bind, who tell the girls ghost-stories till the girls shriek; of stolid Germans, who come to learn one thing, and, having mastered that much, stolidly go away and copy pictures for evermore. Dick listened enraptured because it was Maisie who spoke. He knew the old life.

'It hasn't changed much,' he said. 'Do they still steal colours at lunch-time?'

'Not steal. Attract is the word. Of course they do. I'm good—I only attract ultramarine; but there are students who'd attract flake-white.'

'I've done it myself. You can't help it when the palettes are hung up. Every colour is common property once it runs down,—even though you do start it with a drop of oil. It teaches people not to waste their tubes.'

'I should like to attract some of your colours, Dick. Perhaps I might catch your success with them.'

'I mustn't say a bad word, but I should like to. What in the world, which you've just missed a lovely chance of seeing, does success or want of success, or a three-storied success, matter compared with—No, I won't open that question again. It's time to go back to town.'

'I'm sorry, Dick, but—'

'You're much more interested in that than you are in me.'

'I don't know. I don't think I am.'

'What will you give me if I tell you a sure short-cut to everything you want,—the trouble and the fuss and the tangle and all the rest? Will you promise to obey me?'

'Of course.'

'In the first place, you must never forget a meal because you happen to be at work. You forgot your lunch twice last week,' said Dick, at a venture, for he knew with whom he was dealing.

'No, no,—only once, really.'

'That's bad enough. And you mustn't take a cup of tea and a biscuit in place of a regular dinner, because dinner happens to be a trouble.'

'You're making fun of me!'

'I never was more in earnest in my life. Oh, my love, my love, hasn't it dawned on you yet what you are to me? Here's the whole earth in a conspiracy to give you a chill, or run over you, or drench you to the skin, or cheat you out of your money, or let you die of overwork and underfeeding, and I haven't the mere right to look after you. Why, I don't even know if you have sense enough to put on warm things when the weather's cold.'

'Dick, you're the most awful boy to talk to—really! How do you suppose I managed when you were away?'

'I wasn't here, and I didn't know. But now I'm back I'd give everything I have for the right of telling you to come in out of the rain.'

'Your success too?'

This time it cost Dick a severe struggle to refrain from bad words.

'As Mrs. Jennett used to say, you're a trial, Maisie! You've been cooped up in the schools too long, and you think every one is looking at you. There aren't twelve hundred people in the world who understand pictures. The others pretend and don't care. Remember, I've seen twelve hundred men dead in toadstool-beds. It's only the voice of the tiniest little fraction of people that makes success. The real world doesn't care a tinker's—doesn't care a bit. For aught you or I know, every man in the world may be arguing with a Maisie of his own.'

'Poor Maisie!'

'Poor Dick, I think. Do you believe while he's fighting for what's dearer than his life he wants to look at a picture? And even if he did, and if all the world did, and a thousand million people rose up and shouted hymns to my honour and glory, would that make up to me for the knowledge that you were out shopping in the Edgware Road on a rainy day without an umbrella? Now we'll go to the station.'

'But you said on the beach—' persisted Maisie with a certain fear.

Dick groaned aloud: 'Yes, I know what I said. My work is everything I have, or am, or hope to be, to me, and I believe I've learnt the law that governs it; but I've some lingering sense of fun left, —though you've nearly knocked it out of me. I can just see that it isn't everything to all the world. "Do what I say, and not what I do." '

Maisie was careful not to reopen debatable matters, and they returned to London joyously. The terminus stopped Dick in the midst of an eloquent harangue on the beauties of exercise. He would buy Maisie a horse,—such a horse as never yet bowed head to bit,—would stable it, with a companion, some twenty miles from London, and Maisie, solely for her health's sake, should ride with him twice or thrice a week.

'That's absurd,' said she. 'It wouldn't be proper.'

'Now, who in all London to-night would have sufficient interest or audacity to call us two to account for anything we chose to do?'

Maisie looked at the lamps, the fog, and the hideous turmoil. Dick was right; but horseflesh did not make for Art as she understood it.

'You're very nice sometimes, but you're very foolish more times. I'm not going to let you give me horses, or take you out of your way to-night. I'll go home by myself. Only I want you to promise me something. You won't think any more about that extra threepence, will you? Remember, you've been paid; and I won't allow you to be spiteful and do bad work for a little thing like that.

You can be so big that you mustn't be tiny.'

This was turning the tables with a vengeance. There remained only to put Maisie into her hansom.

'Good-bye,' she said simply. 'You'll come on Sunday. It has been a beautiful day, Dick. Why can't it be like this always?'

'Because love's like line-work: you must go forward or backward; you can't stand still. By the way, go on with your line-work. Good-night, and, for my—for any sake, take care of yourself.'

He turned to walk home, meditating. The day had brought him nothing that he hoped for, but—surely this was worth many days—it had brought him nearer to Maisie. The end was only a question of time now, and the prize well worth the waiting. By instinct, once more, he turned to the river.

'And she understood at once,' he said, looking at the water. 'She found out my pet besetting sin on the spot and paid it off. My God, how she understood! And she said I was better than she was! Better than she was!' He laughed at the absurdity of the notion. 'I wonder if girls guess at one-half a man's life. They can't, or—they wouldn't marry us.' He took her gift out of his pocket, and considered it in the light of a miracle and a pledge of the comprehension that, one day, would lead to perfect happiness. Meantime Maisie was alone in London, with none to save her from danger. And the packed wilderness was very full of danger.

Dick made his prayer to Fate disjointedly after the manner of the heathen as he threw the piece of silver into the river. If any evil were to befall, let him bear the burden and let Maisie go unscathed, since the threepenny piece was dearest to him of all his possessions. It was a small coin in itself, but Maisie had given it, and the Thames held it, and surely the Fates would be bribed for this once.

The drowning of the coin seemed to cut him free from thought of Maisie for the moment. He took himself off the bridge and went whistling to his chambers with a strong yearning for some man-talk and tobacco after his first experience of an entire day spent in the society of a woman. There was a stronger desire at his heart when there rose before him an unsolicited vision of the 'Barralong' dipping deep and sailing free for the Southern Cross.

CHAPTER 8

And these two, as I have told you,
Were the friends of Hiawatha,
Chibiabos, the musician,
And the very strong man, Kwasind.
Hiawatha

Torpenhow was paging the last sheets of some manuscript, while the Nilghai, who had come for chess and remained to talk tactics, was reading through the first part, commenting scornfully the while.

'It's picturesque enough and it's sketchy,' said he; 'but as a serious consideration of affairs in Eastern Europe, it's not worth much.'

'It's off my hands at any rate. . . . Thirty-seven, thirty-eight, thirty-nine slips altogether, aren't there? That should make between eleven and twelve pages of valuable misinformation. Heigho!' Torpenhow shuffled the writing together and hummed—

'Young lambs to sell, young lambs to sell,
If I'd as much money as I could tell,
I never would cry, Young lambs to sell!'

Dick entered, self-conscious and a little defiant, but in the best of tempers with all the world.

'Back at last?' said Torpenhow.

'More or less. What have you been doing?'

'Work. Dickie, you behave as though

the Bank of England were behind you. Here's Sunday, Monday, and Tuesday gone and you haven't done a line. It's scandalous.'

'The notions come and go, my children —they come and go like our 'baccy,' he answered, filling his pipe. 'Moreover,' he stooped to thrust a spill into the grate, 'Apollo does not always stretch his—Oh, confound your clumsy jests, Nilghai!'

'This is not the place to preach the theory of direct inspiration,' said the Nilghai, returning Torpenhow's large and workmanlike bellows to their nail on the wall. 'We believe in cobblers' wax. La!— where you sit down.'

'If you weren't so big and fat,' said Dick, looking round for a weapon, 'I'd—'

'No skylarking in my rooms. You two smashed half my furniture last time you threw cushions about. You might have the decency to say How d'you do? to Binkie. Look at him.'

Binkie had jumped down from the sofa and was fawning round Dick's knee, and scratching at his boots.

'Dear man!' said Dickie, snatching him up, and kissing him on the black patch above his right eye. 'Did ums was, Binks? Did that ugly Nilghai turn you off the sofa? Bite him, Mr. Binkle.' He pitched him on the Nilghai's stomach, as the big man lay at ease, and Binkie pretended to destroy the Nilghai inch by inch, till a sofa-cushion extinguished him, and panting he stuck out his tongue at the company.

'The Binkie-boy went for a walk this morning before you were up, Torp. I saw him making love to the butcher at the corner when the shutters were being taken down—just as if he hadn't enough to eat in his own proper house,' said Dick.

'Binks, is that a true bill?' said Torpenhow severely. The little dog retreated under the sofa-cushion, and showed by the fat white back of him that he really had no further interest in the discussion.

' 'Strikes me that another disreputable dog went for a walk, too,' said the Nilghai. 'What made you get up so early? Torp said you might be buying a horse?'

'He knows it would need three of us for a serious business like that. No, I felt lonesome and unhappy, so I went out to look at the sea, and watch the pretty ships go by.'

'Where did you go?'

'Somewhere on the Channel. Progly or Snigly, or some one-horse watering-place was its name; I've forgotten; but it was only two hours' run from London and the ships went by.'

'Did you see anything you knew?'

'Only the "Barralong" outwards to Australia, and an Odessa grain-boat loaded down by the head. It was a thick day, but the sea smelt good.'

'Wherefore put on one's best trousers to see the "Barralong"?' said Torpenhow, pointing.

'Because I've nothing except these things and my painting duds. Besides, I wanted to do the honour to the sea.'

'Did she make you feel restless?' asked the Nilghai keenly.

'Crazy. Don't speak of it. I'm sorry I went.'

Torpenhow and the Nilghai exchanged a look as Dick, stooping, busied himself among the former's boots and trees.

'These will do,' he said at last; 'I can't say I think much of your taste in slippers, but the fit's the thing.' He slipped his feet into a pair of socklike sambhur-skin foot coverings, found a long chair, and lay at length.

'They're my own pet pair,' Torpenhow said. 'I was just going to put them on myself.'

' 'All your reprehensible selfishness. Just because you see me happy for a minute you want to worry me and stir me up. Find another pair.'

'Good for you that Dick can't wear your clothes, Torp. You two live communistically,' said the Nilghai. 'Dick never has anything that I can wear. He's only useful to sponge upon.'

'Confound you, have you been rummaging round among my caches, then?' said Dick. 'I put a sovereign in the tobacco-jar yesterday. How do you expect a man to keep his accounts properly if you—'

Here the Nilghai began to laugh, and Torpenhow joined him.

'Hid a sovereign yesterday! You're no sort of a financier. You lent me a fiver about a month back. Do you remember?' Torpenhow said.

'Yes, of course.'

'Do you remember that I paid it you ten days later, and you put it at the bottom of the tobacco?'

'By Jove, did I? I thought it was in one of my colour boxes.'

'You thought! About a week ago I went into your studio to get some 'baccy and found it.'

'What did you do with it?'

'Took the Nilghai to a theatre and fed him.'

'You couldn't feed the Nilghai under twice the money—not though you gave him Army beef. Well, I suppose I should have found it out sooner or later. What is there to laugh at?'

'You're a most amazing cuckoo in many directions,' said the Nilghai, still chuckling over the thought of the dinner. 'Never mind. We had both been working very hard, and it was your unearned increment we spent, and as you're only a loafer it didn't matter.'

'That's pleasant—from the man who is bursting with my meat, too. I'll get that dinner back one of these days. Suppose we go to a theatre now.'

' 'Put our boots on,—and dress,—and wash?' The Nilghai spoke very lazily.

'I withdraw the motion.'

'Suppose, just for a change—as a startling variety, you know—we, that is to say we, get our charcoal and our canvas and go on with our work.' Torpenhow spoke pointedly, but Dick only wriggled his toes inside the soft leather moccasins.

'What a one-idea'd clucker it is! If I had any unfinished figures on hand, I haven't any model; if I had my model, I haven't any spray, and I never leave charcoal unfixed over night; and if I had my spray and twenty photographs of backgrounds, I couldn't do anything to-night. I don't feel that way.'

'Binkie-dog, he's a lazy hog, isn't he?' said the Nilghai.

'Very good, I will do some work,' said Dick, rising swiftly. 'I'll fetch the Nungapunga Book, and we'll add another picture to the Nilghai Saga.'

'Aren't you worrying him a little too much?' asked the Nilghai, when Dick had left the room.

'Perhaps, but I know what he can turn out if he likes. It makes me savage to hear him praised for past work when I know what he ought to do. You and I are arranged for—'

'By Kismet and our own powers, more's the pity. I have dreamed of a good deal.'

'So have I, but we know our limitations now. I'm dashed if I know what Dick's may be when he gives himself to his work. That's what makes me so keen about him.'

'And when all's said and done, you will be put aside—quite rightly—for a female girl.'

'I wonder . . . Where do you think he has been to-day?'

'To the sea. Didn't you see the look in his eyes when he talked about her? He's as restless as a swallow in autumn.'

'Yes; but did he go alone?'

'I don't know, and I don't care, but he

has the beginnings of the go-fever upon him. He wants to up-stakes and move out. There's no mistaking the signs. Whatever he may have said before, he has the call upon him now.'

'It might be his salvation,' Torpenhow said.

'Perhaps—if you care to take the responsibility of being a saviour: I'm averse to tampering with souls myself.'

Dick returned with a great clasped sketch-book that the Nilghai knew well and did not love too much. In it Dick had drawn in his playtime all manner of moving incidents, experienced by himself or related to him by the others, of all the four corners of the earth. But the wider range of Nilghai's body and life attracted him most. When truth failed here he fell back on fiction of the wildest, and represented incidents in the Nilghai's career that were unseemly,—his marriages with many African princesses, his shameless betrayal, for Arab wives, of army corps to the Mahdi, his tatooment by skilled operators in Burmah, his interview (and his fears) with the yellow headsman in the blood-stained execution-ground of Canton, and finally, the passings of his spirit into the bodies of whales, elephants, and toucans. Torpenhow from time to time had added rhymed descriptions, and the whole was a curious piece of art, because Dick decided, having regard to the name of the book, which being interpreted means 'naked,' that it would be wrong to draw the Nilghai with any clothes on, under any circumstances. Consequently the last sketch, representing that much-enduring man calling on the War Office to press his claims to the Egyptian medal, was hardly delicate. He settled himself comfortably at Torpenhow's table and turned over the pages.

'What a fortune you would have been to Blake, Nilghai!' he said. 'There's a succulent pinkness about some of these sketches that's more than lifelike. "The

Nilghai surrounded while bathing by the Mahdieh"—that was founded on fact, eh?'

'It was very nearly my last bath, you irreverent dauber. Has Binkie come into the Saga yet?'

'No; the Binkie-boy hasn't done anything except eat and kill cats. Let's see. Here you are as a stained-glass saint in a church. 'Deuced decorative lines about your anatomy; you ought to be grateful for being handed down to posterity in this way. Fifty years hence you'll exist in rare and curious facsimiles at ten guineas each. What shall I try this time? The domestic life of the Nilghai?'

' 'Hasn't got any.'

'The undomestic life of the Nilghai, then. Of course. Mass-meeting of his wives in Trafalgar Square. That's it. They came from the ends of the earth to attend Nilghai's wedding to an English bride. This shall be in sepia. It's a sweet material to work with.'

'It's a scandalous waste of time,' said Torpenhow.

'Don't worry; it keeps one's hand in—specially when you begin without the pencil.' He set to work rapidly. 'That's Nelson's Column. Presently the Nilghai will appear shinning up it.'

'Give him some clothes this time.'

'Certainly—a veil and an orange-wreath, because he's been married.'

'Gad, that's clever enough!' said Torpenhow over his shoulder, as Dick brought out of the paper with three twirls of the brush a very fat back and labouring shoulder pressed against the stone.

'Just imagine,' Dick continued, 'if we could publish a few of these dear little things every time the Nilghai subsidises a man who can write, to give the public an honest opinion of my pictures.'

'Well, you'll admit I always tell you when I have done anything of that kind. I know I can't hammer you as you ought to be hammered, so I give the job to

another. Young Maclagan, for instance—'

'No-o—one half-minute, old man;
stick your hand out against the dark of
the wall-paper—you only burble and call
me names. That left shoulder's out of
drawing. I must literally throw a veil over
that. Where's my pen-knife? Well, what
about Maclagan?'

'I only gave him his riding-orders to—
to lambast you on general principles for
not producing work that will last.'

'Whereupon that young fool,'—Dick
threw back his head and shut one eye as
he shifted the page under his hand,—'being left alone with an ink-pot and what
he conceived were his own notions, went
and spilt them both over me in the
papers. You might have engaged a grown
man for the business, Nilghai. How do
you think the bridal veil looks now,
Torp?'

'How the deuce do three dabs and two
scratches make the stuff stand away from
the body as it does?' said Torpenhow, to
whom Dick's methods were always new.

'It just depends on where you put 'em.
If Maclagan had known that much about
his business he might have done better.'

'Why don't you put the damned dabs
into something that will stay, then?' insisted the Nilghai, who had really taken
considerable trouble in hiring for Dick's
benefit the pen of a young gentleman
who devoted most of his waking hours to
an anxious consideration of the aims
and ends of Art, which, he wrote, was
One and Indivisible.

'Wait a minute till I see how I am
going to manage my procession of wives.
You seem to have married extensively,
and I must rough 'em in with the pencil—Medes, Parthians, Edomites. . . .
Now, setting aside the weakness and the
wickedness and—and the fat-headedness
of deliberately trying to do work that will
live, as they call it, I'm content with the
knowledge that I've done my best up to

date, and I shan't do anything like it
again for some hours at least—probably
years. Most probably never.'

'What! 'Any stuff you have in stock
your best work?' said Torpenhow.

'Anything you've sold?' said the
Nilghai.

'Oh, no. It isn't here and it isn't sold.
Better than that, it can't be sold, and I
don't think any one knows where it is.
I'm sure I don't. . . . And yet more and
more wives, on the north side of the
square. Observe the virtuous horror of
the lions!'

'You may as well explain,' said
Torpenhow, and Dick lifted his head
from the paper.

'The sea reminded me of it,' he said
slowly. 'I wish it hadn't. It weighs some
few thousand tons—unless you cut it out
with a cold chisel.'

'Don't be an idiot. You can't pose with
us here,' said the Nilghai.

'There's no pose in the matter at all.
It's a fact. I was loafing from Lima to
Auckland in a big, old, condemned pas-
senger-ship turned into a cargo-boat and
owned by a second-hand Italian firm.
She was a crazy basket. We were cut
down to fifteen ton of coal a day, and we
thought ourselves lucky when we kicked
seven knots an hour out of her. Then we
used to stop and let the bearings cool
down, and wonder whether the crack in
the shaft was spreading.'

'Were you a steward or a stoker in
those days?'

'I was flush for the time being, so I
was a passenger, or else I should have
been a steward, I think,' said Dick with
perfect gravity, returning to the procession of angry wives. 'I was the only other
passenger from Lima, and the ship was
half empty, and full of rats and cock-
roaches and scorpions.'

'But what has this to do with the
picture?'

'Wait a minute. She had been in the

China passenger trade and her lower deck had bunks for two thousand pigtails. Those were all taken down, and she was empty up to her nose, and the lights came through the port-holes—most annoying lights to work in till you got used to them. I hadn't anything to do for weeks. The ship's charts were in pieces and our skipper daren't run south for fear of catching a storm. So he did his best to knock all the Society Islands out of the water one by one, and I went into the lower deck, and did my picture on the port side as far forward in her as I could go. There was some brown paint and some green paint that they used for the boats, and some black paint for ironwork, and that was all I had.'

'The passengers must have thought you mad.'

'There was only one, and it was a woman; but it gave me the notion of my picture.'

'What was she like?' said Torpenhow.

'She was a sort of Negroid-Jewess-Cuban; with morals to match. She couldn't read or write, and she didn't want to, but she used to come down and watch me paint, and the skipper didn't like it, because he was paying her passage and had to be on the bridge occasionally.'

'I see. That must have been cheerful.'

'It was the best time I ever had. To begin with, we didn't know whether we should go up or go down any minute when there was a sea on; and when it was calm it was paradise; and the woman used to mix the paints and talk broken English, and the skipper used to steal down every few minutes to the lower deck, because he said he was afraid of fire. So, you see, we could never tell when we might be caught, and I had a splendid notion to work out in only three keys of colour.'

'What was the notion?'

'Two lines in Poe—'

'Neither the angels in Heaven above nor the
     demons down under the sea,
Can ever dissever my soul from the soul of
     the beautiful Annabel Lee.

It came out of the sea—all by itself. I drew that fight, fought out in green water over the naked, choking soul, and the woman served as the model for the devils and the angels both—sea-devils and sea-angels, and the soul half drowned between them. It doesn't sound much, but when there was a good light on the lower deck it looked very fine and creepy. It was seven by fourteen feet, all done in shifting light for shifting lights.'

'Did the woman inspire you much?' said Torpenhow.

'She and the sea between them—immensely. There was a heap of bad drawing in that picture. I remember I went out of my way to foreshorten for sheer delight of doing it, and I foreshortened damnably, but for all that it's the best thing I've ever done; and now I suppose the ship's broken up or gone down. Whew! What a time that was!'

'What happened after all?'

'It all ended. They were loading her with wool when I left the ship, but even the stevedores kept the picture clear to the last. The eyes of the demons scared them, I honestly believe.'

'And the woman?'

'She was scared too when it was finished. She used to cross herself before she went down to look at it. Just three colours and no chance of getting any more, and the sea outside and unlimited love-making inside, and the fear of death atop of everything else, O Lord!' He had ceased to look at the sketch, but was staring straight in front of him across the room.

'Why don't you try something of the same kind now?' said the Nilghai.

'Because those things come not by fasting and prayer. When I find a cargo-boat and a Jewess-Cuban and another notion and the same old life, I may.'

'You won't find them here,' said the Nilghai.

'No, I shall not.' Dick shut the sketch-book with a bang. 'This room's as hot as an oven. Open the window, some one.'

He leaned into the darkness, watching the greater darkness of London below him. The chambers stood much higher than the other houses, commanding a hundred chimneys—crooked cowls that looked like sitting cats as they swung round, and other uncouth brick and zinc mysteries supported by iron stanchions and clamped by S-pieces. Northward the lights of Piccadilly Circus and Leicester Square threw a copper-coloured glare above the black roofs, and southward lay all the orderly lights of the Thames. A train rolled out across one of the railway bridges, and its thunder drowned for a minute the dull roar of the streets. The Nilghai looked at his watch and said shortly, 'That's the Paris night-mail. You can book from here to St. Petersburg if you choose.'

Dick crammed head and shoulders out of the window and looked across the river. Torpenhow came to his side, while the Nilghai passed over quietly to the piano and opened it. Binkie, making himself as large as possible, spread out upon the sofa with the air of one who is not to be lightly disturbed.

'Well,' said the Nilghai to the two pairs of shoulders, 'have you never seen this place before?'

A steam-tug on the river hooted as she towed her barges to wharf. Then the boom of the traffic came into the room. Torpenhow nudged Dick. 'Good place to bank in—bad place to bunk in, Dickie, isn't it?'

Dick's chin was in his hand as he answered, in the words of a general not without fame, still looking out on the

darkness—' "My God, what a city to loot!" '

Binkie found the night air tickling his whiskers and sneezed plaintively.

'We shall give the Binkie-dog a cold,' said Torpenhow. 'Come in,' and they withdrew their heads. 'You'll be buried in Kensal Green, Dick, one of these days, if it isn't closed by the time you want to go there—buried within two feet of some one else, his wife and his family.'

'Allah forbid! I shall get away before that time comes. Give a man room to stretch his legs, Mr. Binkle.' Dick flung himself down on the sofa and tweaked Binkie's velvet ears, yawning heavily the while.

'You'll find that wardrobe-case very much out of tune,' Torpenhow said to the Nilghai. 'It's never touched except by you.'

'A piece of gross extravagance,' Dick grunted. 'The Nilghai only comes when I'm out.'

'That's because you're always out. Howl, Nilghai, and let him hear.'

'The life of the Nilghai is fraud and slaughter,
His writings are watered Dickens and water;
But the voice of the Nilghai raised on high
Makes even the Mahdieh glad to die!'

Dick quoted from Torpenhow's letter-press in the Nungapunga Book. 'How do they call moose in Canada, Nilghai?'

The man laughed. Singing was his one polite accomplishment, as many Press-tents in far-off lands had known.

'What shall I sing?' said he, turning in the chair.

' "Moll Roe in the Morning," ' said Torpenhow at a venture.

'No,' said Dick sharply, and the Nilghai opened his eyes. The old chanty whereof he, among a very few, possessed all the words was not a pretty one, but Dick had heard it many times before without wincing. Without prelude he launched into that stately tune that calls together and troubles the hearts of the gipsies of the sea—

'Farewell and adieu to you, Spanish ladies,
Farewell and adieu to you, ladies of Spain.'

Dick turned uneasily on the sofa, for he could hear the bows of the 'Barralong' crashing into the green seas on her way to the Southern Cross. Then came the chorus—

'We'll rant and we'll roar like true British sailors,
We'll rant and we'll roar across the salt seas,
Until we take soundings in the Channel of Old England
From Ushant to Scilly 'tis forty-five leagues.'

'Thirty-five—thirty-five,' said Dick petulantly. 'Don't tamper with Holy Writ. Go on, Nilghai.'

'The first land we made it was called the Deadman,'

and they sang to the end very vigorously.

'That would be a better song if her head were turned the other way—to the Ushant light, for instance,' said the Nilghai.

'Flinging its arms about like a mad windmill,' said Torpenhow. 'Give us something else, Nilghai. You're in fine fog-horn form to-night.'

'Give us the "Ganges Pilot": you sang that in the square the night before El-Maghrib. By the way, I wonder how many of the chorus are alive to-night,' said Dick.

Torpenhow considered for a minute. 'By Jove! I believe only you and I. Raynor, Vickery, and Deenes—all dead; Vincent caught smallpox in Cairo, carried it here and died of it. Yes, only you and I and the Nilghai.'

'Umph! And yet the men here who've done their work in a well-warmed studio all their lives, with a policeman at each corner, say that I charge too much for my pictures.'

'They are buying your work, not your insurance policies, dear child,' said the Nilghai.

'I gambled with one to get at the other. Don't preach. Go on with the "Pilot." Where in the world did you get that song?'

'On a tombstone,' said the Nilghai. 'On a tombstone in a distant land. I made it an accompaniment with heaps of bass chords.'

'Oh, Vanity! Begin.' And the Nilghai began—

'I have slipped my cable, messmates, I'm drifting down with the tide,
I have my sailing orders, while ye at anchor ride.
And never on fair June morning have I put out to sea
With clearer conscience or better hope, or a heart more light and free.

'Shoulder to shoulder, Joe, my boy, into the crowd like a wedge
Strike with the hangers, messmates, but do not cut with the edge.
Cries Charnock, "Scatter the faggots, double that Brahmin in two,
The tall pale widow for me, Joe, the little brown girl for you!"

'Young Joe (you're nearing sixty), why is hide so dark?
Katie has soft fair blue eyes, who blackened yours?—Why, hark!'

They were all singing now, Dick with the roar of the wind of the open sea about his ears as the deep bass voice let itself go.

'The morning gun—Ho, steady!—the arque-buses to me!
I ha' sounded the Dutch High Admiral's heart as my lead doth sound the sea.

'Sounding, sounding the Ganges, floating
   down with the tide,
Moor me close to Charnock, next to my
   nut-brown bride.
My blessing to Kate at Fairlight—Holwell,
   my thanks to you;
Steady! We steer for Heaven, through sand-
   drifts cold and blue.'

'Now what is there in that nonsense to
make a man restless?' said Dick, hauling
Binkie from his feet to his chest.

'It depends on the man,' said Torpenhow.

'The man who has been down to look
at the sea,' said the Nilghai.

'I didn't know she was going to upset
me in this fashion.'

'That's what men say when they go to
say good-bye to a woman. It's more easy,
though, to get rid of three women than a
piece of one's life and surroundings.'

'But a woman can be—' began Dick
unguardedly.

'A piece of one's life,' continued
Torpenhow. 'No, she can't.' His face
darkened for a moment. 'She says she
wants to sympathise with you and help
you in your work, and everything else
that clearly a man must do for himself.
Then she sends round five notes a day to
ask why the dickens you haven't been
wasting your time with her.'

'Don't generalise,' said the Nilghai. 'By
the time you arrive at five notes a day
you must have gone through a good deal
and behaved accordingly. 'Shouldn't begin these things, my son.'

'I shouldn't have gone down to the
sea,' said Dick, just a little anxious to
change the conversation. 'And you
shouldn't have sung.'

'The sea isn't sending you five notes a
day,' said the Nilghai.

'No, but I'm fatally compromised.
She's an enduring old hag, and I'm sorry
I ever met her. Why wasn't I born and
bred and dead in a three-pair back?'

'Hear him blaspheming his first love!

Why in the world shouldn't you listen to
her?' said Torpenhow.

Before Dick could reply the Nilghai
lifted up his voice with a shout that
shook the windows, in 'The Men of the
Sea,' that begins, as all know, 'The sea is
a wicked old woman,' and after racing
through eight lines whose imagery is
truthful, ends in a refrain, slow as the
clacking of a capstan when the boat
comes unwillingly up to the bars where
the men sweat and tramp in the shingle.

' "Ye that bore us, O restore us!
   She is kinder than ye;
   For the call is on our heart-strings!"
   Said The Men of the Sea.'

The Nilghai sang that verse twice, with
simple craft, intending that Dick should
hear. But Dick was waiting for the farewell of the men to their wives.

' "Ye that love us, can ye move us?
   She is dearer than ye;
   And your sleep will be the sweeter,"
   Said The Men of the Sea.'

The rough words beat like the blows of
the waves on the bows of the rickety boat
from Lima in the days when Dick was
mixing paints, making love, drawing
devils and angels in the half dark, and
wondering whether the next minute
would place the Italian captain's knife
between his shoulder-blades. And the go-
fever, which is more real than many
doctors' diseases, waked and raged, urg-
ing him who loved Maisie beyond anything in the world to go away and taste
the old hot, unregenerate life again,—to
scuffle, swear, gamble, and love light
loves with his fellows; to take ship and
know the sea once more, and by her be-
get pictures; to talk to Binat among the
sands of Port Said while Yellow 'Tina
mixed the drinks; to hear the crackle of
musketry, and see the smoke roll outward, thin and thicken again till the shin-

ing black faces came through, and in that hell every man was strictly responsible for his own head, and his own alone, and struck with an unfettered arm. It was impossible, utterly impossible, but—

    ' "Oh, our fathers, in the churchyard,
      She is older than ye,
      And our graves will be the greener,"
    Said The Men of the Sea.'

'What is there to hinder?' said Torpenhow, in the long hush that followed the song.

'You said a little time since that you wouldn't come for a walk round the world, Torp.'

'That was months ago, and I only objected to your making money for travelling expenses. You've shot your bolt here and it has gone home. Go away and do some work, and see some things.'

'Get some of the fat off you; you're disgracefully out of condition,' said the Nilghai, making a plunge from the chair and grasping a handful of Dick generally over the right ribs. 'Soft as putty—pure tallow born of overfeeding. Train it off, Dickie.'

'We're all equally gross, Nilghai. Next time you have to take the field you'll sit down, wink your eyes, gasp, and die in a fit.'

'Never mind. You go away on a ship. Go to Lima again, or to Brazil. There's always trouble in South America.'

'Do you suppose I want to be told where to go? Great Heavens, the only difficulty is to know where I'm to stop. But I shall stay here, as I told you before.'

'Then you'll be buried in Kensal Green and turn into adipocere with the others,' said Torpenhow. 'Are you thinking of commissions in hand? Pay forfeit and go. You've money enough to travel as a king if you please.'

'You've the grisliest notions of amuse-ment, Torp. I think I see myself shipping first class on a six-thousand-ton hotel, and asking the third engineer what makes the engines go round, and whether it isn't very warm in the stokehold. Ho! ho! I should ship as a loafer if ever I shipped at all, which I'm not going to do. I shall compromise, and go for a small trip to begin with.'

'That's something at any rate. Where will you go?' said Torpenhow. 'It would do you all the good in the world, old man.'

The Nilghai saw the twinkle in Dick's eye and refrained from speech.

'I shall go in the first place to Rathray's stable, where I shall hire one horse, and take him very carefully as far as Richmond Hill. Then I shall walk him back again, in case he should accidentally burst into a lather and make Rathray angry. I shall do that to-morrow for the sake of air and exercise.'

'Bah!' Dick had barely time to throw up his arm and ward off the cushion that the disgusted Torpenhow heaved at his head.

'Air and exercise indeed,' said the Nilghai, sitting down heavily on Dick. 'Let's give him a little of both. Get the bellows, Torp.'

At this point the conference broke up in disorder, because Dick would not open his mouth till the Nilghai held his nose fast, and there was some trouble in forcing the nozzle of the bellows between his teeth; and even when it was there he weakly tried to puff against the force of the blast, and his cheeks blew up with a great explosion; and the enemy becoming helpless with laughter he so beat them over the head with a soft sofa-cushion that that became unsewn and distributed its feathers, and Binkie, interfering in Torpenhow's interests, was bundled into the half-empty bag and advised to scratch his way out, which he did after a while, travelling rapidly up and down the floor in the shape of an agitated green haggis, and when he came out looking for satisfaction, the three pillars of his world were picking feathers out of their hair.

'A prophet has no honour in his own country,' said Dick ruefully, dusting his knees. 'This filthy fluff will never brush off my bags.'

'It was all for your good,' said the Nilghai. ' 'Nothing like air and exercise.'

'All for your good,' said Torpenhow, not in the least with reference to past clowning. 'It would let you focus things at their proper worth and prevent your becoming slack in this hothouse of a town. Indeed it would, old man. I shouldn't have spoken if I hadn't thought so. Only, you make a joke of everything.'

'Before God I do no such thing,' said Dick quickly and earnestly. 'You don't know me if you think that.'

'I don't think it,' said the Nilghai.

'How can fellows like ourselves, who know what life and death really mean, dare to make a joke of anything? I know we pretend it, to save ourselves from breaking down or going to the other extreme. Can't I see, old man, how you're always anxious about me, and try to advise me to make my work better? Do you suppose I don't think about that myself? But you can't help me—you can't help me—not even you. I must play my own hand alone in my own way.'

'Hear, hear,' from the Nilghai.

'What's the one thing in the Nilghai Saga that I've never drawn in the Nunga-punga Book?' Dick continued to Torpenhow, who was a little astonished at the outburst.

Now there was one blank page in the book given over to the sketch that Dick had not drawn of the crowning exploit in the Nilghai's life; when that man, being young and forgetting that his body and bones belonged to the paper that employed him, had ridden over sun-burned slippery grass in the rear of Bredow's brigade on the day that the troopers flung themselves at Canrobert's artillery, and for aught they knew twenty battalions in front, to save the battered 24th German Infantry, to give time to decide the fate of Vionville, and to learn ere their remnant came back to Flavigny that cavalry can attack and crumple and break unshaken infantry. Whenever he was inclined to think over a life that might have been better, an income that might have been larger, and a soul that might have been considerably cleaner, the Nilghai would comfort himself with the thought, 'I rode with Bredow's brigade at Vionville,' and take heart for any lesser battle the next day might bring.

'I know,' he said very gravely. 'I was always glad that you left it out.'

'I left it out because Nilghai taught me what the German army learned then, and what Schmidt taught their cavalry. I don't know German. What is it? "Take care of the time and the dressing will take care of itself." I must ride my own line to my own beat, old man.'

'Tempo ist Richtung. You've learned your lesson well,' said the Nilghai. 'He must go alone. He speaks truth, Torp.'

'Maybe I'm as wrong as I can be— hideously wrong. I must find that out for myself, as I have to think things out for myself, but I daren't turn my head to dress by the next man. It hurts me a great deal more than you know not to be able to go, but I cannot, that's all. I must do my own work and live my own life in my own way, because I'm responsible for both. Only don't think I frivol about it, Torp. I have my own matches and sulphur, and I'll make my own hell, thanks.'

There was an uncomfortable pause. Then Torpenhow said blandly, 'What did the Governor of North Carolina say to the Governor of South Carolina?'

'Excellent notion. It is a long time between drinks. There are the makings of a very fine prig in you, Dick,' said the Nilghai.

'I've liberated my mind, estimable Binkie, with the feathers in his mouth.' Dick picked up the still indignant one and shook him tenderly. 'You're tied up in a sack and made to run about blind, Binkie-wee, without any reason, and it has hurt your little feelings. Never mind. Sic volo, sic jubeo, stet pro ratione voluntas, and don't sneeze in my eye because I talk Latin. Good-night.'

He went out of the room.

'That's distinctly one for you,' said the Nilghai. 'I told you it was hopeless to meddle with him. He's not pleased.'

'He'd swear at me if he weren't. I can't make it out. He has the go-fever upon him and he won't go. I only hope that he mayn't have to go some day when he doesn't want to,' said Torpenhow.

· · · · ·

In his room Dick was settling a question with himself—and the question was whether all the world, and all that was therein, and a burning desire to exploit both, was worth one threepenny piece thrown into the Thames.

'It came of seeing the sea, and I'm a cur to think about it,' he decided. 'After all the honeymoon will be that tour—with reservations; only . . . only I didn't realise that the sea was so strong. I didn't feel it so much when I was with Maisie. These damnable songs did it. He's beginning again.'

But it was only Herrick's Nightpiece to Julia that the Nilghai sang, and before it was ended Dick reappeared on the threshold, not altogether clothed indeed, but in his right mind, thirsty and at peace.

The mood had come and gone with the rising and the falling of the tide by Fort Keeling.

CHAPTER 9

'If I have taken the common clay
    And wrought it cunningly
In the shape of a god that was digged a clod,
    The greater honour to me.'

'If thou hast taken the common clay,
    And thy hands be not free
From the taint of the soil, thou hast made
      thy spoil
    The greater shame to thee.'

The Two Potters

He did no work of any kind for the rest of the week. Then came another Sunday. He dreaded and longed for the day always, but since the red-haired girl had sketched him there was rather more dread than desire in his mind.

He found that Maisie had entirely neglected his suggestions about line-work. She had gone off at score filled with some absurd notion for a 'fancy head.' It cost Dick something to command his temper.

'What's the good of suggesting anything?' he said pointedly.

'Ah, but this will be a picture,—a real picture; and I know that Kami will let me send it to the Salon. You don't mind, do you?'

'I suppose not. But you won't have time for the Salon.'

Maisie hesitated a little. She even felt uncomfortable.

'We're going over to France a month sooner because of it. I shall get the idea sketched out here and work it up at Kami's.'

Dick's heart stood still, and he came very near to being disgusted with his queen who could do no wrong. 'Just when I thought I had made some headway, she goes off chasing butterflies. It's too maddening!'

There was no possibility of arguing, for the red-haired girl was in the studio. Dick could only look unutterable reproach.

'I'm sorry,' he said, 'and I think you make a mistake. But what's the idea of your new picture?'

'I took it from a book.'

'That's bad, to begin with. Books aren't the places for pictures. And—'

'It's this,' said the red-haired girl behind him. 'I was reading it to Maisie the other day from "The City of Dreadful Night." D'you know the book?'

'A little. I am sorry I spoke. There are pictures in it. What has taken her fancy?'

'The description of the Melancolia—

'Her folded wings as of a mighty eagle,
But all too impotent to lift the regal
Robustness of her earth-born strength and
    pride.

And here again. (Maisie, get the tea, dear.)

'The forehead charged with baleful thoughts
    and dreams,
The household bunch of keys, the housewife's
    gown,
    Voluminous indented, and yet rigid
    As though a shell of burnished metal frigid,
Her feet thick-shod to tread all weakness
    down.'

There was no attempt to conceal the scorn of the lazy voice. Dick winced.

'But that has been done already by an obscure artist of the name of Durer,' said he. 'How does the poem run?—

'Three centuries and threescore years ago,
With phantasies of his peculiar thought.

You might as well try to rewrite "Hamlet." It will be waste of time.'

'No, it won't,' said Maisie, putting down the teacups with clatter to reassure herself. 'And I mean to do it. Can't you see what a beautiful thing it would make?'

'How in perdition can one do work when one hasn't had the proper training? Any fool can get a notion. It needs train-

ing to drive the thing through,—training and conviction; not rushing after the first fancy.' Dick spoke between his teeth.

'You don't understand,' said Maisie. 'I think I can do it.'

Again the voice of the girl behind him—

'Baffled and beaten back, she works on still;
    Weary and sick of soul, she works the
      more.
Sustained by her indomitable will,
    The hands shall fashion, and the brain
      shall pore,
And all her sorrow shall be turned to
    labour—

I fancy Maisie means to embody herself in the picture.'

'Sitting on a throne of rejected pictures? No, I shan't, dear. The notion in itself has fascinated me.—Of course you don't care for fancy heads, Dick. I don't think you could do them. You like blood and bones.'

'That's a direct challenge. If you can do a Melancolia that isn't merely a sorrowful female head, I can do a better one; and I will, too. What d'you know about Melancolias?' Dick firmly believed that he was even then tasting three-quarters of all the sorrow in the world.

'She was a woman,' said Maisie, 'and she suffered a great deal,—till she could suffer no more. Then she began to laugh at it all, and then I painted her and sent her to the Salon.'

The red-haired girl rose up and left the room, laughing.

Dick looked at Maisie humbly and hopelessly.

'Never mind about the picture,' he said. 'Are you really going back to Kami's a month before your time?'

'I must, if I want to get the picture done.'

'And that's all you want?'

'Of course. Don't be stupid, Dick.'

'You haven't the power. You have only the ideas—the ideas and the little cheap impulses. How you could have kept at your work for ten years steadily is a mystery to me. So you are really going, —a month before you need?'

'I must do my work.'

'Your work—bah! . . . No, I didn't mean that. It's all right, dear. Of course you must do your work, and—I think I'll say good-bye for this week.'

'Won't you even stay for tea?'

'No, thank you. Have I your leave to go, dear? There's nothing more you particularly want me to do, and the line-work doesn't matter.'

'I wish you could stay, and then we could talk over my picture. If only one single picture's a success it draws attention to all the others. I know some of my work is good, if only people could see. And you needn't have been so rude about it.'

'I'm sorry. We'll talk the Melancolia over some one of the other Sundays. There are four more—yes, one, two, three, four—before you go. Good-bye, Maisie.'

Maisie stood by the studio window, thinking, till the red-haired girl returned, a little white at the corners of her lips.

'Dick's gone off,' said Maisie. 'Just when I wanted to talk about the picture. Isn't it selfish of him?'

Her companion opened her lips as if to speak, shut them again, and went on reading 'The City of Dreadful Night.'

Dick was in the Park, walking round and round a tree that he had chosen as his confidante for many Sundays past. He was swearing audibly, and when he found that the infirmities of the English tongue hemmed in his rage, he sought consolation in Arabic, which is expressly designed for the use of the afflicted. He was not pleased with the reward of his patient service; nor was he pleased with

himself; and it was long before he arrived at the proposition that the queen could do no wrong.

'It's a losing game,' he said. 'I'm worth nothing when a whim of hers is in question. But in a losing game at Port Said we used to double the stakes and go on. She do a Melancolia! She hasn't the power, or the insight, or the training. Only the desire. She's cursed with the curse of Reuben. She won't do line-work, because it means real work; and yet she's stronger than I am. I'll make her understand that I can beat her on her own Melancolia. Even then she wouldn't care. She says I can only do blood and bones. I don't believe she has blood in her veins. All the same I love her; and I must go on loving her; and if I can humble her vanity I will. I'll do a Melancolia that shall be something like a Melancolia,— "the Melancolia that transcends all wit." I'll do it at once, con—bless her.'

He discovered that the notion would not come to order, and that he could not free his mind for an hour from the thought of Maisie's departure. He took very small interest in her rough studies for the Melancolia when she showed them next week. The Sundays were racing past, and the time was at hand when all the church bells in London could not ring Maisie back to him. Once or twice he said something to Binkie about 'hermaphroditic futilities,' but the little dog received so many confidences both from Torpenhow and Dick that he did not trouble his tulip-ears to listen.

Dick was permitted to see the girls off. They were going by the Dover night-boat; and they hoped to return in August. It was then February, and Dick felt that he was being hardly used. Maisie was so busy stripping the small house across the Park, and packing her canvases, that she had no time for thought. Dick went down to Dover and wasted a day there fretting over a wonderful possibility. Would Maisie at the very last allow him one small kiss? He reflected that he might capture her by the strong arm, as he had seen women captured in the Southern Soudan, and lead her away; but Maisie would never be led. She would turn her gray eyes upon him and say, 'Dick, how selfish you are!' Then his courage would fail him. It would be better, after all, to beg for that kiss.

Maisie looked more than usually kissable as she stepped from the night-mail on to the windy pier, in a gray waterproof and a little gray cloth travelling-cap. The red-haired girl was not so lovely. Her green eyes were hollow and her lips were dry. Dick saw the trunks aboard, and went to Maisie's side in the darkness under the bridge. The mail-bags were thundering into the forehold, and the red-haired girl was watching them.

'You'll have a rough passage to-night,' said Dick. 'It's blowing outside. I suppose I may come over and see you if I'm good?'

'You mustn't. I shall be busy. At least, if I want you I'll send for you. But I shall write from Vitry-sur-Marne. I shall have heaps of things to consult you about. Oh, Dick, you have been so good to me!—so good to me!'

'Thank you for that, dear. It hasn't made any difference, has it?'

'I can't tell a fib. It hasn't—in that way. But don't think I'm not grateful.'

'Damn the gratitude!' said Dick huskily to the paddle-box.

'What's the use of worrying? You know I should ruin your life, and you'd ruin mine, as things are now. You remember what you said when you were so angry that day in the Park? One of us has to be broken. Can't you wait till that day comes?'

'No, love. I want you unbroken—all to myself.'

Maisie shook her head. 'My poor Dick, what can I say?'

'Don't say anything. Give me a kiss? Only one kiss, Maisie. I'll swear I won't take any more. You might as well, and then I can be sure you're grateful.'

Maisie put her cheek forward, and Dick took his reward in the darkness. It was only one kiss, but, since there was no time-limit specified, it was a long one. Maisie wrenched herself free angrily, and Dick stood abashed and tingling from head to heel.

'Good-bye, darling. I didn't mean to scare you. I'm sorry. Only—keep well and do good work,—specially the Melancolia. I'm going to do one, too. Remember me to Kami, and be careful what you drink. Country drinking-water is bad everywhere, but it's worse in France. Write to me if you want anything, and good-bye. Say good-bye to the what-you-call-um girl, and—can't I have another kiss? No. You're quite right. Good-bye.'

A shout told him that it was not seemly to charge up the mail-bag incline. He reached the pier as the steamer began to move off, and he followed her with his heart.

'And there's nothing—nothing in the wide world—to keep us apart except her obstinacy. These Calais night-boats are much too small. I'll get Torp to write to the papers about it. She's beginning to pitch already.'

Maisie stood where Dick had left her till she heard a little gasping cough at her elbow. The red-haired girl's eyes were alight with cold flame.

'He kissed you!' she said. 'How could you let him, when he wasn't anything to you? How dared you take a kiss from him? Oh, Maisie, let's go to the ladies' cabin. I'm sick,—deadly sick.'

'We aren't into open water yet. Go down, dear, and I'll stay here. I don't like the smell of the engines. . . . Poor

Dick! He deserved one,—only one. But I didn't think he'd frighten me so.'

Dick returned to town next day just in time for lunch, for which he had telegraphed. To his disgust, there were only empty plates in the studio. He lifted up his voice like the bears in the fairy-tale, and Torpenhow entered, looking very guilty.

'H'sh!' said he. 'Don't make such a noise. I took it. Come into my rooms, and I'll show you why.'

Dick paused amazed at the theshold, for on Torpenhow's sofa lay a girl asleep and breathing heavily. The little cheap sailor-hat, the blue-and-white dress, fitter for June than for February, dabbled with mud at the skirts, the jacket trimmed with imitation Astrakhan and ripped at the shoulder-seams, the one-and-eleven-penny umbrella, and, above all, the disgraceful condition of the kid-topped boots, declared all things.

'Oh, I say, old man, this is too bad! You mustn't bring this sort up here. They steal things from the rooms.'

'It looks bad, I admit, but I was coming in after lunch, and she staggered into the hall. I thought she was drunk at first, but it was collapse. I couldn't leave her as she was, so I brought her up here and gave her your lunch. She was fainting from want of food. She went fast asleep the minute she had finished.'

'I know something of that complaint. She's been living on sausages, I suppose. Torp, you should have handed her over to a policeman for presuming to faint in a respectable house. Poor little wretch. Look at that face! There isn't an ounce of immorality in it. Only folly,—slack, fatuous, feeble, futile folly. It's a typical head. D'you notice how the skull begins to show through the flesh padding on the face and cheek-bone?'

'What a cold-blooded barbarian it is! Don't hit a woman when she's down. Can't we do anything? She was simply dropping with starvation. She almost fell into my arms, and when she got to the food she ate like a wild beast. It was horrible.'

'I can give her money, which she would probably spend in drinks. Is she going to sleep for ever?'

The girl opened her eyes and glared at the men between terror and effrontery.

' 'Feeling better?' said Torpenhow.

'Yes. Thank you. There aren't many gentlemen that are as kind as you are. Thank you.'

'When did you leave service?' said Dick, who had been watching the scarred and chapped hands.

'How did you know I was in service? I was. General servant. I didn't like it.'

'And how do you like being your own mistress?'

'Do I look as if I liked it?'

'I suppose not. One moment. Would you be good enough to turn your face to the window?'

The girl obeyed, and Dick watched her face keenly,—so keenly that she made as if to hide behind Torpenhow.

'The eyes have it,' said Dick, walking up and down. 'They are superb eyes for my business. And, after all, every head depends on the eyes. This has been sent from heaven to make up for—what was taken away. Now the weekly strain's off my shoulders, I can get to work in earnest. Evidently sent from heaven. Yes. Raise your chin a little, please.'

'Gently, old man, gently. You're scaring somebody out of her wits,' said Torpenhow, who could see the girl trembling.

'Don't let him hit me! Oh, please don't let him hit me. I've been hit cruel to-day because I spoke to a man. Don't let him look at me like that! He's reg'lar wicked, that one. Don't let him look at me like that, neither! Oh, I feel as if I hadn't nothing on when he looks at me like that!'

The overstrained nerves in the frail body gave way, and the girl wept like a little child and began to scream. Dick threw open the window, and Torpenhow flung the door back.

'There you are,' said Dick soothingly. 'My friend here can call for a policeman, and you can run through that door. Nobody is going to hurt you.'

The girl sobbed convulsively for a few minutes, and then tried to laugh.

'Nothing in the world to hurt you. Now listen to me for a minute. I'm what they call an artist by profession. You know what artists do?'

'They draw the things in red and black ink on the pop-shop labels.'

'I daresay. I haven't risen to pop-shop labels yet. Those are done by the Academicians. I want to draw your head.'

'What for?'

'Because it's pretty. That is why you will come to the room across the landing three times a week at eleven in the morning, and I'll give you three quid a week just for sitting still and being drawn. And there's a quid on account.'

'For nothing? Oh, my!' The girl turned the sovereign in her hand, and with more foolish tears: 'Ain't neither o' you two gentlemen afraid of my bilking you?'

'No. Only ugly girls do that. Try and remember this place. And, by the way, what's your name?'

'I'm Bessie,—Bessie—It's no use giving the rest. Bessie Broke,—Stone-broke if you like. What's your names? But there,—no one ever gives the real ones.'

Dick consulted Torpenhow with his eyes.

'My name's Heldar, and my friend's called Torpenhow; and you must be sure to come here. Where do you live?'

'South-the-water,—one room,—five and sixpence a week. Aren't you making fun of me about that three quid?'

'You'll see later on. And, Bessie, next time you come, remember, you needn't wear that paint. It's bad for the skin, and I have all the colours you'll be likely to need.'

Bessie withdrew, scrubbing her cheek with a ragged pocket-handkerchief. The two men looked at each other.

'You're a man,' said Torpenhow.

'I'm afraid I've been a fool. It isn't our business to run about the earth reforming Bessie Brokes. And a woman of any kind has no right on this landing.'

'Perhaps she won't come back.'

'She will if she thinks she can get food and warmth here. I know she will, worse luck. But remember, old man, she isn't a woman: she's my model; and be careful.'

'The idea! She's a dissolute little scarecrow,—a gutter-snippet and nothing more.'

'So you think. Wait till she has been fed a little and freed from fear. That fair type recovers itself very quickly. You won't know her in a week or two, when that abject fear has died out of her eyes. She'll be too happy and smiling for my purposes.'

'But surely you're taking her out of charity?—to please me?'

'I am not in the habit of playing with hot coals to please anybody. She has been sent from heaven, as I may have remarked before, to help me with my Melancolia.'

' 'Never heard a word about the lady before.'

'What's the use of having a friend if you must sling your notions at him in words? You ought to know what I'm thinking about. You've heard me grunt lately?'

'Even so; but grunts mean anything in your language from bad 'baccy to wicked dealers. And I don't think I've been much in your confidence for some time.'

'It was a high and soulful grunt. You ought to have understood that it meant the Melancolia.' Dick walked Torpenhow up and down the room, keeping silence.

Then he smote him in the ribs. 'Now don't you see it? Bessie's abject futility, and the terror in her eyes, welded on to one or two details in the way of sorrow that have come under my experience lately. Likewise some orange and black,—two keys of each. But I can't explain on an empty stomach.'

'It sounds mad enough. You'd better stick to your soldiers, Dick, instead of maundering about heads and eyes and experiences.'

'Think so?' Dick began to dance on his heels, singing—

'They're as proud as a turkey when they hold
     the ready cash,
   You ought to 'ear the way they laugh an'
     joke;
They are tricky an' they're funny when
     they've got the ready money,—
   Ow! but see 'em when they're all stone-
     broke.'

Then he sat down to pour out his heart to Maisie in a four-sheet letter of counsel and encouragement, and registered an oath that he would get to work with an undivided heart as soon as Bessie should reappear.

The girl kept her appointment un-painted and unadorned, afraid and over-bold by turns. When she found that she was merely expected to sit still, she grew calmer, and criticised the appointments of the studio with freedom and some point. She liked the warmth and the comfort and the release from fear of physical pain. Dick made two or three studies of her head in monochrome, but the actual notion of the Melancolia would not arrive.

'What a mess you keep your things in!' said Bessie, some days later, when she felt herself thoroughly at home. 'I s'pose your clothes are just as bad. Gentlemen never think what buttons and tape are made for.'

'I buy things to wear, and wear 'em till

they go to pieces. I don't know what Torpenhow does.'

Bessie made diligent inquiry in the latter's room, and unearthed a bale of disreputable socks. 'Some of these I'll mend now,' she said, 'and some I'll take home. D'you know, I sit all day long at home doing nothing, just like a lady, and no more noticing them other girls in the house than if they was so many flies? I don't have any unnecessary words, but I put 'em down quick, I can tell you, when they talk to me. No; it's quite nice these days. I lock my door, and they can only call me names through the keyhole, and I sit inside, just like a lady, mending socks. Mr. Torpenhow wears his socks out both ends at once.'

'Three quid a week from me, and the delights of my society. No socks mended. Nothing from Torp except a nod on the landing now and again, and all his socks mended. Bessie is very much a woman,' thought Dick; and he looked at her be-tween half-shut eyes. Food and rest had transformed the girl, as Dick knew they would.

'What are you looking at me like that for?' she said quickly. 'Don't. You look reg'lar bad when you look that way. You don't think much o' me, do you?'

'That depends on how you behave.'

Bessie behaved beautifully. Only it was difficult at the end of a sitting to bid her go out into the gray streets. She very much preferred the studio and a big chair by the stove, with some socks in her lap as an excuse for delay. Then Torpenhow would come in, and Bessie would be moved to tell strange and wonderful stories of her past, and still stranger ones of her present improved circumstances. She would make them tea as though she had a right to make it; and once or twice on these occasions Dick caught Torpen-how's eyes fixed on the trim little figure, and because Bessie's flittings about the room made Dick ardently long for

Maisie, he realised whither Torpenhow's thoughts were tending. And Bessie was exceedingly careful of the condition of Torpenhow's linen. She spoke very little to him, but sometimes they talked together on the landing.

'I was a great fool,' Dick said to himself. 'I know what red firelight looks like when a man's trampling through a strange town; and ours is a lonely, selfish sort of life at the best. I wonder Maisie doesn't feel that sometimes. But I can't order Bessie away. That's the worst of beginning things. One never knows where they stop.'

One evening, after a sitting prolonged to the last limit of the light, Dick was roused from a nap by a broken voice in Torpenhow's room. He jumped to his feet. 'Now what ought I to do? It looks foolish to go in.—Oh, bless you, Binkie!' The little terrier thrust Torpenhow's door open with his nose and came out to take possession of Dick's chair. The door swung wide unheeded, and Dick across the landing could see Bessie in the half-light making her little supplication to Torpenhow. She was kneeling by his side, and her hands were clasped across his knee.

'I know,—I know,' she said thickly. ' 'Tisn't right o' me to do this, but I can't help it; and you were so kind,—so kind; and you never took any notice o' me. And I've mended all your things so carefully,—I did. Oh, please, 'tisn't as if I was asking you to marry me. I wouldn't think of it. But cou—couldn't you take and live with me till Miss Right comes along? I'm only Miss Wrong, I know, but I'd work my hands to the bare bone for you. And I'm not ugly to look at. Say you will?'

Dick hardly recognised Torpenhow's voice in reply—

'But look here. It's no use. I'm liable to be ordered off anywhere at a min-

ute's notice if a war breaks out. At a minute's notice—dear.'

'What does that matter? Until you go, then. Until you go. 'Tisn't much I'm asking, and—you don't know how good I can cook.' She put an arm round his neck and was drawing his head down.

'Until—I—go, then.'

'Torp,' said Dick across the landing. He could hardly steady his voice. 'Come here a minute, old man. I'm in trouble.' —'Heaven send he'll listen to me!' There was something very like an oath from Bessie's lips. She was afraid of Dick, and disappeared down the staircase in panic, but it seemed an age before Torpenhow entered the studio. He went to the mantelpiece, buried his head on his arms, and groaned like a wounded bull.

'What the devil right have you to interfere?' he said, at last.

'Who's interfering with which? Your own sense told you long ago you couldn't be such a fool. It was a tough rack, St. Anthony, but you're all right now.'

'I oughtn't to have seen her moving about these rooms as if they belonged to her. That's what upset me. It gives a lonely man a sort of hankering, doesn't it?' said Torpenhow piteously.

'Now you talk sense. It does. But, since you aren't in a condition to discuss the disadvantages of double housekeeping, do you know what you're going to do?'

'I don't. I wish I did.'

'You're going away for a season on a brilliant tour to regain tone. You're going to Brighton, or Scarborough, or Prawle Point, to see the ships go by. And you're going at once. Isn't it odd? I'll take care of Binkie, but out you go immediately. Never resist the devil. He holds the bank. Fly from him. Pack your things and go.'

'I believe you're right. Where shall I go?'

'And you call yourself a special correspondent! Pack first and inquire afterwards.'

An hour later Torpenhow was despatched into the night in a hansom. 'You'll probably think of some place to go to while you're moving,' said Dick. 'Go to Euston, to begin with, and—oh yes—get drunk to-night.'

He returned to the studio, and lighted more candles, for he found the room very dark.

'Oh, you Jezebel! you futile little Jezebel! Won't you hate me to-morrow?— Binkie, come here.'

Binkie turned over on his back on the hearth-rug, and Dick stirred him with a meditative foot.

'I said she was not immoral. I was wrong. She said she could cook. That showed premeditated sin. Oh, Binkie, if you are a man you will go to perdition; but if you are a woman, and say that you can cook, you will go to a much worse place.'

CHAPTER 10

What's yon that follows at my side?—
   The foe that ye must fight, my lord.—
That hirples swift as I can ride?—
   The shadow of your might, my lord.—
Then wheel my horse against the foe!—
   He's down and overpast, my lord.
Ye war against the sunset glow:
   The darkness gathers fast, my lord.
         The Fight of Heriot's Ford

'This is a cheerful life,' said Dick, some days later. 'Torp's away; Bessie hates me; I can't get at the notion of the Melancolia; Maisie's letters are scrappy; and I believe I have indigestion. What gives a man pains across his head and spots before his eyes, Binkie? Shall us take some liver pills?'

Dick had just gone through a lively scene with Bessie. She had for the fiftieth time reproached him for sending Torpenhow away. She explained her enduring hatred for Dick, and made it clear to him that she only sat for the sake of his money. 'And Mr. Torpenhow's ten times a better man than you,' she concluded.

'He is. That's why he went away. I should have stayed and made love to you.'

The girl sat with her chin on her hand, scowling. 'To me! I'd like to catch you! If I wasn't afraid o' being hung I'd kill you. That's what I'd do. D'you believe me?'

Dick smiled wearily. It is not pleasant to live in the company of a notion that will not work out, a fox-terrier that cannot talk, and a woman who talks too much. He would have answered, but at that moment there unrolled itself from one corner of the studio a veil, as it were, of the filmiest gauze. He rubbed his eyes, but the gray haze would not go.

'This is disgraceful indigestion. Binkie, we will go to a medicine-man. We can't have our eyes interfered with, for by these we get our bread; also mutton-chop bones for little dogs.'

The doctor was an affable local practitioner with white hair, and he said nothing till Dick began to describe the gray film in the studio.

'We all want a little patching and repairing from time to time,' he chirped. 'Like a ship, my dear sir,—exactly like a ship. Sometimes the hull is out of order, and we consult the surgeon; sometimes the rigging, and then I advise; sometimes the engines, and we go to the brain-specialist; sometimes the look-out on the bridge is tired, and then we see an oculist. I should recommend you to see an oculist. A little patching and repairing from time to time is all we want. An oculist, by all means.'

Dick sought an oculist,—the best in London. He was certain that the local practitioner did not know anything about his trade, and more certain that Maisie would laugh at him if he were forced to wear spectacles.

'I've neglected the warnings of my lord the stomach too long. Hence these spots before the eyes, Binkie. I can see as well as I ever could.'

As he entered the dark hall that led to the consulting-room a man cannoned against him. Dick saw the face as it hurried out into the street.

'That's the writer-type. He has the same modelling of the forehead as Torp. He looks very sick. Probably heard something he didn't like.'

Even as he thought, a great fear came upon Dick, a fear that made him hold his breath as he walked into the oculist's waiting-room, with the heavy carved furniture, the dark-green paper, and the sober-hued prints on the wall. He recognised a reproduction of one of his own sketches.

Many people were waiting their turn before him. His eye was caught by a flaming red-and-gold Christmas-carol book. Little children came to that eye-doctor, and they needed large-type amusement.

'That's idolatrous bad Art,' he said, drawing the book towards himself. 'From the anatomy of the angels, it has been made in Germany.' He opened it mechanically, and there leaped to his eyes a verse printed in red ink—

'The next good joy that Mary had,
    It was the joy of three,
To see her good Son Jesus Christ
    Making the blind to see;
Making the blind to see, good Lord,
    And happy may we be.
Praise Father, Son, and Holy Ghost
    To all eternity!'

Dick read and re-read the verse till his turn came, and the doctor was bending above him seated in an armchair. The blaze of a gas-microscope in his eyes made him wince. The doctor's hand touched the scar of the sword-cut on Dick's head, and Dick explained briefly how he had come by it. When the flame was removed, Dick saw the doctor's face, and the fear came upon him again. The doctor wrapped himself in a mist of words. Dick caught allusions to 'scar,' 'frontal bone,' 'optic nerve,' 'extreme caution,' and the 'avoidance of mental anxiety.'

'Verdict?' he said faintly. 'My business is painting, and I daren't waste time. What do you make of it?'

Again the whirl of words, but this time they conveyed a meaning.

'Can you give me anything to drink?'

Many sentences were pronounced in that darkened room, and the prisoners often needed cheering. Dick found a glass of liqueur brandy in his hand.

'As far as I can gather,' he said, coughing above the spirit, 'you call it decay of the optic nerve, or something, and therefore hopeless. What is my time-limit, avoiding all strain and worry?'

'Perhaps one year.'

'My God! And if I don't take care of myself?'

'I really could not say. One cannot ascertain the exact amount of injury inflicted by the sword-cut. The scar is an old one, and—exposure to the strong light of the desert, did you say?—with excessive application to fine work? I really could not say.'

'I beg your pardon, but it has come without any warning. If you will let me, I'll sit here for a minute, and then I'll go. You have been very good in telling me the truth. . . . Without any warning . . . without any warning. Thanks.'

Dick went into the street, and was rapturously received by Binkie. 'We've got it very badly, little dog! Just as badly as we can get it. We'll go to the Park to think it out.'

They headed for a certain tree that Dick knew well, and they sat down to think, because his legs were trembling under him and there was cold fear at the pit of his stomach.

'How could it have come without any warning? It's as sudden as being shot. It's the living death, Binkie. We're to be shut up in the dark in one year if we're careful, and we shan't see anybody, and we shall never have anything we want, not though we live to be a hundred.' Binkie wagged his tail joyously. 'Binkie, we must think. Let's see how it feels to be blind.' Dick shut his eyes, and flaming commas and Catherine-wheels floated inside the lids. Yet when he looked across the Park the scope of his vision was not contracted. He could see perfectly, until a procession of slow-wheeling fireworks defiled across his eyeballs.

'Little dorglums, we aren't at all well. Let's go home. If only Torp were back, now!'

But Torpenhow was in the South of England, inspecting dockyards in the company of the Nilghai. His letters were brief and full of mystery.

Dick had never asked anybody to help him in his joys or his sorrows. He argued, in the loneliness of the studio, henceforward to be decorated with a film of gray gauze in one corner, that, if his fate were blindness, all the Torpenhows in the world could not save him. 'I can't call him off his trip to sit down and sympathise with me. I must pull through the business alone,' he said. He was lying on the sofa eating his moustache and wondering what the darkness of the night would be like. Then came to his mind the memory of a quaint scene in the Soudan. A soldier had been nearly hacked in two by a broad-bladed Arab spear. For one instant the man felt no pain. Looking down, he saw that his life-blood was going from him. The stupid bewilderment on his face was so intensely comic

that both Dick and Torpenhow, still panting and unstrung from a fight for life, had roared with laughter, in which the man seemed as if he would join, but, as his lips parted in a sheepish grin, the agony of death came upon him, and he pitched grunting at their feet. Dick laughed again, remembering the horror. It seemed so exactly like his own case. 'But I have a little more time allowed me,' he said. He paced up and down the room, quietly at first, but afterwards with the hurried feet of fear. It was as though a black shadow stood at his elbow and urged him to go forward; and there were only weaving circles and floating pin-dots before his eyes.

'We must be calm, Binkie; we must be calm.' He talked aloud for the sake of distraction. 'This isn't nice at all. What shall we do? We must do something. Our time is short. I shouldn't have believed that this morning; but now things are different. Binkie, where was Moses when the light went out?'

Binkie smiled from ear to ear, as a well-bred terrier should, but made no suggestion.

' "Were there but world enough and time, This coyness, Binkie, were no crime. . . . But at my back I always hear—" ' He wiped his forehead, which was unpleasantly damp. 'What can I do? What can I do? I haven't any notions left, and I can't think connectedly, but I must do something, or I shall go off my head.'

The hurried walk recommenced, Dick stopping every now and again to drag forth long-neglected canvases and old note-books; for he turned to his work by instinct as a thing that could not fail. 'You won't do, and you won't do,' he said, at each inspection. 'No more soldiers. I couldn't paint 'em. Sudden death comes home too nearly, and this is battle and murder both for me.'

The day was failing, and Dick thought

for a moment that the twilight of the blind had come upon him unawares. 'Allah Almighty!' he cried despairingly, 'help me through the time of waiting, and I won't whine when my punishment comes. What can I do now, before the light goes?'

There was no answer. Dick waited till he could regain some sort of control over himself. His hands were shaking, and he prided himself on their steadiness; he could feel that his lips were quivering, and the sweat was running down his face. He was lashed by fear, driven forward by the desire to get to work at once and accomplish something, and maddened by the refusal of his brain to do more than repeat the news that he was about to go blind. 'It's a humiliating exhibition,' he thought, 'and I'm glad Torp isn't here to see. The doctor said I was to avoid mental worry. Come here and let me pet you, Binkie.'

The little dog yelped because Dick nearly squeezed the bark out of him. Then he heard the man speaking in the twilight and, doglike, understood that his trouble stood off from him—

'Allah is good, Binkie. Not quite so gentle as we could wish, but we'll discuss that later. I think I see my way to it now. All those studies of Bessie's head were nonsense, and they nearly brought your master into a scrape. I hold the notion now as clear as crystal,—"the Melancolia that transcends all wit." There shall be Maisie in that head, because I shall never get Maisie; and Bess, of course, because she knows all about Melancolia, though she doesn't know she knows; and there shall be some drawing in it, and it shall all end up with a laugh. That's for myself. Shall she giggle or grin? No, she shall laugh right out of the canvas, and every man and woman that ever had a sorrow of their own shall—what is it the poem says?—

'Understand the speech and feel a stir
Of fellowship in all disastrous fight.

"In all disastrous fight"? That's better than painting the thing merely to pique Maisie. I can do it now because I have it inside me. Binkie, I'm going to hold you up by your tail. You're an omen. Come here.'

Binkie swung head downward for a moment without speaking.

' 'Rather like holding a guinea-pig; but you're a brave little dog, and you don't yelp when you're hung up. It is an omen.'

Binkie went to his own chair, and as often as he looked, saw Dick walking up and down, rubbing his hands and chuckling. That night Dick wrote a letter to Maisie full of the tenderest regard for her health, but saying very little about his own, and dreamed of the Melancolia to be born. Not till morning did he remember that something might happen to him in the future.

He fell to work, whistling softly, and was swallowed up in the clean, clear joy of creation, which does not come to man too often, lest he should consider himself the equal of his God, and so refuse to die at the appointed time. He forgot Maisie, Torpenhow, and Binkie at his feet, but remembered to stir Bessie, who needed very little stirring, into a tremendous rage, that he might watch the smouldering lights in her eyes. He threw himself without reservation into his work, and did not think of the doom that was to overtake him, for he was possessed with his notion, and the things of this world had no power upon him.

'You're pleased to-day,' said Bessie.

Dick waved his mahl-stick in mystic circles and went to the sideboard for a drink. In the evening, when the exaltation of the day had died down, he went to the sideboard again, and after some visits became convinced that the eye-doctor was a liar, since he still could see everything very clearly. He was of opinion that he would even make a home for Maisie, and that whether she liked it or not she should be his wife. The mood passed next morning, but the sideboard and all upon it remained for his comfort. Again he set to work, and his eyes troubled him with spots and dashes and blurs till he had taken counsel with the sideboard, and the Melancolia both on the canvas and in his own mind appeared lovelier than ever. There was a delightful sense of irresponsibility upon him, such as they feel who walking among their fellow-men know that the death-sentence of disease is upon them, and, since fear is but waste of the little time left, are riotously happy. The days passed without event. Bessie arrived punctually always, and, though her voice seemed to Dick to come from a distance, her face was always very near, and the Melancolia began to flame on the canvas, in the likeness of a woman who had known all the sorrow in the world and was laughing at it. It was true that the corners of the studio draped themselves in gray film and retired into the darkness, that the spots in his eyes and the pains across his head were very troublesome, and that Maisie's letters were hard to read and harder still to answer. He could not tell her of his trouble, and he could not laugh at her accounts of her own Melancolia which was always going to be finished. But the furious days of toil and the nights of wild dreams made amends for all, and the sideboard was his best friend on earth. Bessie was singularly dull. She used to shriek with rage when Dick stared at her between half-closed eyes. Now she sulked or watched him with disgust, saying very little.

Torpenhow had been absent for six weeks. An incoherent note heralded his return. 'News! great news!' he wrote. 'The Nilghai knows, and so does The Keneu. We're all back on Thursday. Get lunch and clean your accoutrements.'

Dick showed Bessie the letter, and she abused him for that he had ever sent Torpenhow away and ruined her life.

'Well,' said Dick brutally, 'you're better as you are, instead of making love to some drunken beast in the street.' He felt that he had rescued Torpenhow from great temptation.

'I don't know if that's any worse than sitting to a drunken beast in a studio. You haven't been sober for three weeks. You've been soaking the whole time; and yet you pretend you're better than me!'

'What d'you mean?' said Dick.

'Mean! You'll see when Mr. Torpenhow comes back.'

It was not long to wait. Torpenhow met Bessie on the staircase without a sign of feeling. He had news that was more to him than many Bessies, and The Keneu and the Nilghai were trampling behind him, calling for Dick.

'Drinking like a fish,' Bessie whispered. 'He's been at it for nearly a month.' She followed the men stealthily to hear judgment done.

They came into the studio, rejoicing, to be welcomed over-effusively by a drawn, lined, shrunken, haggard wreck,—unshaven, blue-white about the nostrils, stooping in the shoulders, and peering under his eyebrows nervously. The drink had been at work as steadily as Dick.

'Is this you?' said Torpenhow.

'All that's left of me. Sit down. Binkie's quite well, and I've been doing some good work.' He reeled where he stood.

'You've done some of the worst work you've ever done in your life. Man alive, you're—'

Torpenhow turned to his companions appealingly, and they left the room to find lunch elsewhere. Then he spoke; but, since the reproof of a friend is much too sacred and intimate a thing to be printed, and since Torpenhow used figures and metaphors which were unseemly, and contempt untranslatable, it will never be known what was actually said to Dick, who blinked and winked and picked at his hands. After a time the culprit began to feel the need of a little self-respect. He was quite sure that he had not in any way departed from virtue, and there were reasons, too, of which Torpenhow knew nothing. He would explain.

He rose, tried to straighten his shoulders, and spoke to the face he could hardly see.

'You are right,' he said. 'But I am right, too. After you went away I had some trouble with my eyes. So I went to an oculist, and he turned a gasogene—I mean a gas-engine—into my eye. That was very long ago. He said, "Scar on the head,—sword-cut and optic nerve." Make a note of that. So I am going blind. I have some work to do before I go blind, and I suppose that I must do it. I cannot see much now, but I can see best when I am drunk. I did not know I was drunk till I was told, but I must go on with my work. If you want to see it, there it is.' He pointed to the all but finished Melancolia and looked for applause.

Torpenhow said nothing, and Dick began to whimper feebly, for joy at seeing Torpenhow again, for grief at misdeeds —if indeed they were misdeeds—that made Torpenhow remote and unsympathetic, and for childish vanity hurt, since Torpenhow had not given a word of praise to his wonderful picture.

Bessie looked through the keyhole after a long pause, and saw the two walking up and down as usual, Torpenhow's hand on Dick's shoulder. Hereat she said something so improper that it shocked even Binkie, who was dribbling patiently on the landing in the hope of seeing his master again.

CHAPTER 11

The lark will make her hymn to God,
  The partridge call her brood,
While I forget the heath I trod,
  The fields wherein I stood.
'Tis dule to know not night from morn,
  But deeper dule to know
I can but hear the hunter's horn
  That once I used to blow.
The Only Son

It was the third day after Torpenhow's return, and his heart was heavy.

'Do you mean to tell me that you can't see to work without whisky? It's generally the other way about.'

'Can a drunkard swear on his honour?' said Dick.

'Yes, if he has been as good a man as you.'

'Then I give you my word of honour,' said Dick, speaking hurriedly through parched lips. 'Old man, I can hardly see your face now. You've kept me sober for two days,—if I ever was drunk,—and I've done no work. Don't keep me back any more. I don't know when my eyes may give out. The spots and dots and the pains and things are crowding worse than ever. I swear I can see all right when I'm—when I'm moderately screwed, as you say. Give me three more sittings from Bessie and all the—stuff I want, and the picture will be done. I can't kill myself in three days. It only means a touch of D.T. at the worst.'

'If I give you three days more will you promise me to stop work and—the other thing, whether the picture's finished or not?'

'I can't. You don't know what that picture means to me. But surely you could get the Nilghai to help you, and knock me down and tie me up. I shouldn't fight for the whisky, but I should for the work.'

'Go on, then. I give you three days; but you're nearly breaking my heart.'

Dick returned to his work, toiling as one possessed; and the yellow devil of whisky stood by him and chased away the spots in his eyes. The Melancolia was nearly finished, and was all or nearly all that he had hoped she would be. Dick jested with Bessie, who reminded him that he was 'a drunken beast'; but the reproof did not move him.

'You can't understand, Bess. We are in sight of land now, and soon we shall lie back and think about what we've done. I'll give you three months' pay when the picture's finished, and next time I have any more work in hand—but that doesn't matter. Won't three months' pay make you hate me less?'

'No, it won't! I hate you, and I'll go on hating you. Mr. Torpenhow won't speak to me any more. He's always looking at map-things and red-backed books.'

Bessie did not say that she had again laid siege to Torpenhow, or that he had at the end of her passionate pleading picked her up, given her a kiss, and put her outside the door with a recommendation not to be a little fool. He spent most of his time in the company of the Nilghai, and their talk was of war in the near future, the hiring of transports, and secret preparations among the dockyards. He did not care to see Dick till the picture was finished.

'He's doing first-class work,' he said to the Nilghai, 'and it's quite out of his regular line. But, for the matter of that, so's his infernal drinking.'

'Never mind. Leave him alone. When he has come to his senses again we'll carry him off from this place and let him breathe clean air. Poor Dick! I don't envy you, Torp, when his eyes fail.'

'Yes, it will be a case of "God help the man who's chained to our Davie." The worst is that we don't know when it will

happen; and I believe the uncertainty and the waiting have sent Dick to the whisky more than anything else.'

'How the Arab who cut his head open would grin if he knew!'

'He's at perfect liberty to grin if he can. He's dead. That's poor consolation now.'

In the afternoon of the third day Torpenhow heard Dick calling for him. 'All finished!' he shouted. 'I've done it! Come in! Isn't she a beauty? Isn't she a darling? I've been down to hell to get her; but isn't she worth it?'

Torpenhow looked at the head of a woman who laughed,—a full-lipped, hollow-eyed woman who laughed from out of the canvas as Dick had intended she should.

'Who taught you how to do it?' said Torpenhow. 'The touch and notion have nothing to do with your regular work. What a face it is! What eyes, and what insolence!' Unconsciously he threw back his head and laughed with her. 'She's seen the game played out,—I don't think she had a good time of it,—and now she doesn't care. Isn't that the idea?'

'Exactly.'

'Where did you get the mouth and chin from? They don't belong to Bess.'

'They're—some one else's. But isn't it good? Isn't it thundering good? Wasn't it worth the whisky? I did it. Alone I did it, and it's the best I can do.' He drew his breath sharply, and whispered, 'Just God! what could I not do ten years hence, if I can do this now!—By the way, what do you think of it, Bess?'

The girl was biting her lips. She loathed Torpenhow because he had taken no notice of her.

'I think it's just the horridest, beastliest thing I ever saw,' she answered, and turned away.

'More than you will be of that way of thinking, young woman.—Dick, there's a sort of murderous, viperine suggestion in the poise of the head that I don't understand,' said Torpenhow.

'That's trick-work,' said Dick, chuckling with delight of being completely understood. 'I couldn't resist one little bit of sheer swagger. It's a French trick, and you wouldn't understand; but it's got at by slewing round the head a trifle, and a tiny, tiny foreshortening of one side of the face from the angle of the chin to the top of the left ear. That, and deepening the shadow under the lobe of the ear. It was flagrant trick-work; but, having the notion fixed, I felt entitled to play with it.—Oh, you beauty!'

'Amen! She is a beauty. I can feel it.'

'So will every man who has any sorrow of his own,' said Dick, slapping his thigh. 'He shall see his trouble there, and, by the Lord Harry, just when he's feeling properly sorry for himself he shall throw back his head and laugh,—as she is laughing. I've put the life of my heart and the light of my eyes into her, and I don't care what comes. . . . I'm tired,—awfully tired. I think I'll get to sleep. Take away the whisky, it has served its turn, and give Bessie thirty-six quid, and three over for luck. Cover the picture.'

He dropped asleep in the long chair, his face white and haggard almost before he had finished the sentence. Bessie tried to take Torpenhow's hand. 'Aren't you never going to speak to me any more?' she said; but Torpenhow was looking at Dick.

'What a stock of vanity the man has! I'll take him in hand to-morrow and make much of him. He deserves it.—Eh! what was that, Bess?'

'Nothing. I'll put things tidy here a little, and then I'll go. You couldn't give me that three months' pay now, could you? He said you were to.'

Torpenhow gave her a cheque and went to his own rooms. Bessie faithfully tidied up the studio, set the door ajar for flight, emptied half a bottle of turpentine on a duster, and began to scrub the face of the Melancolia viciously. The paint did not smudge quickly enough. She took a palette-knife and scraped, following each stroke with the wet duster. In five minutes the picture was a formless, scarred muddle of colours. She threw the paint-stained duster into the studio stove, stuck out her tongue at the sleeper, and whispered, 'Bilked!' as she turned to run down the staircase. She would never see Torpenhow any more, but she had at least done harm to the man who had come between her and her desire and who used to make fun of her. Cashing the cheque was the very cream of the jest to Bessie. Then the little privateer sailed across the Thames, to be swallowed up in the gray wilderness of South-the-water.

Dick slept till late into the evening, when Torpenhow dragged him off to bed. His eyes were as bright as his voice was hoarse. 'Let's have another look at the picture,' he said, insistently as a child.

'You—go—to—bed,' said Torpenhow. 'You aren't at all well, though you mayn't know it. You're as jumpy as a cat.'

'I reform to-morrow. Good-night.'

As he repassed through the studio, Torpenhow lifted the cloth above the picture, and almost betrayed himself by outcries: 'Wiped out!—scraped out and turped out! If Dick knows this to-night he'll go perfectly mad. He's on the verge of jumps as it is. That's Bess,—the little fiend! Only a woman could have done that!—with the ink not dry on the cheque, too! Dick will be raving mad to-morrow. It was all my fault for trying to help gutter-devils. Oh, my poor Dick, the Lord is hitting you very hard!'

Dick could not sleep that night, partly for pure joy, and partly because the well-known Catherine-wheels inside his eyes had given place to crackling volcanoes of many-coloured fire. 'Spout away,' he said aloud. 'I've done my work, and now you can do what you please.' He lay still, staring at the ceiling, the long-pent-up delirium of drink in his veins, his brain on fire with racing thoughts that would not stay to be considered, and his hands crisped and dry. He had just discovered that he was painting the face of the Melancolia on a revolving dome ribbed with millions of lights, and that all his wondrous thoughts stood embodied hundreds of feet below his tiny swinging plank, shouting together in his honour, when something cracked inside his temples like an over-strained bow-string, the glittering dome broke inward, and he was alone in the thick night.

'I'll go to sleep. The room's very dark. Let's light a lamp and see how the Melancolia looks. There ought to have been a moon.'

It was then that Torpenhow heard his name called by a voice that he did not know,—in the rattling accents of deadly fear.

'He's looked at the picture,' was his first thought, as he hurried into the bedroom and found Dick sitting up and beating the air with his hands.

'Torp! Torp! Where are you? For pity's sake, come to me!'

'What's the matter?'

Dick clutched at his shoulder. 'Matter! I've been lying here for hours in the dark, and you never heard me. Torp, old man, don't go away. I'm all in the dark. In the dark, I tell you!'

Torpenhow held the candle within a foot of Dick's eyes, but there was no light in those eyes. He lit the gas, and Dick heard the flame catch. The grip of his fingers on Torpenhow's shoulder made Torpenhow wince.

'Don't leave me. You wouldn't leave me alone now, would you? I can't see. D'you understand? It's black,—quite

black,—and I feel as if I was falling through it all.'

'Steady does it.' Torpenhow put his arm round Dick and began to rock him gently to and fro.

'That's good. Now don't talk. If I keep very quiet for a while this darkness will lift. It seems just on the point of breaking. H'sh!' Dick knit his brows and stared desperately in front of him. The night air was chilling Torpenhow's toes.

'Can you stay like that a minute?' he said. 'I'll get my dressing-gown and some slippers.'

Dick clutched the bed-head with both hands and waited for the darkness to clear away. 'What a time you've been!' he cried, when Torpenhow returned. 'It's as black as ever. What are you banging about in the doorway?'

'Long chair,—horse-blanket,—pillow. Going to sleep by you. Lie down now; you'll be better in the morning.'

'I shan't!' The voice rose to a wail. 'My God! I'm blind! I'm blind, and the darkness will never go away.' He made as if to leap from the bed, but Torpenhow's arms were round him, and Torpenhow's chin was on his shoulder, and his breath was squeezed out of him. He could only gasp, 'Blind!' and wriggle feebly.

'Steady, Dickie, steady!' said the deep voice in his ear, and the grip tightened. 'Bite on the bullet, old man, and don't let them think you're afraid.' The grip could draw no closer. Both men were breathing heavily. Dick threw his head from side to side and groaned.

'Let me go,' he panted. 'You're cracking my ribs. We—we mustn't let them think we're afraid, must we,—all the Powers of Darkness and that lot?'

'Lie down. It's all over now.'

'Yes,' said Dick obediently. 'But would you mind letting me hold your hand? I feel as if I wanted something to hold on to. One drops through the dark so.'

Torpenhow thrust out a large and

hairy paw from the long chair. Dick clutched it tightly, and in half an hour had fallen asleep. Torpenhow withdrew his hand, and, stooping over Dick, kissed him lightly on the forehead, as men do sometimes kiss a wounded comrade in the hour of death, to ease his departure.

In the gray dawn Torpenhow heard Dick talking to himself. He was adrift on the shoreless tides of delirium, speaking very quickly—

'It's a pity,—a great pity; but it's helped, and it must be eaten, Master George. . . . Sufficient unto the day is the blindness thereof, and, further, putting aside all Melancolias and false humours, it is of obvious notoriety—such as mine was—that the queen can do no wrong. Torp doesn't know that. I'll tell him when we're a little farther into the desert. . . . What a bungle those boatmen are making of the steamer-ropes! They'll have that four-inch hawser chafed through in a minute. I told you so—there she goes! . . . White foam on green water, and the steamer slewing round. How good that looks! I'll sketch it. No, I can't. I'm afflicted with ophthalmia. That was one of the ten plagues of Egypt, and it extends up the Nile in the shape of cataract. Ha! that's a joke, Torp. Laugh, you graven image, and stand clear of the hawser. . . . It'll knock you into the water and make your dress all dirty, Maisie dear.'

'Oh!' said Torpenhow. 'This happened before. That night on the river.'

'She'll be sure to say it's my fault if you get muddy, and you're quite near enough to the breakwater. . . . Maisie, that's not fair. Ah! I knew you'd miss. Low and to the left, dear. But you've no conviction. Everything in the world except conviction. Don't be angry, darling. I'd cut my hand off if it would give you anything more than obstinacy. My right hand, if it would serve.'

'Now we mustn't listen. Here's an island shouting across seas of misunderstanding with a vengeance. But it's shouting truth, I fancy,' said Torpenhow.

The babble continued. It all bore upon Maisie. Sometimes Dick lectured at length on his craft, then he cursed himself for his folly in being enslaved. He pleaded to Maisie for a kiss—only one kiss—before she went away, and called to her to come back from Vitry-sur-Marne, if she would; but through all his ravings he bade heaven and earth witness that the queen could do no wrong.

Torpenhow listened attentively, and learned every detail of Dick's life that had been hidden from him. For three days Dick raved through his past, and then slept a natural sleep. 'What a strain he has been running under, poor chap!' said Torpenhow. 'Dick, of all men, handing himself over like a dog. And I was lecturing him on arrogance! I ought to have known that it was no use to judge a man. But I did it. What a demon that girl must be! Dick's given her his life,—confound him!—and she's given him one kiss apparently.'

'Torp,' said Dick from the bed, 'go out for a walk. You've been here too long. I'll get up. Hi! This is annoying. I can't dress myself. Oh, it's too absurd!'

Torpenhow helped him into his clothes and led him to the big chair in the studio. He sat quietly waiting under strained nerves for the darkness to lift. It did not lift that day, nor the next. Dick adventured on a voyage round the walls. He hit his shins against the stove, and this suggested to him that it would be better to crawl on all-fours, one hand in front of him. Torpenhow found him on the floor.

'I'm trying to get the geography of my new possessions,' said he. 'D'you remember that nigger you gouged in the square? Pity you didn't keep the odd eye. It would have been useful. Any letters for me? Give me all the ones in fat gray envelopes with a sort of crown thing outside. They're of no importance.'

Torpenhow gave him a letter with a black M on the envelope flap. Dick put it into his pocket. There was nothing in it that Torpenhow might not have read, but it belonged to himself and to Maisie, who would never belong to him.

'When she finds that I don't write she'll stop writing. It's better so. I couldn't be any use to her now,' Dick argued, and the tempter suggested that he should make known his condition. Every nerve in him revolted. 'I have fallen low enough already. I'm not going to beg for pity. Besides, it would be cruel to her.' He strove to put Maisie out of his thoughts; but the blind have many opportunities for thinking, and as the tides of his strength came back to him in the long employless days of dead darkness, Dick's soul was troubled to the core. Another letter, and another, came from Maisie. Then there was silence, and Dick sat by the window, the pulse of summer in the air, and pictured her being won by another man, stronger than himself. His imagination, the keener for the dark background it worked against, spared him no single detail that might send him raging up and down the studio, to stumble over the stove that seemed to be in four places at once. Worst of all, tobacco would not taste in the darkness. The arrogance of the man had disappeared, and in its place were settled despair that Torpenhow knew, and blind passion that Dick confided to his pillow at night. The intervals between the paroxysms were filled with intolerable waiting and the weight of intolerable darkness.

'Come out into the Park,' said Torpenhow. 'You haven't stirred out since the beginning of things.'

'What's the use? There's no movement in the dark; and, besides,'—he paused

irresolutely at the head of the stairs;—'something will run over me.'

'Not if I'm with you. Proceed gingerly.'

The roar of the streets filled Dick with nervous terror, and he clung to Torpenhow's arm. 'Fancy having to feel for a gutter with your foot!' he said petulantly, as he turned into the Park. 'Let's curse God and die.'

'Sentries are forbidden to pay unauthorized compliments. By Jove, there are the Guards!'

Dick's figure straightened. 'Let's get near 'em. Let's go in and look. Let's get on the grass and run. I can smell the trees.'

'Mind the low railing. That's all right!' Torpenhow kicked out a tuft of grass with his heel. 'Smell that,' he said. 'Isn't it good?' Dick snuffed luxuriously. 'Now pick up your feet and run.' They approached as near to the regiment as was possible. The clank of bayonets being unfixed made Dick's nostrils quiver.

'Let's get nearer. They're in column, aren't they?'

'Yes. How did you know?'

'Felt it. Oh, my men!—my beautiful men!' He edged forward as though he could see. 'I could draw those chaps once. Who'll draw 'em now?'

'They'll move off in a minute. Don't jump when the band begins.'

'Huh! I'm not a new charger. It's the silences that hurt. Nearer, Torp!—nearer! Oh, my God, what wouldn't I give to see 'em for a minute!—one half minute!'

He could hear the armed life almost within reach of him, could hear the slings tighten across the bandsman's chest as he heaved the big drum from the ground.

'Sticks crossed above his head,' whispered Torpenhow.

'I know. I know! Who should know if I don't? H'sh!'

The drumsticks fell with a boom, and

the men swung forward to the crash of the band. Dick felt the wind of the massed movement in his face, heard the maddening tramp of feet and the friction of the pouches on the belts. The big drum pounded out the tune. It was a music-hall refrain that made a perfect quickstep—

'He must be a man of decent height,
  He must be a man of weight,
He must come home on a Saturday night
  In a thoroughly sober state;
He must know how to love me,
  And he must know how to kiss;
And if he's enough to keep us both
  I can't refuse him bliss.'

'What's the matter?' said Torpenhow, as he saw Dick's head fall when the last of the regiment had departed.

'Nothing. I feel a little bit out of the running,—that's all. Torp, take me back. Why did you bring me out?'

CHAPTER 12

There were three friends that buried the
    fourth,
  The mould in his mouth and the dust in
    his eyes;
And they went south, and east, and north,—
  The strong man fights, but the sick man
    dies.

There were three friends that spoke of the
    dead,—
  The strong man fights, but the sick man
    dies.—
'And would he were here with us now,' they
    said,
  'The sun in our face and the wind in our
    eyes.'
                                    Ballad

The Nilghai was angry with Torpenhow. Dick had been sent to bed,—blind men are ever under the orders of those who can see,—and since he had returned

from the Park had fluently sworn at Torpenhow because he was alive, and all the world because it was alive and could see, while he, Dick, was dead in the death of the blind, who, at the best, are only burdens upon their associates. Torpenhow had said something about a Mrs. Gummidge, and Dick had retired in a black fury to handle and rehandle three unopened letters from Maisie.

The Nilghai, fat, burly, and aggressive, was in Torpenhow's rooms. Behind him sat The Keneu, the Great War Eagle, and between them lay a large map embellished with black and white-headed pins.

'I was wrong about the Balkans,' said the Nilghai. 'But I'm not wrong about this business. The whole of our work in the Southern Soudan must be done over again. The public doesn't care, of course, but the Government does, and they are making their arrangements quietly. You know that as well as I do.'

'I remember how the people cursed us when our troops withdrew from Omdurman. It was bound to crop up sooner or later. But I can't go,' said Torpenhow. He pointed through the open door; it was a hot night. 'Can you blame me?'

The Keneu purred above his pipe like a large and very happy cat—

'Don't blame you in the least. It's uncommonly good of you, and all the rest of it, but every man—even you, Torp—must consider his work. I know it sounds brutal, but Dick's out of the race,—down,—gastados, expended, finished, done for. He has a little money of his own. He won't starve, and you can't pull out of your stride for his sake. Think of your own reputation.'

'Dick's was five times bigger than mine and yours put together.'

'That was because he signed his name to everything he did. It's all ended now. You must hold yourself in readiness to move out. You can command your own prices, and you do better work than any three of us.'

'Don't tell me how tempting it is. I'll stay here to look after Dick for a while. He's as cheerful as a bear with a sore head, but I think he likes to have me near him.'

The Nilghai said something uncomplimentary about soft-headed fools who throw away their careers for other fools. Torpenhow flushed angrily. The constant strain of attendance on Dick had worn his nerves thin.

'There remains a third fate,' said The Keneu thoughtfully. 'Consider this, and be not larger fools than is necessary. Dick is—or rather was—an able-bodied man of moderate attractions and a certain amount of audacity.'

'Oho!' said the Nilghai, who remembered an affair at Cairo. 'I begin to see.—Torp, I'm sorry.'

Torpenhow nodded forgiveness: 'You were more sorry when he cut you out, though.—Go on, Keneu.'

'I've often thought, when I've seen men die out in the desert, that if the news could be sent through the world, and the means of transport were quick enough, there would be one woman at least at each man's bedside.'

'There would be some mighty quaint revelations. Let us be grateful things are as they are,' said the Nilghai.

'Let us rather reverently consider whether Torp's three-cornered ministrations are exactly what Dick needs just now.—What do you think yourself, Torp?'

'I know they aren't. But what can I do?'

'Lay the matter before the Board. We are all Dick's friends here. You've been most in his life.'

'But I picked it up when he was off his head.'

'The greater chance of its being true. I thought we should arrive. Who is she?'

Then Torpenhow told a tale in plain words, as a special correspondent who knows how to make a verbal precis should tell it. The men listened without interruption.

'Is it possible that a man can come back across the years to his calf-love?' said Keneu. 'Is it possible?'

'I give the facts. He says nothing about it now, but he sits fumbling three letters from her when he thinks I'm not looking. What am I to do?'

'Speak to him,' said the Nilghai.

'Oh yes! Write to her,—I don't know her full name, remember,—and ask her to accept him out of pity. I believe you once told Dick you were sorry for him, Nilghai. You remember what happened, eh? Go into the bedroom and suggest full confession and an appeal to this Maisie girl, whoever she is. I honestly believe he'd try to kill you; and the blindness has made him rather muscular.'

'Torpenhow's course is perfectly clear,' said The Keneu. 'He will go to Vitry-sur-Marne, which is on the Bezieres-Landes Railway,—single track from Tourgas. The Prussians shelled it out in '70 because there was a poplar on the top of a hill eighteen hundred yards from the church spire. There's a squadron of cavalry quartered there,—or ought to be. Where this studio Torp spoke about may be I cannot tell. That is Torp's business. I have given him his route. He will dispassionately explain the situation to the girl, and she will come back to Dick,—the more especially because, to use Dick's words, "there is nothing but her damned obstinacy to keep them apart." '

'And they have four hundred and twenty pounds a year between 'em. Dick never lost his head for figures, even in his delirium. You haven't the shadow of an excuse for not going,' said the Nilghai.

Torpenhow looked very uncomfortable. 'But it's absurd and impossible. I can't drag her back by the hair.'

'Our business—the business for which we draw our money—is to do absurd and impossible things,—generally with no reason whatever except to amuse the public. Here we have a reason. The rest doesn't matter. I shall share these rooms with the Nilghai till Torpenhow returns. There will be a batch of unbridled "specials" coming to town in a little while, and these will serve as their headquarters. Another reason for sending Torpenhow away. Thus Providence helps those who help others, and'—here The Keneu dropped his measured speech—'we can't have you tied by the leg to Dick when the trouble begins. It's your only chance of getting away; and Dick will be grateful.'

'He will,—worse luck! I can but go and try. I can't conceive a woman in her senses refusing Dick.'

'Talk that out with the girl. I have seen you wheedle an angry Mahdieh woman into giving you dates. This won't be a tithe as difficult. You had better not be here to-morrow afternoon, because the Nilghai and I will be in possession. It is an order. Obey.'

'Dick,' said Torpenhow next morning, 'can I do anything for you?'

'No! Leave me alone. How often must I remind you that I'm blind?'

'Nothing I could go for to fetch for to carry for to bring?'

'No. Take those infernal creaking boots of yours away.'

'Poor chap!' said Torpenhow to himself. 'I must have been sitting on his nerves lately. He wants a lighter step.' Then, aloud, 'Very well. Since you're so independent I'm going off for four or five days. Say good-bye at least. The housekeeper will look after you, and Keneu has my rooms.'

Dick's face fell. 'You won't be longer than a week at the outside? I know I'm touched in the temper, but I can't get on without you.'

'Can't you? You'll have to do without me in a little time, and you'll be glad I'm gone.'

Dick felt his way back to the big chair, and wondered what these things might mean. He did not wish to be tended by the housekeeper, and yet Torpenhow's constant tendernesses jarred on him. He did not exactly know what he wanted. The darkness would not lift, and Maisie's unopened letters felt worn and old from much handling. He could never read them for himself as long as life endured; but Maisie might have sent him some fresh ones to play with. The Nilghai entered with a gift,—a piece of red modelling-wax. He fancied that Dick might find interest in using his hands. Dick poked and patted the stuff for a few minutes, and, 'Is it like anything in the world?' he said drearily. 'Take it away. I may get the touch of the blind in fifty years. Do you know where Torpenhow has gone?'

The Nilghai knew nothing. 'We're staying in his rooms till he comes back. Can we do anything for you?'

'I'd like to be left alone, please. Don't think I'm ungrateful; but I'm best alone.'

The Nilghai chuckled, and Dick resumed his drowsy brooding and sullen rebellion against fate. He had long since ceased to think about the work he had done in the old days, and the desire to do more work had departed from him. He was exceedingly sorry for himself, and the completeness of his tender grief soothed him. But his soul and his body cried for Maisie,—Maisie who would understand. His mind pointed out that Maisie, having her own work to do, would not care. His experience had taught him that when money was exhausted women went away, and that when a man was knocked out of the race the others trampled on him. 'Then at the least,' said Dick, in reply, 'she could use me as I used Binat,—for some sort of a study. I wouldn't ask more than to be near her again, even though I knew that another man was making love to her. Ugh! what a dog I am!'

A voice on the staircase began to sing joyfully—

'When we go—go—go—away from here,
　Our creditors will weep and they will wail,
Our absence much regretting when they find
　　that we've been getting
　Out of England by next Tuesday's Indian
　　mail.'

Following the trampling of feet, slamming of Torpenhow's door, and the sound of voices in strenuous debate, some one squeaked, 'And see, you good fellows, I have found a new water-bottle, —firs'-class patent—eh, how you say? Open himself inside out.'

Dick sprang to his feet. He knew the voice well. 'That's Cassavetti, come back from the Continent.' Now I know why Torp went away. There's a row somewhere, and—I'm out of it!'

The Nilghai commanded silence in vain. 'That's for my sake,' Dick said bitterly. 'The birds are getting ready to fly, and they wouldn't tell me. I can hear Morten-Sutherland and Mackaye. Half the War Correspondents in London are there;—and I'm out of it.'

He stumbled across the landing and plunged into Torpenhow's room. He could feel that it was full of men. 'Where's the trouble?' said he. 'In the Balkans at last? Why didn't some one tell me?'

'We thought you wouldn't be interested,' said the Nilghai shamefacedly. 'It's in the Soudan, as usual.'

'You lucky dogs! Let me sit here while you talk. I shan't be a skeleton at the feast.—Cassavetti, where are you? Your English is as bad as ever.'

Dick was led into a chair. He heard the rustle of the maps, and the talk swept forward, carrying him with it. Everybody spoke at once, discussing press censorships, railway-routes, transport, water-supply, the capacities of generals,—these in language that would have horrified a trusting public,—ranting, asserting, denouncing, and laughing at the top of their voices. There was the glorious certainty of war in the Soudan at any moment. The Nilghai said so, and it was well to be in readiness. The Keneu had telegraphed to Cairo for horses; Cassavetti had stolen a perfectly inaccurate list of troops that would be ordered forward, and was reading it out amid profane interruptions, and The Keneu introduced to Dick some man unknown who would be employed as war artist by the Central Southern Syndicate. 'It's his first outing,' said The Keneu. 'Give him some tips— about riding camels.'

'Oh, those camels?' groaned Cassavetti. 'I shall learn to ride him again, and now I am so much all soft! Listen, you good fellows. I know your military arrangement very well. There will go the Royal Argalshire Sutherlanders. So it was read to me upon best authority.'

A roar of laughter interrupted him.

'Sit down,' said the Nilghai. 'The lists aren't even made out in the War Office.'

'Will there be any force at Suakin?' said a voice.

Then the outcries redoubled, and grew mixed, thus: 'How many Egyptian troops will they use?—God help the Fellaheen! —There's a railway in Plumstead marshes doing duty as a fives-court.—We shall have the Suakin-Berber line built at last.—Canadian voyageurs are too careful. Give me a half-drunk Krooman in a whaleboat.—Who commands the Desert column?—No, they never blew up the big rock at the Ghizeh bend. We shall have to be hauled up, as usual.—Somebody tell me if there's an Indian contingent, or I'll break everybody's head.— Don't tear the map in two.—It's a war of occupation, I tell you, to connect with

the African Companies in the South.—
There's guinea-worm in most of the
wells on that route.' Then the Nilghai,
despairing of peace, bellowed like a fog-
horn and beat upon the table with both
hands.

'But what becomes of Torpenhow?'
said Dick, in the silence that followed.

'Torp's in abeyance just now. He's off
lovemaking somewhere, I suppose,' said
the Nilghai.

'He said he was going to stay at home,'
said The Keneu.

'Is he?' said Dick with an oath. 'He
won't. I'm not much good now, but if
you and the Nilghai hold him down I'll
engage to trample on him till he sees reason. He stay behind, indeed! He's the
best of you all. There'll be some tough
work by Omdurman. We shall come
there to stay, this time. But I forgot. I
wish I were going with you.'

'So do we all, Dickie,' said The Keneu.

'And I most of all,' said the new artist
of the Central Southern Syndicate.
'Could you tell me—'

'I'll give you one piece of advice,' Dick
answered, moving towards the door. 'If
you happen to be cut over the head in a
scrimmage, don't guard. Tell the man to
go on cutting. You'll find it cheapest in
the end. Thanks for letting me look in.'

'There's grit in Dick,' said the Nilghai,
an hour later, when the room was
emptied of all save The Keneu.

'It was the sacred call of the war-
trumpet. Did you notice how he answered to it? Poor fellow! Let's look at
him,' said The Keneu.

The excitement of the talk had died
away. Dick was sitting by the studio
table with his head on his arms, when the
men came in. He did not change his
position.

'It hurts,' he moaned. 'God forgive me,
but it hurts cruelly; and yet, y'know, the
world has a knack of spinning round all
by itself. Shall I see Torp before he goes?'

'Oh yes. You'll see him,' said the
Nilghai.

CHAPTER 13

The sun went down an hour ago,
    I wonder if I face towards home,
If I lost my way in the light of day
    How shall I find now night is come?
                    Old Song

'Maisie, come to bed.'

'It's so hot I can't sleep. Don't worry.'

Maisie put her elbows on the window-
sill and looked at the moonlight on the
straight, poplar-flanked road. Summer
had come upon Vitry-sur-Marne and
parched it to the bone. The grass was dry-
burnt in the meadows, the clay by the
bank of the river was caked to brick, the
roadside flowers were long since dead,
and the roses in the garden hung
withered on their stalks. The heat in the
little low bedroom under the eaves was
almost intolerable. The very moonlight
on the wall of Kami's studio across the
road seemed to make the night hotter,
and the shadow of the big bell-handle by
the closed gate cast a bar of inky black
that caught Maisie's eye and annoyed
her.

'Horrid thing! It should be all white,'
she murmured. 'And the gate isn't in the
middle of the wall, either. I never noticed
that before.'

Maisie was hard to please at that hour.
First, the heat of the past few weeks had
worn her down; secondly, her work, and
particularly the study of a female head,
intended to represent the Melancolia and
not finished in time for the Salon, was
unsatisfactory; thirdly, Kami had said as
much two days before; fourthly,—but so
completely fourthly that it was hardly
worth thinking about,—Dick, her property, had not written to her for more

than six weeks. She was angry with the heat, with Kami, and with her work, but she was exceedingly angry with Dick.

She had written to him three times,— each time proposing a fresh treatment of her Melancolia. Dick had taken no notice of these communications. She had resolved to write no more. When she returned to England in the autumn—for her pride's sake she could not return earlier—she would speak to him. She missed the Sunday afternoon conferences more than she cared to admit. All that Kami said was, 'Continuez, mademoiselle, continuez toujours,' and he had been repeating his wearisome counsel through the hot summer, exactly like a cicala,—an old gray cicala in a black alpaca coat, white trousers, and a huge felt hat. But Dick had tramped masterfully up and down her little studio north of the cool green London park, and had said things ten times worse than 'Continuez,' before he snatched the brush out of her hand and showed her where her error lay. His last letter, Maisie remembered, contained some trivial advice about not sketching in the sun or drinking water at wayside farmhouses; and he had said that not once, but three times,— as if he did not know that Maisie could take care of herself!

But what was he doing, that he could not trouble to write? A murmur of voices in the road made her lean from the window. A cavalryman of the little garrison in the town was talking to Kami's cook. The moonlight glittered on the scabbard of his sabre, which he was holding in his hand lest it should clank inopportunely. The cook's cap cast deep shadows on her face, which was close to the conscript's. He slid his arm round her waist and there followed the sound of a kiss.

'Faugh!' said Maisie, stepping back.

'What's that!' said the red-haired girl, who was tossing uneasily outside her bed.

'Only a conscript kissing the cook,' said Maisie. 'They've gone away now.' She leaned out of the window again, and put a shawl over her nightgown to guard against chills. There was a very small night-breeze abroad, and a sun-baked rose below nodded its head as one who knew unutterable secrets. Was it possible that Dick should turn his thoughts from her work and his own and descend to the degradation of Suzanne and the conscript? He could not! The rose nodded its head and one leaf therewith. It looked like a naughty little devil scratching its ear. Dick could not, 'because,' thought Maisie, 'he is mine,—mine,—mine. He said he was. I'm sure I don't care what he does. It will only spoil his work if he does; and it will spoil mine too.'

The rose continued to nod in the futile way peculiar to flowers. There was no earthly reason why Dick should not disport himself as he chose, except that he was called by Providence, which was Maisie, to assist Maisie in her work. And her work was the preparation of pictures that went sometimes to English provincial exhibitions, as the notices in the scrap-book proved, and that were invariably rejected by the Salon when Kami was plagued into allowing her to send them up. Her work in the future, it seemed, would be the preparation of pictures on exactly similar lines which would be rejected in exactly the same way—

[The red-haired girl threshed distressfully across the sheets. 'It's too hot to sleep,' she moaned; and the interruption jarred.]

Exactly the same way. Then she would divide her years between the little studio in England and Kami's big studio at Vitry-sur-Marne. No, she would go to another master, who should force her into the success that was her right, if patient toil and desperate endeavour gave one a right to anything. Dick had told her that he had worked ten years to understand his craft. She had worked ten years, and ten years were nothing. Dick had said that ten years were nothing,—but that was in regard to herself only. He had said—this very man who could not find time to write—that he would wait ten years for her, and that she was bound to come back to him sooner or later. He had said this in the absurd letter about sunstroke and diphtheria; and then he had stopped writing. He was wandering up and down moonlit streets, kissing cooks. She would like to lecture him now,—not in her nightgown, of course, but properly dressed, severely and from a height. Yet if he was kissing other girls he certainly would not care whether she lectured him or not. He would laugh at her. Very good. She would go back to her studio and prepare pictures that went, etc., etc. The mill-wheel of thought swung round slowly, that no section of it might be slurred over, and the red-haired girl tossed and turned behind her.

Maisie put her chin in her hands and decided that there could be no doubt whatever of the villainy of Dick. To justify herself, she began, unwomanly, to weigh the evidence. There was a boy, and he had said he loved her. And he kissed her,—kissed her on the cheek,—by a yellow sea-poppy that nodded its head exactly like the maddening dry rose in the garden. Then there was an interval, and men had told her that they loved her—just when she was busiest with her work. Then the boy came back, and at their very second meeting had told her that he loved her. Then he had— But there was no end to the things he had done. He had given her his time and his powers. He had spoken to her of Art, housekeeping, technique, teacups, the abuse of pickles as a stimulant,—that was rude,—sable-hair brushes,—he had given her the best in her stock,—she used them daily; he had given her advice that

she profited by, and now and again—a look. Such a look! The look of a beaten hound waiting for the word to crawl to his mistress's feet. In return she had given him nothing whatever, except—here she brushed her mouth against the open-work sleeve of her nightgown—the privilege of kissing her once. And on the mouth, too. Disgraceful! Was that not enough, and more than enough? and if it was not, had he not cancelled the debt by not writing and—probably kissing other girls?

'Maisie, you'll catch a chill. Do go and lie down,' said the wearied voice of her companion. 'I can't sleep a wink with you at the window.'

Maisie shrugged her shoulders and did not answer. She was reflecting on the meannesses of Dick, and on other meannesses with which he had nothing to do. The remorseless moonlight would not let her sleep. It lay on the skylight of the studio across the road in cold silver; she stared at it intently, and her thoughts began to slide one into the other. The shadow of the big bell-handle in the wall grew short, lengthened again, and faded out as the moon went down behind the pasture and a hare came limping home across the road. Then the dawn-wind washed through the upland grasses, and brought coolness with it, and the cattle lowed by the drought-shrunk river. Maisie's head fell forward on the window-sill, and the tangle of black hair covered her arms.

'Maisie, wake up. You'll catch a chill.'

'Yes, dear; yes, dear.' She staggered to her bed like a wearied child, and as she buried her face in the pillows she muttered, 'I think—I think. . . . But he ought to have written.'

Day brought the routine of the studio, the smell of paint and turpentine, and the monotonous wisdom of Kami, who was a leaden artist, but a golden teacher if the pupil were only in sympathy with him.

Maisie was not in sympathy that day, and she waited impatiently for the end of the work. She knew when it was coming; for Kami would gather his black alpaca coat into a bunch behind him, and, with faded blue eyes that saw neither pupils nor canvas, look back into the past to recall the history of one Binat. 'You have all done not so badly,' he would say. 'But you shall remember that it is not enough to have the method and the art, and the power, nor even that which is touch, but you shall have also the conviction that nails the work to the wall. Of the so many I have taught,'—here the students would begin to unfix drawing-pins or get their tubes together,—'the very so many that I have taught, the best was Binat. All that comes of the study and the work and the knowledge was to him even when he came. After he left me he should have done all that could be done with the colour, the form, and the knowledge. Only, he had not the conviction. So to-day I hear no more of Binat,—the best of my pupils,—and that is long ago. So to-day, too, you will be glad to hear no more of me. Continuez, mesdemoiselles, and, above all, with conviction.'

He went into the garden to smoke and mourn over the lost Binat as the pupils dispersed to their several cottages or loitered in the studio to make plans for the cool of the afternoon.

Maisie looked at her very unhappy Melancolia, restrained a desire to grimace before it, and was hurrying across the road to write a letter to Dick, when she was aware of a large man on a white troop-horse. How Torpenhow had managed in the course of twenty hours to find his way to the hearts of the cavalry officers in quarters at Vitry-sur-Marne to discuss with them the certainty of a glorious revenge for France, to reduce the colonel to tears of pure affability, and to borrow the best horse in the squadron for the journey to Kami's studio, is a

mystery that only special correspondents can unravel.

'I beg your pardon,' said he. 'It seems an absurd question to ask, but the fact is that I don't know her by any other name: Is there any young lady here that is called Maisie?'

'I am Maisie,' was the answer from the depths of a great sun-hat.

'I ought to introduce myself,' he said, as the horse capered in the blinding white dust. 'My name is Torpenhow. Dick Heldar is my best friend, and—and—the fact is that he has gone blind.'

'Blind?' said Maisie stupidly. 'He can't be blind.'

'He has been stone-blind for nearly two months.'

Maisie lifted up her face, and it was pearly white. 'No! No! Not blind! I won't have him blind!'

'Would you care to see for yourself?' said Torpenhow.

'Now,—at once?'

'Oh no! The Paris train doesn't go through this place till eight to-night. There will be ample time.'

'Did Mr. Heldar send you to me?'

'Certainly not. Dick wouldn't do that sort of thing. He's sitting in his studio, turning over some letters that he can't read because he's blind.'

There was a sound of choking from the sun-hat. Maisie bowed her head and went into the cottage, where the red-haired girl was on a sofa, complaining of a headache.

'Dick's blind!' said Maisie, taking her breath quickly as she steadied herself against a chair-back. 'My Dick's blind!'

'What?' The girl was on the sofa no longer.

'A man has come from England to tell me. He hasn't written to me for six weeks.'

'Are you going to him?'

'I must think.'

'Think! I should go back to London

and see him, and I should kiss his eyes, and kiss them and kiss them until they got well again! If you don't go I shall. Oh, what am I talking about? You wicked little idiot! Go to him at once. Go!'

Torpenhow's neck was blistering, but he preserved a smile of infinite patience as Maisie appeared bareheaded in the sunshine.

'I am coming,' said she, her eyes on the ground.

'You will be at Vitry Station, then, at seven this evening.' This was an order delivered by one who was used to being obeyed. Maisie said nothing, but she felt grateful that there was no chance of disputing with this big man who took everything for granted and managed a squealing horse with one hand. She returned to the red-haired girl, who was weeping bitterly, and between tears, kisses,—very few of those,—menthol, packing, and an interview with Kami, the sultry afternoon wore away. Thought might come afterwards. Her present duty was to go to Dick,—Dick who owned the wondrous friend and sat in the dark playing with her unopened letters.

'But what will you do?' she said to her companion.

'I? Oh, I shall stay here and—finish your Melancolia,' she said, smiling pitifully. 'Write to me afterwards.'

That night there ran a legend through Vitry-sur-Marne of a mad Englishman, doubtless suffering from sunstroke, who had drunk all the officers of the garrison under the table, had borrowed a horse from the lines, and had then and there eloped, after the English custom, with one of those more than mad English girls who drew pictures down there under the care of that good Monsieur Kami.

'They are very droll,' said Suzanne to the conscript in the moonlight by the studio wall. 'She walked always with those big eyes that saw nothing, and yet she kisses me on both cheeks as though she were my sister, and gives me—see—ten francs!'

The conscript levied a contribution on both gifts; for he prided himself on being a good soldier.

Torpenhow spoke very little to Maisie during the journey to Calais; but he was careful to attend to all her wants, to get her a compartment entirely to herself, and to leave her alone. He was amazed at the ease with which the matter had been accomplished.

'The safest thing would be to let her think things out. By Dick's showing,—when he was off his head,—she must have ordered him about very thoroughly. Wonder how she likes being under orders.'

Maisie never told. She sat in the empty compartment often with her eyes shut, that she might realise the sensation of blindness. It was an order that she should return to London swiftly, and she found herself at last almost beginning to enjoy the situation. This was better than looking after luggage and a red-haired friend who never took any interest in her surroundings. But there appeared to be a feeling in the air that she, Maisie,—of all people,—was in disgrace. Therefore she justified her conduct to herself with great success, till Torpenhow came up to her on the steamer, and without preface began to tell the story of Dick's blindness, suppressing a few details, but dwelling at length on the miseries of delirium. He stopped before he reached the end, as though he had lost interest in the subject, and went forward to smoke. Maisie was furious with him and with herself.

She was hurried on from Dover to London almost before she could ask for breakfast, and—she was past any feeling of indignation now—was bidden curtly to wait in a hall at the foot of some lead-covered stairs while Torpenhow went up to make inquiries. Again the knowledge that she was being treated like a naughty little girl made her pale cheeks flame. It was all Dick's fault for being so stupid as to go blind.

Torpenhow led her up to a shut door, which he opened very softly. Dick was sitting by the window, with his chin on his chest. There were three envelopes in his hand, and he turned them over and over. The big man who gave orders was no longer by her side, and the studio door snapped behind her.

Dick thrust the letters into his pocket as he heard the sound. 'Hullo, Torp! Is that you? I've been so lonely.'

His voice had taken the peculiar flatness of the blind. Maisie pressed herself up into a corner of the room. Her heart was beating furiously, and she put one hand on her breast to keep it quiet. Dick was staring directly at her, and she realised for the first time that he was blind. Shutting her eyes in a railway-carriage to open them when she pleased was child's play. This man was blind though his eyes were wide open.

'Torp, is that you? They said you were coming.' Dick looked puzzled and a little irritated at the silence.

'No: it's only me,' was the answer, in a strained little whisper. Maisie could hardly move her lips.

'H'm!' said Dick composedly, without moving. 'This is a new phenomenon. Darkness I'm getting used to; but I object to hearing voices.'

Was he mad, then, as well as blind, that he talked to himself? Maisie's heart beat more wildly, and she breathed in gasps. Dick rose and began to feel his way across the room, touching each table and chair as he passed. Once he caught his foot on a rug, and swore, dropping on his knees to feel what the obstruction might be. Maisie remembered him walking in the Park as though all the earth belonged to him, tramping up and down her studio two months ago, and flying up

the gangway of the Channel steamer. The beating of her heart was making her sick, and Dick was coming nearer, guided by the sound of her breathing. She put out a hand mechanically to ward him off or to draw him to herself, she did not know which. It touched his chest, and he stepped back as though he had been shot.

'It's Maisie!' said he, with a dry sob. 'What are you doing here?'

'I came—I came—to see you, please.' Dick's lips closed firmly.

'Won't you sit down, then? You see, I've had some bother with my eyes, and—'

'I know. I know. Why didn't you tell me?'

'I couldn't write.'

'You might have told Mr. Torpenhow.'

'What has he to do with my affairs?'

'He—he brought me from Vitry-sur-Marne. He thought I ought to see you.'

'Why, what has happened? Can I do anything for you? No, I can't. I forgot.'

'Oh, Dick, I'm so sorry! I've come to tell you, and—Let me take you back to your chair.'

'Don't! I'm not a child. You only do that out of pity. I never meant to tell you anything about it. I'm no good now. I'm down and done for. Let me alone!'

He groped back to his chair, his chest labouring as he sat down.

Maisie watched him, and the fear went out of her heart, to be followed by a very bitter shame. He had spoken a truth that had been hidden from the girl through every step of the impetuous flight to London; for he was, indeed, down and done for—masterful no longer, but rather a little abject; neither an artist stronger than she, nor a man to be looked up to—only some blind one that sat in a chair and seemed on the point of crying. She was immensely and unfeignedly sorry for him—more sorry than she had ever been for any one in her life, but not sorry enough to deny his words. So she stood still and felt ashamed and a little hurt, because she had honestly intended that her journey should end triumphantly; and now she was only filled with pity most startlingly distinct from love.

'Well?' said Dick, his face steadily turned away. 'I never meant to worry you any more. What's the matter?'

He was conscious that Maisie was catching her breath, but was as unprepared as herself for the torrent of emotion that followed. People who cannot cry easily weep unrestrainedly when the fountains of the great deep are broken up. She had dropped into a chair and was sobbing with her face hidden in her hands.

'I can't—I can't!' she cried desperately. 'Indeed, I can't. It isn't my fault. I'm so sorry. Oh, Dickie, I'm so sorry.'

Dick's shoulders straightened again, for the words lashed like a whip. Still the sobbing continued. It is not good to realise that you have failed in the hour of trial or flinched before the mere possibility of making sacrifices.

'I do despise myself—indeed I do. But I can't. Oh, Dickie, you wouldn't ask me—would you?' wailed Maisie.

She looked up for a minute, and by chance it happened that Dick's eyes fell on hers. The unshaven face was very white and set, and the lips were trying to force themselves into a smile. But it was the worn-out eyes that Maisie feared. Her Dick had gone blind and left in his place some one that she could hardly recognise till he spoke.

'Who is asking you to do anything, Maisie? I told you how it would be. What's the use of worrying? For pity's sake don't cry like that; it isn't worth it.'

'You don't know how I hate myself. Oh, Dick, help me—help me!' The passion of tears had grown beyond her control and was beginning to alarm the man.

He stumbled forward and put his arm round her, and her head fell on his shoulder.

'Hush, dear, hush! Don't cry. You're quite right, and you've nothing to reproach yourself with—you never had. You're only a little upset by the journey, and I don't suppose you've had any breakfast. What a brute Torp was to bring you over.'

'I wanted to come. I did indeed,' she protested.

'Very well. And now you've come and seen, and I'm—immensely grateful. When you're better you shall go away and get something to eat. What sort of a passage did you have coming over?'

Maisie was crying more subduedly, for the first time in her life glad that she had something to lean against. Dick patted her on the shoulder tenderly but clumsily, for he was not quite sure where her shoulder might be.

She drew herself out of his arms at last and waited, trembling and most unhappy. He had felt his way to the window to put the width of the room between them, and to quiet a little the tumult in his heart.

'Are you better now?' he said.

'Yes, but—don't you hate me?'

'I hate you? My God! I?'

'Isn't—isn't there anything I could do for you, then? I'll stay here in England to do it, if you like. Perhaps I could come and see you sometimes.'

'I think not, dear. It would be kindest not to see me any more, please. I don't want to seem rude, but—don't you think—perhaps you had almost better go now.'

He was conscious that he could not bear himself as a man if the strain continued much longer.

'I don't deserve anything else. I'll go, Dick. Oh, I'm so miserable.'

'Nonsense. You've nothing to worry about; I'd tell you if you had. Wait a moment, dear. I've got something to give you first. I meant it for you ever since this little trouble began. It's my Melancolia; she was a beauty when I last saw her. You can keep her for me, and if ever you're poor you can sell her. She's worth a few hundreds at any state of the market.' He groped among his canvases. 'She's framed in black. Is this a black frame that I have my hand on? There she is. What do you think of her?'

He turned a scarred, formless muddle of paint towards Maisie, and the eyes strained as though they would catch her wonder and surprise. One thing and one thing only could she do for him.

'Well?'

The voice was fuller and more rounded, because the man knew he was speaking of his best work. Maisie looked at the blur, and a lunatic desire to laugh caught her by the throat. But for Dick's sake—whatever this mad blankness might mean—she must make no sign. Her voice choked with hard-held tears as she answered, still gazing on the wreck—

'Oh, Dick, it is good!'

He heard the little hysterical gulp and took it for tribute. 'Won't you have it, then? I'll send it over to your house if you will.'

'I? Oh, yes—thank you. Ha! ha!' If she did not fly at once the laughter that was worse than tears would kill her. She turned and ran, choking and blinded, down the staircases that were empty of life, to take refuge in a cab and go to her house across the Park. There she sat down in the almost dismantled drawing-room and thought of Dick in his blindness, useless till the end of life, and of herself in her own eyes. Behind the sorrow, the shame, and the humiliation, lay fear of the cold wrath of the red-haired girl when Maisie should return. Maisie had never feared her companion before. Not until she found herself saying, 'Well, he never asked me,' did she realise her scorn of herself.

And that is the end of Maisie.

For Dick was reserved more searching torment. He could not realise at first that Maisie, whom he had ordered to go, had left him without a word of farewell. He was savagely angry against Torpenhow, who had brought upon him this humiliation and troubled his miserable peace. Then his dark hour came, and he was alone with himself and his desires to get what help he could from the darkness. The queen could do no wrong, but in following the right, so far as it served her work, she had wounded her one subject more than his own brain would let him know.

'It's all I had and I've lost it,' he said, as soon as the misery permitted clear thinking. 'And Torp will think that he has been so infernally clever that I shan't have the heart to tell him. I must think this out quietly.'

'Hullo!' said Torpenhow, entering the studio after Dick had enjoyed two hours of thought. 'I'm back. Are you feeling any better?'

'Torp, I don't know what to say. Come here.' Dick coughed huskily, wondering indeed, what he should say and how to say it temperately.

'What's the need for saying anything? Get up and tramp.' Torpenhow was perfectly satisfied.

They walked up and down as of custom, Torpenhow's hand on Dick's shoulder, and Dick buried in his own thoughts.

'How in the world did you find it all out?' said Dick at last.

'You shouldn't go off your head if you want to keep secrets, Dickie. It was absolutely impertinent on my part; but if you'd seen me rocketing about on a half-trained French troop-horse under a blazing sun you'd have laughed. There will be a charivari in my rooms to-night. Seven other devils—'

'I know—the row in the Southern Soudan. I surprised their councils the other day, and it made me unhappy. Have you fixed your flint to go? Who d'you work for?'

' 'Haven't signed any contracts yet. I wanted to see how your business would turn out.'

'Would you have stayed with me, then, if—things had gone wrong?' He put his question cautiously.

'Don't ask me too much. I'm only a man.'

'You've tried to be an angel very successfully.'

'Oh ye—es! . . . Well, do you attend the function to-night? We shall be half screwed before the morning. All the men believe the war's a certainty.'

'I don't think I will, old man, if it's all the same to you. I'll stay quiet here.'

'And meditate? I don't blame you. You deserve a good time if ever a man did.'

That night there was tumult on the stairs. The correspondents poured in from theatre, dinner and music-hall to Torpenhow's room that they might discuss their plan of campaign in the event of military operations being a certainty. Torpenhow, The Keneu, and the Nilghai had bidden all the men they had worked with to the orgy; and Mr. Beeton, the housekeeper, declared that never before in his checkered experience had he seen quite such a fancy lot of gentlemen. They waked the chambers with shoutings and song; and the elder men were quite as bad as the younger. For the chances of war were in front of them, and all knew what those meant.

Sitting in his own room a little perplexed by the noise across the landing, Dick suddenly began to laugh to himself.

'When one comes to think of it the situation is intensely comic. Maisie's

quite right—poor little thing. I didn't know she could cry like that before; but now I know what Torp thinks, I'm sure he'd be quite fool enough to stay at home and try to console me—if he knew. Besides, it isn't nice to own that you've been thrown over like a broken chair. I must carry this business through alone—as usual. If there isn't a war, and Torp finds out, I shall look foolish, that's all. If there is a war I mustn't interfere with another man's chances. Business is business, and I want to be alone—I want to be alone. What a row they're making!'

Somebody hammered at the studio door.

'Come out and frolic, Dickie,' said the Nilghai.

'I should like to, but I can't. I'm not feeling frolicsome.'

'Then I'll tell the boys and they'll draw you like a badger.'

'Please not, old man. On my word, I'd sooner be left alone just now.'

'Very good. Can we send anything in to you? Fizz, for instance. Cassavetti is beginning to sing songs of the Sunny South already.'

For one minute Dick considered the proposition seriously.

'No, thanks. I've a headache already.'

'Virtuous child. That's the effect of emotion on the young. All my congratulations, Dick. I also was concerned in the conspiracy for your welfare.'

'Go to the devil and—oh, send Binkie in here.'

The little dog entered on elastic feet, riotous from having been made much of all the evening. He had helped to sing the choruses; but scarcely inside the studio he realised that this was no place for tail-wagging, and settled himself on Dick's lap till it was bedtime. Then he went to bed with Dick, who counted every hour as it struck, and rose in the morning with a painfully clear head to receive Torpenhow's more formal congratulations and a particular account of the last night's revels.

'You aren't looking very happy for a newly-accepted man,' said Torpenhow.

'Never mind that—it's my own affair, and I'm all right. Do you really go?'

'Yes. With the old Central Southern as usual. They wired and I accepted on better terms than before.'

'When do you start?'

'The day after to-morrow—for Brindisi.'

'Thank God.' Dick spoke from the bottom of his heart.

'Well, that's not a pretty way of saying you're glad to get rid of me. But men in your condition are allowed to be selfish.'

'I didn't mean that. Will you get a hundred pounds cashed for me before you leave?'

'That's a slender amount for housekeeping, isn't it?'

'Oh, it's only for—marriage expenses.'

Torpenhow brought him the money, counted it out in fives and tens, and carefully put it away in the writing-table.

'Now I suppose I shall have to listen to his ravings about his girl until I go. Heaven send us patience with a man in love!' said he to himself.

But never a word did Dick say of Maisie or marriage. He hung in the doorway of Torpenhow's room when the latter was packing, and asked innumerable questions about the coming campaign, till Torpenhow began to feel annoyed.

'You're a secretive animal, Dickie, and you consume your own smoke, don't you?' he said on the last evening.

'I—I suppose so. By the way, how long do you think this war will last?'

'Days, weeks, or months. One can never tell. It may go on for years.'

'I wish I were going.'

'Good heavens! You're the most unaccountable creature! Hasn't it occurred to you that you're going to be married—thanks to me?'

'Of course, yes. I'm going to be married—so I am. Going to be married. I'm awfully grateful to you. Haven't I told you that?'

'You might be going to be hanged by the look of you,' said Torpenhow.

And the next day Torpenhow bade him good-bye and left him to the loneliness he had so much desired.

CHAPTER 14

Yet at the last, ere our spearmen had found him,
 Yet at the last, ere a sword-thrust could save,
Yet at the last, with his masters around him,
 He of the Faith spoke as master to slave;
Yet at the last, tho' the Kafirs had maimed him,
 Broken by bondage and wrecked by the reiver,—
Yet at the last, tho' the darkness had claimed him,
 He called upon Allah and died a believer.
        Kizilbashi

'Beg your pardon, Mr. Heldar, but—but isn't nothin' going to happen?' said Mr. Beeton.

'No!' Dick had just waked to another morning of blank despair and his temper was of the shortest.

'Taint my regular business o' course, sir; and what I say is, "Mind your own business and let other people mind theirs"; but just before Mr. Torpenhow went away he give me to understand, like, that you might be moving into a house of your own, so to speak—a sort of house with rooms upstairs and downstairs where you'd be better attended to, though I try to act just by all our tenants. Don't I?'

'Ah! That must have been a madhouse. I shan't trouble you to take me there yet. Get me my breakfast, please, and leave me alone.'

'I hope I haven't done anything wrong, sir, but you know, I hope, that as far as a man can I tries to do the proper thing by all the gentlemen in chambers—and more particular those whose lot is hard— such as you, for instance, Mr. Heldar. You likes soft-roe bloater, don't you? Soft-roe bloaters is scarcer than hard-roe, but what I say is, "Never mind a little extra trouble so long as you gives satisfaction to the tenants." '

Mr. Beeton withdrew and left Dick to himself. Torpenhow had been long away; there was no more rioting in the chambers, and Dick had settled down to his new life, which he was weak enough to consider nothing better than death.

It is hard to live alone in the dark, confusing the day and night; dropping to sleep through sheer weariness at mid-day, and rising restless in the chill of the dawn. At first Dick, on his awakenings, would grope along the corridors of the chambers till he heard some one snore. Then he would know that the day had not yet come and return wearily to his bedroom. Later he learned not to stir till there was a noise and movement in the house and Mr. Beeton advised him to get up. Once dressed—and dressing, now that Torpenhow was away, was a lengthy business, because collars, ties, and the like, hid themselves in far corners of the room, and search meant headbeating against chairs and trunks—once dressed, there was nothing whatever to do except to sit still and brood till the three daily meals came. Centuries separated breakfast from lunch, and lunch from dinner, and though a man prayed for hundreds of years that his mind might be taken from

him, God would never hear. Rather the mind was quickened and the revolving thoughts ground against each other as millstones grind when there is no corn between; and yet the brain would not wear out and give him rest. It continued to think, at length, with imagery and all manner of reminiscences. It recalled Maisie and past success, reckless travels by land and sea, the glory of doing work and feeling that it was good, and suggested all that might have happened had the eyes only been faithful to their duty. When thinking ceased through sheer weariness, there poured into Dick's soul tide on tide of overwhelming, purposeless fear—dread of starvation always, terror lest the unseen ceiling should crush down upon him, fear of fire in the chambers and a louse's death in red flame, and agonies of fiercer horror that had nothing to do with any fear of death. Then Dick bowed his head, and clutching the arms of his chair fought with his sweating self till the tinkle of plates told him that something to eat was being set before him.

Mr. Beeton would bring the meal when he had time to spare, and Dick learned to hang upon his speech which dealt with badly-fitted gas-plugs, waste-pipes out of repair, little tricks for driving picture-nails into walls, and the sins of the charwoman or the housemaids. In the lack of better things the small gossip of a servants' hall becomes immensely interesting, and the screwing of a washer on a tap an event to be talked over for days.

Once or twice a week, too, Mr. Beeton would take Dick out with him when he went marketing in the morning to haggle with tradesmen over fish, lamp-wicks, mustard, tapioca, and so forth, while Dick rested his weight first on one foot and then on the other, and played aimlessly with the tins and string-ball on the counter. Then they would, perhaps, meet one of Mr. Beeton's friends, and Dick, standing aside a little, would hold his peace till Mr. Beeton was willing to go on again.

The life did not increase his self-respect. He abandoned shaving as a dangerous exercise, and being shaved in a barber's shop meant exposure of his infirmity. He could not see that his clothes were properly brushed, and since he had never taken any care of his personal appearance he became every known variety of sloven. A blind man cannot eat with cleanliness till he has been some months used to the darkness. If he demand attendance and grow angry at the want of it, he must assert himself and stand upright. Then the meanest menial can see that he is blind and, therefore, of no consequence. A wise man will keep his eyes on the floor and sit still. For amusement he may pick coal lump by lump out of the scuttle with the tongs, and pile it in a little heap in the fender, keeping count of the lumps, which must all be put back again, one by one and very carefully. He may set himself sums if he cares to work them out; he may talk to himself or to the cat if she chooses to visit him; and if his trade has been that of an artist, he may sketch in the air with his forefinger; but that is too much like drawing a pig with the eyes shut. He may go to his bookshelves and count his books, ranging them in order of their size, or to his wardrobe and count his shirts, laying them in piles of two or three on the bed, as they suffer from frayed cuffs or lost buttons. Even this entertainment wearies after a time; and all the times are very, very long.

Dick was allowed to sort a tool-chest where Mr. Beeton kept hammers, taps and nuts, lengths of gas-pipes, oil-bottles and string.

'If I don't have everything just where I know where to look for it, why, then, I can't find anything when I do want it.

You've no idea, sir, the amount of little things that these Chambers uses up,' said Mr. Beeton. Fumbling at the handle of the door as he went out: 'It's hard on you, sir, I do think it's hard on you. Ain't you going to do anything, sir?'

'I'll pay my rent and messing. Isn't that enough?'

'I wasn't doubting for a moment that you couldn't pay your way, sir; but I 'ave often said to my wife, "It's 'ard on 'im because it isn't as if he was an old man, nor yet a middle-aged one, but quite a young gentleman. That's where it comes so 'ard." '

'I suppose so,' said Dick absently. This particular nerve through long battering had ceased to feel—much.

'I was thinking,' continued Mr. Beeton, still making as if to go, 'that you might like to hear my boy Alf read you the papers sometimes of an evening. He do read beautiful, seeing he's only nine.'

'I should be very grateful,' said Dick. 'Only let me make it worth his while.'

'We wasn't thinking of that, sir, but of course it's in your own 'ands; but only to 'ear Alf sing "A Boy's Best Friend Is 'is Mother"! Ah!'

'I'll hear him sing that too. Let him come in this evening with the news-papers.'

Alf was not a nice child, being puffed up with many school-board certificates for good conduct, and inordinately proud of his singing. Mr. Beeton remained, beaming, while the child wailed his way through a song of some eight eight-line verses in the usual whine of the young Cockney, and, after compliments, left him to read Dick the foreign telegrams. Ten minutes later Alf returned to his parents rather pale and scared.

' 'E said 'e couldn't stand it no more,' he explained.

'He never said you read badly, Alf?' Mrs. Beeton spoke.

'No. 'E said I read beautiful. Said 'e

never 'eard any one read like that, but 'e said 'e couldn't abide the stuff in the papers.'

'P'raps he's lost some money in the Stocks. Were you readin' him about Stocks, Alf?'

'No; it was all about fightin' out there where the soldiers is gone—a great long piece with all the lines close together and very hard words in it. 'E give me 'arf a crown because I read so well. And 'e says the next time there's anything 'e wants read 'e'll send for me.'

'That's good hearing, but I do think for all the half-crown—put it into the kicking-donkey money-box, Alf, and let me see you do it—he might have kept you longer. Why, he couldn't have begun to understand how beautiful you read.'

'He's best left to hisself—gentlemen always are when they're downhearted,' said Mr. Beeton.

Alf's rigorously limited powers of comprehending Torpenhow's special correspondence had waked the devil of unrest in Dick. He could hear, through the boy's nasal chant, the camels grunting in the squares behind the soldiers outside Suakin; could hear the men swearing and chaffing across the cooking-pots, and could smell the acrid wood-smoke as it drifted over the camp before the wind of the desert.

That night he prayed to God that his mind might be taken from him, offering for proof that he was worthy of this favour the fact that he had not shot himself long ago. That prayer was not answered, and indeed Dick knew in his heart of hearts that only a lingering sense of humour and no special virtue had kept him alive. Suicide, he had persuaded himself, would be a ludicrous insult to the gravity of the situation as well as a weak-kneed confession of fear.

'Just for the fun of the thing,' he said to the cat, who had taken Binkie's place in his establishment, 'I should like to know how long this is going to last. I can live for a year on the hundred pounds Torp cashed for me. I must have two or three thousand at least at the Bank—twenty or thirty years more provided for, that is to say. Then I fall back on my hundred and twenty a year which will be more by that time. Let's consider. Twenty-five—thirty-five—a man's in his prime then, they say—forty-five—a middle-aged man just entering politics—fifty-five—"died at the comparatively early age of fifty-five," according to the newspapers. Bah! How these Christians funk death! Sixty-five—we're only getting on in years. Seventy-five is just possible though. Great Hell, cat O! fifty years more of solitary confinement in the dark! You'll die, and Beeton will die, and Torp will die, and Mai—everybody else will die, but I shall be alive and kicking with nothing to do. I'm very sorry for myself. I should like some one else to be sorry for me. Evidently I'm not going mad before I die, but the pain's just as bad as ever. Some day when you're vivisected cat! O! they'll tie you down on a little table and cut you open—but don't be afraid; they'll take precious good care that you don't die. You'll live, and you'll be very sorry then that you weren't sorry for me. Perhaps Torp will come back or . . . I wish I could go to Torp and the Nilghai, even though I were in their way.'

Pussy left the room before the speech was ended, and Alf, as he entered, found Dick addressing the empty hearth-rug.

'There's a letter for you, sir,' he said. 'Perhaps you'd like me to read it.'

'Lend it to me for a minute and I'll tell you.'

The outstretched hand shook just a little and the voice was not over-steady. It was within the limits of human possibility that—that was no letter from Maisie. He knew the heft of three closed envelopes only too well. It was a foolish hope that the girl should write to him, for he did not realise that there is a wrong which admits of no reparation though the evildoer may with tears and the heart's best love strive to mend all. It is best to forget that wrong whether it be caused or endured, since it is as remediless as bad work once put forward.

'Read it, then,' said Dick, and Alf began intoning according to the rules of the Board School—

' "I could have given you love, I could have given you loyalty, such as you never dreamed of. Do you suppose I cared what you were? But you chose to whistle everything down the wind for nothing. My only excuse for you is that you are so young." '

'That's all,' he said, returning the paper to be dropped into the fire.

'What was in the letter?' asked Mrs. Beeton when Alf returned.

'I don't know. I think it was a circular or a tract about not whistlin' at everything when you're young.'

'I must have stepped on something when I was alive and walking about, and it has bounced up and hit me. God help it, whatever it is—unless it was all a joke. But I don't know any one who'd take the trouble to play a joke on me. . . . Love and loyalty for nothing. It sounds tempting enough. I wonder whether I have lost anything really?'

Dick considered for a long time, but could not remember when or how he had put himself in the way of winning these trifles at a woman's hands.

Still, the letter as touching on matters that he preferred not to think about stung him into a fit of frenzy that lasted for a day and night. When his heart was so full of despair that it would hold no more, body and soul together seemed to be dropping without check through the darkness. Then came fear of darkness and desperate attempts to reach the light again. But there was no light to be reached. When that agony had left him sweating and breathless, the downward flight would recommence till the gathering torture of it spurred him into another fight as hopeless as the first. Followed some few minutes of sleep in which he dreamed that he saw. Then the procession of events would repeat itself till he was utterly worn out, and the brain took up its everlasting consideration of Maisie and might-have-beens.

At the end of everything Mr. Beeton came to his room and volunteered to take him out. 'Not marketing this time, but we'll go into the Parks if you like.'

'Be damned if I do,' quoth Dick. 'Keep to the streets and walk up and down. I like to hear the people round me.'

This was not altogether true. The blind in the first stages of their infirmity dislike those who can move with a free stride and unlifted arms—but Dick had no earthly desire to go to the Parks. Once and only once since Maisie had shut the door he had gone there under Alf's charge. Alf forgot him and fished for minnows in the Serpentine with some companions. After half an hour's waiting Dick, almost weeping with rage and wrath, caught a passer-by who introduced him to a friendly policeman, who led him to a four-wheeler opposite the Albert Hall. He never told Mr. Beeton of Alf's forgetfulness, but . . . this was not the manner in which he was used to walk the Parks aforetime.

'What streets would you like to walk down, then?' said Mr. Beeton sympathetically. His own ideas of a riotous holiday meant picnicking on the grass of the Green Park with his family, and half a dozen paper bags full of food.

'Keep to the river,' said Dick, and they kept to the river, and the rush of it was in his ears till they came to Blackfriars Bridge and struck thence on to the Waterloo Road, Mr. Beeton explaining the beauties of the scenery as he went on.

'And walking on the other side of the pavement,' said he, 'unless I'm much mistaken, is the young woman that used to come to your rooms to be drawed. I never forgets a face and I never remembers a name, except paying tenants o'course!'

'Stop her,' said Dick. 'It's Bessie Broke. Tell her I'd like to speak to her again. Quick, man!'

Mr. Beeton crossed the road under the noses of the omnibuses and arrested Bessie then on her way northward. She recognised him as the man in authority who used to glare at her when she passed up Dick's staircase, and her first impulse was to run.

'Wasn't you Mr. Heldar's model?' said Mr. Beeton, planting himself in front of her. 'You was. He's on the other side of the road and he'd like to see you.'

'Why?' said Bessie faintly. She remembered—indeed had never for long forgotten—an affair connected with a newly-finished picture.

'Because he has asked me to do so, and because he's most particular blind.'

'Drunk?'

'No. 'Orspital blind. He can't see. That's him over there.'

Dick was leaning against the parapet of the bridge as Mr. Beeton pointed him out—a stub-bearded, bowed creature wearing a dirty magenta-coloured neck-cloth outside an unbrushed coat. There was nothing to fear from such an one. Even if he chased her, Bessie thought he could not follow far. She crossed over and Dick's face lighted up. It was long since a woman of any kind had taken the trouble to speak to him.

'I hope you're well, Mr. Heldar?' said Bessie, a little puzzled. Mr. Beeton stood by with the air of an ambassador and breathed responsibly.

'I'm very well indeed, and, by Jove! I'm glad to see—hear you, I mean, Bess. You never thought it worth while to turn up and see us again after you got your money. I don't know why you should. Are you going anywhere in particular just now?'

'I was going for a walk,' said Bessie.

'Not the old business?' Dick spoke under his breath.

'Lor', no! I paid my premium'—Bessie was very proud of that word—'for a barmaid, sleeping in, and I'm at the bar now quite respectable. Indeed I am.'

Mr. Beeton had no special reason to believe in the loftiness of human nature. Therefore he dissolved himself like a mist and returned to his gas-plugs without a word of apology. Bessie watched the flight with a certain uneasiness; but so long as Dick appeared to be ignorant of the harm that had been done to him . . .

'It's hard work pulling the beer-handles,' she went on, 'and they've got one of them penny-in-the-slot cash-machines, so if you get wrong by a penny at the end of the day—but then I don't believe the machinery is right. Do you?'

'I've only seen it work. Mr. Beeton?'

'He's gone.'

'I'm afraid I must ask you to help me home, then. I'll make it worth your while. You see?' The sightless eyes turned towards her and Bessie saw.

'It isn't taking you out of your way?' he said hesitatingly. 'I can ask a policeman if it is.'

'Not at all. I come on at seven and I'm off at four. That's easy hours.'

'Good God!—but I'm on all the time. I wish I had some work to do too. Let's go home, Bess.'

He turned and cannoned into a man on the sidewalk, recoiling with an oath. Bessie took his arm and said nothing—as she had said nothing when he had ordered her to turn her face a little more to the light. They walked for some time in silence, the girl steering him deftly through the crowd.

'And where's—where's Mr. Torpenhow?' she inquired at last.

'He has gone away to the desert.'

'Where's that?'

Dick pointed to the right. 'East—out of the mouth of the river,' said he. 'Then west, then south, and then east again, all along the underside of Europe. Then south again. God knows how far.' The explanation did not enlighten Bessie in the least, but she held her tongue and looked to Dick's path till they came to the chambers.

'We'll have tea and muffins,' he said joyously. 'I can't tell you, Bessie, how glad I am to find you again. What made you go away so suddenly?'

'I didn't think you'd want me any more,' she said, emboldened by his ignorance.

'I didn't as a matter of fact—but afterwards— At any rate I'm glad you've come. You know the stairs.'

So Bessie led him home to his own place—there was no one to hinder—and shut the door of the studio.

'What a mess!' was her first word. 'All these things haven't been looked after for months and months.'

'No, only weeks, Bess. You can't expect them to care.'

'I don't know what you expect them to do. They ought to know what you've paid them for. The dust's just awful. It's all over the easel.'

'I don't use it much now.'

'All over the pictures and the floor, and all over your coat. I'd like to speak to them housemaids.'

'Ring for tea, then.' Dick felt his way to the one chair he used by custom.

Bessie saw the action and, as far as in her lay, was touched. But there remained always a keen sense of new-found superiority, and it was in her voice when she spoke.

'How long have you been like this?' she said wrathfully, as though the blindness were some fault of the housemaids.

'How?'

'As you are.'

'The day after you went away with the cheque, almost as soon as my picture was finished; I hardly saw her alive.'

'Then they've been cheating you ever since, that's all. I know their nice little ways.'

A woman may love one man and despise another, but on general feminine principles she will do her best to save the man she despises from being defrauded. Her loved one can look to himself, but the other man, being obviously an idiot, needs protection.

'I don't think Mr. Beeton cheats much,' said Dick. Bessie was flouncing up and down the room, and he was conscious of a keen sense of enjoyment as he heard the swish of her skirts and the light step between.

'Tea and muffins,' she said shortly, when the ring at the bell was answered; 'two teaspoonfuls and one over for the pot. I don't want the old teapot that was here when I used to come. It don't draw. Get another.'

The housemaid went away scandalised, and Dick chuckled. Then he began to cough as Bessie banged up and down the studio disturbing the dust.

'What are you trying to do?'

'Put things straight. This is like unfurnished lodgings. How could you let it go so?'

'How could I help it? Dust away.'

She dusted furiously, and in the midst of all the pother entered Mrs. Beeton. Her husband on his return had explained the situation, winding up with the peculiarly felicitous proverb, 'Do unto others as you would be done by.' She had descended to put into her place the person who demanded muffins and an uncracked teapot as though she had a right to both.

'Muffins ready yet?' said Bess, still dusting. She was no longer a drab of the streets, but a young lady who, thanks to Dick's cheque, had paid her premium and was entitled to pull beer-handles with the best. Being neatly dressed in black she did not hesitate to face Mrs. Beeton, and there passed between the two women certain regards that Dick would have appreciated. The situation adjusted itself by eye. Bessie had won, and Mrs. Beeton returned to cook muffins and make scathing remarks about models, hussies, trollops, and the like, to her husband.

'There's nothing to be got of interfering with him, Liza,' he said. 'Alf, you go along into the street to play. When he isn't crossed he's as kindly as kind, but when he's crossed he's the devil and all. We took too many little things out of his rooms since he was blind to be that particular about what he does. They ain't no objects to a blind man, of course, but if it was to come into court we'd get the sack. Yes, I did introduce him to that girl because I'm a feelin' man myself.'

'Much too feelin'!' Mrs. Beeton slapped the muffins into the dish, and thought of comely housemaids long since dismissed on suspicion.

'I ain't ashamed of it, and it isn't for us to judge him hard so long as he pays quiet and regular as he do. I know how to manage young gentlemen, you know how to cook for them, and what I says is, let each stick to his own business and then there won't be any trouble. Take them muffins down, Liza, and be sure you have no words with that young woman. His lot is cruel hard, and if he's crossed he do swear worse than any one I've ever served.'

'That's a little better,' said Bessie, sitting down to the tea. 'You needn't wait, thank you, Mrs. Beeton.'

'I had no intention of doing such, I do assure you.'

Bessie made no answer whatever. This, she knew, was the way in which real ladies routed their foes, and when one is a barmaid at a first-class public-house one may become a real lady at ten minutes' notice.

Her eyes fell on Dick opposite her and she was both shocked and displeased. There were droppings of food all down the front of his coat; the mouth, under the ragged ill-grown beard, drooped sullenly; the forehead was lined and contracted; and on the lean temples the hair was a dusty, indeterminate colour that might or might not have been called gray. The utter misery and self-abandonment of the man appealed to her, and at the bottom of her heart lay the wicked feeling that he was humbled and brought low who had once humbled her.

'Oh! it is good to hear you moving about,' said Dick, rubbing his hands. 'Tell us all about your bar successes, Bessie, and the way you live now.'

'Never mind that. I'm quite respectable, as you'd see by looking at me. You don't seem to live too well. What made you go blind that sudden? Why isn't there any one to look after you?'

Dick was too thankful for the sound of her voice to resent the tone of it.

'I was cut across the head a long time ago, and that ruined my eyes. I don't suppose anybody thinks it worth while to look after me any more. Why should they?—and Mr. Beeton really does everything I want.'

'Don't you know any gentlemen and ladies, then, while you was—well?'

'A few, but I don't care to have them looking at me.'

'I suppose that's why you've growed a beard. Take it off, it don't become you.'

'Good gracious, child, do you imagine that I think of what becomes me these days?'

'You ought. Get that taken off before I come here again. I suppose I can come, can't I?'

'I'd be only too grateful if you did. I don't think I treated you very well in the old days. I used to make you angry.'

'Very angry, you did.'

'I'm sorry for it, then. Come and see me when you can and as often as you can. God knows, there isn't a soul in the world to take that trouble except you and Mr. Beeton.'

'A lot of trouble he's taking and she too.' This with a toss of the head. 'They've let you do anyhow, and they haven't done anything for you. I've only to look to see that much. I'll come, and I'll be glad to come, but you must go and be shaved, and you must get some other clothes—those ones aren't fit to be seen.'

'I have heaps somewhere,' he said help-lessly.

'I know you have. Tell Mr. Beeton to give you a new suit and I'll brush it and keep it clean. You may be as blind as a barn-door, Mr. Heldar, but it doesn't excuse you looking like a sweep.'

'Do I look like a sweep then?'

'Oh, I'm sorry for you. I'm that sorry for you!' she cried impulsively, and took Dick's hands. Mechanically, he lowered his head as if to kiss—she was the only woman who had taken pity on him, and he was not too proud for a little pity now. She stood up to go.

'Nothing o' that kind till you look more like a gentleman. It's quite easy when you get shaved, and some clothes.'

He could hear her drawing on her gloves and rose to say good-bye. She passed behind him, kissed him auda-ciously on the back of the neck, and ran away as swiftly as on the day when she had destroyed the Melancolia.

'To think of me kissing Mr. Heldar,' she said to herself, 'after all he's done to me and all! Well, I'm sorry for him, and if he was shaved he wouldn't be so bad to look at, but . . . Oh them Beetons, how shameful they've treated him! I know Beeton's wearing his shirts on his back to-day just as well as if I'd aired it. To-morrow, I'll see . . . I wonder if he has much of his own. It might be worth more than the bar—I wouldn't have to do any work—and just as respectable if no one knew.'

Dick was not grateful to Bessie for her parting gift. He was acutely conscious of it in the nape of his neck throughout the night, but it seemed, among very many other things, to enforce the wisdom of getting shaved. He was shaved accord-ingly in the morning, and felt the better for it. A fresh suit of clothes, white linen, and the knowledge that some one in the world said that she took an interest in his personal appearance, made him carry himself almost upright; for the brain was relieved for a while from thinking of Maisie, who, under other circumstances, might have given that kiss and a million others.

'Let us consider,' said he after lunch. 'The girl can't care, and it's a toss-up whether she comes again or not, but if money can buy her to look after me she shall be bought. Nobody else in the world would take the trouble, and I can make it worth her while. She's a child of the gutter holding brevet rank as a bar-maid; so she shall have everything she wants if she'll only come and talk and look after me.' He rubbed his newly-shorn chin and began to perplex himself with the thought of her not coming. 'I suppose I did look rather a sweep,' he went on. 'I had no reason to look other-wise. I knew things dropped on my clothes, but it didn't matter. It would be cruel if she didn't come. She must. Maisie came once, and that was enough for her. She was quite right. She had something to work for. This creature has only beer-handles to pull, unless she has deluded some young man into keeping company with her. Fancy being cheated for the sake of a counter-jumper! We're falling pretty low.'

Something cried aloud within him:— This will hurt more than anything that has gone before. It will recall and remind and suggest and tantalise, and in the end drive you mad.

'I know it, I know it!' Dick cried, clenching his hands despairingly; 'but good heavens! is a poor blind beggar never to get anything out of his life except three meals a day and a greasy waistcoat? I wish she'd come.'

Early in the afternoon time she came, because there was no young man in her life just then, and she thought of material advantages which would allow her to be idle for the rest of her days.

'I shouldn't have known you,' she said approvingly. 'You look as you used to look—a gentleman that was proud of himself.'

'Don't you think I deserve another kiss then?' said Dick, flushing a little.

'Maybe—but you won't get it yet. Sit down and let's see what I can do for you. I'm certain sure Mr. Beeton cheats you, now that you can't go through the house-keeping books every month. Isn't that true?'

'You'd better come and housekeep for me then, Bessie.'

' 'Couldn't do it in these chambers— you know that as well as I do.'

'I know, but we might go somewhere else, if you thought it worth your while.'

'I'd try to look after you, anyhow; but I shouldn't care to have to work for both of us.' This was tentative.

Dick laughed.

'Do you remember where I used to keep my bankbook?' said he. 'Torp took it to be balanced just before he went away. Look and see.'

'It was generally under the tobacco-jar. Ah!'

'Well?'

'Oh! Four thousand two hundred and ten pounds nine shillings and a penny! Oh my!'

'You can have the penny. That's not bad for one year's work. Is that and a hundred and twenty pounds a year good enough?'

The idleness and the pretty clothes were almost within her reach now, but she must, by being housewifely, show that she deserved them.

'Yes; but you'd have to move, and if we took an inventory, I think we'd find that Mr. Beeton has been prigging little things out of the rooms here and there. They don't look as full as they used.'

'Never mind, we'll let him have them. The only thing I'm particularly anxious to take away is that picture I used you for—when you used to swear at me. We'll pull out of this place, Bess, and get away as far as ever we can.'

'Oh yes,' she said uneasily.

'I don't know where I can go to get away from myself, but I'll try, and you shall have all the pretty frocks that you care for. You'll like that. Give me that kiss now, Bess. Ye gods! it's good to put one's arm round a woman's waist again.'

Then came the fulfilment of the prophecy within the brain. If his arm were thus round Maisie's waist and a kiss had just been given and taken between them,—why then. . . . He pressed the girl more closely to himself because the pain whipped him. She was wondering how to explain a little accident to the Melancolia. At any rate, if this man really desired the solace of her company —and certainly he would relapse into his original slough if she withdrew it—he would not be more than just a little vexed. It would be delightful at least to see what would happen, and by her teachings it was good for a man to stand in certain awe of his companion.

She laughed nervously, and slipped out of his reach.

'I shouldn't worrit about that picture if I was you,' she began, in the hope of turning his attention.

'It's at the back of all my canvases somewhere. Find it, Bess; you know it as well as I do.'

'I know—but—'

'But what? You've wit enough to manage the sale of it to a dealer. Women haggle much better than men. It might be a matter of eight or nine hundred pounds to—to us. I simply didn't like to think about it for a long time. It was mixed up with my life so.—But we'll cover up our tracks and get rid of everything, eh? Make a fresh start from the beginning, Bess.'

Then she began to repent very much indeed, because she knew the value of money. Still, it was probable that the blind man was overestimating the value of his work. Gentlemen, she knew, were absurdly particular about their things. She giggled as a nervous housemaid giggles when she tries to explain the breakage of a pipe.

'I'm very sorry, but you remember I was—I was angry with you before Mr. Torpenhow went away?'

'You were very angry, child; and on my word I think you had some right to be.'

'Then I—but aren't you sure Mr. Torpenhow didn't tell you?'

'Tell me what? Good gracious, what are you making such a fuss about when you might just as well be giving me another kiss.'

He was beginning to learn, not for the first time in his experience, that kissing is a cumulative poison. The more you get of it, the more you want. Bessie gave the kiss promptly, whispering, as she did so, 'I was so angry I rubbed out that picture with the turpentine. You aren't angry, are you?'

'What? Say that again.' The man's hand had closed on her wrist.

'I rubbed it out with turps and the knife,' faltered Bessie. 'I thought you'd only have to do it over again. You did do it over again, didn't you? Oh, let go of my wrist; you're hurting me.'

'Isn't there anything left of the thing?'

'N'nothing that looks like anything. I'm sorry—I didn't know you'd take on about it; I only meant to do it in fun. You aren't going to hit me?'

'Hit you! No! Let's think.'

He did not relax his hold upon her wrist, but stood staring at the carpet. Then he shook his head as a young steer shakes it when the lash of the stock-whip across his nose warns him back to the path to the shambles that he would escape. For weeks he had forced himself not to think of the Melancolia, because she was a part of his dead life. With Bessie's return and certain new prospects that had developed themselves the Melancolia—lovelier in his imagination than she had ever been on canvas—reappeared. By her aid he might have procured more money wherewith to amuse Bess and to forget Maisie, as well as another taste of an almost forgotten success. Now, thanks to a vicious little housemaid's folly, there was nothing to look for—not even the hope that he might some day take an abiding interest in the housemaid. Worst of all, he had been made to appear ridiculous in Maisie's eyes. A woman will forgive the man who has ruined her life so long as he gives her love: a man may forgive those who ruin the love of his life, but he will never forgive the destruction of his work.

'Tck—tck—tck,' said Dick between his teeth, and then laughed softly. 'It's an omen, Bessie, and—a good many things considered, it serves me right for doing what I have done. By Jove! that accounts for Maisie's running away. She must have thought me perfectly mad—small blame to her! The whole picture ruined, isn't it so? What made you do it?'

'Because I was that angry. I'm not angry now—I'm awful sorry.'

'I wonder.—It doesn't matter, anyhow. I'm to blame for making the mistake.'

'What mistake?'

'Something you wouldn't understand, dear. Great heavens! to think that a little piece of dirt like you could throw me out of my stride!' Dick was talking to himself as Bessie tried to shake off his grip on her wrist.

'I ain't a piece of dirt, and you shouldn't call me so! I did it 'cause I hated you, and I'm only sorry now 'cause you're—'cause you're—'

'Exactly—because I'm blind. There's nothing like tact in little things.'

Bessie began to sob. She did not like being shackled against her will; she was afraid of the blind face and the look upon it, and was sorry too that her great revenge had only made Dick laugh.

'Don't cry,' he said, and took her into his arms. 'You only did what you thought right.'

'I—I ain't a little piece of dirt, and if you say that I'll never come to see you again.'

'You don't know what you've done to me. I'm not angry—indeed, I'm not. Be quiet for a minute.'

Bessie remained in his arms shrinking. Dick's first thought was connected with Maisie, and it hurt him as white-hot iron hurts an open sore.

Not for nothing is a man permitted to ally himself to the wrong woman. The first pang—the first sense of things lost is but the prelude to the play, for the very just Providence who delights in causing pain has decreed that the agony shall return, and that in the midst of keenest pleasure. They know this pain equally who have forsaken or been forsaken by

the love of their life, and in their new wives' arms are compelled to realise it. It is better to remain alone and suffer only the misery of being alone, so long as it is possible to find distraction in daily work. When that resource goes the man is to be pitied and left alone.

These things and some others Dick considered while he was holding Bessie to his heart.

'Though you mayn't know it,' he said, raising his head, 'the Lord is a just and a terrible God, Bess; with a very strong sense of humour. It serves me right— how it serves me right! Torp could understand it if he were here; he must have suffered something at your hands, child, but only for a minute or so. I saved him. Set that to my credit, some one.'

'Let me go,' said Bess, her face darkening. 'Let me go.'

'All in good time. Did you ever attend Sunday school?'

'Never. Let me go, I tell you; you're making fun of me.'

'Indeed, I'm not. I'm making fun of myself. . . . Thus. "He saved others, himself he cannot save." It isn't exactly a school-board text.' He released her wrist, but since he was between her and the door she could not escape. 'What an enormous amount of mischief one little woman can do!'

'I'm sorry; I'm awful sorry about the picture.'

'I'm not. I'm grateful to you for spoiling it. . . . What were we talking about before you mentioned the thing?'

'About getting away—and money. Me and you going away.'

'Of course. We will get away—that is to say, I will.'

'And me?'

'You shall have fifty whole pounds for spoiling a picture.'

'Then you won't—?'

'I'm afraid not, dear. Think of fifty

pounds for pretty things all to yourself.'

'You said you couldn't do anything without me.'

'That was true a little while ago. I'm better now, thank you. Get me my hat.'

'S'pose I don't?'

'Beeton will, and you'll lose fifty pounds. That's all. Get it.'

Bessie cursed under her breath. She had pitied the man sincerely, had kissed him with almost equal sincerity, for he was not unhandsome; it pleased her to be in a way and for a time his protector, and above all there were four thousand pounds to be handled by some one. Now through a slip of the tongue and a little feminine desire to give a little, not too much, pain she had lost the money, the blessed idleness and the pretty things, the companionship, and the chance of looking outwardly as respectable as a real lady.

'Now fill me a pipe. Tobacco doesn't taste, but it doesn't matter, and I'll think things out. What's the day of the week, Bess?'

'Tuesday.'

'Then Thursday's mail-day. What a fool—what a blind fool I have been! Twenty-two pounds covers my passage home again. Allow ten for additional expenses. We must put up at Madame Binat's for old sake's sake. Thirty-two pounds altogether. Add a hundred for the cost of the last trip—Gad, won't Torp stare to see me!—a hundred and thirty-two leaves seventy-eight for baksheesh—I shall need it—and to play with. What are you crying for, Bess? It wasn't your fault, child; it was mine altogether. Oh, you funny little opossum, mop your eyes, and take me out! I want the pass-book and the cheque-book. Stop a minute. Four thousand pounds at four per cent—that's safe interest—means a hundred and sixty pounds a year; one hundred and twenty pounds a year—also safe—is

two eighty, and two hundred and eighty pounds added to three hundred a year means gilded luxury for a single woman. Bess, we'll go to the bank."

Richer by two hundred and ten pounds stored in his money-belt, Dick caused Bessie, now thoroughly bewildered, to hurry from the bank to the P. and O. offices, where he explained things tersely.

'Port Said, single first; cabin as close to the baggage-hatch as possible. What ship's going?'

'The "Colgong," ' said the clerk.

'She's a wet little hooker. Is it Tilbury and a tender, or Galleons and the docks?'

'Galleons. Twelve-forty, Thursday.'

'Thanks. Change, please. I can't see very well—will you count it into my hand?'

'If they all took their passages like that instead of talking about their trunks, life would be worth something,' said the clerk to his neighbour, who was trying to explain to a harassed mother of many that condensed milk is just as good for babes at sea as daily dairy. Being nineteen and unmarried, he spoke with conviction.

'We are now,' quoth Dick, as they returned to the studio, patting the place where his money-belt covered ticket and money, 'beyond the reach of man, or devil, or woman—which is much more important. I've three little affairs to carry through before Thursday, but I needn't ask you to help, Bess. Come here on Thursday morning at nine. We'll breakfast, and you shall take me down to Galleons Station.'

'What are you going to do?'

'Going away of course. What should I stay for?'

'But you can't look after yourself?'

'I can do anything. I didn't realise it before, but I can. I've done a great deal already. Resolution shall be treated to one kiss if Bessie doesn't object.'

Strangely enough, Bessie objected and Dick laughed. 'I suppose you're right. Well, come at nine the day after to-morrow and you'll get your money.'

'Shall I sure?'

'I don't bilk, and you won't know whether I do or not unless you come. Oh, but it's long and long to wait! Good-bye, Bessie,—send Beeton here as you go out.'

The housekeeper came.

'What are all the fittings of my rooms worth?' said Dick imperiously.

' 'Tisn't for me to say, sir. Some things is very pretty and some is wore out dreadful.'

'I'm insured for two hundred and seventy.'

'Insurance policies is no criterion, though I don't say—'

'Oh, damn your longwindedness! You've made your pickings out of me and the other tenants. Why, you talked of retiring and buying a public-house the other day. Give a straight answer to a straight question.'

'Fifty,' said Mr. Beeton, without a moment's hesitation.

'Double it; or I'll break up half my sticks and burn the rest.'

He felt his way to a bookstand that supported a pile of sketch-books, and wrenched out one of the mahogany pillars.

'That's sinful, sir,' said the house-keeper, alarmed.

'It's my own. One hundred or—'

'One hundred it is. It'll cost me three and six to get that there pilaster mended.'

'I thought so. What an out-and-out swindler you must have been to spring that price at once!'

'I hope I've done nothing to dissatisfy any of the tenants, least of all you, sir.'

'Never mind that. Get me the money to-morrow, and see that all my clothes are packed in the little brown bullock-trunk. I'm going.'

'But the quarter's notice?'

'I'll pay forfeit. Look after the packing and leave me alone.'

Mr. Beeton discussed this new departure with his wife, who decided that Bessie was at the bottom of it all. Her husband took a more charitable view.

'It's very sudden—but then he was always sudden in his ways. Listen to him now!'

There was a sound of chanting from Dick's room.

'We'll never come back any more, boys,
We'll never come back no more;
We'll go to the deuce on any excuse,
And never come back no more!
Oh say we're afloat or ashore, boys,
Oh say we're afloat or ashore;
But we'll never come back any more, boys,
We'll never come back no more!'

'Mr. Beeton! Mr. Beeton! Where the deuce is my pistol?'

'Quick, he's going to shoot himself—'avin' gone mad!' said Mrs. Beeton.

Mr. Beeton addressed Dick soothingly, but it was some time before the latter, threshing up and down his bedroom, could realise the intention of the promises to 'find everything to-morrow, sir.'

'Oh, you copper-nosed old fool—you impotent Academician!' he shouted at last. 'Do you suppose I want to shoot myself? Take the pistol in your silly shaking hand then. If you touch it, it will go off, because it's loaded. It's among my campaign-kit somewhere—in the parcel at the bottom of the trunk.'

Long ago Dick had carefully possessed himself of a forty-pound weight field-equipment constructed by the knowledge of his own experience. It was this put-away treasure that he was trying to find and rehandle. Mr. Beeton whipped the revolver out of its place on the top of the package, and Dick drove his hand among the khaki coat and breeches, the blue cloth leg-bands, and the heavy flannel shirts doubled over a pair of swan-neck

THE LIGHT THAT FAILED

spurs. Under these and the water-bottle lay a sketchbook and a pigskin case of stationery.

'These we don't want; you can have them, Mr. Beeton. Everything else I'll keep. Pack 'em on the top right-hand side of my trunk. When you've done that come into the studio with your wife. I want you both. Wait a minute; get me a pen and a sheet of notepaper.'

It is not an easy thing to write when you cannot see, and Dick had particular reasons for wishing that his work should be clear. So he began, following his right hand with his left: ' "The badness of this writing is because I am blind and cannot see my pen." H'mph!—Even a lawyer can't mistake that. It must be signed, I suppose, but it needn't be witnessed. Now an inch lower—why did I never learn to use a type-writer?—"This is the last will and testament of me, Richard Heldar. I am in sound bodily and mental health, and there is no previous will to revoke."—That's all right. Damn the pen! Whereabouts on the paper was I?— "I leave everything that I possess in the world, including four thousand pounds, and two thousand seven hundred and twenty-eight pounds held for me"—Oh, I can't get this straight.' He tore off half the sheet and began again with the caution about the handwriting. Then: 'I leave all the money I possess in the world to'—here followed Maisie's name, and the names of the two banks that held his money.

'It mayn't be quite regular, but no one has a shadow of a right to dispute it, and I've given Maisie's address. Come in, Mr. Beeton. This is my signature; you've seen it often enough to know it; I want you and your wife to witness it. Thanks. To-morrow you must take me to the land-lord and I'll pay forfeit for leaving with-out notice, and I'll lodge this paper with him in case anything happens when I'm away. Now we're going to light up the studio stove. Stay with me, and give me my papers as I want 'em.'

No one knows until he has tried how fine a blaze a year's accumulation of bills, letters, and dockets can make. Dick stuffed into the stove every document in the studio—saving only three unopened letters: destroyed sketch-books, rough note-books, new and half-finished canvases alike.

'What a lot of rubbish a tenant gets about him if he stays long enough in one place, to be sure,' said Mr. Beeton at last.

'He does. Is there anything more left?' Dick felt round the walls.

'Not a thing, and the stove's nigh red-hot.'

'Excellent, and you've lost about a thousand pounds' worth of sketches. Ho! ho! Quite a thousand pounds' worth, if I can remember what I used to be.'

'Yes sir,' politely. Mr. Beeton was quite sure that Dick had gone mad, otherwise he would have never parted with his excellent furniture for a song. The canvas things took up storage room and were much better out of the way.

There remained only to leave the little will in safe hands: that could not be ac-complished till to-morrow. Dick groped about the floor picking up the last pieces of paper, assured himself again and again that there remained no written word or sign of his past life in drawer or desk, and sat down before the stove till the fire died out and the contracting iron cracked in the silence of the night.

CHAPTER 15

With a heart of furious fancies,
  Whereof I am commander;
With a burning spear and a horse of air,
  To the wilderness I wander.
With a knight of ghosts and shadows
  I summoned am to tourney—
Ten leagues beyond the wide world's end,
  Methinks it is no journey.
                    Tom o'Bedlam's Song

'Good-bye, Bess; I promised you fifty. Here's a hundred—all that I got for my furniture from Beeton. That will keep you in pretty frocks for some time. You've been a good little girl, all things considered, but you've given me and Torpenhow a fair amount of trouble.'

'Give Mr. Torpenhow my love if you see him, won't you?'

'Of course I will, dear. Now take me up the gang-plank and into the cabin. Once aboard the lugger and the maid is—and I am free, I mean.'

'Who'll look after you on the ship?'

'The head-steward, if there's any use in money. The doctor when we come to Port Said, if I know anything of P. and O. doctors. After that, the Lord will provide, as He used to do.'

Bess found Dick his cabin in the wild turmoil of a ship full of leavetakers and weeping relatives. Then he kissed her, and laid himself down in his bunk until the decks should be clear. He who had taken so long to move about his own darkened rooms well understood the geography of a ship, and the necessity of seeing to his own comforts was as wine to him. Before the screw began to thrash the ship along the Docks he had been introduced to the head-steward, had royally tipped him, secured a good place at table, opened out his baggage, and settled himself down with joy in the cabin. It was scarcely necessary to feel his way as he moved about, for he knew everything so well. Then God was very kind: a deep sleep of weariness came upon him just as he would have thought of Maisie, and he slept till the steamer had cleared the mouth of the Thames and was lifting to the pulse of the Channel.

The rattle of the engines, the reek of oil and paint, and a very familiar sound in the next cabin roused him to his new inheritance.

'Oh, it's good to be alive again!' He yawned, stretched himself vigorously, and went on deck to be told that they were almost abreast of the lights of Brighton. This is no more open water than Trafalgar Square is a common; the free levels begin at Ushant; but none the less Dick could feel the healing of the sea at work upon him already. A boisterous little cross-swell swung the steamer disrespectfully by the nose; and one wave breaking far aft spattered the quarterdeck and the pile of new deck chairs. He heard the foam fall with the clash of broken glass, was stung in the face by a cupful, and sniffing luxuriously, felt his way to the smoking-room by the wheel. There a strong breeze found him, blew his cap off and left him bareheaded in the doorway, and the smoking-room steward, understanding that he was a voyager of experience, said that the weather would be stiff in the chops off the Channel and more than half a gale in the Bay. These things fell as they were foretold, and Dick enjoyed himself to the utmost. It is allowable and even necessary at sea to lay firm hold upon tables, stanchions, and ropes in moving from place to place. On land the man who feels with his hands is patently blind. At sea even a blind man who is not sea-sick can jest with the doctor over the weakness of his fellows. Dick told the doctor many tales—and these are coin of more value than silver if properly handled—smoked with him till unholy hours of the night, and so won his short-lived regard that he promised Dick a few hours of his time when they came to Port Said.

And the sea roared or was still as the winds blew, and the engines sang their song day and night, and the sun grew stronger day by day, and Tom the Lascar barber shaved Dick of a morning under the opened hatch-grating where the cool winds blew, and the awnings were spread and the passengers made merry, and at last they came to Port Said.

'Take me,' said Dick to the doctor, 'to Madame Binat's—if you know where that is.'

'Whew!' said the doctor, 'I do. There's not much to choose between 'em; but I suppose you're aware that that's one of the worst houses in the place. They'll rob you to begin with, and knife you later.'

'Not they. Take me there, and I can look after myself.'

So he was brought to Madame Binat's and filled his nostrils with the well-remembered smell of the East, that runs without a change from the Canal head to Hong-Kong, and his mouth with the villainous Lingua Franca of the Levant. The heat smote him between the shoulder-blades with the buffet of an old friend, his feet slipped on the sand, and his coat-sleeve was warm as new-baked bread when he lifted it to his nose.

Madame Binat smiled with the smile that knows no astonishment when Dick entered the drinking-shop which was one source of her gains. But for a little accident of complete darkness he could hardly realise that he had ever quitted the old life that hummed in his ears. Somebody opened a bottle of peculiarly strong Schiedam. The smell reminded Dick of Monsieur Binat, who, by the way, had spoken of art and degradation. Binat was dead; Madame said as much when the doctor departed, scandalised, so far as a ship's doctor can be at the warmth of Dick's reception. Dick was delighted at it. 'They remember me here after a year. They have forgotten me across the water by this time. Madame, I want a long talk with you when you're at liberty. It is good to be back again.'

In the evening she set an iron-topped cafe-table out on the sands, and Dick and she sat by it, while the house behind them filled with riot, merriment, oaths, and threats. The stars came out and the lights of the shipping in the harbour twinkled by the head of the Canal.

'Yes. The war is good for trade, my friend; but what dost thou do here? We have not forgotten thee.'

'I was over there in England and I went blind.'

'But there was the glory first. We heard of it here, even here—I and Binat; and thou hast used the head of Yellow 'Tina—she is still alive—so often and so well that 'Tina laughed when the papers arrived by the mailboats. It was always something that we here could recognize in the paintings. And then there was always the glory and the money for thee.'

'I am not poor—I shall pay you well.'

'Not to me. Thou hast paid for everything.' Under her breath, 'Mon Dieu, to be blind and so young! What horror!'

Dick could not see her face with the pity on it, or his own with the discoloured hair at the temples. He did not feel the need of pity; he was too anxious to get to the front once more, and explained his desire.

'And where? The Canal is full of the English ships. Sometimes they fire as they used to do when the war was here—ten years ago. Beyond Cairo there is fighting, but how canst thou go there without a correspondent's passport? And in the desert there is always fighting, but that is impossible also,' said she.

'I must go to Suakin.' He knew, thanks to Alf's readings, that Torpenhow was at work with the column that was protecting the construction of the Suakin-Berber line. P. and O. steamers do not touch at that port, and, besides, Madame Binat knew everybody whose help or advice was worth anything. They were not respectable folk, but they could cause things to be accomplished, which is much more important when there is work toward.

'But at Suakin they are always fighting. That desert breeds men always—and always more men. And they are so bold! Why to Suakin?'

'My friend is there.'

'Thy friend! Chtt! Thy friend is death, then.'

Madame Binat dropped a fat arm on the table-top, filled Dick's glass anew, and looked at him closely under the stars. There was no need that he should bow his head in assent and say—

'No. He is a man, but—if it should arrive . . . blamest thou?'

'I blame?' she laughed shrilly. 'Who am I that I should blame any one—except those who try to cheat me over their consummations. But it is very terrible.'

'I must go to Suakin. Think for me. A great deal has changed within the year, and the men I knew are not here. The Egyptian lighthouse steamer goes down the Canal to Suakin—and the post-boats —But even then—'

'Do not think any longer. I know, and it is for me to think. Thou shalt go— thou shalt go and see thy friend. Be wise. Sit here until the house is a little quiet—I must attend to my guests—and afterwards go to bed. Thou shalt go, in truth, thou shalt go.'

'To-morrow?'

'As soon as may be.' She was talking as though he were a child.

He sat at the table listening to the voices in the harbour and the streets, and wondering how soon the end would come, till Madame Binat carried him off to bed and ordered him to sleep. The house shouted and sang and danced and revelled, Madame Binat moving through it with one eye on the liquor payments and the girls and the other on Dick's interests. To this latter end she smiled upon scowling and furtive Turkish officers of Fellaheen regiments, was gracious to Cypriote commissariat underlings, and more than kind to camel agents of no nationality whatever.

In the early morning, being then appropriately dressed in a flaming red silk ball-dress, with a front of tarnished gold embroidery and a necklace of plate-glass diamonds, she made chocolate and carried it in to Dick.

'It is only I, and I am of discreet age, eh? Drink and eat the roll too. Thus in France mothers bring their sons, when those behave wisely, the morning chocolate.' She sat down on the side of the bed whispering: —

'It is all arranged. Thou wilt go by the lighthouse boat. That is a bribe of ten pounds English. The captain is never paid by the Government. The boat comes to Suakin in four days. There will go with thee George, a Greek muleteer. Another bribe of ten pounds. I will pay; they must not know of thy money. George will go with thee as far as he goes with his mules. Then he comes back to me, for his well-beloved is here, and if I do not receive a telegram from Suakin saying that thou art well, the girl answers for George.'

'Thank you.' He reached out sleepily for the cup. 'You are much too kind, Madame.'

'If there were anything that I might do I would say, stay here and be wise; but I do not think that would be best for thee.' She looked at her liquor-stained dress with a sad smile. 'Nay, thou shalt go, in truth, thou shalt go. It is best so. My boy, it is best so.'

She stooped and kissed Dick between the eyes. 'That is for good-morning,' she said, going away. 'When thou art dressed we will speak to George and make everything ready. But first we must open the little trunk. Give me the keys.'

'The amount of kissing lately has been simply scandalous. I shall expect Torp to kiss me next. He is more likely to swear at me for getting in his way, though. Well, it won't last long—Oh, Madame, help me to my toilette of the guillotine! There will be no chance of dressing properly out yonder.'

He was rummaging among his new

campaign-kit, and rowelling his hands with the spurs. There are two ways of wearing well-oiled ankle-jacks, spotless blue leg-bands, khaki coat and breeches, and a perfectly pipe-clayed helmet. The right way is the way of the untired man, master of himself, setting out upon an expedition, well pleased.

'Everything must be very correct,' Dick explained. 'It will become dirty afterwards, but now it is good to feel well dressed. Is everything as it should be?'

He patted the revolver neatly hidden under the fulness of the blouse on the right hip and fingered his collar.

'I can do no more,' Madame said, between laughing and crying. 'Look at thyself—but I forgot.'

'I am very content.' He stroked the creaseless spirals of his leggings. 'Now let us go and see the captain and George and the lighthouse boat. Be quick, Madame.'

'But thou canst not be seen by the harbour walking with me in the daylight. Figure to yourself if some English ladies—'

'There are no English ladies; and if there are, I have forgotten them. Take me there.'

In spite of his burning impatience it was nearly evening ere the lighthouse boat began to move. Madame had said a great deal both to George and the captain touching the arrangements that were to be made for Dick's benefit. Very few men who had the honour of her acquaintance cared to disregard Madame's advice. That sort of contempt might end in being knifed by a stranger in a gambling-hell upon surprisingly short provocation.

For six days—two of them were wasted in the crowded Canal—the little steamer worked her way to Suakin, where she was to pick up the superintendent of lighthouses; and Dick made it his business to propitiate George, who was distracted with fears for the safety of his light-of-love and half inclined to make Dick responsible for his own discomfort. When they arrived George took him under his wing, and together they entered the red-hot seaport, encumbered with the material and wastage of the Suakin-Berber line, from locomotives in disconsolate fragments to mounds of chairs and pot-sleepers.

'If you keep with me,' said George, 'nobody will ask for passports or what you do. They are all very busy.'

'Yes; but I should like to hear some of the Englishmen talk. They might remember me. I was known here a long time ago—when I was some one indeed.'

'A long time ago is a very long time ago here. The graveyards are full. Now listen. This new railway runs out so far as Tanai-el-Hassan—that is seven miles. Then there is a camp. They say that beyond Tanai-el-Hassan the English troops go forward, and everything that they require will be brought to them by this line.'

'Ah! Base camp. I see. That's a better business than fighting Fuzzies in the open.'

'For this reason even the mules go up in the iron-train.'

'Iron what?'

'It is all covered with iron, because it is still being shot at.'

'An armoured train. Better and better! Go on, faithful George.'

'And I go up with my mules to-night. Only those who particularly require to go to the camp go out with the train. They begin to shoot not far from the city.'

'The dears—they always used to!' Dick snuffed the smell of parched dust, heated iron, and flaking paint with delight. Certainly the old life was welcoming him back most generously.

'When I have got my mules together I

go up to-night, but you must first send a telegram to Port Said, declaring that I have done you no harm.'

'Madame has you well in hand. Would you stick a knife into me if you had the chance?'

'I have no chance,' said the Greek. 'She is there with that woman.'

'I see. It's a bad thing to be divided between love of woman and the chance of loot. I sympathise with you, George.'

They went to the telegraph-office unquestioned, for all the world was desperately busy and had scarcely time to turn its head, and Suakin was the last place under sky that would be chosen for holiday-ground. On their return the voice of an English subaltern asked Dick what he was doing. The blue goggles were over his eyes and he walked with his hand on George's elbow as he replied—

'Egyptian Government—mules. My orders are to give them over to the A.C.G. at Tanai-el-Hassan. Any occasion to show my papers?'

'Oh, certainly not. I beg your pardon. I'd no right to ask, but not seeing your face before I—'

'I go out in the train to-night, I suppose,' said Dick boldly. 'There will be no difficulty in loading up the mules, will there?'

'You can see the horse-platforms from here. You must have them loaded up early.' The young man went away wondering what sort of broken-down waif this might be who talked like a gentleman and consorted with Greek muleteers. Dick felt unhappy. To outface an English officer is no small thing, but the bluff loses relish when one plays it from the utter dark, and stumbles up and down rough ways, thinking and eternally thinking of what might have been if things had fallen out otherwise, and all had been as it was not.

George shared his meal with Dick and went off to the mule-lines. His charge sat alone in a shed with his face in his hands. Before his tight-shut eyes danced the face of Maisie, laughing, with parted lips. There was a great bustle and clamour about him. He grew afraid and almost called for George.

'I say, have you got your mules ready?' It was the voice of the subaltern over his shoulder.

'My man's looking after them. The— the fact is I've a touch of ophthalmia and I can't see very well.'

'By Jove! that's bad. You ought to lie up in hospital for a while. I've had a turn of it myself. It's as bad as being blind.'

'So I find it. When does this armoured train go?'

'At six o'clock. It takes an hour to cover the seven miles.'

'Are the Fuzzies on the rampage—eh?'

'About three nights a week. 'Fact is I'm in acting command of the night-train. It generally runs back empty to Tanai for the night.'

'Big camp at Tanai, I suppose?'

'Pretty big. It has to feed our desert-column somehow.'

'Is that far off?'

'Between thirty and forty miles—in an infernal thirsty country.'

'Is the country quiet between Tanai and our men?'

'More or less. I shouldn't care to cross it alone, or with a subaltern's command for the matter of that, but the scouts get through in some extraordinary fashion.'

'They always did.'

'Have you been here before, then?'

'I was through most of the trouble when it first broke out.'

'In the service and cashiered,' was the subaltern's first thought, so he refrained from putting any questions.

'There's your man coming up with the mules. It seems rather queer—'

'That I should be mule-leading?' said Dick.

'I didn't mean to say so, but it is. Forgive me—it's beastly impertinence I know, but you speak like a man who has been at a public school. There's no mistaking the tone.'

'I am a public school man.'

'I thought so. I say, I don't want to hurt your feelings, but you're a little down on your luck, aren't you? I saw you sitting with your head in your hands, and that's why I spoke.'

'Thanks. I am about as thoroughly and completely broke as a man need be.'

'Suppose—I mean I'm a public school man myself. Couldn't I perhaps—take it as a loan y'know and—'

'You're much too good, but on my honour I've as much money as I want. . . . I tell you what you could do for me, though, and put me under an everlasting obligation. Let me come into the bogie truck of the train. There is a foretruck, isn't there?'

'Yes. How d'you know?'

'I've been in an armoured train before. Only let me see—hear some of the fun I mean, and I'll be grateful. I go at my own risk as a non-combatant.'

The young man thought for a minute. 'All right,' he said. 'We're supposed to be an empty train, and there's no one to blow me up at the other end.'

George and a horde of yelling amateur assistants had loaded up the mules, and the narrow-gauge armoured train, plated with three-eighths-inch boiler-plate till it looked like one long coffin, stood ready to start.

Two bogie trucks running before the locomotive were completely covered in with plating, except that the leading one was pierced in front for the nozzle of a machine-gun, and the second at either side for lateral fire. The trucks together made one long iron-vaulted chamber in which a score of artillerymen were rioting.

'Whitechapel—last train! Ah, I see yer kissin' in the first class there!' somebody shouted, just as Dick was clambering into the forward truck.

'Lordy! 'Ere's a real live passenger for the Kew, Tanai, Acton, and Ealin' train. "Echo," sir. Speshul edition! "Star," sir.' —'Shall I get you a foot-warmer?' said another.

'Thanks. I'll pay my footing,' said Dick, and relations of the most amicable were established ere silence came with the arrival of the subaltern, and the train jolted out over the rough track.

'This is an immense improvement on shooting the unimpressionable Fuzzy in the open,' said Dick from his place in the corner.

'Oh, but he's still unimpressed. There he goes!' said the subaltern, as a bullet struck the outside of the truck. 'We always have at least one demonstration against the night-train. Generally they attack the rear-truck where my junior commands. He gets all the fun of the fair.'

'Not to-night, though! Listen!' said Dick. A flight of heavy-handed bullets was succeeded by yelling and shouts. The children of the desert valued their nightly amusement, and the train was an excellent mark.

'Is it worth while giving them half a hopper full?' the subaltern asked of the engine which was driven by a Lieutenant of Sappers.

'I should just think so! This is my section of the line. They'll be playing old Harry with my permanent way if we don't stop 'em.'

'Right O!'

'Hrrmph!' said the machine-gun through all its five noses as the subaltern drew the lever home. The empty cartridges clashed on the floor and the smoke blew back through the truck. There was indiscriminate firing at the rear of the train, a return fire from the darkness without and unlimited howling. Dick stretched himself on the floor, wild with delight at the sounds and the smells.

'God is very good—I never thought I'd hear this again. Give 'em hell, men. Oh, give 'em hell!' he cried.

The train stopped for some obstruction on the line ahead and a party went out to reconnoitre, but came back cursing, for spades. The children of the desert had piled sand and gravel on the rails, and twenty minutes were lost in clearing it away. Then the slow progress recommenced, to be varied with more shots, more shoutings, the steady clack and kick of the machine-guns, and a final difficulty with a half-lifted rail ere the train came under the protection of the roaring camp at Tanai-el-Hassan.

'Now, you see why it takes an hour and a half to fetch her through,' said the subaltern, unshipping the cartridge-hopper above his pet gun.

'It was a lark, though. I only wish it had lasted twice as long. How superb it must have looked from outside!' said Dick, sighing regretfully.

'It palls after the first few nights. By the way, when you've settled about your mules, come and see what we can find to eat in my tent. I'm Bennil of the Gunners —in the Artillery lines—and mind you don't fall over my tent-ropes in the dark.'

But it was all dark to Dick. He could only smell the camels, the hay-bales, the cooking, the smoky fires, and the tanned canvas of the tents as he stood, where he had dropped from the train, shouting for George. There was a sound of light-hearted kicking on the iron skin of the rear trucks, with squealing and grunting. George was unloading the mules.

The engine was blowing off steam nearly in Dick's ear; a cold wind of the desert danced between his legs; he was hungry, and felt tired and dirty—so dirty that he tried to brush his coat with his hands. That was a hopeless job; he thrust his hands into his pockets and began to count over the many times that he had waited in strange or remote places for trains or camels, mules or horses, to carry him to his business. In those days he could see—few men more clearly— and the spectacle of an armed camp at dinner under the stars was an ever fresh pleasure to the eye. There was colour, light, and motion, without which no man has much pleasure in living. This night there remained for him only one more journey through the darkness that never lifts to tell a man how far he has travelled. Then he would grip Torpenhow's hand again—Torpenhow, who was alive and strong, and lived in the midst of the action that had once made the reputation of a man called Dick Heldar: not in the least to be confused with the blind, bewildered vagabond who seemed to answer to the same name. Yes, he would find Torpenhow, and come as near to the old life as might be. Afterwards he would forget everything: Bessie, who had wrecked the Melancolia and so nearly wrecked his life; Beeton, who lived in a strange unreal city full of tin-tacks and gas-plugs, and matters that no men needed; that irrational being who had offered him love and loyalty for nothing, but had not signed her name; and most of all Maisie, who, from her own point of view, was undeniably right in all she did, but oh, at this distance, so tantalisingly fair.

George's hand on his arm pulled him back to the situation.

'And what now?' said George.

'Oh yes, of course. What now? Take me to the camel-men. Take me to where the scouts sit when they come in from the desert. They sit by their camels, and the camels eat grain out of a black blanket held up at the corners, and the men eat by their side just like camels. Take me there!'

The camp was rough and rutty, and

Dick stumbled many times over the stumps of scrub. The scouts were sitting by their beasts, as Dick knew they would. The light of the dung-fires flickered on their bearded faces, and the camels bubbled and mumbled beside them at rest. It was no part of Dick's policy to go into the desert with a convoy of supplies. That would lead to impertinent questions, and since a blind non-combatant is not needed at the front, he would probably be forced to return to Suakin. He must go up alone, and go immediately.

'Now for one last bluff—the biggest of all,' he said. 'Peace be with you, brethren!' The watchful George steered him to the circle of the nearest fire. The heads of the camel-sheiks bowed gravely, and the camels, scenting a European, looked sideways curiously like brooding hens, half ready to get to their feet.

'A beast and a driver to go to the fighting line to-night,' said Dick.

'A Mulaid?' said a voice, scornfully naming the best baggage-breed that he knew.

'A Bisharin,' returned Dick with perfect gravity. 'A Bisharin without saddle-galls. Therefore no charge of thine, shock-head.'

Two or three minutes passed. Then—

'We be knee-haltered for the night. There is no going out from the camp.'

'Not for money?'

'H'm! Ah! English money?'

Another depressing interval of silence. 'How much?'

'Twenty-five pounds English paid into the hand of the driver at my journey's end, and as much more into the hand of the camel-sheik here, to be paid when the driver returns.'

This was royal payment, and the sheik, who knew that he would get his commission on the deposit, stirred in Dick's behalf.

'For scarcely one night's journey—

fifty pounds. Land and wells and good trees and wives to make a man content for the rest of his days. Who speaks?' said Dick.

'I,' said a voice. 'I will go—but there is no going from the camp.'

'Fool! I know that a camel can break his knee-halter, and the sentries do not fire if one goes in chase. Twenty-five pounds and another twenty-five pounds. But the beast must be a good Bisharin; I will take no baggage-camel.'

Then the bargaining began, and at the end of half an hour the first deposit was paid over to the sheik, who talked in low tones to the driver. Dick heard the latter say: 'A little way out only. Any baggage-beast will serve. Am I a fool to waste my cattle for a blind man?'

'And though I cannot see'—Dick lifted his voice a little—'yet I carry that which has six eyes, and the driver will sit before me. If we do not reach the English troops in the dawn he will be dead.'

'But where, in God's name, are the troops?'

'Unless thou knowest let another man ride. Dost thou know? Remember it will be life or death to thee.'

'I know,' said the driver sullenly. 'Stand back from my beast. I am going to slip him.'

'Not so swiftly. George, hold the camel's head a moment. I want to feel his cheek.' The hands wandered over the hide till they found the branded half-circle that is the mark of the Bisharin, the light-built riding camel. 'That is well. Cut this one loose. Remember no blessing of God comes on those who try to cheat the blind.'

The men chuckled by the fires at the camel-driver's discomfiture. He had intended to substitute a slow, saddle-galled baggage-colt.

'Stand back!' one shouted, lashing the Bisharin under the belly with a quirt.

Dick obeyed as soon as he felt the nose-string tighten in his hand,—and a cry went up, 'Illaha! Aho! He is loose.'

With a roar and a grunt the Bisharin rose to his feet and plunged forward towards the desert, his driver following with shouts and lamentation. George caught Dick's arm and hurried him stumbling and tripping past a disgusted sentry who was used to stampeding camels.

'What's the row now?' he cried.

'Every stitch of my kit on that blasted dromedary,' Dick answered, after the manner of a common soldier.

'Go on, and take care your throat's not cut outside—you and your dromedary's.'

The outcries ceased when the camel had disappeared behind a hillock, and his driver had called him back and made him kneel down.

'Mount first,' said Dick. Then climbing into the second seat and gently screwing the pistol muzzle into the small of his companion's back, 'Go on, in God's name, and swiftly. Good-bye, George. Remember me to Madame, and have a good time with your girl. Get forward, child of the Pit!'

A few minutes later he was shut up in a great silence, hardly broken by the creaking of the saddle and the soft pad of the tireless feet. Dick adjusted himself comfortably to the rock and pitch of the pace, girthed his belt tighter, and felt the darkness slide past. For an hour he was conscious only of the sense of rapid progress.

'A good camel,' he said at last.

'He has never been underfed. He is my own and clean bred,' the driver replied.

'Go on.'

His head dropped on his chest and he tried to think, but the tenor of his thoughts was broken because he was very sleepy. In the half doze it seemed that he was learning a punishment hymn at Mrs.

Jennett's. He had committed some crime as bad as Sabbath-breaking, and she had locked him up in his bedroom. But he could never repeat more than the first two lines of the hymn—

'When Israel of the Lord beloved
Out of the land of bondage came.'

He said them over and over thousands of times. The driver turned in the saddle to see if there were any chance of capturing the revolver and ending the ride. Dick roused, struck him over the head with the butt, and stormed himself wide awake. Somebody hidden in a clump of camel-thorn shouted as the camel toiled up rising ground. A shot was fired, and the silence shut down again, bringing the desire to sleep. Dick could think no longer. He was too tired and stiff and cramped to do more than nod uneasily from time to time, waking with a start and punching the driver with the pistol.

'Is there a moon?' he asked drowsily.

'She is near her setting.'

'I wish that I could see her. Halt the camel. At least let me hear the desert talk.'

The man obeyed. Out of the utter stillness came one breath of wind. It rattled the dead leaves of a shrub some distance away and ceased. A handful of dry earth detached itself from the edge of a rain trench and crumbled softly to the bottom.

'Go on. The night is very cold.'

Those who have watched till the morning know how the last hour before the light lengthens itself into many eternities. It seemed to Dick that he had never since the beginning of original darkness done anything at all save jolt through the air. Once in a thousand years he would finger the nail-heads on the saddle-front and count them all carefully. Centuries later he would shift his revolver from his right hand to his left, and allow the eased arm

[218]

to drop down at his side. From the safe distance of London he was watching himself thus employed,—watching critically. Yet whenever he put out his hand to the canvas that he might paint the tawny yellow desert under the glare of the sinking moon, the black shadow of the camel and the two bowed figures atop, that hand held a revolver and the arm was numbed from wrist to collarbone. Moreover, he was in the dark, and could see no canvas of any kind whatever.

The driver grunted, and Dick was conscious of a change in the air.

'I smell the dawn,' he whispered.

'It is here, and yonder are the troops. Have I done well?'

The camel stretched out its neck and roared as there came down wind the pungent reek of camels in square.

'Go on. We must get there swiftly. Go on.'

'They are moving in their camp. There is so much dust that I cannot see what they do.'

'Am I in better case? Go forward.'

They could hear the hum of voices ahead, the howling and the bubbling of the beasts and the hoarse cries of the soldiers girthing up for the day. Two or three shots were fired.

'Is that at us? Surely they can see that I am English,' Dick spoke angrily.

'Nay, it is from the desert,' the driver answered, cowering in his saddle. 'Go forward, my child! Well it is that the dawn did not uncover us an hour ago.'

The camel headed straight for the column and the shots behind multiplied. The children of the desert had arranged that most uncomfortable of surprises, a dawn attack for the English troops, and were getting their distance by snap-shots at the only moving object without the square.

'What luck! What stupendous and imperial luck!' said Dick. 'It's "just before the battle, mother." Oh, God has been most good to me! Only'—the agony of the thought made him screw up his eyes for an instant—'Maisie . . .'

'Allahu! We are in,' said the man, as he drove into the rearguard and the camel knelt.

'Who the deuce are you? Despatches or what? What's the strength of the enemy behind that ridge? How did you get through?' asked a dozen voices. For all answer Dick took a long breath, unbuckled his belt, and shouted from the saddle at the top of a wearied and dusty voice, 'Torpenhow! Ohe, Torp! Coo-ee, Tor-pen-how.'

A bearded man raking in the ashes of a fire for a light to his pipe moved very swiftly towards that cry, as the rearguard, facing about, began to fire at the puffs of smoke from the hillocks around. Gradually the scattered white cloudlets drew out into long lines of banked white that hung heavily in the stillness of the dawn before they turned over wave-like and glided into the valleys. The soldiers in the square were coughing and swearing as their own smoke obstructed their view, and they edged forward to get beyond it. A wounded camel leaped to its feet and roared aloud, the cry ending in a bubbling grunt. Some one had cut its throat to prevent confusion. Then came the thick sob of a man receiving his death-wound from a bullet; then a yell of agony and redoubled firing.

There was no time to ask any questions.

'Get down, man! Get down behind the camel!'

'No. Put me, I pray, in the forefront of the battle.' Dick turned his face to Torpenhow and raised his hand to set his helmet straight, but, miscalculating the distance, knocked it off. Torpenhow saw that his hair was gray on the temples, and that his face was the face of an old man.

'Come down, you damned fool! Dickie, come off!"

And Dick came obediently, but as a tree falls, pitching sideways from the Bisharin's saddle at Torpenhow's feet. His luck had held to the last, even to the crowning mercy of a kindly bullet through his head.

Torpenhow knelt under the lee of the camel, with Dick's body in his arms.

THE LIFE AND WORKS OF
RUDYARD KIPLING

By RAYMOND LAS VERGNAS

RUDYARD KIPLING was born in Bombay on December 30, 1865. His mother, Alice McDonald, came from a family of Scottish extraction, some of whose branches extended as far as Ulster. She was the daughter of a Methodist minister and had several brothers and sisters. One of them, Georgiana, had married the painter Burne-Jones, who subsequently became famous and was the greatly admired uncle to whom young Rudyard turned for guidance. Another sister later married Alfred Baldwin, who was to become a very powerful iron master and, more important still, the father of a Prime Minister of Britain. Alice, Kipling's mother, apparently made the least brilliant match. John Lockwood Kipling was also the son of a Methodist minister; his family, who came from Yorkshire, bore a surname that was rather uncommon in England. The two young people were attracted to one another and John proposed to Alice on the shores of Lake Rudyard. He was then a modest designer working in a factory in the Potteries, the famous region of the "five towns" so accurately described by the novelist Arnold Bennett, but had obtained a post as professor of sculpture at the Fine Arts School in Bombay. The wedding took place before his departure on March 18, 1865.

Young "Ruddy" spent the first years of his life in India, brought up to the sound of the vernacular spoken by the porter and his "ayah," or nurse; he took to it so naturally that when he went to join his parents in the drawing room, he had to be reminded that his mother tongue was English. But the children had to be sent away for proper education, a moment dreaded by all British families in India. The moment for young Rudyard came particularly early, apparently because of Alice Kipling's poor health; worn out by the birth of her daughter Trix, in 1868, she lost a third child during the scorchingly hot summer of 1870. At any rate, Ruddy was only five and a half years old and his sister three when their parents, anxious to conform to tradition, left them with strange foster parents in Southsea at the end of a trip to England. Alice and John went back to India without even warning Trix or Ruddy of the fate in store for them.

This was a disastrous experience for the little boy, as we can see from its reflections in two of his works; one is *Baa Baa, Black Sheep,* published in 1888; the other is of more immediate interest here, being the first chapter of *The Light that Failed* (1891). Here, the actual facts were set down with very little manipulation.

The only relatively acceptable member of the foster family in Southsea was the father, "Uncle" Harry, who was quite kind to the children. But when he died, Rudyard was left at the mercy of his wife, "Aunty" Rosa. She had a son who was jealous of the young lodger and poor Rudyard led a life of humiliation and mental wretchedness which, in his pride, he revealed to no one except his readers later on under the cloak of fiction. It was not until his autobiography appeared that the cloak fell away and the real significance of the picture he had drawn in *The Light that Failed* finally emerged.

During the five years that Ruddy spent in Southsea his only happy times were the summer holidays he spent with his real aunt, Georgiana, his mother's sister. But at the end of each holiday, he always had to go back. To make things worse, Ruddy's eyesight was gradually deteriorating—he always read a great deal, for reading was his solace—and he feared the worst. However, an oculist simply ordered him to give up reading for a time and wear spectacles.

One day, in March 1877, Ruddy's mother arrived unexpectedly from India. When she entered his room at night, he automatically flung up an arm to protect himself; this put an end to his misfortunes. Alice Kipling took her son and daughter away from Aunty Rosa.

Ruddy was now twelve years old. He was sent to a public school and, in spite of the harsh discipline, he liked it. This was where he formed a friendship with two other boys whom he described much later in one of his works that has remained extremely popular in Britain, *Stalky and Co.* (1899).

In September 1882, at the age of seventeen, Rudyard left England for India, where he was to rejoin his family in Lahore. There had been disturbances in Egypt and Prime Minister Gladstone had ordered the bombardment of Alexandria while the young man was en route. When he reached Port Said, he did not, of course, see the battlefield strewn with corpses, for it lay forty miles away. But he must have imagined what the atmosphere was like, to judge by the scenes he introduced into *The Light that Failed*.

In Lahore he first helped his father, who was now curator of the museum there, and then went to work for a provincial newspaper, *The Civil and Military Gazette*. He worked there for four years, training his mind while carrying out duties that were often humble, but full of interest for him. His only worry (apart from the breaking off of a tentative engagement in 1884 by Florence Garrard, a girl for whom he had formed an attachment in England) was his eyesight, which was causing him serious anxiety again.

During the hot season he visited the summer resort of Simla, one of the most talked-of towns of the day because of the lavish style in which the Viceroy, Lord Dufferin, held court there. And it was here that Kipling wrote the first stories that were worthy of his future reputation. But these were not his first attempts at writing. While he was still at school he had, with the headmaster's encouragement, written some poems which he had sent his parents, lovingly copied out on expensive paper. They were so proud of their son's poems that they had them printed in book form in Lahore, under the title *Schoolboy Lyrics* (1883). About fifty copies were printed and distributed to a few friends. But now things went further. In a Christmas collection published under the sponsorship of *The Civil and Military Gazette*, Kipling had two short stories, of which "The Phantom

Rickshaw" (1884) is still regarded as one of his most typical tales.

The next year Kipling became a Free-mason. He joined the Hope and Perseverance lodge as a result of his yearning for a universal religion transcending the taboos and mazes of caste pride, while creating a spirit of brotherhood among the members of an international elite.

During the winter of 1886–1887, Rudyard Kipling, only twenty-one years old, began to write the poems and stories that were to open the gateway to fame for him.

· *Departmental Ditties* (1886) was a collection of somewhat free-and-easy ballads, bordering on farce and interspersed with witty allusions to personalities of local officialdom. Kipling considered this book of only minor importance and it was published anonymously. Nevertheless, when it appeared it was highly successful locally and, more important still, produced the first English reaction in a London magazine. In an article signed by Andrew Lang, the critic expressed regret that the poet's name had not been disclosed. No one in India was ignorant of the book's authorship.

The Indian edition of the *Plain Tales from the Hills* (1888), a book that is today still so full of life, was soon out of print. In England the enthusiasm with which it was first received gradually flagged, but abroad its popularity was more easily maintained.

Kipling's professional activity took him to many parts of northern India, where he made copious notes on local scenery and customs. He was to draw upon this material later for his highly picturesque effects. After his first successes, he began writing short stories for the *Week's News,* a weekly newspaper, then for the *Pioneer Mail.* A series of small, inexpensive volumes intended for Indian railway bookstores was written for the Indian Railway Library. These in-clude some excellent tales, such as "Soldiers Three," "Wee Willie Winkie," "The Man Who Would Be King," "Baa Baa, Black Sheep," and "Under the Deodars."

During these years Kipling struck up a close friendship with some fellow boarders in Allahabad, a Professor Hill and his young American lady. When Mrs. Hill, after recovering from a serious illness, decided to leave with her husband for the United States to recuperate, Kipling suddenly made up his mind to join them. He left from Calcutta in March 1889. His wanderings took him to Japan, California, Oregon, Salt Lake City, Chicago, New York, and finally London, where he decided to stay.

After an absence of seven years, Rudyard Kipling was back on English soil. He was faced with the difficulties of establishing new connections, making useful contacts, and winning a name for himself with his pen, and found the going very hard at first. He was also homesick for India and his distant friends. Rudyard's sister, who was now married, arrived in England in 1890. When she went to see her brother, she found him depressed and worried about his eyesight again. The Bohemian life he was leading at the time, partly to forget his earlier disappointments in love, was scarcely conducive to improving his condition, and in addition, he was wearing himself out with work. During the spring he had written most of the *Barrack-Room Ballads,* half a dozen long short stories, and part of *The Light that Failed,* which he finished, absolutely exhausted, in August of the same year. The announcement in the press of the forthcoming publication of the novel was accompanied by the news that the author was leaving for Naples to take a badly needed rest.

In spite of his many different successes his reputation up to now had been confined to a limited circle of readers. But he awoke famous one morning (rather as

Byron had done) as a result of an article in the *Times* that excited public interest. In a lead article published on March 25, 1890, this influential paper stated that the young author of *Plain Tales from the Hills* had not only struck a new vein, but was tapping its resources with true originality.

On his return from Italy in November 1890, *The Light that Failed,* was scheduled to be brought out as magazine pieces in two versions, an American and an English one. In both cases, the publisher was an American firm, Lippincott, which owned monthlies appearing in New York and London respectively. These magazines always contained a short, unpublished novel. (Lippincott did very well indeed, for in that one year, 1890, he published *The Sign of Four* by Conan Doyle, *The Picture of Dorian Gray* by Oscar Wilde, and *The Light that Failed.*)

A mystery involving *The Light that Failed* came to the fore with the publication of the novel in England by Macmillan in March of 1891. An American edition, originally published by Lovell shortly before Lippincott's magazine version appeared, was substantially different from the new English edition. Not only was the English version about one-third longer, but it ended in a pessimistic note quite opposite to the happy ending of the American version. Kipling did not hesitate to declare where he stood in the matter, stating in the preface to the new English version that this was the story "as it was originally conceived by the writer."

In spite of the scholarly work of those who have made critical studies of Kipling, particularly Charles Carrington, author of an admirable monograph published in 1955, a great deal of obscurity still surrounds this strange book. Obviously it contains some childhood memories, in which the boy and girl are no longer brother and sister, but future sweethearts; the Indian setting is changed into a Sudanese and Egyptian one; the blindness with which Dick Heldar, the painter, is threatened may to some extent be linked up with young Kipling's own fears, yet the main plot is still an enigma. Who is Maisie? As she develops, she no longer seems to be the same person. The child Maisie seems to remind us of Trix; later on, she seems more like Florence Garrard, Kipling's former fiancée, whom he had met again in London while writing the book and to whom he could well have been attracted again with no prospect of success.

Though it appears unlikely that Kipling was ready at this time to give up his bachelorhood, the time for marriage had almost come. On his arrival in London, Rudyard had met a young American of French descent, Wolcott Balestier, who was a well-known figure in the literary society of the day. Balestier induced Kipling to collaborate with him in writing an exotic novel, *The Naulahka.* During their conversations, Rudyard had many opportunities to see his friend's sister, Caroline. She made a profound impression on him. He was still in delicate health, however, and decided on his doctor's advice to try out the beneficial effects of a change of air. He set out on a long journey for this purpose, traveling to India via South Africa and Australia. He was staying with his parents in Lahore when, in December 1891, he received a cable from Caroline Balestier informing him that Wolcott had died. Deeply distressed, Kipling returned to England at once, only stopping briefly at Bombay to see the ayah who had looked after him in his infancy.

He arrived in London on January 10, 1892, and arrangements were made for his marriage to Caroline within a week. He married Carrie on January 18; he was twenty-seven, she was thirty. Their honeymoon took them to North America, the home of Caroline's family, Japan, and Canada. They finally settled in Vermont, where their daughter Josephine was born on December 29, 1892.

There, early in 1893, Rudyard was delighted to receive a visit from his father. The elder Kipling had retired and published a book that contained a mixture of legends, personal observations, and local folk tales under the title of *Beast and Man in India.* His arrival in Vermont happened to coincide with a period in Rudyard's career when he most needed his father's advice. For some months he had been thinking of writing animal stories. He had just finished the tale called "Mowgli's Brothers" and his talks with his father apparently led him to continue with the *Jungle Books* (1894).

H. Rider Haggard, the author of *King Solomon's Mines,* and Kipling agreed that the idea of writing animal fables was first suggested to Kipling by one of Haggard's stories, *Nada the Lily,* which is set in Zululand. But in Kipling's works the philosophy of life, moral code, and, in particular, politics, as laid down by the dictates of the law of the jungle, bear the indelible stamp of his own genius.

Kipling continued writing the *Jungle* stories at intervals until March 1895, when he suddenly lost interest in Mowgli. Meanwhile, the Kiplings had gone on traveling while keeping their home base in Vermont. It was at this point that Kipling's creative demon turned to reminiscences about his wanderings through India and the idea of *Kim* first occurred to him. In February 1896, Carrie gave birth to a second daughter, Elsie, and a chance conversation with the doctor who attended her set Rudyard working on new material for a romance. He dropped *Kim* to concentrate on writing a book about life among the cod-fishing fleets off the Newfoundland banks. He called it

Captains Courageous (1897); it is a book that became and remained more popular in the United States than in England.

Before the Kiplings went to live in England, he had finished a collection of poems which was published in book form in November 1896, under the title of *The Seven Seas.* In England, the Kiplings settled themselves in Rottingdean, a small village on the Channel coast near Brighton. Here his poetry gained strength and depth. It was here that he wrote his famous "Recessional" for the *Times* to mark Queen Victoria's jubilee; when the hymn appeared on July 17, 1897, its author became, although not the official Poet Laureate, the nation's most honored poet.

A month later Kipling's third child was born, a son, this time, who was called John.

Now the Kiplings set off on their travels again, first of all to South Africa, where they arrived in January 1898, and met Cecil Rhodes. This was a period of tension when empires were being built up on the Dark Continent and the English wanted to acquire a major share of them. In Cecil Rhodes, Kipling felt that he had found a kindred spirit, who thought as he did that white men, particularly Anglo-Saxons, should unite on both sides of the Atlantic to fulfill a mission of prestige and example in relation to the less favored races.

At the time, the war between the Americans and Spain over Cuba had just ended and it was the American people that Kipling had in mind when he wrote his famous poem, *The White Man's Burden* (1898). In this hymn to the glory of imperialist energy he evoked a sense of common responsibility which he believed English-speaking white men ought to have. As soon as he finished it, he sent it to Theodore Roosevelt, whom he had once met and who had just been elected Vice President of the United States. Roosevelt commented that the poem made "good sense from the expansionist standpoint." A few weeks later, the Philippines came under American control; the white men's burden was growing.

During the summer of 1899, to his great sorrow, Kipling lost his Uncle Ned, Sir Edward Burne-Jones, for whom he had always had the deepest affection. He was then writing the *Just So Stories* (1902), which he enjoyed telling and acting out before an audience of the youngsters in his family. He was very good at reading aloud, instinctively finding the right intonation and rhythm and making the most of the drollness of the sounds. These stories are full of zest, with free play for Kipling's comic vein in explaining, for instance, how the elephant got his trunk or the camel his hump.

These entertaining activities did not prevent Kipling from working on more serious subjects. He had returned to the story of *Kim* again for the fourth time, but he still had not found a form that satisfied him completely; he had also discussed and approved a stage adaptation of *The Light that Failed,* which was produced in 1903.

When Kipling was at the height of his fame, he entered upon a period of family misfortunes, starting with the temporary mental illness of his sister Trix. She became sick at the end of 1898 and had to be placed in her mother's care. In the meantime, the Kiplings had left England for the United States. They crossed the Atlantic in January 1899, during a terrible storm and were in very poor shape on arrival in America. The children had caught chills and developed whooping cough and Carrie was confined to bed with a high temperature. On February 20th, Rudyard came home to his New York hotel complaining of aches and pains and fatigue. The next day the doctor diagnosed pneumonia. The patient had a high fever, was delirious, and hovered between life and death for several days. It was not until the 29th that a slight improvement set in; at last, on March 4th, the doctors pronounced him out of danger.

But while congratulatory telegrams were pouring in from all over the world, the condition of his daughter Josephine, who was still dangerously ill, suddenly deteriorated on March 5th. She died on the morning of the 6th. Kipling was so weak that his wife decided on a secret funeral and kept the terrible news from him for a long time. He never recovered from it emotionally. Physically, it took a rest of several months in Scotland to recover.

Here he finished writing *Stalky and Co.,* in which he recalled his public-school days. He then returned to his house in Rottingdean and began to take a passionate interest in the noisy, backfiring motor cars which were making rare appearances on the roads, surrounded by uproar. He even rented one himself.

At the end of 1899, war broke out between the Boers of South Africa and Britain, which had colonies neighboring the states of the South Africans of Dutch descent. The Boers took the offensive and invaded Mafeking, Kimberley, and Ladysmith, where British troops were stationed. The Kiplings, who had set out for Cape Town at the beginning of 1900, arrived there on February 5th, just in time to learn that British forces had suffered another defeat in Natal.

A few days later the position looked more hopeful. Kimberley had been relieved in mid-February and Cecil Rhodes, who was there at that time, was able to return to his activities. Kipling was one of the first people to see him after his rescue. He then traveled all over the country as journalist and patriot, visiting hospitals, encouraging the troops, and once coming under fire as a very close eyewitness at the battle of Karee Siding.

Despite his trips and articles as a war correspondent, Kipling found time in 1900 to finish *Kim* (1901), the novel about India which he had begun many years earlier. This book, which is one of his most characteristic and surely one of his most interesting, was completed in August of that year. But reminiscences about his days in India were not enough to engross a man like Kipling, whose mind was always attracted to matters of topical interest. For the moment the situation in South Africa was a matter of critical interest. After spending a few months in England, the Kiplings returned to the war zone at the end of the year.

Shortly before his departure, at the end of 1901, Kipling published a somewhat unexpected poem in the *Times* which made him a good many enemies in England. His main purpose was to induce his fellow countrymen to concern themselves more closely with the drama being enacted on the opposite side of the globe. The poem violently attacked British contempt for soldiering and ridiculed the snobbery of the "flannelled fools at the wicket" who thought they showed they were men because they played cricket. This satire of a national sport and a symbol of a way of life in the British Isles caused a great commotion. Kipling's popularity suffered as a result.

There had been little improvement in the war. The British authorities had set up camps as reception centers for enemy women and children, but the sanitary conditions were very poor and thousands of people came to a pitiable end there. This time Kipling did not travel far inland, where guerrilla warfare had broken out again more violently than ever. Cecil Rhodes provided him with a house in

which, incidentally, he spent every winter with his wife from 1901 to 1908.

Rhodes died shortly afterward. The war drew to a close when peace negotiations started in April 1902. The Kiplings were about to return to England, to be joined there by Trix, who had recovered from her mental illness. Peace was concluded on June 1, 1902, but the joy felt in Britain at the news of the victory was dimmed when, during the same month, Edward VII's subjects learned of the sudden illness of their King, whose coronation was to take place shortly. Kipling was deeply affected by the danger hanging over the court. He turned his mind to the problem of the function and meaning of the monarchy. These subjects were to preoccupy him more and more as time went on.

With the dawn of the twentieth century, Kipling, a man ahead of his time in many areas of technology, a man who loved to drive through the English countryside in his Locomobile, started writing science fiction. For example, he dreamed up a sort of commentary on a flight across the Atlantic Ocean in the year 2000 by a gas-turbine propelled aircraft escorted all the way by a system of safety devices (weather, radio, flight, and landing control). These predictions are truly amazing considering their date, 1903; they were to be followed by others in 1907 contained in a political satire, *As Easy as ABC,* which describes the consequences of a new system of government based on air supremacy over the whole planet.

The prospects he saw for the future were actually not very rosy; perhaps this is why he turned to the past, or perhaps it was just because he enjoyed tracing out the course of history for children, especially his own. In any event, in January 1905, he started work on the series called *Puck of Pook's Hill,* which was published in book form in 1906, and was followed later by a continuation, *Rewards and Fairies*. His principal audience in both cases consisted of his children, Elsie and John, ten and nine years old respectively at the time when the first of the two books was published, fourteen and thirteen when the second one appeared. A change in direction and tone between the two books was only to be expected.

It was partly because of the children's age that the Kiplings stopped dividing up their time between England and South Africa. They had been in the habit of spending three months in Cape Town and the rest of the year in Sussex. The requirements of the children's education, especially John's, made them discontinue this practice. (Although Kipling never returned to South Africa after 1908, he made a point of retaining his exclusive right to the house he had been given there until the end of his life.)

Death carried both of Kipling's parents off almost at the same time. His mother, who had become a more or less helpless invalid, died at the end of 1910 and her husband, who was a little younger, then became seriously ill. In January 1911, Rudyard received an urgent telegram calling him to his father's bedside. He arrived too late; John Lockwood Kipling had succumbed to a heart attack.

After this double loss, life was never quite the same for Rudyard Kipling, even though he continued to lead a life governed by a peaceful routine which outwardly appeared to be perfectly satisfactory. From 1909 until the outbreak of war the Kipling family went to Switzerland every winter. They spent a month or six weeks there; then, when John went back to school, the three remaining members of the family usually stayed in France, a country of which Kipling was especially fond.

In 1913, the Kiplings visited Egypt

and the novelist saw for the first time the Nile valley, the setting for *The Light that Failed* twenty-two years earlier. One year later the tragedy of World War I began to unfold.

John Kipling left for the front in France in August 1915. He was reported missing in October. This was the start for his parents of the agony of hoping against hope. It was two years before they learned how their son had met his death. He had been shot through the head and his sergeant had laid him down in a trench while the attack continued. But his comrades had been forced to retreat and give up the position. When it was retaken much later, blasted and ravaged by battle, ten thousand British soldiers were gone without a trace.

It was no doubt the cruel anguish which he and his wife had suffered that moved Kipling to devote his energies to honoring the memory of those who were killed in the war, particularly those whose names were not known. By the end of 1917, he had become a member of the War Graves Commission; it was he who suggested the wording of the inscription "Their name liveth for evermore," later engraved in stone in every military cemetery in England. He also played a part in gaining approval for the idea of a monument to the Unknown Soldier in Britain, which was subsequently adopted by the other nations involved in the war.

Kipling's duties as a War Graves Commissioner brought him the honor of meeting the King in person. In 1922, the King and Queen, on behalf of the nation, went on a pilgrimage to the Continent, as a tribute to the British soldiers who had fallen and were buried there. Kipling and his wife were presented to them and, on his return to England, the King asked the writer to visit him. This was the first of a series of private conversations in the course of which a bond of friendship was gradually formed between the two men.

All his life, Kipling had held himself aloof from offers of preferment from his government and even the monarch himself. He refused an offer to become Poet Laureate in 1895, as well as the offer of a title in 1899. He even declined membership in the British Academy (founded in 1901), a precedent which enabled him to refuse election on two occasions to the American Academy of Arts and Sciences. But when McGill University in Montreal awarded him an honorary doctor's degree in 1899 he accepted. He of course accepted the Nobel Prize for Literature in 1907 and subsequently doctor's degrees were conferred on him by the universities of Durham, Oxford, Cambridge, Edinburgh, Strasbourg, and Paris. In 1926, after refusing the presidency of the Society of Authors, he did accept the Gold Medal of the Royal Society of Literature, which had only been awarded three times previously in the history of Great Britain: to Walter Scott, George Meredith, and Thomas Hardy. In 1933, he accepted membership in the French Academy of Moral and Political Sciences.

A group of admirers decided in 1927 to start a Kipling Society; General Dunsterville (the original of Stalky in *Stalky and Co.*) became president. Although this tribute offended Kipling's modesty, he felt obliged to acquiesce. The Society prospered and is still flourishing today in England and the United States.

It was in 1932 that Kipling started on his autobiography. It was published the next year. As its title, *Something of Myself,* suggests, it is by no means exhaustive, but in the psychological insight it provides, it is a record of basic importance.

Rudyard Kipling reached the age of seventy on December 30, 1935; the many tokens of affection which he received on this occasion included a personal letter from the King which moved him deeply. The beginning of January was spent in preparations for the approaching customary trip to France. On January 12, the day before he was due to leave, Kipling seemed in excellent health. During the night, however, he had a severe hemorrhage and was taken to the hospital for an emergency operation. He died there on the 18th. On the 22nd his ashes were taken to Westminster Abbey to await the official funeral ceremony that was to take place the next day. The death of King George V, which occurred at this time, plunged the whole country into deep sorrow and formed a closer link still between the writer who was borne to Poets' Corner with an escort of the most prominent men in the Empire and the sovereign who had deeply understood, honored, and loved him.

This was the end of the life of a poet in the fullest sense of the word: a creative spirit in the realms of thought, art, and action. More than thirty years after his death, Rudyard Kipling is still one of the most widely read authors in the world.

Translated by A. Jackson.

Raymond Las Vergnas, a novelist, literary critic, and historian, is professor of English literature and languages at the Sorbonne.

THE 1907 PRIZE

By GUNNAR AHLSTRÖM

In 1907 the Nobel Committee lost little time getting started to pick a winner for the Literature award. By August, rumors were already circulating, and several more or less impressive names were often mentioned. *L'Intransigeant* of Paris wrote, "Who will receive the great prize this year? One of our Swedish colleagues claims to know. At first they thought of Mark Twain, the American humorist whose popularity has been revived by his recent visit to England, but it seems that the Nobel Committee will make a better choice—the great novelist and poet of Empire, Rudyard Kipling, who has sung of the British Tommy with such lyricism and patriotism, and whose *Jungle Book* is so popular, even here."

The source of this information was a squib in a Swedish newspaper. The fact that this report attracted the attention of the press outside Sweden showed that the Nobel Prize for Literature had come of age. The names of the candidates under consideration had become news. The discussions which raged about them had enough news value and teased people's curiosity sufficiently to overcome the torpor of the August heat.

The year 1907 was to bring something new and unexpected. It was no longer simply enough to find candidates—it had become necessary to consider certain countries, certain nationalities as well.

Which nation would be selected this time? With Sully Prudhomme and Mistral, France had already received its due homage. The laurel had gone to Germany with the choice of Mommsen in 1902, Bjørnson had planted the Scandinavian flag on the heights, and the Slavs had been honored in the person of Sienkiewicz. Carducci, with his award, had brought glory to Italy. In England people were waiting for the Swedish Academy to recognize not only the fatherland of Shakespeare but also the reality of a great empire. The wait, however, was long, very long.

"I desire expressly that the prizes be awarded without considerations of nationality," Nobel had stipulated in his last will and testament. This provision, like the entire Nobel Prize institution, sought to express the golden dream of progress and peace among peoples. The air of the cultural world quivered with generous projects. Those who cherished them were apparently unaware that these serene harmonies awakened only the feeblest echo in the real world. For the world had already entered the era of armed peace, and no knowledgeable political weatherman could help being disturbed.

It is one of the more ironic paradoxes of history that the early twentieth century resounded with declarations of peace and international appeals. Idealistic congresses were born everywhere. In those years, when the political world was really moving along the fatal road which ineluctably led in the opposite direction, the energies which charged the atmosphere were of quite a different stamp. Statesmen discussed spheres of economic influence as they lay in wait for colonies to seize while economic antagonisms were ripening in rhythm with the battles flaring up in the international marketplace. Cynical calculations followed one on the other, joined hands, mingled, always disguised as pure gold. And the gold medal of the Nobel Prize, insignia of the old idealism, had a sinister reverse side—national prestige. The year 1914 was not really very far off.

In Stockholm, the worthy Academy was opposed to this unidealistic tendency. Even so, it was scarcely possible to ignore the fact that from one year to the next the literary awards were beginning to involve national options. One of the members of the Swedish Academy, a sly old bishop for whom parliamentary tactics held no secrets, argued energetically that in spite of the wishes of the late Alfred Nobel it was necessary to pass the cup of Nobel wine among the various nations, to observe the rules of the diplomatic game. What the good bishop finally said aloud, plenty of people had been thinking silently.

Under such circumstances, how were the British to act? They had begun by not acting at all—in the first year England had not proposed any candidate. The Academy was reproved for not having informed British literary institutions of their right to do so then. The Society of Authors in London soon organized a Nobel Prize Committee which collected names from the members. From then on, interest in the Prize was lively among the British, perhaps more so than in any other country. In 1902 Stockholm received no less than sixty nominations from them; in 1903 there were forty-four, in 1905 there were thirty-five. The Prize and the heft of its gold medal seemed to excite the Society of Authors. The names they proposed were, moreover, of the highest rank. The first year Herbert Spencer headed the list, supported by forty-eight admirers. He died the following year, however, and efforts were then concentrated on Charles Algernon Swinburne. The majority voted for him, and he could boast among his supporters many notable figures of Edwardian letters, including J. M. Barrie, Austin Dobson, Thomas Hardy, Arthur Wing Pinero, Conan Doyle, and George Meredith. Meredith also garnered a fair vote, and his name figured among those sent on to Stockholm. Swinburne and Meredith became perennials, but years passed while the Prize still refused to travel across the North Sea.

The year 1907 came. Britain was regrouping its forces behind the aged Swinburne. This time the number of his partisans had swelled to twenty-seven, and this domestic chorus was reinforced by the voice of a Swede, the diplomat Baron Bildt, who in 1906 had successfully guided the candidacy of Giosuè Carducci to victory. By late summer, Kipling's name began to appear in the press, awakening spirited comment. It was with mitigated feelings that the British saw Swinburne spurned once again. The *Daily News* printed a substantial interview with Edmund Gosse, secretary of the Nobel Prize Committee of the Society of Authors. Prudently weighing his words, Gosse seemed to be preparing public opinion for the award of the Prize to someone other than the candidate recommended by the Society of Authors. The fact that the patriarch Carducci had died six weeks after receiving the award in 1906 was thought to have convinced the Swedish Academy, Gosse reported, that it was better to recompense some younger writer who still had work to do. Age could possibly work against the seventy-year-old Swinburne, and if that proved indeed to be the case it would be more a question of chronology than of literary values.

Gosse had good reasons to prepare his fellow countrymen for an unexpected choice. Kipling was by no means an official candidate and the men who had proposed him were considered outsiders by the orthodox literary world. After the early success of *Plain Tales from the Hills,* his reputation had gone down. Kipling was one of those English writers who have become famous rather in spite of public opinion at home than because of it. In this sense he is comparable to Defoe or Dickens. The admiration which surrounded this fabulous Englishman abroad offered a striking contrast. In France he had won immediate popularity, as he had also in Sweden. The reasons were the same as elsewhere in Europe. In the northern countries narrative talent was in the doldrums during this period of self-analysis, a time characterized by an anemic need for dissection. Kipling's voice was an invigorating breath for such writers as Selma Lagerlöf, who had actually undergone the valuable influence of the British master. Readers were attracted by the imaginative power, the exotic settings, the original characters, the communicative power, the narrative ease. All of these were understood to be the revelations of a primitive genius, of a mysterious inspiration of folklore and fairy tales.

An air of wonderment was in the air when Kipling arrived in Stockholm to pick up his prize. The short British gentleman with the black mustache, nearsighted but with friendly eyes gazing out from behind steel-framed spectacles, was besieged by a host of zealous interviewers.

The authentic Kipling was expected to lope in, wolflike, as Mowgli did, together with Baloo and Bagheera among these academic sahibs—or to come in like Kim with his lama, who, on catching sight of the Nobel Prize, would presumably forget the Arrow River. Or perhaps he should have been wearing khaki, like Tommy Atkins, and bellowing a departmental ditty or a barrack-room ballad in the solemn gathering. "To discover that Kipling is a man like other men, that he wears a black overcoat and a white necktie, rather shakes a chap a bit," wrote one Swedish journalist. "If only he had been holding a cobra in his hand!" As it was, the celebrated author seemed a likeable, modest, informal fellow, perfectly adapted to the Nobelian scene.

A few days before the ceremony, scheduled for December 10, Oscar II, the venerable King of Sweden, had died. The grieving nation was waiting for the funeral. In his autobiographical sketch, *Something of Myself,* Kipling gives an evocative description of Stockholm as he saw it. A winter twilight was falling on the city as he made his way to the somber palace to be presented to the new King. Snow blanketed the interior courtyard, the sentinels' cloaks, and the ancient cannon. Passing through the many corridors, he came into the presence of Gustav V. The King, exhausted, his eyes downcast, addressed a few words to the laureates. Round about, the mournful silence of the court was relieved only by the clicking of the medals and the decorations.

The traditional banquet following the awards was canceled. The prizes were awarded in a simple ceremony in the hall of the Academy of Sciences. Few persons attended, and ovations would have been out of place. Nevertheless, Kipling was able to realize clearly how much he was loved in Sweden. One of the newspapers did him the honor of publishing a front-page article in English, a teachers' journal published a profile of the celebrated visitor, thanking him for everything which, directly or indirectly, he had given Swedish children. Children in the schools near Stockholm paid him tribute by sending delegations to the Grand Hotel, where he was lodged. A little girl gave a fine speech in English, carefully learned by heart, then they all sang *Home, Sweet Home* and the Swedish national anthem. The guest was not the only person to be deeply moved. Another story is told of how Kipling had promised to send one of his young readers his *Jungle Book* in English. He kept his promise and the book arrived with this dedication: "Promises made to boys must be kept."

After these days in Stockholm, Kipling disappeared as discreetly as he had arrived. His new destination was South Africa, where he was to vacation with his family. In his luggage he carried not only his souvenirs of the northern kingdom but the Nobel diploma, which spoke of "the power of observation, the originality of imagination, the virility of his ideas, and the remarkable talent for narration which characterize the creations of this world-famous author."

Translated by Dale McAdoo.

Sinclair Lewis

1930

"For his vigorous and graphic art

of description and his ability

to create, with wit and humor,

new types of characters"

Illustrated by GÉRARD ÉCONOMOS

PRESENTATION ADDRESS

By ERIK AXEL KARLFELDT

PERMANENT SECRETARY
OF THE SWEDISH ACADEMY

———

THIS YEAR'S WINNER of the Nobel Prize for Literature is a native of a part of America which for a long time has had Swedish contacts. He was born at Sauk Centre, a place of about two or three thousand inhabitants in the great cornland of Minnesota. He describes the place in his novel *Main Street* (1920), though there it is called Gopher Prairie. It is the great prairie, an undulating land with lakes and oak groves, which has produced that little town and many others exactly like it. The pioneers have need of places to sell their grain, shops to purchase their supplies, banks for their mortgage loans, doctors for their bodies, and clergymen for their souls. There is cooperation between the country and the town, but at the same time there is conflict. Does the town exist for the sake of the country, or the country for the town?

The prairie makes its power felt. During the winters, as long and cold as ours, terrific storms dump their snow in the wide streets, between low and shabby houses. The summer scorches with an intense heat and the town smells, because it lacks both sewers and street cleaning. Yet the town naturally feels its superiority; it is the flower of the prairie. It has the economic threads in its hands, and it is the focus of civilization—a concentrated, proud America amidst these earthbound thralls of foreign origin, Germans and Scandinavians.

Thus the town lives happily in its self-confidence and its belief in true democracy, which does not exclude a proper stratification of the people, its faith in a sound business morality, and the blessings of being motorized; for there are many Fords in Main Street. To this town comes a young woman filled with rebellious emotions. She wants to reform the town, inside and out, but fails completely, almost going under in the attempt.

As a description of life in a small town, *Main Street* is certainly one of the best ever written. To be sure, the town is first and foremost American, but it could, as a spiritual milieu, be situated just as well in Europe. Like Mr. Lewis, many of us have suffered from its ugliness and bigotry. The strong satire has aroused local protests, but one need not be keen sighted to see the tolerant strain in Lewis's sketch of his native town and its people.

Behind the puffed-up complacency of Gopher Prairie, however, lurks jealousy. At the edge of the plain stand cities like St. Paul and Minneapolis, already little metropolitan centers with their skyscraper windows gleaming in the sunlight or the evening's electricity. Gopher Prairie wants to be like them and finds the time ripe for a campaign of progress, based on the rising price of wheat in war time.

A stump orator is imported, a real rabblerouser of the peppiest kind, and with blatant eloquence he demonstrates that nothing will be easier than for Gopher Prairie to take the lead and reach the 200,000-population class.

Mr. Babbitt—George Follansbee Babbitt—is the happy citizen of such a city (*Babbitt,* 1922). It is called Zenith, but probably it cannot be found on the map under that name. This city with its enlarged horizons hereafter becomes the starting point for Mr. Lewis's critical raids into the territories of Americanism. The city is a hundred times larger than Gopher Prairie and, therefore, a hundred times richer in one hundred percent Americanism and one hundred times as satisfied with itself, and the enchantment of its optimism and progressive spirit is embodied in George F. Babbitt.

As a matter of fact, Babbitt probably approaches the ideal of an American popular hero of the middle class. The relativity of business morals as well as private rules of conduct is for him an accepted article of faith, and without hesitation he considers it God's purpose that man should work, increase his income, and enjoy modern improvements. He feels that he obeys these commandments and therefore lives in complete harmony with himself and society.

His profession, real estate, is the highest in existence, and his house near the city, with its trees and lawn, is standard, inside and out. The make of his car corresponds to his position, and in it he whizzes through the streets, proud as a young hero amidst the perils of the traffic. His family life also corresponds to the bourgeois average. His wife has become used to his masculine grumblings at home, and the children are impertinent, but that is what one expects.

He enjoys excellent health, is well fed and thriving, alert and good natured. His daily lunches at the club are feasts of instructive business conversation and stimulating anecdotes; he is sociable and winning. Babbitt is furthermore a man with the gift of speech. He has learned all the national slogans and whirls them about with his flowing tongue in his popular talks before clubs and mass meetings. Not even for the most elevated spirituality does he lack sympathy. He basks in the company of the noted poet, Cholmondeley Frink, who concentrates his genius on the composition of striking, rhymed advertisements for various firms and thereby earns a good annual income.

Thus Babbitt lives the life of the irreproachable citizen conscious of his respectability. But the jealousy of the gods broods over a mortal whose happiness grows too great. A soul such as Babbitt's is, of course, incapable of growth; it is a readymade article from the start. Then Babbitt discovers that he has tendencies toward vice which he has neglected —although not wholly, one ought to add. As he approaches fifty, he hastens to make up for the neglect. He enters into an irregular relationship and joins a frivolous gang of youths, in which he plays the role of a generous sugar daddy. But his deeds find him out. His lunches at the club become more and more painful through the silence and aloofness of his friends. They hint that he is spoiling his chance of future membership in the committee of progress. Here it is naturally New York and Chicago that loom before him. He succeeds in recovering his better self, and it is edifying to see him kneel in his pastor's study, where he receives absolution. And then Babbitt can once more devote himself to the Sunday school and other socially useful activities. His story ends as it began.

With his satire Mr. Lewis wishes to attack institutions as representatives of false ideas, and not individuals. It is then a triumph for his art, a triumph almost unique in literature, that he has been able to make this Babbitt, who fatalistically lives within the borders of an earthbound but at the same time pompous utilitarianism, an almost lovable individual.

Babbitt is naïve, and a believer who speaks up for his faith. At bottom

SINCLAIR LEWIS

there is nothing wrong with the man, and he is so festively refreshing
that he almost serves as a recommendation for American snap and
vitality. There are bounders and Philistines in all countries, and one can
only wish that half of them were half as amusing as Babbitt.

To the splendor of the figure, as well as to other speaking characters
in the book, Mr. Lewis has added his unparalleled gift of words. Listen,
for example, to the conversation of a few commercial travelers, sitting together in a compartment of the New York express. An unsuspected halo
falls over the profession of selling. "To them, the Romantic Hero was
no longer the knight, the wandering poet, the cowpuncher, the aviator,
nor the brave young district attorney, but the great sales manager, who
had an Analysis of Merchandising Problems on his glass-topped desk,
whose title of nobility was 'Go-getter,' and who devoted himself and all
his young samurai to the cosmic purpose of Selling—not of selling anything in particular, for or to anybody in particular, but pure Selling."

Arrowsmith (1925) is a work of a more serious nature. Lewis has
there attempted to represent the medical profession and science in all its
manifestations. As is well known, American research in the natural
sciences, physics, chemistry, and medicine ranks with the best of our age,
and it has several times been recognized as such from this very platform.
Tremendous resources have been placed at its command. Richly endowed
institutions work unceasingly on its development.

That even here some speculative persons want to take advantage of
their opportunities may be regarded as inevitable. Private industries are
on the alert for scientific discoveries and want to profit from them before
they have been tested and finally established. The bacteriologist, for instance, searches with infinite care for vaccines to cure widespread diseases, and the manufacturing chemist wants to snatch them prematurely
from his hand for mass production.

Under the guidance of a gifted and conscientious teacher, Martin
Arrowsmith develops into one of the idealists of science. The tragedy of
his life as a research worker is that, after making an important discovery,
he delays its announcement for constantly renewed tests until he is
anticipated by a Frenchman in the Pasteur Institute.

The book contains a rich gallery of different medical types. We have
the hum of the medical schools with their quarreling and intriguing professors. Then there is the unpretentious country doctor, recalled from

Main Street, who regards it as an honor to merge with his patients and become their support and solace. Then we have the shrewd organizer of public health and general welfare, who works himself into popular favor and political power. Next we have the large institutes with their apparently royally independent investigators, under a management which to a certain extent must take into consideration the commercial interests of the donors and drive the staff to forced work for the honor of the institutes.

Above these types rises Arrowsmith's teacher, the exiled German Jew, Gottlieb, who is drawn with a warmth and admiration that seem to suggest a living model. He is an incorruptibly honest servant of science, but at the same time a resentful anarchist and a standoffish misanthrope, who doubts whether the humanity whose benefactor he is amounts to as much as the animals he kills with his experiments. Further, we meet the Swedish doctor, Gustaf Sondelius, a radiant Titan, who with singing and courage pursues pests in their lairs throughout the world, exterminates poisonous rats and burns infected villages, drinks and preaches his gospel that hygiene is destined to kill the medical art.

Alongside all of this runs the personal history of Martin Arrowsmith. Lewis is much too clever to make his characters without blemish, and Martin suffers from faults which at times seem obstructive to his development, both as a man and as a scientist. As a restless and irresolute young man he gets his best help from a little woman he encountered at a hospital where she was an insignificant nurse. When he begins to drift about the country as an unsuccessful medical student, he looks her up in a little village in the Far West, and there she becomes his wife. She is a devoted and simple soul, who demands nothing and who patiently waits in her solitude when, bewitched by the siren of science, her husband loses himself in the labyrinths of his work.

Later she accompanies him and Sondelius to the plague-infected island where Arrowsmith wants to test his serum. Her death in the abandoned hut, while her husband listens distractedly to another and more earthy siren than that of science, seems like a poetically crowning final act to a life of primitive self-sacrificing femininity.

The book is full of admirable learning, certified by experts as being accurate. Though a master of light-winged words, Lewis is never superficial when it comes to the foundations of his art. His study of details is always as careful and thorough as that of such a scientist as Arrowsmith or Gottlieb. In this work he has built a monument to the profession of his own father, that of the physician, which certainly is not represented by a charlatan or a faker.

His big novel *Elmer Gantry* (1927) is like a surgical operation on one of the most delicate parts of the social body. Presumably it would not pay to search anywhere in the world for the old Puritanical virtues, but possibly one might find in some of the oldest corners of America a remnant of the sect which regarded it as a sin to remarry, once it had pleased God to make one a widower or widow, and wicked to lend money at interest. But otherwise America has no doubt had to moderate its religious rigidity. To what extent a pulpiteer like Elmer Gantry is common over there, we cannot here have the slightest idea. Neither his slap-dash style of preaching with his cocky pugilistic manners ("Hello, Mr. Devil") nor his successful collecting of money and men inside the gates of the church can hide the sad fact that he is an unusually foul fish. Mr. Lewis has been neither willing nor able to give him any attractive traits. But as description the book is a feat of strength, genuine and powerful, and its full-flavored, somber satire has a devastating effect. It is unnecessary to point out that hypocrisy thrives a little everywhere and that any one who attacks it at such a close range places himself before a hydra with many dangerous heads.

Sinclair Lewis's latest work is called *Dodsworth* (1929). In his books we have previously caught glimpses of the family as one of the most aristocratic in Zenith—a circle where no Babbitt ever gains admission. "Most aristocratic" probably often means in America "richest," but Sam Dodsworth is both aristocratic and rich. Even after three hundred years he notes the English blood in his veins and wants to know the land of his ancestors. He is an American, but not a jingo. With him travels his wife, Fran. She is already over forty, while he is fifty. She is a cool beauty, "virginal as the winter wind," though she has grown children. In the European atmosphere she blossoms as a brilliant flower of luxury, reveling in vanity, pleasure, and selfishness. She goes so far that the quiet man who loves her has to leave her to her fate.

Once alone he meditates on the problem "Europe–America," and as a real business man he wants to clear up his accounts with both. He thinks of many things, honestly and without prejudice. One of his observations is that the very soil of Europe has some of the old-time quiet, which is scorned by America, the land of restless record-hunters. But America is the land of youth and daring experiments. And when he returns there, we understand that the heart of Sinclair Lewis follows him.

Yes, Sinclair Lewis is an American. He writes the new language—American—as one of the representatives of 120,000,000 souls. He asks us to consider that this nation is not yet finished or melted down; that it is still in the turbulent years of adolescence.

The new great American literature has started with national self-criticism. It is a sign of health. Sinclair Lewis has the blessed gift of wielding his land-clearing implement not only with a firm hand but with a smile on his lips and youth in his heart. He has the manners of a new settler, who takes new land into cultivation. He is a pioneer.

Mr. Sinclair Lewis—I have spoken of you to this assembly in a language which you do not understand. I might have abused the occasion to speak ill of you. I have not done it. I have spoken of you as one of the strong, young chieftains of the great new American literature. Besides, you have a special recommendation to Swedish hearts. You were born among our countrymen in America, and you have mentioned them in friendly terms in your renowned books. We are glad to see you here today and glad that our nation has a laurel of its own to bestow on you. And now I ask you to descend with me and receive it from the hand of our King.

Mr. Lewis made no formal acceptance speech at the banquet. In impromptu remarks he expressed his gratitude and declared that he felt closely related to the Swedish people because of his many acquaintances among the Swedish families of Minnesota. He said that the Nobel Prize had a great significance for him, that it had in fact created a new standard which implied an obligation to improve on what he had done so far. Furthermore, he considered it a high honor to have been awarded the Nobel Prize along with the renowned scholars who received the distinction. He said that he himself had the most profound respect for the integrity of the scientist, and thought that a man of letters, himself included, should strive for the same integrity.

THE MAN WHO KNEW COOLIDGE[1]

By SINCLAIR LEWIS

[Excerpt]

—And I certainly do enjoy listening to you gentlemen and getting your views. That's one of the nice things about being on a Pullman like this: you can guarantee that you'll meet a lot of regular he-Americans with sound opinions and ideas.

And now let me tell you: the way I look at these things—

I don't mean to suggest for one second that I've got any better bean than the plain ordinary average citizen, but I've given a whole lot of attention to politics and such matters and—In fact, strikes me that it's the duty of all the better-educated citizens to take an interest in the affairs of the State, for what, after all, as a fellow was saying to us at the Kiwanis Club the other day—what is the Government but the union of all of us put together for mutual advantage and protection?

And me—why say, I read the political editorials in the *Advocate*—that's the

leading paper in my town—Zenith—I read 'em like most folks read the sporting page. And as a result of all this and certain personal information that I can't disclose the sources of, I've come to the firm conclusion—

Here's something maybe you gentlemen never thought of:

They can all say all they want to about how President Coolidge—good old silent Cal Coolidge!—isn't maybe as flashy as some of these statesmen. Maybe he isn't as much given to shooting off his mouth as certain other public figures that I could name. Maybe he isn't what my daughter would call so "Ritzy"—

And say, by golly it's beyond me where the young generation of today, taking them by and large, get all this slang that they pull. Why, here just the other day my daughter was talking to her brother, and Robby—That's the boy's name; only fifteen; three years younger than his sister, but smart's a whip. There's certainly one up-and-coming kid, if I do say so.

Why say—

Now I never put him up to it, y'understand. The Lord knows I can afford to give him the best the land affords, at least to a reasonable extent, I mean as much

---

[1] Mr. Calvin Coolidge was the President of the United States of North America from 1923 to 1929. He fulfilled many of the soundest American ideals, and he stands, along with the Ford motor car, the Rev. Dr. William Sunday, and the *Saturday Evening Post,* as the symbol of his era.

comfort and even luxury as is good for him. I'd never made a peep about how maybe it'd be a good stunt for him to go out and maybe earn a little money on the side. But he comes in one evening just before supper—before dinnertime, with his hat on one side of his head, looking proud as Punch.

So I says to him, "Well, Robert Livingston—"

As a matter of fact, his middle name isn't Livingston at all, it's Otto, but we often call him Robert Livingston, jokingly.

"Well, Robert Livingston," I says to him, "who do you think you are? Thomas Edison or Napoleon or somebody? Or maybe Red Grange![2] Sit down, Mr. Grange, and let me hang up your hat."

You know, jokingly.

Well, he just looks at me—

I'm afraid if the truth were known the kid is pretty gosh-awful fresh, but he's so darn' cute about it that you can't get sore at him, the darn' little cuss—just as up-and-coming as I was at his age. He just stands and looks at me and sticks his hands in his pants-pockets and then—

Say, what do you think he went and done? He put a record on the Recto-phone.

You know—that's this new kind of phonograph that reproduces every tone of the human voice or music. It's some kind of new scientific invention that for a long time the scientists couldn't ever achieve it. But they got it now so they don't miss any of these undertones—or overtones or whatever it is—that they used to miss by earlier methods of reproduction. It costs a lot more than the old-fashioned phonograph, but way I look at it, the best is the cheapest in the long run.

Well, Robby, the little rascal, he goes to work and puts on a record, something about "I may have been a private in the A.E.F., but believe me I'm a general with the dames." Then he says, "Dad," he says, "in me you behold the feline's *robe de nuit*. I've gone and—"

Mind you, 's I said, I'd never even suggested to him that he get a job out of school-hours and earn a little money. I most certainly do believe that it's a mighty fine thing for a boy to do a little work, no matter how well fixed his folks are, and learn the value of money; learn how doggone hard it is to sneak up on ole Mr. Dollar and get a strangle hold on him.

I swear, a lot of the young folks today seem to think the Old Man is simply made of money and don't have to sweat for every cent he makes. But same time, I hadn't figured it was time yet to explain this to Robby, though maybe that was a mistake on my part, and if it was, I'm perfectly willing to admit it—confession is good for the soul, as they say.

Maybe I should have drummed it into him long ago. I've got it on mighty straight inside information—in fact one of my best friends is acquainted with a man who knows the Rockefellers intimately—and he tells me that the Rockefellers,[3] people with all their jack, they bring their families up to be just as careful of money as any of us: *they* don't let their kids run away with the notion that it don't take any trouble to collect the dough.

Well, this gentleman related a significant little incident regarding the Rockefellers that he heard personally. Seems he was right there at the time. Here was old John D., probably with half the money-kings in the world waiting to see him, talking to young John D., just as simple and quiet as any one of us. And he said,

[2] A professional athlete renowned circ. 1926.

[3] First of the American ducal families.

and I've never forgotten his words—in fact I repeated them to Robby that day—the old gentleman looked at young John D., and prob'ly I imagine he put his hand on his shoulder, and he looked at him and said, *"My boy, waste not, want not!"*

Yes sir!

But anyway—

I'm afraid I'm getting a little off the subject of Coolidge, and if there's anything I hate it's a fellow that if he starts to talk about a subject he can't stick to it.

I remember one time we had one of these book-authors speaking at the Kiwanis Club, and say, that fellow, maybe he could write all right (though at that I'd like to see him sit down and dictate a letter to some fellow that would make him pay his account and yet not make him get sore!)—and as I say, I don't know anything about his writing, but when it came to *talking*, why say, he wandered all round Robin Hood's barn! Shows what a lack of business-training does to these fellows that think they're so gosh-awful smart and superior!

Well, as I say, Robby puts this record on the Rectophone—and that's an instrument you gentlemen certainly want to try—and he looks at me, and he says, "Well, Dad, I've got me a job in Zabriskie's Drug Store for Saturday afternoons, and I draw down one and one-half bucks for each and every said same!"

Pretty good, eh? I'll say it is! And him only fifteen.

But what I started to say was: The way that kid and his sister torture the English language to death just about gets my goat. Here him and his sister was talking one time, and he starts kidding her about some bird she was sweet on, and he says, "That guy's all wet."

But she come back at him, quick's a flash, "Yeh, he's wet like a Methodist Sunday School!"

Yes sir, it beats the cars how this new generation takes the Queen's English like you and I was brought up to speak it in the good old-fashioned schools where there was some thoroughness and discipline and not just a lot of these flashy fads, and they just practically ruin it, and as I was saying, if Sister—that's what we often call my daughter—if *she* was talking about Coolidge, she'd probably say he wasn't "Ritzy."

Well, if you want to look at it that way, all right. Maybe he isn't as high-falutin as some people I could name. But I wonder if any of you gentlemen ever thought of this?

He may not shoot off a lot of fireworks, but do you know what he is? He's SAFE.

Yes sir, Cal is the President for real honest-to-God Americans like us.

There's a lot of folks that pan him, but what are they? You can bet your sweet life he isn't popular with the bums or yeggs or anarchists or highbrows or cynics—

I remember our pastor saying one time, "A cynic is a man who sneers, and a man who sneers is setting himself up to tell God that he doesn't approve of God's handiwork!" No sir! You can bet Coolidge ain't popular with the Bolsheviks or the lazy boob of a workman that wants fifteen bucks a day for doing nothing! No sir, nor with the cocaine fiends or the drunkards or the fellows that don't want the prohibition law enforced—

Not that I never take a drink. What I say about prohibition is:

Once a law has been passed by the duly elected and qualified representatives of the people of these United States, in fact once it's on the statute books, it's *there*, and it's there to be enforced. There hadn't ought to be any blind pigs or illegal stills. But same time, that don't mean you got to be a fanatic.

If a fellow feels like making some

good home-brewed beer or wine, or if you go to a fellow's house and he brings out some hootch or gin that *you* don't know where he got it and it isn't any of your business, or if you have a business acquaintance coming to your house and you figure he won't loosen up and talk turkey without a little spot and you know a good dependable bootlegger that you can *depend* on, why, then that's a different matter, and there ain't any reason on God's green earth that *I* can see why you shouldn't take advantage of it, always providing you aren't setting somebody a bad example or making it look like you sympathized with law-breaking.

No, sir!

But now to come down to the point of my story, I hope to be able to give you gentlemen an agreeable little surprise.

I know Coolidge personally!

Yes sir, in fact I was a classmate of his! Sure as I'm telling you! I'll give you gentlemen an inside view of him, not only as I saw him in college but as I've studied him at the White House!

When I say I was a classmate of his—

Well, the fact is that certain unfortunate family circumstances, that I needn't go into and that wouldn't interest you, prevented me from completing my college course—

My father, and a fine, upstanding, cultured gentleman of the old school he was, too, always ready with a helping hand for any mortal that needed it, a man of A 1 standing in his community— Fall River, Mass., that was; in fact I was born and brought up in Fall River, which is, as you may know, one of the most beautiful and enterprising and go-ahead communities in the fair state of Massachusetts—he was, in fact, the leading corn and feed merchant in all his section of Fall River.

But I'm afraid he put a little too much confidence in the advice of an alleged friend.

Fact is, he invested his savings in a perpetual motion machine company that had little or no value. He died, and it was quite sudden, in December of my Freshman year, so I had to go back home and take up the burden of helping support the family.

But I certainly got a lot of value out of even that comparatively short time at Amherst, and the fellows at the Kiwanis Club tell me that they can see certain educational advantages in the quality of such speeches or motions as I may be called upon to deliver at the club, and welcomes to the speakers.

So it was at college that I was able to get an inside view of Cal Coolidge that has maybe been denied to even his more intimate associates in these later busy years when he has been so engrossed in the cares of the nation.

I don't suppose I could have been called one of Cal's closest friends in college, but I knew him pretty well. In fact we lived not far from each other, and I used to see him frequently. I'll admit that I never had any notion that he'd climb to his present high position and international and historical fame, but even in those days you could see from the way he worked, and the way he looked at a thing from all sides before he went off half-cocked, that in whatever department of life he might choose, he would make his mark. And the next time you hear one of these birds criticizing Coolidge, you just tell 'em *that,* will you, from one who knew him in the days when he wasn't surrounded with adulations!

I can remember just's well as if it was yesterday, Cal and me happened to come out of a class together, and I said, "Well, it's going to be a cold winter," and he came right back, "Yep."

Didn't waste a lot of time arguing and discussing! He knew!

And another time: I never could get

along any too good in Latin. My talent, you might say, is more along practical lines. I asked Cal—we happened to be going into class together, and I asked him, "Say, what's the Latin for 'defy'?"

"Don't know," he said. No beating around the bush and pretending and four-flushing, but coming right out with it, bang! That's the kind of man he is, you take it from one who *knows* him!

Yes sir, I knew the boy and had the greatest affection and respect for him, like all of us who had the rare opportunity of *understanding* him!

And to think that I might not have gotten acquainted with him if we hadn't been chums together in one of the smaller colleges!

I tell you gentlemen, the way I figure it: the great, you might say the invincible advantage of the smaller educational institutions is that they throw the boys together in such intimate contact and— as Dr. Frank Crane[4] says in one of his pieces somewhere—they provide that close knowledge of human beings which fits a boy for supremacy in the future walks and struggles of life. That's been my experience.

Still, same time—

These great modern universities, with their laboratories and stadiums and everything— They do have an advantage; and fact is, my son is preparing to enter the state university.

But anyway:

Naturally, considering that I had the privilege—through no virtue of my own, mind you—of being in my modest way rather chummy with Coolidge, I've watched his rise to world-wide fame with peculiar interest, and after he became President I often said to my wife, "By

golly, I'd like to see the boy and just shake hands with him again."

Not, mind you, because he was President. After all, I've reached a position where I'm just as independent as the other fellow. An American citizen doesn't have to bow down and kowtow to anybody, whether it be the President or a millionaire or Queen Marie[5] of Bulgaria or anybody—

By the way, Queen Marie made quite a stay at Zenith. She stopped over pretty near an hour between trains, and say, we certainly gave her a good time. The mayor read her an address and presented her with a gold-mounted polished cow's-foot combination ink-well, thermometer, and daily text calendar that I'll bet she's showing the folks in her palace right now. But I mean:

It wasn't because he was President, as I explained to the wife, but—

"Besides," I said to her, "just between you and me, I bet it would give the boy a real kick, after having to associate with ambassadors and generals and Frank Kellogg[6] and all those high-up guys, to be able to let down for a minute and shake the mitt of a fellow that he used to laugh and joke with in the old care-free days before we both assumed the responsibilities of our present careers."

So here about six months ago, when we were planning to take a little trip to New York—

I had to go to New York to look over a new mimeographing machine. You see, I'm in the office-supply business, and let me tell you gentlemen that though I'm the first to respect other professions, though I honor the surgeon who can snatch you from the very gates of death, the lawyer who can so brilliantly argue your case—though personally I always

---

[4] A clergyman often known, about 1927, as "the Christian Voltaire of America."

[5] A lady formerly a queen.
[6] A former American cabinet minister.

think it's better to settle out of court—or the great banker or department-store owner, yet in all fairness let me put this to you:

Who is it that enables these gentlemen to do business and get their great ideas across in an up-to-date, efficient, time-saving manner? Who is it but the office-supply man! Yes sir, I'm proud of my profession, and as a matter of fact I have the honor of representing the office-supply category in our great Zenith Kiwanis Club!

Just take filing-cabinets alone!

I always say, and sometimes the boys laugh at me at the Athletic Club, but good-naturedly, because I've got as fine a lot of friends as anybody I know, and believe me I'm mighty good and proud of them, and I tell 'em, "Boys," I say, "excuse me if I get flowery, but you must always remember I'm a great reader of Colonel Bob Ingersoll—though I'm the first to deprecate the unfortunate religious ideas and skepticism that marred that otherwise great philosopher and public speaker, and probably it's from him that I got the idea of talking without having to resort to cheap and vulgar phrases, besides being a college man and—

"Excuse me if I get highfalutin," I often say to them—you know, at lunch at the Athletic Club—you know how a lot of fellows will get to reminiscing and chewing the rag when maybe they ought to be beating it back to their offices and getting on the job, but—

"Maybe you think I'm getting kind of woozy about it," I tell 'em, "but to me the beauties of modern filing-systems, which enable a man to instantly and without the least loss of time or effort find a letter on which, perhaps, depends the closing of an important deal, is in its practical way, to say nothing of the physical appearance of modern up-to-date filing-cabinets, no longer mere wooden boxes but whether in steel or fireproofed wood, the finest example of the cabinet-maker's art and imitating perfectly the rarest woods—To me," I often tell them, "these filing-systems are in every way as beautiful as the poet's song, as the flush on the maiden's cheek when she first hears the first whispered words of love, or the soft chirp of the mother bird at eveningtide, chirping to her birdlings. Yes sir, you bet your sweet life they are, and you can laugh all you want to!"

So as I say, I had to go on to New York to look over—

I usually do my buying in Chicago, but this was a new caper that the wholesalers in Chicago hadn't got hold of yet. I'd been working pretty hard, and my wife was kind of a little run down from the after-effects of the flu—

And say, God, what a curse *that* is! I wonder if you gentlemen ever stopped to think that though the flu is in each individual case so much less fatal than diseases like the plague or brain-fever, yet considering the *number* of those afflicted with it—and after all, when you look at a subject, you've got to go into the statistics of it—of course naturally an office-supply man has great advantages that way, being in the business— When you think how *many* folks get flu, it seems like one of the most important of all diseases.

I tell you, I'm as religious as the next fellow, and I never'd for one moment dream of criticizing the preachers' doctrines—let them figure out theology and religion, I say, and I'll stick to the office-supply business. But don't it sometimes almost make you question the workings of Providence when you see the mysterious way in which disease smites down the just with the unjust?

Why, my wife went on sniveling and subject to constant headaches for more than six weeks after the doctor *said* he'd got her all cured of the flu!

So I said to her, "Honey," as I often call her, "what say you and me and Delmerine—"

Delmerine, that's my daughter's name. Don't know, by the way, that I've introduced myself. Lowell Schmaltz is my name—

Funny! Whole lot of people take Schmaltz for a German name, but of course as a matter of fact, when you look into the matter, it isn't German at all but Pennsylvania Dutch, which is almost the same as saying New England Yankee and—

Well, I figured Delmerine could get away all right, because she's finished high school.

I'd asked her if she wanted to go to college—I could perfectly well afford to send her, of course—but she thought it over and she felt more kind of called to the musical line, and she was taking vocal and piano. But I figured she could drop them all right for a few weeks and I said—

Robby (that's my son), of course he couldn't get away, because he was in school, but—

I says to my wife, "Mamie, how'd it strike you—I've simply got to go to New York on a business trip and things are kind of slack now, and how'd it be if Delmerine and you went along and saw the sights and everything?"

Say, she was tickled pink! She'd never seen New York, and of course—

Not that I'd want to live in the Big Burg. What I always say is: New York is a swell hang-out for a few days' visit, and theaters and all like that, but when it comes to living there—say, I wouldn't live there if they gave me Times Square and threw in Riverside Drive to boot. Compared with Zenith—

And believe me, gentlemen—

I don't believe in going around boosting your own burg all the time. I don't suppose Zenith is any better, practically, than Minneapolis or Cincinnati or Pittsburgh, say. But it certainly is one high-class city, and you may or may not know that not only do we lead the world in the manufacture of loud speakers and overalls, but we have, since Lindbergh's transoceanic flight, made all the plans and raised quite a lot of the money to construct the largest and finest flying-field between Chicago and New York, excepting Detroit and Dayton of course, and we plan to have a restaurant at the areodrome there serving short-orders twenty-four hours a day.

And I must say Mamie and I are pretty well fixed there. Believe me, we don't have to travel to get any ideas how to live! Just a couple of years ago I finished building a dandy little Italian villa-style bungalow, with a Spanish mission entrance. We've got two bathrooms, and a fireplace, and everything fixed up first-rate, and in the basement I've installed an electric washing-machine and a garbage-incinerator, and we got something that you don't find in many houses: in both bathrooms I've got a slit in the wall, right by the stationary bowls, for the disposal of safety razor blades.

And say! I've got a great plan. Some day I'm—I am, by golly, no kid!—sounds crazy, but it'd be the greatest luxury you gentlemen ever heard of; just think, when you were taking a nice, long, lazy hot bath; some day I'm going to put a radio in my bathroom! But that's an ideal to be worked out in the future. Maybe it'll be my contribution to American progress. But still, let that pass, for the moment. As I say, we don't live so bad.

And of course I drive a Chrysler myself and I gave my wife a Chevrolet coop—

Say, I certainly got a rise out of her. She's one darn' nice little woman, if I do say so; been an A 1 wife in every way, even if she does kick a little sometimes about my driving too fast. Well, here her last birthday I come home and I could see she was mouching around skittish as a wasp, because 'most always on her birthdays I've got something tucked inside my pocket for her.

"Do you know what day this is?" I finally says to her, after I'd looked over the paper and listened in on the radio a little—though I remember there wasn't anything on then except the daily stock receipt reports from the Omaha packing yards.

She brightens up and tries to look kittenish and makes out like she doesn't know, and she says, "No, what?"

"It's the day—or it will be the evening—of the Kid Milligan-Pooch Federstein fight, and we better invite in some of the folks and listen to the fight on the radio," I says.

Well sir, the poor kid, she certainly did look awful' down in the mouth. I didn't know whether she was going to be plucky, or whether she'd bawl me out—I got to admit she does, sometimes. But she was game and didn't say anything, and pretty soon, 'long about fifteen, maybe twenty minutes, I suggested we go out and have a little walk before dinner. Well, meantime, you get me, I'd had the fellow bring this Chevrolet coop around and park it right in front of the house.

"Here's a nice little car," I says when I sees the Chev. "Wonder how she runs."

And I goes and gets in and starts it!

Well sir— You know how women carry on. She cusses me out, and she beefs, and she gets on a rampage, and she says, "Why Lowell Schmaltz," she says, "what do you mean! What'll the owner say?"

"I'll bet he'll do a lot of saying," I

laughs, "if he—or she—happens to see me in it!"

"Why, I never *knew* you to do a thing like that!" she says. "You get right out of that car!"

Say, I had her wild!

"So that's how a fellow gets treated, is it," I says, and I pretend to look hurt, and I gets out, and then I draws her attention to a little card that I'd had tied on the door handle—'d tied it on myself, matter of fact—that said, "To Mamie on her birthday from Woofums"—Woofums —kind of a nut name, but that's what she calls me sometimes when we're kind of fooling around.

Say, maybe she didn't pretty nearly keel over!

Yes sir, you bet, both of us have our own cars, though mine—

It ain't the fault of the Chrysler itself, I'm certain of that, certainly a high-grade A 1 machine, but the garage got to fooling with it, and my car's got a squeak in it somewhere that I by golly simply can *not* locate, and say, if there's anything gets me wild when I'm driving—

I can stand the big gaff— Why say, when I had a tire blow out on me after only two thousand miles (any of you gentlemen ever try the Melps tire? Well, don't, that's my advice to you, and believe me I know, I've tried two of them, and in my opinion this monkey-business they advertise about wrapping the fabric crosswise or whatever it is is all the bugs; don't get the result they claim at all)—

I can stand those big things, but say, even the littlest squeak, why say, it simply drives me crazy when I'm driving.

Why, here just last Sunday I was driving the family out to a cousin of ours that lives in Elmwood for Sunday dinner, and it was as fine a day as you ever saw, but just about the time I began to enjoy myself, and I was going past the Seven Corners and looking at the new filling-station they got there—say, man, I'll bet that's one of the finest filling-stations in the United States: twelve pumps they got, and a comfort station fixed up to look like an old-fashioned log cabin, and a supply store with a great big huge enormous fish-aquarium simply chuck full of goldfish right in the window. And geraniums.

And just when I was calling it to Mame's attention—by golly all of a sudden that squeak started again.

Well say, I couldn't enjoy anything all day. After dinner, I took Cousin Ed out for a drive, to see if he could locate the squeak, and we drove right down through a woods, a park they got there, mighty pretty and I'd 've enjoyed it like the dickens—I always was a great believer in Nature—but every time I looked at a tree or a nice rustic-style bench or something like that, that darn' squeak would start in again, and Cousin Ed—he thinks he's such a wiz at cars, but Lord love you, he couldn't locate that squeak any more'n I could.

But's I say: I guess we're about as well fixed as most folks and we certainly don't have to get away from home to enjoy ourselves, but when I said to my wife, "I kind of got an idea you and Delmerine might come along with me and give New York the once-over," she looked like somebody'd left her a million dollars.

And Delmerine she just hollers, "Oh boy! I'll give those Manhattan cabarets a look at a live one for once!"

"And we might stop at Cousin Walter's in Troy, on the way," I says.

"Oh no, let's not," says my wife.

"But we *got* to go there! Ain't Cousin Walter living there?" I says.

"Well, what of that?" she says. "Haven't you and he always hated each other?"

"Well, maybe we have," I says, "but he's a *relative,* ain't he? And when you

travel you got to look up your relatives, ain't you?"

Well, make a long story short, we decided to stop at Cousin Walter's for a few days—and then—man!—then I springs the big surprise!

"And after New York," I says, "we'll come home by way of Washington, and we'll stop in and call on the President!"

"Oh Papa, we couldn't do *that!*" Delmerine hollers.

"I'd like to know why not!" I says. "Ain't he and I classmates?"

"Yes, but maybe he wouldn't remember you," she says.

"Now you look here!" I says. "If you think for one moment that I wasn't just as important in college as he was, and maybe then some—they told me if I could have stayed till spring I'd 've been on the baseball team— But that isn't the point! Let me tell you right now that words like that are an insult not to me, my fine young lady, but to the Great Executive himself!

"What is it that more than any other one quality distinguishes leaders of men like Cal? It isn't merely his profound thought, his immovable courage, his genial and democratic manners, but it's the fact that he's so close a student of human nature that he quickly but thoroughly studies each man as he meets him, and so never *can* forget him! Understand now," I says to them, "I understand that the President is one of the busiest men in the country, what with having to sign documents, and shake hands with delegations of Elks, and so on, and I certainly don't intend to intrude, but we'll just drop in and give him a pleasant surprise—think how many years it is since we've seen each other!—and just shake hands and pass on. And you'll be able, Delmerine, to tell your grandchildren that once you heard the voice of Calvin Coolidge!"

Well, of course when I made it clear

they were tickled to death at the prospect, and so we started making plans— personally I was for just taking some suitcases along, but my wife held out for the black trunk, and I must say—I'm always the first one to admit it when I'm licked, and Mamie certainly won that time!— she pointed out I'd have to have my dress-suit in New York and it wouldn't get wrinkled in a wardrobe trunk—and now say, while we're speaking of that, I'll bet it's struck you gentlemen as it has me: there's one of the highest-class and most significant of modern inventions that do so much to make life happy, the wardrobe trunk, and what a lot it adds to ease of travel and seeing the world, yes sir, she sure won that time and—

And just then—

Say, isn't it funny how a fellow will remember comparatively unimportant details even at a critical time! Happened just then that Robby—that's my son, he's only fifteen, and the little cuss had started smoking, seems like I'd done everything I could to make him stop, but he's such a cute little beggar the way he comes back at you when you try to bawl him out that I never could get a word in edgeways. Well, he comes in—

And besides, I must say I still ain't sold on the idea of cigarettes.

I think I can with justification call myself what you might call a modern, up-to-date liberal man. I was the first fellow in my neighborhood to put in a radio, and I never did believe they ought to have hung Sacco and Vanzetti if they were innocent. But when it comes to smoking, I still prefer a pipe or a good cigar.

But's I was saying, he comes in smoking a cigarette, and Delmerine—that's my daughter, a girl that I want to tell you gentlemen can in my judgment sing just as good right this minute as Schumann-Heink or Sophie Tucker or any of these famous prima donnas—and she

hollers at him, "Say, Dad's going to take us to see President Coolidge."

And he says, "Gee whiz! Are you going to give him enough warning so he can get away?"

Well say, maybe I didn't light into him then! I believe in giving kids their freedom, but I've told Robby time and time again that it's nice language and nice manners that enable a fellow to get along in this world, and if he'd study his mother and me a little more instead of a lot of these smart-aleck cigarette-sucking high-school fraternity yahoos, he'd be a lot better off! You bet! Every time!

Well, so we decided to go and got started. I don't want to bore you gentlemen with a lot of details of our trip. Of course what you want to hear about is the inside glimpse of Coolidge and the White House that I was privileged to have. So I'll cut it short and come right down to the real meat of the story.

So we got off on the noon train in about a week and— Say, it certainly is remarkable, ain't it, the conveniences of railroad travel today—in America, I mean, not abroad. A fellow that knows every inch of Europe was telling me there ain't a what you might call really comfortable train in the whole length and breadth of the Old Country. But here—

There I sits in the club car, with every convenience and luxury—soft drinks (personally I always find the Loganberry Highball the best drink on a Pullman)— and soft drinks to be had just by touching a button, and a regular library of free magazines and everything, especially the *Saturday Evening Post,* which is, taking it by and large, my favorite magazine, especially the advertisements, now that they've taken to printing 'em in colors.

Say! they can keep their old masters; give me some of these advertisements!

Yes sir, it's wonderful what strides advertising has made these last few years.

Of course I admire the really great and leading American authors—Mrs. Rinehart and Peter B. Kyne and Arthur Brisbane[7]—but I doubt if even they can touch the fellows that get up these advertisements nowadays. And it was a mighty bright idea—I don't know who started it, but this idea of working in a girl with pretty legs in all sorts of ads; not only stocking ads, but auto ads, showing her climbing into a car; and machinery, showing her giving it the North and South, and so on. Yes sir, a fellow that wants to understand the United States, all he has to do is study the *Saturday Evening Post* ads, and he'll see why we're the most advanced nation in the world, and the most individual.

There's a lot of sorehead critics of America that claim we're standardized, but—

Well, to take an example, let me take—well, just for an example let me take the fellow that I happened to be lunching with before I caught this train —just take the differences between him and me. We both belong to the Athletic Club, we both belong to service clubs, we have our places of business in the same block, we live within a quarter of a mile of each other, we both like golf and a good lively jazz on the radio. And yet this fellow and me—his name is Babbitt, G. F. Babbitt, fellow in the real estate game—we're as different as Moses and Gene Tunney.[8]

Where these poor devils of Europeans are crushed down and prevented from having their characters developed by the wide and free initiative so characteristic of American life, George and me can be friendly, yet as different—

Well, like this, for instance: I drive a Chrysler, and Babbitt doesn't. I'm a Congregationalist, and Babbitt has no use whatsomever for anything but his old Presbyterian church. He wears these big round spectacles, and you couldn't hire me to wear anything but eyeglasses— much more dignified, *I* think. He's got so he likes golf for its own sake, and I'd rather go fishing, any day. And—and so on. Yes sir, it's a wonderful thing how American civilization, as represented, you might say, by modern advertising, has encouraged the, as a speaker at the Kiwanis recently called it, free play of individualism.

But as I say—

Make a long story short, we got to Cousin Walter's at Troy all right, and on to New York—

But say, Walt certainly did entertain us in fine style—I got to thinking he wasn't such a bad cuss after all. And he's got a new house that, and I'm the first to admit it, is just as modern as mine is! A modern homey home! Vacuum cleaner and gas clothes-dryer and one of these new noiseless electric refrigerators—

Man, what a convenience that is! I never could understand why they make so much fuss over Babe Ruth or even a real scientific pioneer like Lindbergh, when we haven't yet done anything to boost the honest-to-God master genius that invented the electric refrigerator.

Think of what it'll do! Give you every sort of frozen dessert! Get rid of the iceman that tracks mud on the back porch! Provide ice-water so you can have a refreshing drink night or day! What I always say is: these fellows can have their big libraries, their blinking art galleries, their private pipe organs, their rose gardens, but when it comes down to the *practical* things that make home an inspiration and solid comfort to a real family, give me an electric refrigerator! And I got to admit that Walt's radio

---

[7] Three distinguished writers of fiction of the first quarter of the twentieth century in America.

[8] Another celebrated athlete, much influenced by G. Bernard Shaw.

shades mine just the least little bit. And there's mighty few things that indicate a fellow's social rank and progress better than his radio.

And what an invention *that* is! *What* an invention! Talk about miracles—

Just think of it! Here you sit at home in the ole over-stuffed chair, happy as a clam at low tide (or is it high tide?— whichever it is). You sit there and smoke your pipe and twiddle the knob and what do you get? *Think* of it! Right there at home you hear the best jazz music in the country, bands in the best hotels in Chicago, and that wonderful orchestra at Zion City! All the hockey matches right while they're going on! Jokes by the best comedians in the country—

Say, I heard a crackajack over the radio the other day. Seems there was a couple of fellows sitting chinning in a Pullman, just like we are. "Haven't I met you in Buffalo?" one fellow says to the other, and the other says, "I've never been in Buffalo," and the first fellow says, "Neither have I—must 've been a couple o' other fellows!"

Yes sir! and then think of the instructive lectures you get on the radio—why say, just the other night I heard that in the eye of the ordinary house-fly there are several thousand, I think it was, separate lenses. Ever know that?

And then the sermons on Sunday morning. Why, that alone would make the radio one of the most world-revolutionizing inventions the world has ever known.

I tell you, it gives a real spiritual uplift to a poor devil that all week, excepting maybe at the Kiwanis lunch, he's had to toil and moil amid the dust of busy affairs and forget higher things. You bet! I'll never forget one sermon that I wouldn't ever 've heard, if I hadn't had the radio, it being 'way off in Youngstown, Ohio—Reverend Wayo on how he

didn't want to say that every atheist was a bootlegger, but you could bet your sweet life every bootlegger was an atheist!

Cute idea for a sermon, eh? and—

Yes sir, there's never been anything that makes for sound internationalism, nothing that combats the destructive and malign propaganda of the Bolsheviks and pacifists and all like that like the radio, and personally I class it right in with card-catalogues as an inspiration to the New Era.

So as I say, Walt's radio was every bit as good as mine, and we had some dandy drives around Troy and a big beer party Sunday evening—the only evening we stayed up late—I was mighty glad to find that Walt still kept regular hours and turned in about ten.

I tell you there never was a truer saying than "Early to bed, early to rise, makes a man healthy, wealthy, and wise"—I've certainly found it true in my own case—and we drove out for a few rounds of golf—

Now you take golf. By golly, if anybody'd told me fifteen years ago that I'd be out on the links chasing a little white pill around, I'd 've told 'em they were crazy, but let me tell you, I found one of the best ways to get acquainted with customers was to play round with 'em, and I saw what a mossback I'd been, and I've got so I like the game itself a good deal— take like my playing there at Troy even when I wasn't making any valuable contacts—and even though the weather was pretty chilly and—

Seems to me that on the whole the weather has gotten warmer than it used to be when we were kids. You read in the papers how it hasn't changed materially, but they can say what they want to, don't you remember how doggone cold it used to be mornings when we had to get up and chase off to school, and now it seems like we don't have any more old-fashioned winters—maybe that's one reason why the kids today aren't as self-reliant as we were—

But to get back to my subject. As I say, I certainly did enjoy my stay with Walt as I hadn't expected to, especially his stories and inside information about the War, he was a lieutenant in the quartermaster's corps at Camp Devon—

You know, there's a lot of false ideas about the War. I don't want to criticize General Pershing—I know he ranks among the greatest generals we've ever had, right along with Grant and Lee and Israel Putnam, but same time what we ought to done, what I'd 've done if I'd been running things, was to march right straight through to Berlin, and make them Germans suffer *good*—suffer like we did.

I was explaining this to my wife, and she says, "Why, Lowell T. Schmaltz," she says, "I'm ashamed of you! Don't we know some Germans that are awful' nice folks?"

"You don't know the Germans like I do," I says to her. "They haven't got any forward-looking ideas. They believe in rule by tyranny and despotism and compulsion and all that, and if they haven't understood our democratic ideas, they ought to 've been *forced* to, that's what they ought to 've been!" I told her. "But same time you got to hand it to 'em— they certainly have buckled down to work ever since the War. Be a good thing if *our* workmen worked like that, 'stead of watching the clock and thinking about a raise all the time!"

But make a long story short, we certainly enjoyed our stay, and we went on to New York.

I was kind of sore all the time I was in New York, though. These damn' New Yorkers—I hope none of you gentlemen come from New York—they seem to think they run the nation, and what I always say is, as a matter of fact they're the most provincial town in the country! Give me Chicago every time.

You see, when I go to Chicago, in the first place I always stay at the Hotel Grand Imperial Palace, it's a nice quiet little place and the clerks *know* me and try to give me a little service, but in those big New York hotels, they're so darn' independent, you'd think they were doing you a favor.

Then when it comes to business—

In Chicago I usually do the bulk, you might say, of my business with Starbright, Horner, and Dodd; and Billy Dodd himself looks after me, and say, there's a man that it's a pleasure to do business with, a square-shooter if ever there was one, and always got a good story and a two-bit cigar for you, and acts like he was glad to see you, and he isn't one of those fellows to throw seven kind of cat-fits if maybe a fellow is temporarily a little short and wants an extension of a couple of days or a month or so. Yes sir, and many's the good lunch I've had with Billy in the old Palmer House before they tore it down, and though of course this new Palmer House is you might say a regular palace, still, there was kind of an atmosphere about the old place, and say, they certainly did know how to cook steak and fried onions to a turn. Um! And oyster stew. But in New York—

All this darn' fancy French food, and the *prices*—

"My God," I says to one of these smart-aleck headwaiters, or maybe he was what they call a captain, anyway he was the fellow that takes the order and then he hands it on to the regular waiter. "My God," I said to him, when I looks at the prices on the bill of fare, "I just come in here to eat," I says. "I don't want to buy the hotel!"

And just the same way in the business world.

Why say, the firm that was handling these new mimeograph machines, they said they were behind on their orders and they couldn't make a delivery right away. Oh, that's all right, I told 'em—why couldn't they fill my order and keep some other fellow waiting?

No sir, they said, they wouldn't do it. They were just naturally arbitrary about it, and when I tried to make 'em understand that with the class and volume of business that *I* do, they ought to be willing to make some concessions, they acted like a bunch of human icicles. Some day I'm going to write a letter to the New York newspapers and tell 'em what a real he-American from the Middle West thinks about their town—

The noise, and traffic so thick you can't get anywhere, and the outrageous prices and—

And no home-life. Folks all out in the evening, hitting it up at these night clubs and everything. Now you take us, back home, for instance. Evenings, except maybe when I have to be at the lodge or some Kiwanis committee meetings, or maybe Delmerine or Robby are at the movies or a party or something, we all just settle down around the radio and have a real old-fashioned homey time together. But not in New York! No sir! I swear, I don't know what the nation's coming to—

And too many foreigners—fellows with Wop names and Hunky names and Lord knows what all—and this corrupt politics—

Oh say, speaking of politics, if I may interrupt myself a moment and take the risk of straying from my story, I got to tell you what I heard at the Kiwanis luncheon just this past week. Our congressman, and I think it's pretty generally conceded even right in Washington that he's got one of the ablest minds in the entire House of Representatives, he got back from an extensive investigation of the European status—spent six weeks in Germany, France, and Italy, and he gave it as his measured opinion that all these countries are so prosperous now that we certainly ought to press for the payment of our debt in full! Why, he said that in the better class of hotels in those countries, you could get just as good food and nearly as expensive as in New York itself! And they complaining about being poor!

But to get back to my story, I didn't think so much of New York, though we did have one dandy evening—we ran into some folks from home at the hotel lobby, and we all went out to a Chink restaurant and threw in some of the best chicken chow mein that I ever ate in my life, and then we went to a movie that I knew was good because I'd seen it in Zenith—Hoot Gibson in a crackajack western film.

But Delmerine, she liked New York, and my Lord, how that girl did keep nagging and teasing and complaining—

She wanted to go to one of these night clubs. I pointed out to her that all day long while I had to work, talking to a lot of different firms, she and her mother were free to enjoy themselves—go to a matinée or look over the stores and shop a little (though I didn't encourage 'em to buy too much— "Why not wait till you get back home—the stores there are just as up-to-date as New York, far's I can see," I pointed out to 'em). But she kept insisting, and her mother more or less agreed with her, and so one night I took 'em to a swell night club that was recommended to me by one of the bell-boys at the hotel, cute little tad, knew the town like a book.

Well, thinks I, here's where I have a punk evening, but I want to admit that I was wrong. Not but what it was expensive, and I certainly wouldn't want to go to one of those places more'n once or twice a year, but say, that was some place!

First off, we was all kind of disappointed. We drives up to a house in the Fifties, just an ordinary-looking place, and all dark.

"This can't be the place," I says to the taxi driver.

"Sure, this is the joint all right," he says.

"Are you sure?" I says.

"Sure, you bet," he says. "I've driven lots of folks here. You just ring that basement bell and they'll let you in," he says.

Well, I figured he probably knew his business, so my wife and Delmerine and I, we all piled out of the taxi, and I went and rang the bell at the basement door—well, they call it the basement; it was really practically the ground floor, but this was one of those houses that they got so many of in New York, or used to have anyway, though now a lot of 'em are being torn down to make way for modern apartment houses—graystone houses they call 'em, and you go up a flight of steps from the street to the front door, so the door to this basement floor, as they call it, was really kind of under these steps practically on the ground level, only of course you go down into a kind of areaway that's a step or maybe it might have been two steps below the pavement level but not more than that if I remember rightly, and there was a kind of iron grilled door, but, 's I said, there weren't any lights or anything that *we* could see, and I wondered if the taxi-driver could've been right and—

But I rung the bell and pretty soon, sure enough, the door opened, and by golly there was a fellow in one of these funny Lord High Admiral uniforms, and

I says to him, "Is this the Nouvelle Desire—" That was the name of the joint I was looking for— "Is this the Nouvelle Desire?" I says.

"Yes, but I haven't the pleasure of knowing your face," he says—you know, some highfalutin comeback like that.

Well, I kidded him along—I told him it wasn't such a hard face to know when you put your mind to it. Delmerine—she stood right back of me, and I must say, maybe it was just because she was my girl, but she wore a kind of light violet dress and shiny spangles and gold slippers, and say, she certainly looked as elegant as anybody there that night, and my wife wasn't such a slouch herself, for a Mid Western girl and—

But as I was saying, Delmerine was standing right near me, and she kind of whispers to me, "Say, you hadn't ought to kid the servants like that."

But I knew this guy in the uniform wasn't any ordinary servant and I wanted to show him I was just as used to the Gay Life as anybody (of course I was wearing my dress-suit) and—

But anyway, he calls what I figured out to be the assistant manager—nice-looking fellow in a dress-suit, kind of dark-complected, Italian I guess, but a nice-spoken fellow.

He explained that this Nouvelle Desire was a club and they couldn't let in nobody that didn't belong, but I introduced him to the wife and Delmerine, and I explained we come from Zenith and was only in town for about a week, and I showed him my Elks card, and he looked us over good, and he said maybe he could fix it—the regular membership cost two hundred bucks a head a year, but finally he let me have a temporary membership for that week for only five bucks a head.

So we got in all safe and—

Maybe you couldn't see any lights outside, but inside, oh boy! It was fixed up as elegant as if it was the Vanderbilts' ballroom. They'd turned the whole parlor floor—that is, the floor above the basement, I guess they had the kitchen and all like that on the basement floor—

And here was a funny thing: this assistant manager—he and I got to be quite chummy; he told me to call him Nick, and I said he was to call me Low, but he said that was against the rules—and Nick told me something that may surprise you gentlemen as it certainly surprised me at the time: he told me that they did all their cooking by electricity!

Then as I say, there was this kind of ballroom. Halfway up, the wall was all red satin or silk or something, with a lot of what they call Modern Art decoration, or that's what Nick called it—all kinds of zigzags and big flowers and everything in gold; and then above that the walls was all hung with flowers. I found they was artificial flowers, but they looked so real you had to touch 'em before you'd believe it. And some of the tables was in kind of booths fixed up so that they looked like grape arbors and all like that. And at the end of the room there was some great big yellow marble columns—it looked like real genuwine marble, though it may not have been—in front of where the orchestra played—and say, the boys in that orchestra certainly were some jazz babies all right, all coons, but they had a regular high-class musical education, Nick told me later, and the fellow that played the saxophone—say, if they got anybody better'n him in Paul Whiteman's[9] band, I want to hear him, that's all— Why say, he could make that ole saxophone sound like a fog horn or a sick cow or anything he wanted.

Well, before we got settled down—there weren't many folks there yet—Nick took me aside and said they had a regular

sure-enough old-fashioned bar on the floor above, and he thought maybe he could fix it so I could go up and get outside of a little real liquor. The rules of the club, or so he said anyway, the rules of the club made every fellow buy wine at his table, and when it comes to fizz, of course it's a grand high-class wine, but it ain't got the authority like hootch, like the fellow says.

Well, make a long story short, he went away and he fixed it so we could go up to the bar.

I'd just intended to let Delmerine and her mother have some ginger ale up there, but seems they didn't stock any soft drinks, and anyway Delmerine put up a holler.

"I want a cocktail," she says, "and I'll bet so does Mamma, if she tells the truth. Maybe we'll never get to another night club again," she says. "And besides," she says, "you've let me taste a sip of your cocktail when you've had 'em at home. And think of what my bunch will say if I go back home and tell 'em we went to a night club and I couldn't have a cocktail. I'm not a kid," she says.

Well, anyway, I kicked, and I pointed out her mother didn't want any—my wife's a great believer in prohibition—but her mother, doggone her, she went and laid right down on me and didn't back me up— Just kind of giggled, and said she wouldn't mind one herself, just this once. So, make a long story short, we all had a cocktail— Mame took a Bronx, and Delmerine took a side-car, if I remember rightly, and I ordered a Martini and then I said, "By golly, I believe I'll have a Manhattan. Must be five years since I've had a Manhattan cocktail." And so I had a Manhattan. And then I sneaked in a couple highballs while Mame and the girl was in the ladies' dressing-room, and say, by that time I certainly did feel primed for one high, wide and fancy evening.

[9] The Ysaye and Toscanini of America.

And I want to say that, think what you may of New York, we certainly had said evening.

Nick had fixed us up a nice little table almost right next to where they danced.

We looked around and there was a nice-looking lot of people there—they was just coming in. Delmerine was just saying, "Oh, I wish we knew somebody here—I won't have anybody to dance with except you, Papa," and I was informing her that I was regarded as by golly just as good a dancer as anybody at the Country Club, when—Say, you could 've knocked me down with a feather! Yes sir, I hears a familiar voice, and there stands Sam Geierstein of the Mammoth Clothing Company of Zenith—fellow I'd often met at the Athletic Club.

Now there's a whole lot of fellows I'd rather seen than Sam. To tell the truth, just between ourselves, he hasn't got any too good a reputation for square dealing, and I've heard some mighty queer rumors about the way him and his lady secretary carry on. But same time—you know how it is when you're away from home—especially in a city like New York where they're such a chilly lot of stiffs: familiar face sure does look good to you.

So we invites Sam to sit down, and say, I will say one thing for him, he certainly did insist on buying his share of wine and then some. And he sure could dance. I never did like his looks—kind of too dark and good-looking, and big black eyes like you don't really like to see in a real he-male, but he certainly did spin Delmerine and even the wife around that ole floor all right. And me, after I'd got a little champagne into my system, I guess I wouldn't have hardly beefed much even if he'd kissed Delmerine—

Not that he did anything like that, you understand; he acted like a perfect gentleman, you understand; and once

when I was dancing with Mame, and I kind of slipped and almost fell down—they had that floor altogether too slippery for any use—why, it was Sam that grabbed me and kept me from falling.

Though I don't like the way he's been hanging around the house since we been back in Zenith—seems he's got a wife somewhere only they're separated. Delmerine, she says I'm crazy. She says she just discusses music with Sam—seems he knows a lot about it. But I don't like her being out late—

Oh, I guess I'm an old crank. But Del is so young, and she thinks she knows everything but she's innocent as a baby, but— Oh, I'm a regular fusser. But anyway, we certainly did have one large round time that evening—evening, huh! Say, we certainly were high-rollers for once! I'll bet it was three o'clock before we hit the hay. I remember—

It was kind o' comic! Here was Mame—that's my wife—supposed to be a good respectable dame, and me, a deacon in the church, and us coming down Broadway at three A.M. singing "We Won't Go Home Until Morning!"

You see, Sam—he's got the nerve of the devil—he picked up a couple from Fort Worth, Texas (and maybe she wasn't some baby; say, she had all the regular New York dames there beat a mile), and somehow, I don't exactly remember how, we got acquainted with another couple from San José, California, a gentleman that was in the fruit ranching business and his wife and son, he took a shine to Delmerine; and up in the bar I got talking to a gentleman and lady from Kansas City, Missouri—or it may have been Kansas City, Kansas. I can't exactly remember, at this late date —and the whole lot of us carried on like we'd always known each other, dancing and laughing and drinking toasts and singing and drinking and cutting up—

Say! But I hate to think of what it cost me. But as I told my wife, that's the way of it, in New York.

But I don't need to tell you gentlemen about New York. Probably you know it better'n I do, and you want me to sing my little song and get it finished and get on to Washington and my experiences at the White House. Yes sir, the less said about New York the better. Money-mad, that's what the New Yorkers are.

If I wanted to sacrifice other more worth-while things, like our home-life and friendships and reading worth-while literature, and getting in a good fish every summer— And let me tell you that they can talk about Canada all they want to, but if they can show me any better fishing than I get up in Northern Michigan, right within you'd hardly call it more'n an overnight ride from Zenith, why just let 'em show it to me, that's all!

But the way I look at it, a fellow ought to be prosperous for his family's sake and that of his own position in the community, but money-making can be overdone, and what I always say is, Ideals before Dollars every time.

So that's what I think of New York and— And then we packed up and went on to Washington, and say, Delmerine pretended she didn't care, but she was so excited over the prospect of having a chat with the President that she couldn't hardly sit still on the train. Well, so was I—hadn't seen Cal for so many years. I got to thinking maybe he might invite us to lunch or supper, but still, I knew that was unreasonable—having to entertain so many people—ambassadors, and officials of the Order of Moose, and so on— but I guess I was pretty excited just the same.

I don't know how well you gentlemen know Washington, but the new station there is very handsome and up-to-date in every respect, with a great big open space—the Plaza I believe they call it— in front; and what I'd never known is, you can see the dome of the Capitol right from the front of the station. I tell you I got a mighty big thrill out of that.

Well, Mame wanted us to get a room in the hotel first and get washed up, but I says, "No sir, we better see the President first and see what his plans are; we'll just keep the taxi waiting and I don't care if it costs a dollar and a half; 'tisn't often in your life that you're going to sit in with a President of these United States!"

So we got into a taxi and we started off all het up, and all of a sudden I says to my wife, "Say, do you notice anything funny about this taxi?"

"Why no," she says, "I don't know's I do; it looks all right to me. Why?"

"Looks all right!" I says. "I should say it does! Do you mean to tell me you don't notice something different about this taxi?"

"Why no," she says.

"Well, what make of car is it?" I says.

Of course Delmerine has to horn in. "It's a Studebaker, isn't it?" she says.

"Oh it is, is it, Miss Smarty!" I says. "My God, and me teaching you to drive! It is not a Studebaker, and it isn't a Cadillac, no, and it isn't a flivver either! It's a Buick. See the significance?"

Well, they both stared at me—couldn't get the idea at all—just like women, even the brightest of 'em.

"Can't you see?" I says. "Here's the Buick, the biggest-selling six-cylinder car in the United States if not in the world. And yet how often do you see a Buick taxi? Not very often. Ever think of that? Yes sir, it's a mighty peculiar thing, and I'm sure I don't know why it is. At least I'm practically certain it's a Buick—of course with a taxi body on it—I didn't happen to notice the hood, but from the looks of the dashboard— Anyway—"

So I tapped on the window, and the

driver—he probably thought we were just ordinary tourists that wanted to see the town, and we were passing some building or other and he just hardly turns his head and he says, "It's the Pensions Building." (Or it may have been the Patent Building—I didn't pay much attention, I was so worked up and excited about seeing the President, and I can't exactly remember at this late date.)

"No," I hollers to him, "what I want to know is: isn't this a Buick taxi?"

"Yeh," he says.

"There!" I says to the girls. "What did I tell you!"

You bet!

So we came to the White House and—

Now even you gentlemen that 've been to Washington and seen the White House may not know that the offices, including the President's own private office, are in wings stretching out on either side of the old main structure. The wings are new, I should think, and they're so low that you wouldn't hardly notice 'em from the street in front—not hardly know they were there unless you'd happened, like I was, to be privileged to enter 'em.

So there we came up the avenue to that famous old place—

I tell you it was a mighty moving thing to think of the famous men that had inhabited that structure. Grant and McKinley and Harding and Garfield and everybody! By golly, as I told the Kiwanis when I addressed them about my trip, it certainly gave a fellow inspiration. For what after all is a greater inspiration than the lives of our heroes—

That reminds me that recently—why, in fact, it was just a couple of nights ago, and a neighbor and I were having a little visit, and he says to me, "Lowell, who do you think have been the greatest heroes of the United States since 1900 and the geniuses?"

Well, a question like that certainly makes a fellow think, and him and I, we began making lists, and it just happens I've still got mine in my pocket here, and here's how I figured out our leading intellects:

Coolidge, Harding, Wilson (though I'm a Republican), Ford, Lindbergh, Billy Sunday,[10] Pershing, Roosevelt, John Roach Stratton,[11] Judge Gary and—

Now here's a couple more names that may surprise you gentlemen; maybe you never looked at it like this. I figure that what you might call the arts ought to be represented, and I put in Anne Nichols—say, the author of a play like "Abie's Irish Rose," that can run five years, is in my mind—maybe it's highbrow and impractical to look at it that way, but the way I see it, she's comparable to any business magnate, and besides, they say she's made as much money as Jack Dempsey.[12]

And here's a name that may surprise you still more: Samuel Gompers!

Yes, I knew that would surprise you, my putting in a man that lots of folks think he merely stood for union labor and labor disturbances and all those kind of Bolshevik activities. But it seems that Gompers—a fellow, some kind of professor he was, was explaining this to us at the Kiwanis Club here just recently—Gompers stood right square *against* labor disturbances. He thought that laboring men ought to have their rights, and I suppose that's true, but the way he looked at it, he wanted employees and employers and the general public to join hands in one great brotherhood for the glory of the Union and the extension of our markets into lands now unfairly monopolized by England and Germany. Yes sir!

[10] The Protestant Pope.
[11] The editor has not been able to discover who this person was.
[12] A famous actor.

So, as I say, we drove up to the White House—

I'd told the chauffeur to go right up to the front door—just like I'd expect Cal Coolidge to come right up to *my* front door, if he came to call on me in Zenith. I didn't understand then about the arrangement of the White House.

But there was some kind of cop at the gate and he says, "What do you want, please?"

"What do I want, officer?" I says. "What do I *want?* Why, I just want to call on the President, that's all!" I says. "I'm an old friend of his, that's all!" I says.

Well, I explains, and he tells me the proper caper is to go round to the office entrance, so I says all right; I'd be the last, I says to him, as a friend of the President, to want to break any proper regulations.

Well, make a long story short, at last there we were, in one of the waiting-rooms to the President's own offices, and a gentleman came in—fine-looking gentleman he was, all dressed up like Sunday morning, in a cutaway coat and striped pants and seems he was practically the President's first main secretary, and I presented my wife and Delmerine to him, and I explained about the President and me being classmates.

"I know the President's a busy man, but I'd like a look at the old kid," I tells him, "and I kind of thought I'd like to have my wife and daughter shake hands with him."

Well sir, he understood perfectly.

He went right in and saw the President—didn't keep me waiting one minute, no sir, not hardly a minute.

He came back and said the President was awful' sorry he couldn't have us come in just that second, but seems he was all tied up with an important international conference about—I think it was about Geneva he said—and would I

wait. This secretary was mighty nice, too; he didn't let us sit there like bumps on a log; he sat and visited with us, and that's how I had the chance to get the real low-down on so many of the President's opinions and activities, but I don't want you gentlemen to give any of this stuff to the newspapers.

I asked this secretary, Mr. Jones his name was—I said to him, "What does the President think about disarmament, Mr. Jones?"

"Well, it just happens," he says, "that I can tell you in the President's own words. I heard him talking to the Secretary of State," he says—say, maybe that didn't give me a kick, sitting in as it were on a conference between the President and the Secretary of State! But anyway: "I heard him talking to the Secretary," Mr. Jones told me, "and he said, 'Frank, big navies cost a lot of money and in my opinion it would be a saving if we could get the different nations to reduce them.' "

"Well, well, I'm mighty glad to find that out, Mr. Jones," I said, "and it confirms my own opinion about disarmament. Say, tell me," I says, "how does the President live, in his personal life? What does he take for breakfast?"

Well, Mr. Jones explained that the President took a simple breakfast just like the rest of us—just some coffee and toast and eggs and porridge and so on. I was mighty proud and glad to hear that Cal was unspoiled by all his fame and was still just the same simple direct fellow he'd been when we were chums.

"What does the President think of the situation in China?" I asked Mr. Jones.

"Well, I think I can say without violating any confidences that contrary to the opinion of certain senators, the President feels the situation in China is serious and in fact almost critical and that—but this mustn't go any farther," Mr. Jones told me, "he feels decidedly that while the rights and properties of the Great Powers must be safeguarded, yet we must consider patiently and fairly the rights of the Chinese themselves."

"Well sir, I certainly am interested to hear that," I told him. "There's no question about it. That's exactly how I feel myself."

You see, I'd had a kind of you might call it a special opportunity of getting the real inside dope about the Chinese situation and the Bolshevik influence there. I heard a missionary, just recently back from the scene of disturbance in China, speak at the Wednesday Evening Supper at our church—the Pilgrim Congregational Church of Zenith—Dr. G. Prosper Edwards is the pastor, very famous pulpit orator, you've quite probably heard him on the radio, tunes in on WWWL every second Sunday morning at eleven-fifteen, very eloquent man and a rip-snorting good scholar, too, but very liberal. As he always says, he's more than ready to fellowship with any Christian body no matter what their differences in theology, providing they merely accept the fundamental and indisputable elements of Christianity, such as the Virgin Birth and the proven fact of after-life.

I tell you how I feel about religion, anyway.

I'm a Congregationalist myself, and it isn't for one second just because I happened to be born one, as one of these smart-aleck infidels was trying to prove to me one day, but because of my deep reverence for the great leaders of our church, like Jonathan Edwards and Roger Baldwin—no, come to think of it, he was a Baptist, wasn't he, that Rhode Island guy?

But anyway: just the same today: fellows like Newell Dwight Hillis and S. Parkes Cadman,[13] that during the War

they did as much to win the struggle for world-wide democracy as any soldier, the way they showed up the secret plans of Germany to dominate the world—and the way Dr. Cadman writes this column in the newspapers; say, he knows just about everything, and he can clear up your troubles about anything whether it's an incurable sickness or who wrote Shakespeare—yes sir, a real big typical American leader.

But same time, way I look at it, the other denominations—the Methodists and Baptists and Presbyterians and Campbellites—they're all working together to make a greater and purer America.

Our generation, I guess we still got a lot of the Old Harry in us. Me, I admit, I smoke and sometimes I take a little drink —but never to excess; if there's anything I despise it's a man that can't hold his liquor—and I do like a nice drive on Sunday, and sometimes I cuss a little, and I guess I ain't above looking at a pretty ankle even yet. But it's my firm belief—maybe you gentlemen never thought about it this way—if we'll just support the churches and give the preachers a chance, a generation will come which won't even *want* to do those things, and then America will stand forth before the world such a nation as has never been seen, yes sir, and I'm mighty glad to fellowship with Methodists or—

Not that I think so much of these Christian Scientists and Seventh Day Adventists and all them, though. They carry things too far, and I don't believe in going to extremes in anything; and as for the Catholics—I hope none of you gentlemen are Catholics and I wouldn't want this to go any farther, but I've always felt the Catholics were too tolerant toward drinking and smoking and so aren't, you might say, really hardly typically American at all.

And as to religion in general, they tell

_____
13 The Protestant Erasmus, but a man of broader culture and greater positiveness.

me there's a lot of smart-aleck highbrows today that are calling the truth of Christianity in question. Well, I may not be any theologian, but I wish I could meet one of these fellows, and believe me, I'd settle his hash.

"Look here," I'd tell him; "in the first place, it stands to reason, don't it, that fellows specially trained in theology, like the preachers, know more than us laymen, don't it? And in the second, if the Christian religion has lasted two thousand years and is today stronger than ever—just look, for instance, at that skyscraper church they're building in New York—is it likely that a little handful of you smart galoots are going to be able to change it?"

I guess they never thought of that. Trouble with fellows like agnostics is that you simply can't get 'em to stop and think and use their minds!

And what have they got to put in the *place* of religion? Know what the trouble with those fellows is? *They're destructive and not constructive!*

But as I was saying, our church has a regular Wednesday Evening Supper, before prayer-meeting, and say, the ladies of the church certainly do serve one of the tastiest suppers you ever ate, and for only forty cents—Hamburg steak with Spanish sauce, or creamed chipped beef, or corn beef and cabbage, and sometimes ice cream for dessert, all A 1. And they usually have a speaker, and this evening I was speaking of, the speaker that spoke on China was a missionary, and he gave us the real low-down on China, and he told us it was fierce the way the Chinks were carrying on, and not respecting either their trade treaties—and what a *damn'* fool thing *that* was, because here they had a chance to get in contact with America and England and get civilized and give up worshiping idols—But he showed a real Christian spirit. He said

that even though the Chinks had practically kicked him out, he believed they ought to be allowed to have another chance to try to run their own country.

Well, I could see that was fair, and I was real interested to see the President agreed with him in this point of view, and then I asked Mr. Jones—

"Mr. Jones," I said, "what's the real truth about the President's fishing? Is he a good fisherman?" I said.

"He's one of the best. His catch always compares favorably with that of any other member of the party, when he sets his mind to it, but you must remember that he's constantly weighed down by the cares of state," Mr. Jones said.

"Yes, I can see that," I told him, "and personally, I think it's a shame for some of these newspapers that haven't got anything better to write to make fun of him. Say, another thing," I asked him, "does the President belong to any of the service clubs—Rotary and Kiwanis and so on?"

"No, in his position," Mr. Jones explained to me, "in his position he couldn't hardly discriminate between them, but I think I'm not betraying any secret when I say that the President has the highest admiration for the great service and ideals of all these organizations."

Well, I was mighty glad to hear that, and I think you gentlemen will be, too, whether you belong to 'em or not. For after all, what organizations are doing a greater good and providing more real happiness today than the service clubs, all of 'em, though I myself am a Kiwanian and I can't help feeling that maybe our own organization has got the edge on the other fellows—we aren't as darned snobbish as these Rotarians, and yet we aren't, you might say, as common as the Civitans and the Lions and— Yes sir!

Think what these clubs provide. A chance for a lot of the most responsible and forward-looking men of the community to get together once a week, and not only have a high old time, with all the dignity of our positions checked at the door, calling each other by our first names— Think of what that means! Say here's some high muckamuck of a judge; for that hour or so I call him "Pete," and slap him on the back and kid him about his family, and stands to reason that any man enjoys having a chance to let down and be human like that.

And then the good we do! Why say, just this past year our Zenith Kiwanians have put up not less than two hundred and sixty-three highway markers within forty miles of Zenith, and we gave the kids at an orphan asylum a dandy auto ride and free feed. And believe me it was one fine ad for the Kiwanians, because we took the kids out in trucks, and every truck had on it a great big red sign, "Free Outing for the Unfortunate Kiddies, Provided Free by Zenith Kiwanis Club."

To say nothing of the fine speakers we have each week—the mayor and cancer specialists and authors and vaudeville artists and everybody. And these soreheads that make fun of—

But be that as it may, I was mighty glad to hear the President speak like that and to get his real inside view, and so I asks Mr. Jones, "What's, uh—what's the President's views on taxation, if it isn't impertinent to ask?"

Now you gentlemen will be interested to learn what Mr. Jones told me, because of course that's one of the most important topics of the day, and Jones spoke right up, without hesitation:

"I know for a fact," he told me, "that the President feels that the burdens of taxation should be so equably distributed that they shall lay no undue burden on the poor and unfortunate, yet at the same time they must in no sense be prejudicial to honest business interests or cramp the necessary conduct and expansion of commerce."

And some fly-by-nights claim that the President isn't a deep thinker!

And then— Delmerine had been on pins and needles at the prospect of talking with the President; couldn't hardly keep still in her chair. Mr. Jones was real nice to her, and I certainly was proud of the way one of our home girls could answer up to a man in official position like that.

"So you come from Zenith," he says to her. "Do you like it?"

"Oh you bet," she said. "I just think Zenith is the nicest city in America. Of course I'd rather live in New York, but my, do you know we have the finest park system in the United States?"

"Is that a fact!" he says. "No, I didn't know that. And I guess you like to Charleston," he says. "Or have you gone out for the black bottom? Do you like it?"

"Do I?" she says. "Oh boy! I'd show you, but I guess this isn't hardly the place."

"No, I'm afraid it isn't," he says, and we all four bust right out laughing together—wasn't that a comical idea—to dance the Charleston in the President's offices!

I was just going to ask Mr. Jones how the President felt about socialism when there was a messenger come out and called him in and he was gone about a couple minutes, it couldn't have been more than that, and he come back, and say, he did look real sorry.

"I've got terrible news," he told me. "The President was just ready to see you when the British ambassador come in with some important business that'll take a couple of hours, and then he has to hustle down to the *Mayflower*—that's his yacht—and be gone maybe four-five days, on an important secret conference.

But he specially sent me to tell you that he's heart-broken he can't see you, and he hopes you'll drop in any time you're in Washington."

So you gentlemen can see that it isn't by accident but by real thinking and good fellowship that President Coolidge —yes, or any other president we've had recently—maintains his position, and I hope I haven't bored you and now I'll dry up and let some other fellow talk and—

But just to speak of socialism a moment. I'm willing to give every man a fair square deal, but when it comes to supporting a lot of loafers, the way I look at it is that the constructive, practical people like ourselves, who control the country, ought, you might say—

A LETTER FROM THE QUEEN

By SINCLAIR LEWIS

Doctor Selig was an adventurer. He did not look it, certainly. He was an amiable young bachelor with thin hair. He was instructor in history and economics in Erasmus College, and he had to sit on a foolish little platform and try to coax some fifty young men and women, who were interested only in cuddling and four-door sedans, to become hysterical about the law of diminishing returns.

But at night, in his decorous boarding house, he sometimes smoked a pipe, which was viewed as obscene in the religious shades of Erasmus, and he was boldly writing a book which was to make him famous.

Of course everyone is writing a book. But Selig's was different. It was profound. How good it was can be seen from the fact that with only three quarters of it done, it already had fifteen hundred footnotes—such lively comments as *"Vid. J. A. S. H. S. VIII, 234 et seq."* A real book, nothing flippant or commercialized.

It was called *The Influence of American Diplomacy on the Internal Policies of Paneuropa.*

"Paneuropa," Selig felt, was a nice and scholarly way of saying "Europe."

It would really have been an interesting book if Doctor Selig had not believed that all literature is excellent in proportion as it is hard to read. He had touched a world romantic and little known. Hidden in old documents, like discovering in a desert an oasis where girls laugh and fountains chatter and the market place is noisy, he found the story of Franklin, who in his mousy fur cap was the Don Juan of Paris, of Adams fighting the British Government to prevent their recognizing the Confederacy, of Benjamin Thompson, the Massachusetts Yankee who in 1791 was chief counselor of Bavaria, with the title of Count Rumford.

Selig was moved by these men who made the young America more admired than she is today. And he was moved and, in a most unscholarly way, he became a little angry as he reviewed the story of Senator Ryder.

He knew, of course, that Lafayette Ryder had prevented war between England and America in the first reign of Grover Cleveland; he knew that Ryder had been Secretary of State, and Ambassador to France, courted by Paris for his wisdom, his manners, his wit; that as Senator he had fathered (and mothered and wet-nursed) the Ryder-Hanklin Bill, which had saved our wheat markets; and that his two books, *Possibilities of Disarmament* and *The Anglo-American Empire,* were not merely glib propaganda for peace, but such inspired documents as would have prevented the Boer War, the Spanish-American War, the Great War, if there had been in his Victorian world a dozen men with minds like his. This Selig knew, but he could not remember when Ryder had died.

Then he discovered with aghast astonishment that Senator Ryder was not dead, but still alive at ninety-two forgotten by the country he had helped to build.

Yes, Selig felt bitterly, we honor our great men in America—sometimes for as much as two months after the particular act of greatness that tickles us. But this is a democracy. We mustn't let anyone suppose that because we have given him an (undesired) parade up Broadway and a (furiously resented) soaking of publicity on March first, he may expect to be taken seriously on May second.

The Admiral Dewey whom the press for a week labeled as a combination of Nelson, Napoleon, and Chevalier Bayard, they later nagged to his grave. If a dramatist has a success one season, then may the gods help him, because for the rest of his life everyone will attend his plays only in the hope that he will fail.

But sometimes the great glad-hearted hordes of boosters do not drag down the idol in the hope of finding clay feet, but just forget him with the vast, contemptuous, heavy indifference of a hundred and twenty million people.

So felt Doctor Selig, angrily, and he planned for the end of his book a passionate resurrection of Senator Ryder. He had a shy hope that his book would appear before the Senator's death, to make him happy.

Reading the Senator's speeches, studying his pictures in magazine files, he felt that he knew him intimately. He could see, as though the Senator were in the room, that tall ease, the contrast of long thin nose, gay eyes, and vast globular brow that made Ryder seem a combination of Puritan, clown, and benevolent scholar.

Selig longed to write to him and ask— oh, a thousand things that only he could explain; the proposals of Lionel Sackville-West regarding Colombia; what Queen Victoria really had said in that famous but unpublished letter to President Harrison about the Newfoundland fisheries. Why couldn't he write to him?

No! The man was ninety-two, and Selig had too much reverence to disturb him, along with a wholesome suspicion that his letter would be kicked out by the man who had once told Gladstone to go to the devil.

So forgotten was the Senator that Selig could not, at first, find where he lived. Who's Who gave no address. Selig's superior, Professor Munk, who was believed to know everything in the world except the whereabouts of his last-season's straw hat, bleated, "My dear chap, Ryder is dwelling in some cemetery! He passed beyond, if I remember, in 1901."

The mild Doctor Selig almost did homicide upon a venerable midwestern historian.

At last, in a bulletin issued by the Anti-Prohibition League, Selig found among the list of directors: "Lafayette Ryder (form. U.S. Sen., Sec'y State), West Wickley, Vermont." Though the Senator's residence could make no difference to him, that night Selig was so excited that he smoked an extra pipe of tobacco.

He was planning his coming summer vacation, during which he hoped to finish his book. The presence of the Senator drew him toward Vermont, and in an educational magazine he found the advertisement: "Sky Peaks, near Wickley, Vt., woodland nook with peace and a library—congenial and intellectual company and writers—tennis, handball, riding—nightly Sing round Old-time Bonfire —fur. bung. low rates."

That was what he wanted: a nook and a library and lots of low rates, along with nearness to his idol. He booked a fur. bung. for the summer, and he carried his suitcase to the station on the beautiful day when the young fiends who through the year had tormented him with un-answerable questions streaked off to all parts of the world and for three tremen-dous months permitted him to be a private human being.

When he reached Vermont, Selig found Sky Peaks an old farm, redecorated in a distressingly tea-roomy fashion. His single bungalow, formerly an honest corncrib, was now painted robin's-egg blue with yellow trimmings and christened "Shel-ley." But the camp was on an upland, and air sweet from hayfield and spruce grove healed his lungs, spotted with classroom dust.

At his first dinner at Sky Peaks, he demanded of the host, one Mr. Iddle, "Doesn't Senator Ryder live somewhere near here?"

"Oh, yes, up on the mountain, about four miles south."

"Hope I catch a glimpse of him some day."

"I'll run you over to see him any time you'd like."

"Oh, I couldn't do that! Couldn't in-trude!"

"Nonsense! Of course he's old, but he takes quite an interest in the countryside. Fact, I bought this place from him and— Don't forget the Sing tonight."

At eight that evening Iddle came to drag Selig from the security of his corn-crib just as he was getting the relations of the Locarno Pact and the Versailles Treaty beautifully coördinated.

It was that kind of Sing. "The Long, Long Trail," and "All God's Chillun Got Shoes." (God's Chillun also possessed coats, pants, vests, flivvers, and water-melons, interminably.) Beside Selig at the campfire sat a young woman with eyes, a nose, a sweater, and an athletic skirt, none of them very good or particularly bad. He would not have noticed her, but she picked on him:

"They tell me you're in Erasmus, Doctor Selig."

"Um."

"Real attention to character. And after all, what benefit is there in developing the intellect if the character isn't developed to keep pace with it? You see, I'm in educational work myself—oh, of course nothing like being on a college faculty, but I teach history in the Lincoln High School at Schenectady—my name is Selma Swanson. We must have some good talks about teaching history, mustn't we!"

"Um!" said Selig, and escaped, though it was not till he was safely in his corn-crib that he said aloud, "We must *not!*"

For three months he was not going to be a teacher, or heed the horrors of character-building. He was going to be a great scholar. Even Senator Ryder might be excited to know how powerful an in-tellect was soothing itself to sleep in a corncrib four miles away!

He was grinding hard next afternoon when his host, Iddle, stormed in with: "I've got to run in to Wickley Center. Go right near old Ryder's. Come on. I'll in-troduce you to him."

"Oh, no, honestly!"

"Don't be silly: I imagine he's lonely. Come on!"

Before Selig could make up his mind to get out of Iddle's tempestuous flivver and walk back, they were driving up a mountain road and past marble gateposts into an estate. Through a damp grove of birches and maples they came out on meadows dominated by an old brick house with a huge porch facing the checkered valley. They stopped with a dash at the porch, and on it Selig saw an old man sunk in a canvas deck chair and covered with a shawl. In the shadow the light seemed to concentrate on his bald head, like a sphere of polished vellum, and on long bloodless hands lying as in death on shawl-draped knees. In his eyes there was no life nor desire for it.

Iddle leaped out, bellowing, "Afternoon, Senator! Lovely day, isn't it? I've brought a man to call on you. This is Mr. Selig of—uh—one of our colleges. I'll be back in an hour."

He seized Selig's arm—he was abominably strong—and almost pulled him out of the car. Selig's mind was one wretched puddle of confusion. Before he could dredge any definite thought out of it, Iddle had rattled away, and Selig stood below the porch, hypnotized by the stare of Senator Ryder—too old for hate or anger, but not too old for slow contempt.

Not one word Ryder said.

Selig cried, like a schoolboy unjustly accused:

"Honestly, Senator, the last thing I wanted to do was to intrude on you. I thought Iddle would just introduce us and take me away. I suppose he meant well. And perhaps subconsciously I did want to intrude! I know your *Possibilities of Disarmament* and *Anglo-American Empire* so well—"

The Senator stirred like an antediluvian owl awakening at twilight. His eyes came to life. One expected him to croak, like a cynical old bird, but his still voice was fastidious:

"I didn't suppose anyone had looked at my books since 1910." Painful yet gracious was the gesture with which he waved Selig to a chair. "You are a teacher?"

"Instructor in a small Ohio college. Economics and history. I'm writing a monograph on our diplomacy, and naturally— There are so many things that only you could explain!"

"Because I'm so old?"

"No! Because you've had so much knowledge and courage—perhaps they're the same thing! Every day, literally, in working on my book I've wished I could consult you. For instance— Tell me, sir,

didn't Secretary of State Olney really want war with England over Venezuela? Wasn't he trying to be a tin hero?"

"No!" The old man threw off his shawl. It was somehow a little shocking to find him not in an ancient robe laced with gold, but in a crisp linen summer suit with a smart bow tie. He sat up, alert, his voice harsher. "No! He was a patriot. Sturdy. Honest. Willing to be conciliatory but not flinching. Miss Tully!"

At the Senator's cry, out of the wide fanlighted door of the house slid a trained nurse. Her uniform was so starched that it almost clattered, but she was a peony sort of young woman, the sort who would insist on brightly mothering any male, of any age, whether or not he desired to be mothered. She glared at the intruding Selig; she shook her finger at Senator Ryder, and simpered:

"Now I do hope you aren't tiring yourself, else I shall have to be ever so stern and make you go to bed. The doctor said—"

"Damn the doctor! Tell Mrs. Tinkham to bring me down the file of letters from Richard Olney, Washington, for 1895— O-l-n-e-y—and hustle it!"

Miss Tully gone, the Senator growled, "Got no more use for a nurse than a cat for two tails! It's that mutton-headed doctor, the old fool! He's seventy-five years old, and he hasn't had a thought since 1888. Doctors!"

He delivered an address on the art of medicine with such vigorous blasphemy that Selig shrank in horrified admiration. And the Senator didn't abate the blazing crimson of his oration at the entrance of his secretary, Mrs. Tinkham, a small, narrow, bleached, virginal widow.

Selig expected her to leap off the porch and commit suicide in terror. She didn't. She waited, she yawned gently, she handed the Senator a manila envelope, and gently she vanished.

The Senator grinned. "She'll pray at

me tonight! She daren't while you're here. There! I feel better. Good cussing is a therapeutic agent that has been forgotten in these degenerate days. I could teach you more about cussing than about diplomacy—to which cussing is a most valuable aid. Now here is a letter that Secretary Olney wrote me about the significance of his correspondence with England."

It was a page of history. Selig handled it with more reverence than he had given to any material object in his life.

He exclaimed, "Oh, yes, you used—of course I've never seen the rest of this letter, and I can't tell you, sir, how excited I am to see it. But didn't you use this first paragraph—it must be about on page 276 of your *Anglo-American Empire?*"

"I believe I did. It's not my favorite reading!"

"You know, of course, that it was reprinted from your book in the *Journal of the American Society of Historical Sources* last year?"

"Was it?" The old man seemed vastly pleased. He beamed at Selig as at a young but tested friend. He chuckled, "Well, I suppose I appreciate now how King Tut felt when they remembered him and dug him up. . . . Miss Tully! Hey! Miss Tully, will you be so good as to tell Martens to bring us whisky and soda, with two glasses? Eh? Now you look here, young woman; we'll fight out the whole question of my senile viciousness after our guest has gone. Two glasses, I said! . . . Now about Secretary Olney. The fact of the case was . . ."

Two hours later, Senator Ryder was still talking and in that two hours he had given Selig such unrecorded information as the researcher could not have found in two years of study.

Selig had for two hours walked with presidents and ambassadors; he had the dinner conversation of foreign ministers, conversations so private, so world-affecting, that they never had been set down, even in letters. The Senator had revealed his friendship with King Edward, and the predictions about the future World War the King had made over a glass of mineral water.

The mild college instructor, who till this afternoon had never spoken to anyone more important than the president of a prairie college, was exalted with a feeling that he had become the confidant of kings and field marshals, of Anatole France and Lord Haldane, of Sarah Bernhardt and George Meredith.

He had always known but till now he had never understood that in private these great personages were plain human beings, like Doctor Wilbur Selig of Erasmus. It made him feel close to King Edward to hear (though the Senator may have exaggerated) that the King could not pronounce his own name without a German accent; it made him feel a man of the world to learn the details of a certain not very elevating party at which an English duke and a German prince and a Portuguese king, accompanied by questionable ladies, had in bibulous intimacy sung to Senator Ryder's leadership the lyric, "How Dry I Am."

During that two hours, there had been ten minutes when he had been entirely off in a Conan Doyle spirit world. His notion of prodigious alcoholic dissipation was a bottle of home-brewed beer once a month. He had tried to mix himself a light whisky and soda—he noted, with some anxiety about the proper drinking-manners in diplomatic society, that he took approximately one third as much whisky as the Senator.

But while the old man rolled his drink in his mouth and shook his bald head rapturously and showed no effect, Selig was suddenly lifted six million miles above the earth, through pin-gray clouds shot with lightning, and at that altitude

[273]

he floated dizzily while below him the Senator discoursed on the relations of Cuban sugar to Colorado beets.

And once Iddle blatted into sight, in his dirty flivver, suggested taking him away, and was blessedly dismissed by the Senator's curt, "Doctor Selig is staying here for dinner. I'll send him back in my car."

Dinner . . . Selig, though he rarely read fiction, had read in some novel about "candle-flames, stilled in the twilight and reflected in the long stretch of waxed mahogany as in a clouded mirror —candles and roses and old silver." He had read, too, about stag horns and heraldic shields and the swords of old warriors.

Now, actually, the Senator's dining room had neither stag horn nor heraldic shield nor sword, and if there were still candle-flames, there was no mahogany to reflect them, but instead a silver stretch of damask. It was a long room, simple, with old portraits against white panels. Yet Selig felt that he was transported into all the romance he had ever read.

The dinner was countrylike. By now, Selig expected peacocks' tongues and caviar; he got steak and cantaloupe and corn pudding. But there were four glasses at each plate, and along with water, which was the familiar drink at Erasmus, he had, and timidly, tasted sherry, Burgundy, and champagne.

If Wilbur Selig of Iowa and Erasmus had known anything, it was that champagne was peculiarly wicked, associated with light ladies, lewd talk, and losses at roulette invariably terminating in suicide. Yet it was just as he was nibbling at his very first glass of champagne that Senator Ryder began to talk of his delight in the rise of Anglo-Catholicism.

No. It was none of it real.

If he was exhilarated that he had been kept for dinner, he was ecstatic when the Senator said, "Would you care to come for dinner again day after tomorrow? Good. I'll send Martens for you at seven-thirty. Don't dress."

In a dream phantasmagoria he started home, driven by Martens, the Senator's chauffeur-butler, with unnumbered things that had puzzled him in writing his book made clear.

When he arrived at the Sky Peaks camp, the guests were still sitting about the dull campfire.

"My!" said Miss Selma Swanson, teacher of history. "Mr. Iddle says you've spent the whole evening with Senator Ryder. Mr. Iddle says he's a grand person —used to be a great politician."

"Oh, he was kind enough to help me about some confused problems," murmured Selig.

But as he went to bed—in a reformed corncrib—he exulted, "I bet I could become a good friend of the Senator! Wouldn't that be wonderful!"

Lafayette Ryder, when his visitor—a man named Selig or Selim—was gone, sat at the long dining table with a cigarette and a distressingly empty cognac glass. He was meditating. "Nice eager young chap. Provincial. But mannerly. I wonder if there really are a few people who know that Lafe Ryder once existed?"

He rang, and the crisply coy Miss Tully, the nurse, waltzed into the dining room bubbling, "So we're all ready to go to bed now, Senator!"

"We are not! I didn't ring for you; I rang for Martens."

"He's driving your guest."

"Humph! Send in cook. I want some more brandy."

"Oh, now, Daddy Ryder! You aren't going to be naughty, are you?"

"I am! And who the deuce ever told you to call me 'Daddy'? Daddy!"

"You did. Last year."

"I don't—this year. Bring me the brandy bottle."

"If I do, will you go to bed then?"

"I will not!"

"But the doctor—"

"The doctor is a misbegotten hound with a face like a fish. And other things. I feel cheerful tonight. I shall sit up late. Till All Hours."

They compromised on eleven-thirty instead of All Hours, and one glass of brandy instead of the bottle. But, vexed at having thus compromised—as so often, in ninety-odd years, he had been vexed at having compromised with Empires—the Senator was (said Miss Tully) very naughty in his bath.

"I swear," said Miss Tully afterward, to Mrs. Tinkham, the secretary, "if he didn't pay so well, I'd leave that horrid old man tomorrow. Just because he was a politician or something, once, to think he can sass a trained nurse!"

"You would not!" said Mrs. Tinkham. "But he *is* naughty."

And they did not know that, supposedly safe in his four-poster bed, the old man was lying awake, smoking a cigarette and reflecting:

"The gods have always been much better to me than I have deserved. Just when I thought I was submerged in a flood of women and doctors, along comes a man for companion, a young man who seems to be a potential scholar, and who might preserve for the world what I tried to do. Oh, stop pitying yourself, Lafe Ryder! . . . I wish I could sleep."

Senator Ryder reflected, the next morning, that he had probably counted too much on young Selig. But when Selig came again for dinner, the Senator was gratified to see how quickly he was already fitting into a house probably more elaborate than any he had known. And quite easily he told of what the Senator accounted his uncivilized farm boyhood, his life in a state university.

"So much the better that he is naïve, not one of these third-secretary cubs who think they're cosmopolitan because they went to Groton," considered the Senator. "I must do something for him."

Again he lay awake that night, and suddenly he had what seemed to him an inspired idea.

"I'll give young Selig a lift. All this money and no one but hang-jawed relatives to give it to! Give him a year of freedom. Pay him—he probably earns twenty-five hundred a year; pay him five thousand and expenses to arrange my files. If he makes good, I'd let him publish my papers after I pass out. The letters from John Hay, from Blaine, from Choate! No set of unpublished documents like it in America! It would *make* the boy!

"Mrs. Tinkham would object. Be jealous. She might quit. Splendid! Lafe, you arrant old coward, you've been trying to get rid of that woman without hurting her feelings for three years! At that, she'll probably marry you on your dying bed!"

He chuckled, a wicked, low, delighted sound, the old man alone in darkness.

"Yes, and if he shows the quality I think he has, leave him a little money to carry on with while he edits the letters. Leave him—let's see."

It was supposed among Senator Ryder's lip-licking relatives and necessitous hangers-on that he had left of the Ryder fortune perhaps two hundred thousand dollars. Only his broker and he knew that he had by secret investment increased it to a million, these ten years of dark, invalid life.

He lay planning a new will. The present one left half his fortune to his university, a quarter to the town of Wickley for a community center, the rest to nephews and nieces, with ten thousand each for the Tully, the Tinkham, Martens, and the much-badgered doctor, with a grave proviso that the doctor should never again dictate to any patient how much he should smoke.

Now to Doctor Selig, asleep and not even dream-warned in his absurd corn-crib, was presented the sum of twenty-five thousand dollars, the blessings of an old man, and a store of historical documents which could not be priced in coin.

In the morning, with a headache, and very strong with Miss Tully about the taste of the aspirin—he suggested that she had dipped it in arsenic—the Senator reduced Selig to five thousand, but that night it went back to twenty-five.

How pleased the young man would be.

Doctor Wilbur Selig, on the first night when he had unexpectedly been bidden to stay for dinner with Senator Ryder, was as stirred as by— What *would* most stir Doctor Wilbur Selig? A great play? A raise in salary? An Erasmus football victory?

At the second dinner, with the house and the hero less novel to him, he was calmly happy, and zealous about getting information. The third dinner, a week after, was agreeable enough, but he paid rather more attention to the squab in casserole than to the Senator's revelations about the Baring panic, and he was a little annoyed that the Senator insisted (so selfishly) on his staying till midnight, instead of going home to bed at a reasonable hour like ten—with, perhaps, before retiring, a few minutes of chat with that awfully nice bright girl, Miss Selma Swanson.

And through that third dinner he found himself reluctantly critical of the Senator's morals.

Hang it, here was a man of good family, who had had a chance to see all that was noblest and best in the world, and why did he feel he had to use such bad language, why did he drink so much? Selig wasn't (he proudly reminded him-

self) the least bit narrow-minded. But an old man like this ought to be thinking of making his peace; ought to be ashamed of cursing like a stableboy.

He reproved himself next morning, "He's been mighty nice to me. He's a good old coot—at heart. And of course a great statesman."

But he snapped back to irritation when he had a telephone call from Martens, the chauffeur: "Senator Ryder would like you to come over for tea this afternoon. He has something to show you."

"All right, I'll be over."

Selig was curt about it, and he raged, "Now, by thunder, of all the thoughtless, selfish old codgers! As if I didn't have anything to do but dance attendance on him and amuse him! And here I'd planned to finish a chapter this afternoon! 'Course he does give me some inside information, but still—as if I needed all the tittle-tattle of embassies for my book! Got all the stuff I need now. And how am I to get over there? The selfish old hound never thinks of that! Does he suppose I can afford a car to go over? I'll have to walk! Got half a mind not to go!"

The sulkiness with which he came to tea softened when the Senator began to talk about the Queen Victoria letter.

Historians knew that during the presidency of Benjamin Harrison, when there was hostility between America and Britain over the seizure by both sides of fishing boats, Queen Victoria had written in her own hand to President Harrison. It was believed that she deplored her royal inability to appeal directly to Parliament, and suggested his first taking the difficulty up with Congress. But precisely what was in this unofficial letter, apparently no one knew.

This afternoon Senator Ryder said placidly, "I happen to have the original of the letter in my possession."

"What?"

"Perhaps some day I'll give you a glimpse of it. I think I have the right to let you quote it."

Selig was electrified. It would be a sensation—*he* would be a sensation! He could see his book, and himself, on the front pages. But the Senator passed on to a trivial, quite improper anecdote about a certain Brazilian ambassador and a Washington milliner, and Selig was irritable again. Darn it, it was indecent for a man of over ninety to think of such things! And why the deuce was he so skittish and secretive about his old letter? If he was going to show it, why not do it?

So perhaps Doctor Selig of Erasmus was not quite so gracious as a Doctor Selig of Erasmus should have been when, at parting, the old man drew from under his shawl a worn blue-gray pamphlet, and piped:

"I'm going to give you this, if you'd like it. There's only six copies left in the world, I believe. It's the third one of my books—privately printed and not ordinarily listed with the others. It has, I imagine, a few things in it the historians don't know; the real story of the Paris commune."

"Oh, thanks," Selig said brusquely and, to himself, in the Senator's car, he pointed out that it showed what an egotistic old codger Ryder was to suppose that just because he'd written something, it must be a blooming treasure!

He glanced into the book. It seemed to have information. But he wasn't stirred, for it was out of line with what he had decided were the subjects of value to Doctor Selig and, therefore, of general interest.

After tea, now, it was too late for work before dinner, and he had Ryder's chauffeur set him down at Tredwell's General Store, which had become for members of the Sky Peaks camp a combination of department store, post office and café, where they drank wild toasts in lemon pop.

Miss Selma Swanson was there, and Selig laughingly treated her to chewing gum, Attaboy Peanut Candy Rolls, and seven fishhooks. They had such a lively time discussing that funny Miss Elkington up at the camp.

When he started off, with Miss Swanson, he left the Senator's book behind him in the store. He did not miss it till he had gone to bed.

Two days afterward, the Senator's chauffeur again telephoned an invitation to tea for that afternoon, but this time Selig snapped, "Sorry! Tell the Senator I unfortunately shan't be able to come!"

"Just a moment, please," said the chauffeur. "The Senator wishes to know if you care to come to dinner tomorrow evening—eight—he'll send for you."

"Well— Yes, tell him I'll be glad to come."

After all, dinner here at Sky Peaks was pretty bad, and he'd get away early in the evening.

He rejoiced in having his afternoon free for work. But the confounded insistence of the Senator had so bothered him that he banged a book on his table and strolled outside.

The members of the camp were playing One Old Cat, with Selma Swanson, very jolly in knickerbockers, as cheer leader. They yelped at Selig to join them and, after a stately refusal or two, he did. He had a good time. Afterward he pretended to wrestle with Miss Swanson— she had the supplest waist, and, seen close up, the moistest eyes. So he was glad that he had not wasted his afternoon listening to that old bore.

The next afternoon, at six, a splendid chapter done, he went off for a climb up Mount Poverty with Miss Swanson. The late sun was so rich on pasture, pine clumps, and distant meadows, and Miss

Swanson was so lively in tweed skirt and brogues—but the stockings were silk—that he regretted having promised to be at the Senator's at eight.

"But of course I always keep my promises," he reflected proudly.

They sat on a flat rock perched above the valley, and he observed in rather a classroom tone, "How remarkable that light is—the way it picks out that farmhouse roof, and then the shadow of those maples on the grass. Did you ever realize that it's less the shape of things than the light that gives a landscape beauty?"

"No, I don't think I ever did. That's so. It's the light! My, how observant you are!"

"Oh, no, I'm not. I'm afraid I'm just a bookworm."

"Oh, you are not! Of course you're tremendously scholarly—my, I've learned so much about study from you—but then, you're so active—you were just a circus playing One Old Cat yesterday. I do admire an all-round man."

At seven-thirty, holding her firm hand, he was saying, "But really, there's so much that I lack that— But you do think I'm right about it's being so much manlier not to drink like that old man? By the way, we must start back."

At a quarter to eight, after he had kissed her and apologized and kissed her, he remarked, "Still, he can wait a while—won't make any difference."

At eight: "Golly, it's so late! Had no idea. Well, I better not go at all now. I'll just phone him this evening and say I got balled up on the date. Look! Let's go down to the lake and dine on the wharf at the boathouse, just you and I."

"Oh, that would be grand!" said Miss Selma Swanson.

Lafayette Ryder sat on the porch that, along with his dining room and bedroom, had become his entire world, and waited for the kind young friend who was giving back to him the world he had once known. His lawyer was coming from New York in three days, and there was the matter of the codicil of his will. But—the Senator stirred impatiently—this money matter was grubby; he had for Selig something rarer than money—a gift for a scholar.

He looked at it and smiled. It was a double sheet of thick bond, with "Windsor Castle" engraved at the top. Above this address was written in a thin hand: "To my friend L. Ryder, to use if he ever sees fit. Benj. Harrison."

The letter began, "To His Excellency, the President," and it was signed, "Victoria R." In a few lines between inscription and signature there was a new history of the great Victoria and of the Nineteenth Century. . . . Dynamite does not come in large packages.

The old man tucked the letter into a pocket down beneath the rosy shawl that reached up to his gray face.

Miss Tully rustled out, to beg, "Daddy, you won't take more than one cocktail tonight? The doctor says it's so bad for you!"

"Heh! Maybe I will and maybe I won't! What time is it?"

"A quarter to eight."

"Doctor Selig will be here at eight. If Martens doesn't have the cocktails out on the porch three minutes after he gets back, I'll skin him. And you needn't go looking for the cigarettes in my room, either! I've hidden them in a brand-new place, and I'll probably sit up and smoke till dawn. Fact: doubt if I shall go to bed at all. Doubt if I'll take my bath."

He chuckled as Miss Tully wailed, "You're so naughty!"

The Senator need not have asked the time. He had groped down under the shawl and looked at his watch every five minutes since seven. He inwardly glared at himself for his foolishness in anticipating his young friend, but—all the old ones were gone.

That was the devilishness of living so many years. Gone, so long. People wrote idiotic letters to him, still, begging for his autograph, for money, but who save this fine young Selig had come to him? . . . So long now!

At eight, he stirred, not this time like a drowsy old owl, but like an eagle, its lean head thrusting forth from its pile of hunched feathers, ready to soar. He listened for the car.

At ten minutes past, he swore, competently. Confound that Martens!

At twenty past, the car swept up the driveway. Out of it stepped only Martens, touching his cap, murmuring:

"Very sorry, sir. Mr. Selig was not at the camp."

"Then why the devil didn't you wait?"

"I did, sir, as long as I dared."

"Poor fellow! He may have been lost on the mountain. We must start a search!"

"Very sorry, sir, but if I may say so, as I was driving back past the foot of the Mount Poverty trail, I saw Mr. Selig with a young woman, sir, and they were talking and laughing and going away from the camp, sir. I'm afraid—"

"Very well. That will do."

"I'll serve dinner at once, sir. Do you wish your cocktail out here?"

"I won't have one. Send Miss Tully."

When the nurse had fluttered to him, she cried out with alarm. Senator Ryder was sunk down into his shawl. She bent over him to hear his whisper:

"If it doesn't keep you from your dinner, my dear, I think I'd like to be helped up to bed. I don't care for anything to eat. I feel tired."

While she was anxiously stripping the shawl from him, he looked long, as one seeing it for the last time, at the darkening valley. But as she helped him up, he suddenly became active. He snatched from his pocket a stiff double sheet of paper and tore it into fragments which he fiercely scattered over the porch with one sweep of his long arm.

Then he collapsed over her shoulder.

BABBITT

By SINCLAIR LEWIS

[Excerpt]

CHAPTER 1

The towers of Zenith aspired above the morning mist; austere towers of steel and cement and limestone, sturdy as cliffs and delicate as silver rods. They were neither citadels nor churches, but frankly and beautifully office-buildings.

The mist took pity on the fretted structures of earlier generations: the Post Office with its shingle-tortured mansard, the red brick minarets of hulking old houses, factories with stingy and sooted windows, wooden tenements colored like mud. The city was full of such grotesqueries, but the clean towers were thrusting them from the business center, and on the farther hills were shining new houses, homes—they seemed—for laughter and tranquillity.

Over a concrete bridge fled a limousine of long sleek hood and noiseless engine. These people in evening clothes were returning from an all-night rehearsal of a Little Theater play, an artistic adventure considerably illuminated by champagne. Below the bridge curved a railroad, a maze of green and crimson lights. The New York Flyer boomed past, and twenty lines of polished steel leaped into the glare.

In one of the skyscrapers the wires of the Associated Press were closing down. The telegraph operators wearily raised their celluloid eye-shades after a night of talking with Paris and Peking. Through the building crawled the scrubwomen, yawning, their old shoes slapping. The dawn mist spun away. Cues of men with lunch-boxes clumped toward the immensity of new factories, sheets of glass and hollow tile, glittering shops where five thousand men worked beneath one roof, pouring out the honest wares that would be sold up the Euphrates and across the veldt. The whistles rolled out in greeting a chorus cheerful as the April dawn; the song of labor in a city built—it seemed—for giants.

II

There was nothing of the giant in the aspect of the man who was beginning to awaken on the sleeping-porch of a Dutch Colonial House in that residential district of Zenith known as Floral Heights.

His name was George F. Babbitt. He was forty-six years old now, in April, 1920, and he made nothing in particular, neither butter nor shoes nor poetry, but he was nimble in the calling of selling houses for more than people could afford to pay.

His large head was pink, his brown hair thin and dry. His face was babyish in slumber, despite his wrinkles and the red spectacle-dents on the slopes of his nose. He was not fat but he was exceedingly well fed; his cheeks were pads, and the unroughened hand which lay helpless upon the khaki-colored blanket was slightly puffy. He seemed prosperous, extremely married and unromantic; and altogether unromantic appeared this sleeping-porch, which looked on one sizable elm, two respectable grass-plots, a cement driveway, and a corrugated iron garage. Yet Babbitt was again dreaming of the fairy child, a dream more romantic than scarlet pagodas by a silver sea.

For years the fairy child had come to him. Where others saw but Georgie Babbitt, she discerned gallant youth. She waited for him, in the darkness beyond mysterious groves. When at last he could slip away from the crowded house he darted to her. His wife, his clamoring friends, sought to follow, but he escaped, the girl fleet beside him, and they crouched together on a shadowy hillside. She was so slim, so white, so eager! She cried that he was gay and valiant, that she would wait for him, that they would sail—

Rumble and bang of the milk-truck.

Babbitt moaned, turned over, struggled back toward his dream. He could see only her face now, beyond misty waters. The furnace-man slammed the basement door. A dog barked in the next yard. As Babbitt sank blissfully into a dim warm tide, the paper-carrier went by whistling, and the rolled-up *Advocate* thumped the front door. Babbitt roused, his stomach constricted with alarm. As he relaxed, he was pierced by the familiar and irritating rattle of some one cranking a Ford: snap-ah-ah, snap-ah-ah, snap-ah-ah. Himself a pious motorist, Babbitt cranked with the unseen driver, with him waited through taut hours for the roar of the starting engine, with him agonized as the roar ceased and again began the infernal patient snap-ah-ah—a round, flat sound, a

shivering cold-morning sound, a sound infuriating and inescapable. Not till the rising voice of the motor told him that the Ford was moving was he released from the panting tension. He glanced once at his favorite tree, elm twigs against the gold patina of sky, and fumbled for sleep as for a drug. He who had been a boy very credulous of life was no longer greatly interested in the possible and improbable adventures of each new day.

He escaped from reality till the alarm-clock rang, at seven-twenty.

III

It was the best of nationally advertised and quantitatively produced alarm-clocks, with all modern attachments, including cathedral chime, intermittent alarm, and a phosphorescent dial. Babbitt was proud of being awakened by such a rich device. Socially it was almost as creditable as buying expensive cord tires.

He sulkily admitted now that there was no more escape, but he lay and detested the grind of the real-estate business, and disliked his family, and disliked himself for disliking them. The evening before, he had played poker at Vergil Gunch's till midnight, and after such holidays he was irritable before breakfast. It may have been the tremendous home-brewed beer of the prohibition-era and the cigars to which that beer enticed him; it may have been resentment of return from this fine, bold man-world to a restricted region of wives and stenographers, and of suggestions not to smoke so much.

From the bedroom beside the sleeping-porch, his wife's detestably cheerful "Time to get up, Georgie boy," and the itchy sound, the brisk and scratchy sound, of combing hairs out of a stiff brush.

He grunted; he dragged his thick legs,

in faded baby-blue pajamas, from under the khaki blanket; he sat on the edge of the cot, running his fingers through his wild hair, while his plump feet mechanically felt for his slippers. He looked regretfully at the blanket—forever a suggestion to him of freedom and heroism. He had bought it for a camping trip which had never come off. It symbolized gorgeous loafing, gorgeous cursing, virile flannel shirts.

He creaked to his feet, groaning at the waves of pain which passed behind his eyeballs. Though he waited for their scorching recurrence, he looked blurrily out at the yard. It delighted him, as always; it was the neat yard of a successful business man of Zenith, that is, it was perfection, and made him also perfect. He regarded the corrugated iron garage. For the three-hundred-and-sixty-fifth time in a year he reflected, "No class to that tin shack. Have to build me a frame garage. But by golly it's the only thing on the place that isn't up-to-date!" While he stared he thought of a community garage for his acreage development, Glen Oriole. He stopped, puffing and jiggling. His arms were akimbo. His petulant, sleep-swollen face was set in harder lines. He suddenly seemed capable, an official, a man to contrive, to direct, to get things done.

On the vigor of his idea he was carried down the hard, clean, unused-looking hall into the bathroom.

Though the house was not large it had, like all houses on Floral Heights, an altogether royal bathroom of porcelain and glazed tile and metal sleek as silver. The towel-rack was a rod of clear glass set in nickel. The tub was long enough for a Prussian Guard, and above the set bowl was a sensational exhibit of toothbrush holder, shaving-brush holder, soap-dish, sponge-dish, and medicine-cabinet, so glittering and so ingenious that they resembled an electrical instrument-board.

But the Babbitt whose god was Modern Appliances was not pleased. The air of the bathroom was thick with the smell of a heathen toothpaste. "Verona been at it again! 'Stead of sticking to Lilidol, like I've re-peat-ed-ly asked her, she's gone and gotten some confounded stinkum stuff that makes you sick!"

The bath-mat was wrinkled and the floor was wet. (His daughter Verona eccentrically took baths in the morning, now and then.) He slipped on the mat, and slid against the tub. He said "Damn!" Furiously he snatched up his tube of shaving-cream, furiously he lathered, with a belligerent slapping of the unctuous brush, furiously he raked his plump cheeks with a safety-razor. It pulled. The blade was dull. He said, "Damn—oh—oh—damn it!"

He hunted through the medicine cabinet for a packet of new razor-blades (reflecting, as invariably, "Be cheaper to buy one of these dinguses and strop your own blades,") and when he discovered the packet, behind the round box of bicarbonate of soda, he thought ill of his wife for putting it there and very well of himself for not saying "Damn." But he did say it, immediately afterward, when with wet and soap-slippery fingers he tried to remove the horrible little envelope and crisp clinging oiled paper from the new blade.

Then there was the problem, oft-pondered, never solved, of what to do with the old blade, which might imperil the fingers of his young. As usual, he tossed it on top of the medicine-cabinet, with a mental note that some day he must remove the fifty or sixty other blades that were also temporarily, piled up there. He finished his shaving in a growing testiness increased by his spinning headache and by the emptiness in his stomach. When he was done, his round face smooth and streamy and his eyes stinging from soapy water, he reached for a towel. The family towels were wet, wet and clammy and vile, all of them wet, he found, as he blindly snatched them—his own face-towel, his wife's, Verona's, Ted's, Tinka's, and the lone bath-towel with the huge welt of initial. Then George F. Babbitt did a dismaying thing. He wiped his face on the guest-towel! It was a pansy-embroidered trifle which always hung there to indicate that the Babbitts were in the best Floral Heights society. No one had ever used it. No guest had ever dared to. Guests secretively took a corner of the nearest regular towel.

He was raging, "By golly, here they go and use up all the towels, every doggone one of 'em, and they use 'em and get 'em all wet and sopping, and never put out a dry one for me—of course, I'm the goat!—and then I want one and—I'm the only person in the doggone house that's got the slightest doggone bit of consideration for other people and thoughtfulness and consider there may be others that may want to use the doggone bathroom after me and consider—"

He was pitching the chill abominations into the bath-tub, pleased by the vindictiveness of that desolate flapping sound; and in the midst his wife serenely trotted in, observed serenely, "Why Georgie dear, what are you doing? Are you going to wash out the towels? Why, you needn't wash out the towels. Oh, Georgie, you didn't go and use the guest-towel, did you?"

It is not recorded that he was able to answer.

For the first time in weeks he was sufficiently roused by his wife to look at her.

IV

Myra Babbitt—Mrs. George F. Babbitt—was definitely mature. She had creases from the corners of her mouth to the bottom of her chin, and her plump neck bagged. But the thing that marked her as having passed the line was that she no longer had reticences before her husband, and no longer worried about not having reticences. She was in a petticoat now, and corsets which bulged, and unaware of being seen in bulgy corsets. She had become so dully habituated to married life that in her full matronliness she was as sexless as an anemic nun. She was a good woman, a kind woman, a diligent woman, but no one, save perhaps Tinka her ten-year-old, was at all interested in her or entirely aware that she was alive.

After a rather thorough discussion of all the domestic and social aspects of towels she apologized to Babbitt for his having an alcoholic headache; and he recovered enough to endure the search for a B.V.D. undershirt which had, he pointed out, malevolently been concealed among his clean pajamas.

He was fairly amiable in the conference on the brown suit.

"What do you think, Myra?" He pawed at the clothes hunched on a chair in their bedroom, while she moved about mysteriously adjusting and patting her petticoat and, to his jaundiced eye, never seeming to get on with her dressing. "How about it? Shall I wear the brown suit another day?"

"Well, it looks awfully nice on you."

"I know, but gosh, it needs pressing."

"That's so. Perhaps it does."

"It certainly could stand being pressed, all right."

"Yes, perhaps it wouldn't hurt it to be pressed."

"But gee, the coat doesn't need pressing. No sense in having the whole darn suit pressed, when the coat doesn't need it."

"That's so."

"But the pants certainly need it, all right. Look at them—look at those wrinkles—the pants certainly do need pressing."

"That's so. Oh, Georgie, why couldn't you wear the brown coat with the blue trousers we were wondering what we'd do with them?"

"Good Lord! Did you ever in all my life know me to wear the coat of one suit and the pants of another? What do you think I am? A busted bookkeeper?"

"Well, why don't you put on the dark gray suit to-day, and stop in at the tailor and leave the brown trousers?"

"Well, they certainly need— Now where the devil is that gray suit? Oh, yes, here we are."

He was able to get through the other crises of dressing with comparative resoluteness and calm.

His first adornment was the sleeveless dimity B.V.D. undershirt, in which he resembled a small boy humorlessly wearing a cheesecloth tabard at a civic pageant. He never put on B.V.D.'s without thanking the God of Progress that he didn't wear tight, long, old-fashioned undergarments, like his father-in-law and partner, Henry Thompson. His second embellishment was combing and slicking back his hair. It gave him a tremendous forehead, arching up two inches beyond the former hair-line. But most wonder-working of all was the donning of his spectacles.

There is character in spectacles—the pretentious tortoise-shell, the meek pince-nez of the school teacher, the twisted silver-framed glasses of the old villager. Babbitt's spectacles had huge, circular, frameless lenses of the very best glass; the ear-pieces were thin bars of gold. In them he was the modern business man; one who gave orders to clerks and drove a car and played occasional golf and was scholarly in regard to Salesmanship. His head suddenly appeared not babyish but weighty, and you noted his heavy, blunt nose, his straight mouth and thick, long

upper lip, his chin overfleshy but strong; with respect you beheld him put on the rest of his uniform as a Solid Citizen.

The gray suit was well cut, well made, and completely undistinguished. It was a standard suit. White piping on the V of the vest added a flavor of law and learning. His shoes were black laced boots, good boots, honest boots, standard boots, extraordinarily uninteresting boots. The only frivolity was in his purple knitted scarf. With considerable comment on the matter to Mrs. Babbitt (who, acrobatically fastening the back of her blouse to her skirt with a safety-pin, did not hear a word he said), he chose between the purple scarf and a tapestry effect with stringless brown harps among blown palms, and into it he thrust a snake-head pin with opal eyes.

A sensational event was changing from the brown suit to the gray the contents of his pockets. He was earnest about these objects. They were of eternal importance, like baseball or the Republican Party. They included a fountain pen and a silver pencil (always lacking a supply of new leads) which belonged in the righthand upper vest pocket. Without them he would have felt naked. On his watch-chain were a gold penknife, silver cigar-cutter, seven keys (the use of two of which he had forgotten), and incidentally a good watch. Depending from the chain was a large, yellowish elk's-tooth—proclamation of his membership in the Brotherly and Protective Order of Elks. Most significant of all was his loose-leaf pocket note-book, that modern and efficient note-book which contained the addresses of people whom he had forgotten, prudent memoranda of postal money-orders which had reached their destinations months ago, stamps which had lost their mucilage, clippings of verses by T. Cholmondeley Frink and of the newspaper editorials from which Babbitt got his opinions and his polysyllables, notes to be sure and do things which he did not intend to do, and one curious inscription—D.S.S.D.M.Y.P.D.F.

But he had no cigarette-case. No one had ever happened to give him one, so he hadn't the habit, and people who carried cigarette-cases he regarded as effeminate.

Last, he stuck in his lapel the Boosters' Club button. With the conciseness of great art the button displayed two words: "Boosters—Pep!" It made Babbitt feel loyal and important. It associated him with Good Fellows, with men who were nice and human, and important in business circles. It was his V.C., his Legion of Honor ribbon, his Phi Beta Kappa key.

With the subtleties of dressing ran other complex worries. "I feel kind of punk this morning," he said. "I think I had too much dinner last evening. You oughtn't to serve those heavy banana fritters."

"But you asked me to have some."

"I know, but— I tell you, when a fellow gets past forty he has to look after his digestion. There's a lot of fellows that don't take proper care of themselves. I tell you at forty a man's a fool or his doctor— I mean, his own doctor. Folks don't give enough attention to this matter of dieting. Now I think— Course a man ought to have a good meal after the day's work, but it would be a good thing for both of us if we took lighter lunches."

"But Georgie, here at home I always do have a light lunch."

"Mean to imply I make a hog of myself, eating down-town? Yes, sure! You'd have a swell time if you had to eat the truck that new steward hands out to us at the Athletic Club! But I certainly do feel out of sorts this morning. Funny, got a pain down here on the left side—but no, that wouldn't be appendicitis, would it? Last night, when I was driving over to Verg Gunch's, I felt a pain in my stomach, too. Right here it was—kind of

a sharp shooting pain. I— Where'd that dime go to? Why don't you serve more prunes at breakfast? Of course I eat an apple every evening—an apple a day keeps the doctor away—but still, you ought to have more prunes, and not all these fancy doodads."

"The last time I had prunes you didn't eat them."

"Well, I didn't feel like eating 'em, I suppose. Matter of fact, I think I did eat some of 'em. Anyway— I tell you it's mighty important to— I was saying to Verg Gunch, just last evening, most people don't take sufficient care of their diges—"

"Shall we have the Gunches for our dinner, next week?"

"Why sure; you bet."

"Now see here, George: I want you to put on your nice dinner-jacket that evening."

"Rats! The rest of 'em won't want to dress."

"Of course they will. You remember when you didn't dress for the Littlefields' supper-party, and all the rest did, and how embarrassed you were."

"Embarrassed, hell! I wasn't embarrassed. Everybody knows I can put on as expensive a Tux. as anybody else, and I should worry if I don't happen to have it on sometimes. All a darn nuisance, anyway. All right for a woman, that stays around the house all the time, but when a fellow's worked like the dickens all day, he doesn't want to go and hustle his head off getting into the soup-and-fish for a lot of folks that he's seen in just reg'lar ordinary clothes that same day."

"You know you enjoy being seen in one. The other evening you admitted you were glad I'd insisted on your dressing. You said you felt a lot better for it. And oh, Georgie, I do wish you wouldn't say 'Tux.' It's 'dinner-jacket.' "

"Rats, what's the odds?"

"Well, it's what all the nice folks say.

Suppose Lucile McKelvey heard you calling it a 'Tux.' "

"Well, that's all right now! Lucile McKelvey can't pull anything on me! Her folks are common as mud, even if her husband and her dad are millionaires! I suppose you're trying to rub in *your* exalted social position! Well, let me tell you that your revered paternal ancestor, Henry T., doesn't even call it a 'Tux.'! He calls it a 'bobtail jacket for a ringtail monkey,' and you couldn't get him into one unless you chloroformed him!"

"Now don't be horrid, George."

"Well, I don't want to be horrid, but Lord! you're getting as fussy as Verona. Ever since she got out of college she's been too rambunctious to live with—doesn't know what she wants—well, I know what she wants!—all she wants is to marry a millionaire, and live in Europe, and hold some preacher's hand, and simultaneously at the same time stay right here in Zenith and be some blooming kind of a socialist agitator or boss charity-worker or some damn thing! Lord, and Ted is just as bad! He wants to go to college, and he doesn't want to go to college. Only one of the three that knows her own mind is Tinka. Simply can't understand how I ever came to have a pair of shillyshallying children like Rone and Ted. I may not be any Rockefeller or James J. Shakespeare, but I certainly do know my own mind, and I do keep right on plugging along in the office and— Do you know the latest? Far as I can figure out, Ted's new bee is he'd like to be a movie actor and— And here I've told him a hundred times, if he'll go to college and law-school and make good, I'll set him up in business and— Verona just exactly as bad. Doesn't know what she wants. Well, well, come on! Aren't you ready yet? The girl rang the bell three minutes ago."

Before he followed his wife, Babbitt stood at the western-most window of their room. This residential settlement, Floral Heights, was on a rise; and though the center of the city was three miles away—Zenith had between three and four hundred thousand inhabitants now—he could see the top of the Second National Tower, an Indiana limestone building of thirty-five stories.

Its shining walls rose against April sky to a simple cornice like a streak of white fire. Integrity was in the tower, and decision. It bore its strength lightly as a tall soldier. As Babbitt stared, the nervousness was soothed from his face, his slack chin lifted in reverence. All he articulated was "That's one lovely sight!" but he was inspired by the rhythm of the city; his love of it renewed. He beheld the tower as a temple-spire of the religion of business, a faith passionate, exalted, surpassing common men; and as he clumped down to breakfast he whistled the ballad "Oh, by gee, by gosh, by jingo" as though it were a hymn melancholy and noble.

CHAPTER 2

Relieved of Babbitt's bumbling and the soft grunts with which his wife expressed the sympathy she was too experienced to feel and much too experienced not to show, their bedroom settled instantly into impersonality.

It gave on the sleeping-porch. It served both of them as dressing-room, and on the coldest nights Babbitt luxuriously gave up the duty of being manly and retreated to the bed inside, to curl his toes in the warmth and laugh at the January gale.

The room displayed a modest and pleasant color-scheme, after one of the best standard designs of the decorator who "did the interiors" for most of the speculative-builders' houses in Zenith. The walls were gray, the woodwork white, the rug a serene blue; and very much like mahogany was the furniture— the bureau with its great clear mirror, Mrs. Babbitt's dressing-table with toilet-articles of almost solid silver, the plain twin beds, between them a small table holding a standard electric bedside lamp, a glass for water, and a standard bedside book with colored illustrations—what particular book it was cannot be ascertained, since no one had ever opened it. The mattresses were firm but not hard, triumphant modern mattresses which had cost a great deal of money; the hot-water radiator was of exactly the proper scientific surface for the cubic contents of the room. The windows were large and easily opened, with the best catches and cords, and Holland roller-shades guaranteed not to crack. It was a masterpiece among bedrooms, right out of Cheerful Modern Houses for Medium Incomes. Only it had nothing to do with the Babbitts, nor with any one else. If people had ever lived and loved here, read thrillers at midnight and lain in beautiful indolence on a Sunday morning, there were no signs of it. It had the air of being a very good room in a very good hotel. One expected the chambermaid to come in and make it ready for people who would stay but one night, go without looking back, and never think of it again.

Every second house in Floral Heights had a bedroom precisely like this.

The Babbitts' house was five years old. It was all as competent and glossy as this bedroom. It had the best of taste, the best of inexpensive rugs, a simple and laudable architecture, and the latest conveniences. Throughout, electricity took the place of candles and slatternly hearth-fires. Along the bedroom baseboard were three plugs for electric lamps, concealed by little brass doors. In the halls were plugs for the vacuum cleaner, and in the living-room plugs for the piano lamp, for the electric fan. The trim dining-room (with its admirable oak buffet, its leaded-glass cupboard, its creamy plaster walls, its modest scene of a salmon expiring upon a pile of oysters) had plugs which supplied the electric percolator and the electric toaster.

In fact there was but one thing wrong with the Babbitt house: It was not a home.

II

Often of a morning Babbitt came bouncing and jesting in to breakfast. But things were mysteriously awry to-day. As he pontifically tread the upper hall he looked into Verona's bedroom and protested, "What's the use of giving the family a high-class house when they don't appreciate it and tend to business and get down to brass tacks?"

He marched upon them: Verona, a dumpy brown-haired girl of twenty-two, just out of Bryn Mawr, given to solicitudes about duty and sex and God and the unconquerable bagginess of the gray sports-suit she was now wearing. Ted— Theodore Roosevelt Babbitt—a decorative boy of seventeen. Tinka—Katherine— still a baby at ten, with radiant red hair and a thin skin which hinted of too much candy and too many ice cream sodas. Babbitt did not show his vague irritation as he tramped in. He really disliked being a family tyrant, and his nagging was as meaningless as it was frequent. He shouted at Tinka, "Well, kittiedoolie!" It was the only pet name in his vocabulary, except the "dear" and "hon." with which he recognized his wife, and he flung it at Tinka every morning.

He gulped a cup of coffee in the hope

of pacifying his stomach and his soul. His stomach ceased to feel as though it did not belong to him, but Verona began to be conscientious and annoying, and abruptly there returned to Babbitt the doubts regarding life and families and business which had clawed at him when his dream-life and the slim fairy girl had fled.

Verona had for six months been filing-clerk at the Gruensberg Leather Company offices, with a prospect of becoming secretary to Mr. Gruensberg and thus, as Babbitt defined it, "getting some good out of your expensive college education till you're ready to marry and settle down."

But now said Verona: "Father! I was talking to a classmate of mine that's working for the Associated Charities—oh, Dad, there's the sweetest little babies that come to the milk-station there!—and I feel as though I ought to be doing something worth while like that."

"What do you mean 'worth while'? If you get to be Gruensberg's secretary—and maybe you would, if you kept up your shorthand and didn't go sneaking off to concerts and talk-fests every evening—I guess you'll find thirty-five or forty bones a week worth while!"

"I know, but—oh, I want to—contribute— I wish I were working in a settlement-house. I wonder if I could get one of the department-stores to let me put in a welfare-department with a nice rest-room and chintzes and wicker chairs and so on and so forth. Or I could—"

"Now you look here! The first thing you got to understand is that all this uplift and flipflop and settlement-work and recreation is nothing in God's world but the entering wedge for socialism. The sooner a man learns he isn't going to be coddled, and he needn't expect a lot of free grub and, uh, all these free classes and flipflop and doodads for his kids unless he earns 'em, why, the sooner he'll

get on the job and produce—produce—produce! That's what the country needs, and not all this fancy stuff that just enfeebles the will-power of the working man and gives his kids a lot of notions above their class. And you—if you'd tend to business instead of fooling and fussing— All the time! When I was a young man I made up my mind what I wanted to do, and stuck to it through thick and thin, and that's why I'm where I am to-day, and—Myra! What do you let the girl chop the toast up into these dinky little chunks for? Can't get your fist onto 'em. Half cold, anyway!"

Ted Babbitt, junior in the great East Side High School, had been making hiccup-like sounds of interruption. He blurted now, "Say, Rone, you going to—"

Verona whirled. "Ted! Will you kindly not interrupt us when we're talking about serious matters!"

"Aw punk," said Ted judicially. "Ever since somebody slipped up and let you out of college, Ammonia, you been pulling these nut conversations about what-nots and so-on-and-so-forths. Are you going to— I want to use the car to-night."

Babbitt snorted, "Oh, you do! May want it myself!" Verona protested, "Oh, you do, Mr. Smarty! I'm going to take it myself!" Tinka wailed, "Oh, papa, you said maybe you'd drive us down to Rose-dale!" and Mrs. Babbitt, "Careful, Tinka, your sleeve is in the butter." They glared, and Verona hurled, "Ted, you're a perfect pig about the car!"

"Course you're not! Not a-tall!" Ted could be maddeningly bland. "You just want to grab it off, right after dinner, and leave it in front of some skirt's house all evening while you sit and gas about lit-e'ature and the highbrows you're going to marry—if they only propose!"

"Well, Dad oughtn't to *ever* let you have it! You and those beastly Jones boys drive like maniacs. The idea of your taking the turn on Chautauqua Place at forty miles an hour!"

"Aw, where do you get that stuff! You're so darn scared of the car that you drive up-hill with the emergency brake on!"

"I do not! And you— Always talking about how much you know about motors, and Eunice Littlefield told me you said the battery fed the generator!"

"You—why, my good woman, you don't know a generator from a differential." Not unreasonably was Ted lofty with her. He was a natural mechanic, a maker and tinkerer of machines; he lisped in blueprints for the blueprints came.

"That'll do now!" Babbitt flung in mechanically, as he lighted the gloriously satisfying first cigar of the day and tasted the exhilarating drug of the *Advocate-Times* headlines.

Ted negotiated: "Gee, honest, Rone, I don't want to take the old boat, but I promised couple o' girls in my class I'd drive 'em down to the rehearsal of the school chorus, and, gee, I don't want to, but a gentleman's got to keep his social engagements."

"Well, upon my word! You and your social engagements! In high school!"

"Oh, ain't we select since we went to that hen college! Let me tell you there isn't a private school in the state that's got as swell a bunch as we got in Gamma Digamma this year. There's two fellows that their dads are millionaires. Say, gee, I ought to have a car of my own, like lots of the fellows."

Babbitt almost rose. "A car of your own! Don't you want a yacht, and a house and lot? That pretty nearly takes the cake! A boy that can't pass his Latin examinations, like any other boy ought to, and he expects me to give him a motor-car, and I suppose a chauffeur, and an aeroplane maybe, as a reward for

the hard work he puts in going to the movies with Eunice Littlefield! Well, when you see me giving you—"

Somewhat later, after diplomacies, Ted persuaded Verona to admit that she was merely going to the Armory, that evening, to see the dog and cat show. She was then, Ted planned, to park the car in front of the candy-store across from the Armory and he would pick it up. There were masterly arrangements regarding leaving the key, and having the gasoline tank filled; and passionately, devotees of the Great God Motor, they hymned the patch on the spare inner-tube, and the lost jack-handle.

Their truce dissolving, Ted observed that her friends were "a scream of a bunch—stuck-up gabby four-flushers." His friends, she indicated, were "disgusting imitation sports, and horrid little shrieking ignorant girls." Further: "It's disgusting of you to smoke cigarettes, and so on and so forth, and those clothes you've got on this morning, they're too utterly ridiculous—honestly, simply disgusting."

Ted balanced over to the low beveled mirror in the buffet, regarded his charms, and smirked. His suit, the latest thing in Old Eli Togs, was skin-tight, with skimpy trousers to the tops of his glaring tan boots, a chorus-man waistline, pattern of an agitated check, and across the back a belt which belted nothing. His scarf was an enormous black silk wad. His flaxen hair was ice-smooth, pasted back without parting. When he went to school he would add a cap with a long vizor like a shovel-blade. Proudest of all was his wasit-coat, saved for, begged for, plotted for; a real Fancy Vest of fawn with polka dots of a decayed red, the points astoundingly long. On the lower edge of it he wore a high-school button, a class button, and a fraternity pin.

And none of it mattered. He was supple and swift and flushed; his eyes (which he believed to be cynical) were candidly eager. But he was not over-gentle. He waved his hand at poor dumpy Verona and drawled: "Yes, I guess we're pretty ridiculous and dis-gusticulus, and I rather guess our new necktie is some smear!"

Babbitt barked: "It is! And while you're admiring yourself, let me tell you it might add to your manly beauty if you wiped some of that egg off your mouth!"

Verona giggled, momentary victor in the greatest of Great Wars, which is the family war. Ted looked at her hopelessly, then shrieked at Tinka: "For the love o' Pete, quit pouring the whole sugar bowl on your corn flakes!"

When Verona and Ted were gone and Tinka upstairs, Babbitt groaned to his wife: "Nice family, I must say! I don't pretend to be any baa-lamb, and maybe I'm a little cross-grained at breakfast sometimes, but the way they go on jab-jab-jabbering, I simply can't stand it. I swear, I feel like going off some place where I can get a little peace. I do think after a man's spent his lifetime trying to give his kids a chance and a decent edu-cation, it's pretty discouraging to hear them all the time scrapping like a bunch of hyenas and never—and never— Curi-ous; here in the paper it says— Never silent for one mom— Seen the morning paper yet?"

"No, dear." In twenty-three years of married life, Mrs. Babbitt had seen the paper before her husband just sixty-seven times.

"Lots of news. Terrible big tornado in the South. Hard luck, all right. But this, say, this is corking! Beginning of the end for those fellows! New York Assembly has passed some bills that ought to com-pletely outlaw the socialists! And there's an elevator-runners' strike in New York and a lot of college boys are taking their places. That's the stuff! And a mass-meeting in Birmingham's demanded that

this Mick agitator, this fellow De Valera, be deported. Dead right, by golly! All these agitators paid with German gold anyway. And we got no business interfer-ing with the Irish or any other foreign government. Keep our hands strictly off. And there's another well-authenticated rumor from Russia that Lenin is dead. That's fine. It's beyond me why we don't just step in there and kick those Bolshe-vik cusses out."

"That's so," said Mrs. Babbitt.

"And it says here a fellow was inaugu-rated mayor in overalls—a preacher, too! What do you think of that!"

"Humph! Well!"

He searched for an attitude, but neither as a Republican, a Presbyterian, an Elk, nor a real-estate broker did he have any doctrine about preacher-mayors laid down for him, so he grunted and went on. She looked sympathetic and did not hear a word. Later she would read the headlines, the society columns, and the department-store advertisements.

"What do you know about this! Charley McKelvey still doing the sassiety stunt as heavy as ever. Here's what that gushy woman reporter says about last night:

Never is Society with the big, big S more flattered than when they are bidden to partake of good cheer at the distinguished and hospitable residence of Mr. and Mrs. Charles L. McKelvey as they were last night. Set in its spacious lawns and landscaping, one of the notable sights crowning Royal Ridge, but merry and homelike despite its mighty stone walls and its vast rooms famed for their decoration, their home was thrown open last night for a dance in honor of Mrs. McKelvey's notable guest, Miss J. Sneeth of Washington. The wide hall is so generous in its proportions that it made a perfect ball-room, its hardwood floor reflecting the charming pageant above its polished sur-face. Even the delights of dancing paled be-fore the alluring opportunities for tête-à-têtes that invited the soul to loaf in the long library before the baronial fireplace, or in the drawing-room with its deep comfy armchairs, its shaded lamps just made for a sly whisper of pretty nothings all a deux; or even in the billiard room where one could take a cue and show a prowess at still another game than that sponsored by Cupid and Terpsichore.

There was more, a great deal more, in the best urban journalistic style of Miss Elnora Pearl Bates, the popular society editor of the *Advocate-Times*. But Babbitt could not abide it. He grunted. He wrinkled the newspaper. He protested: "Can you beat it! I'm willing to hand a lot of credit to Charley McKelvey. When we were in college together, he was just as hard up as any of us, and he's made a million good bucks out of contracting and hasn't been any dishonester or bought any more city councils than was necessary. And that's a good house of his—though it ain't any 'mighty stone walls' and it ain't worth the ninety thousand it cost him. But when it comes to talking as though Charley McKelvey and all that booze-hoisting set of his are any blooming bunch of of, of Vanderbilts, why, it makes me tired!"

Timidly from Mrs. Babbitt: "I would like to see the inside of their house though. It must be lovely. I've never been inside."

"Well, I have! Lots of—couple of times. To see Chaz about business deals, in the evening. It's not so much. I wouldn't *want* to go there to dinner with that gang of, of high-binders. And I'll bet I make a whole lot more money than some of those tin-horns that spend all they got on dress-suits and haven't got a decent suit of underwear to their name! Hey! What do you think of this!"

Mrs. Babbitt was strangely unmoved by the tidings from the Real Estate and Building column of the *Advocate-Times*:

Ashtabula Street, 496—J. K. Dawson to Thomas Mullally, April 17, 15.7 x 112.2, mtg. $4000 .... Nom.

And this morning Babbitt was too disquieted to entertain her with items from Mechanics' Liens, Mortgages Recorded, and Contracts Awarded. He rose. As he looked at her his eyebrows seemed shaggier than usual. Suddenly:

"Yes, maybe— Kind of shame to not keep in touch with folks like the McKelveys. We might try inviting them to dinner, some evening. Oh, thunder, let's not waste our good time thinking about 'em! Our little bunch has a lot livelier times than all those plutes. Just compare a real human like you with these neurotic birds like Lucile McKelvey—all high-brow talk and dressed up like a plush horse! You're a great old girl, hon!"

He covered his betrayal of softness with a complaining: "Say, don't let Tinka go and eat any more of that poison nutfudge. For Heaven's sake, try to keep her from ruining her digestion. I tell you, most folks don't appreciate how important it is to have a good digestion and regular habits. Be back 'bout usual time, I guess."

He kissed her—he didn't quite kiss her—he laid unmoving lips against her unflushing cheek. He hurried out to the garage, muttering: "Lord, what a family! And now Myra is going to get pathetic on me because we don't train with this millionaire outfit. Oh, Lord, sometimes I'd like to quit the whole game. And the office worry and detail just as bad. And I act cranky and— I don't mean to, but I get— So darn tired!"

CHAPTER 3

To George F. Babbitt, as to most prosperous citizens of Zenith, his motor car was poetry and tragedy, love and heroism. The office was his pirate ship but the car his perilous excursion ashore.

Among the tremendous crises of each day none was more dramatic than starting the engine. It was slow on cold mornings; there was the long, anxious whirr of the starter; and sometimes he had to drip ether into the cocks of the cylinders, which was so very interesting that at lunch he would chronicle it drop by drop, and orally calculate how much each drop had cost him.

This morning he was darkly prepared to find something wrong, and he felt belittled when the mixture exploded sweet and strong, and the car didn't even brush the door-jamb, gouged and splintery with many bruisings by fenders, as he backed out of the garage. He was confused. He shouted "Morning!" to Sam Doppelbrau with more cordiality than he had intended.

Babbitt's green and white Dutch Colonial house was one of three in that block on Chatham Road. To the left of it was the residence of Mr. Samuel Doppelbrau, secretary of an excellent firm of bathroom-fixture jobbers. His was a comfortable house with no architectural manners whatever; a large wooden box with a squat tower, a broad porch, and glossy paint yellow as a yolk. Babbitt disapproved of Mr. and Mrs. Doppelbrau as "Bohemian." From their house came midnight music and obscene laughter; there were neighborhood rumors of bootlegged whisky and fast motor rides. They furnished Babbitt with many happy evenings of discussion, during which he announced firmly, "I'm not strait-laced, and I don't mind seeing a fellow throw in a drink once in a while, but when it comes to deliberately trying to get away with a lot of hell-raising all the while like the Doppelbraus do, it's too rich for my blood!"

On the other side of Babbitt lived Howard Littlefield, Ph.D., in a strictly modern house whereof the lower part was dark red tapestry brick, with a leaded oriel, the upper part of pale stucco like spattered clay, and the roof red-tiled. Littlefield was the Great Scholar of the neighborhood; the authority on everything in the world except babies, cooking, and motors. He was a Bachelor of Arts of Blodgett College, and a Doctor of Philosophy in economics of Yale. He was the employment-manager and publicity-counsel of the Zenith Street Traction Company. He could, on ten hours' notice, appear before the board of aldermen or the state legislature and prove, absolutely, with figures all in rows and with precedents from Poland and New Zealand, that the street-car company loved the Public and yearned over its employees; that all its stock was owned by Widows and Orphans; and that whatever it desired to do would benefit property-owners by increasing rental values, and help the poor by lowering rents. All his acquaintances turned to Littlefield when they desired to know the date of the battle of Saragossa, the definition of the word "sabotage," the future of the German mark, the translation of *"hinc illæ lachrimæ,"* or the number of products of coal tar. He awed Babbitt by confessing that he often sat up till midnight reading the figures and footnotes in Government reports, or skimming (with amusement at the author's mistakes) the latest volumes of chemistry, archeology, and ichthyology.

But Littlefield's great value was as a spiritual example. Despite his strange learnings he was as strict a Presbyterian and as firm a Republican as George F. Babbitt. He confirmed the business men in the faith. Where they knew only by passionate instinct that their system of industry and manners was perfect, Dr. Howard Littlefield proved it to them, out of history, economics, and the confessions of reformed radicals.

Babbitt had a good deal of honest pride in being the neighbor of such a savant, and in Ted's intimacy with Eunice Littlefield. At sixteen Eunice was interested in no statistics save those regarding the ages and salaries of motion-picture stars, but—as Babbitt definitively put it—"she was her father's daughter."

The difference between a light man like Sam Doppelbrau and a really fine character like Littlefield was revealed in their appearances. Doppelbrau was disturbingly young for a man of forty-eight. He wore his derby on the back of his head, and his red face was wrinkled with meaningless laughter. But Littlefield was old for a man of forty-two. He was tall, broad, thick; his gold-rimmed spectacles were engulfed in the folds of his long face; his hair was a tossed mass of greasy blackness; he puffed and rumbled as he talked; his Phi Beta Kappa key shone against a spotty black vest; he smelled of old pipes; he was altogether funereal and archidiaconal; and to real-estate brokerage and the jobbing of bathroom-fixtures he added an aroma of sanctity.

This morning he was in front of his house, inspecting the grass parking between the curb and the broad cement sidewalk. Babbitt stopped his car and leaned out to shout "Mornin'!" Littlefield lumbered over and stood with one foot up on the running-board.

"Fine morning," said Babbitt, lighting—illegally early—his second cigar of the day.

"Yes, it's a mighty fine morning," said Littlefield.

"Spring coming along fast now."

"Yes, it's real spring now, all right," said Littlefield.

"Still cold nights, though. Had to have a couple blankets, on the sleeping-porch last night."

"Yes, it wasn't any too warm last night," said Littlefield.

"But I don't anticipate we'll have any more real cold weather now."

"No, but still, there was snow at Tiflis, Montana, yesterday," said the Scholar, "and you remember the blizzard they had out West three days ago—thirty inches of snow at Greeley, Colorado—and two years ago we had a snow-squall right here in Zenith on the twenty-fifth of April."

"Is that a fact! Say, old man, what do you think about the Republican candidate? Who'll they nominate for president? Don't you think it's about time we had a real business administration?"

"In my opinion, what the country needs, first and foremost, is a good, sound, business-like conduct of its affairs. What we need is—a business administration!" said Littlefield.

"I'm glad to hear you say that! I certainly am glad to hear you say that! I didn't know how you'd feel about it, with all your associations with colleges and so on, and I'm glad you feel that way. What the country needs—just at this present juncture—is neither a college president nor a lot of monkeying with foreign affairs, but a good—sound—economical—business—administration, that will give us a chance to have something like a decent turnover."

"Yes. It isn't generally realized that even in China the schoolmen are giving way to more practical men, and of course you can see what that implies."

"Is that a fact! Well, well!" breathed Babbitt, feeling much calmer, and much happier about the way things were going in the world. "Well, it's been nice to stop and parleyvoo a second. Guess I'll have to get down to the office now and sting a few clients. Well, so long, old man. See you to-night. So long."

II

They had labored, these solid citizens. Twenty years before, the hill on which Floral Heights was spread, with its bright roofs and immaculate turf and amazing comfort, had been a wilderness of rank second-growth elms and oaks and maples. Along the precise streets were still a few wooded vacant lots, and the fragment of an old orchard. It was brilliant to-day; the apple boughs were lit with fresh leaves like torches of green fire. The first white of cherry blossoms flickered down a gully, and robins clamored.

Babbitt sniffed the earth, chuckled at the hysteric robins as he would have chuckled at kittens or at a comic movie. He was, to the eye, the perfect office-going executive—a well-fed man in a correct brown soft hat and frameless spectacles, smoking a large cigar, driving a good motor along a semi-suburban parkway. But in him was some genius of authentic love for his neighborhood, his city, his clan. The winter was over; the time was come for the building, the visible growth, which to him was glory. He lost his dawn depression; he was ruddily cheerful when he stopped on Smith Street to leave the brown trousers, and to have the gasoline-tank filled.

The familiarity of the rite fortified him: the sight of the tall red iron gasoline-pump, the hollow-tile and terra-cotta garage, the window full of the most agreeable accessories—shiny casings, spark-plugs with immaculate porcelain jackets, tire-chains of gold and silver. He was flattered by the friendliness with which Sylvester Moon, dirtiest and most skilled of motor mechanics, came out to

serve him. "Mornin', Mr. Babbitt!" said Moon, and Babbitt felt himself a person of importance, one whose name even busy garagemen remembered—not one of these cheap-sports flying around in flivvers. He admired the ingenuity of the automatic dial, clicking off gallon by gallon; admired the smartness of the sign: "A fill in time saves getting stuck—gas to-day 31 cents"; admired the rhythmic gurgle of the gasoline as it flowed into the tank, and the mechanical regularity with which Moon turned the handle.

"How much we takin' to-day?" asked Moon, in a manner which combined the independence of the great specialist, the friendliness of a familiar gossip, and respect for a man of weight in the community, like George F. Babbitt.

"Fill 'er up."

"Who you rootin' for for Republican candidate, Mr. Babbitt?"

"It's too early to make any predictions yet. After all, there's still a good month and two weeks—no, three weeks—must be almost three weeks—well, there's more than six weeks in all before the Republican convention, and I feel a fellow ought to keep an open mind and give all the candidates a show—look 'em all over and size 'em up, and then decide carefully."

"That's a fact, Mr. Babbitt."

"But I'll tell you—and my stand on this is just the same as it was four years ago, and eight years ago, and it'll be my stand four years from now—yes, and eight years from now! What I tell everybody, and it can't be too generally understood, is that what we need first, last, and all the time is a good, sound business administration!"

"By golly, that's right!"

"How do those front tires look to you?"

"Fine! Fine! Wouldn't be much work

for garages if everybody looked after their car the way you do."

"Well, I do try and have some sense about it." Babbitt paid his bill, said adequately, "Oh, keep the change," and drove off in an ecstasy of honest self-appreciation. It was with the manner of a Good Samaritan that he shouted at a respectable-looking man who was waiting for a trolley car, "Have a lift?" As the man climbed in Babbitt condescended, "Going clear down-town? Whenever I see a fellow waiting for a trolley, I always make it a practice to give him a lift—unless, of course, he looks like a bum."

"Wish there were more folks that were so generous with their machines," dutifully said the victim of benevolence.

"Oh, no, 'tain't a question of generosity, hardly. Fact, I always feel—I was saying to my son just the other night—it's a fellow's duty to share the good things of this world with his neighbors, and it gets my goat when a fellow gets stuck on himself and goes around tooting his horn merely because he's charitable."

The victim seemed unable to find the right answer. Babbitt boomed on:

"Pretty punk service the Company giving us on these carlines. Nonsense to only run the Portland Road cars once every seven minutes. Fellow gets mighty cold on a winter morning, waiting on a street corner with the wind nipping at his ankles."

"That's right. The Street Car Company don't give a damn what kind of a deal they give us. Something ought to happen to 'em."

Babbitt was alarmed. "But still, of course it won't do to just keep knocking the Traction Company and not realize the difficulties they're operating under, like these cranks that want municipal ownership. The way these workmen hold up the Company for high wages is simply a crime, and of course the burden falls on you and me that have to pay a seven-

cent fare! Fact, there's remarkable service on all their lines—considering."

"Well—" uneasily.

"Darn fine morning," Babbitt explained. "Spring coming along fast."

"Yes, it's real spring now."

The victim had no originality, no wit, and Babbitt fell into a great silence and devoted himself to the game of beating trolley cars to the corner: a spurt, a tail-chase, nervous speeding between the huge yellow side of the trolley and the jagged row of parked motors, shooting past just as the trolley stopped—a rare game and valiant.

And all the while he was conscious of the loveliness of Zenith. For weeks together he noticed nothing but clients and the vexing To Rent signs of rival brokers. To-day, in mysterious malaise, he raged or rejoiced with equal nervous swiftness, and to-day the light of spring was so winsome that he lifted his head and saw.

He admired each district along his familiar route to the office: The bungalows and shrubs and winding irregular driveways of Floral Heights. The one-story shops on Smith Street, a glare of plate-glass and new yellow brick; groceries and laundries and drug-stores to supply the more immediate needs of East Side housewives. The market gardens in Dutch Hollow, their shanties patched with corrugated iron and stolen doors. Billboards with crimson goddesses nine feet tall advertising cinema films, pipe tobacco, and talcum powder. The old "mansions" along Ninth Street, S.E., like aged dandies in filthy linen; wooden castles turned into boarding-houses, with muddy walks and rusty hedges, jostled by fast-intruding garages, cheap apartment-houses, and fruit-stands conducted by bland, sleek Athenians. Across the belt of railroad-tracks, factories with high-perched water-tanks and tall stacks—factories producing condensed milk, paper boxes, lighting-fixtures, motor cars. Then the business center, the thickening dart-ing traffic, the crammed trolleys unload-ing, and high doorways of marble and polished granite.

It was big—and Babbitt respected big-ness in anything; in mountains, jewels, muscles, wealth, or words. He was, for a spring-enchanted moment, the lyric and almost unselfish lover of Zenith. He thought of the outlying factory suburbs; of the Chaloosa River with its strangely eroded banks; of the orchard-dappled Tonawanda Hills to the North, and all the fat dairy land and big barns and comfortable herds. As he dropped his passenger he cried, "Gosh, I feel pretty good this morning!"

III

Epochal as starting the car was the drama of parking it before he entered his office. As he turned from Oberlin Avenue round the corner into Third Street, N.E., he peered ahead for a space in the line of parked cars. He angrily just missed a space as a rival driver slid into it. Ahead, another car was leaving the curb, and Babbitt slowed up, holding out his hand to the cars pressing on him from behind, agitatedly motioning an old woman to go ahead, avoiding a truck which bore down on him from one side. With front wheels nicking the wrought-steel bumper of the car in front, he stopped, feverishly cramped his steering-wheel, slid back into the vacant space and, with eighteen inches of room, manœuvered to bring the car level with the curb. It was a virile adventure masterfully executed. With satisfaction he locked a thief-proof steel wedge on the front wheel, and crossed the street to his real-estate office on the ground floor of the Reeves Building.

The Reeves Building was as fireproof as a rock and as efficient as a typewriter; fourteen stories of yellow pressed brick, with clean, upright, unornamented lines.

It was filled with the offices of lawyers, doctors, agents for machinery, for emery wheels, for wire fencing, for mining-stock. Their gold signs shone on the windows. The entrance was too modern to be flamboyant with pillars; it was quiet, shrewd, neat. Along the Third Street side were a Western Union Tele-graph Office, the Blue Delft Candy Shop, Shotwell's Stationery Shop, and the Bab-bitt-Thompson Realty Company.

Babbitt could have entered his office from the street, as customers did, but it made him feel an insider to go through the corridor of the building and enter by the back door. Thus he was greeted by the villagers.

The little unknown people who inhab-ited the Reeves Building corridors—ele-vator-runners, starter, engineers, superin-tendent, and the doubtful-looking lame man who conducted the news and cigar stand—were in no way city-dwellers. They were rustics, living in a constricted valley, interested only in one another and in The Building. Their Main Street was the entrance hall, with its stone floor, severe marble ceiling, and the inner win-dows of the shops. The liveliest place on the street was the Reeves Building Barber Shop, but this was also Babbitt's one embarrassment. Himself, he patronized the glittering Pompeian Barber Shop in the Hotel Thornleigh, and every time he passed the Reeves shop—ten times a day, a hundred times—he felt untrue to his own village.

Now, as one of the squirearchy, greeted with honorable salutations by the villagers, he marched into his office, and peace and dignity were upon him, and the morning's dissonances all unheard.

They were heard again, immediately. Stanley Graff, the outside salesman, was talking on the telephone with tragic lack of that firm manner which disci-plines clients: "Say, uh, I think I got just the house that would suit you—the Percival House, in Linton. . . . Oh, you've seen it. Well, how'd it strike you? . . . Huh? . . . Oh," irresolutely, "oh, I see."

As Babbitt marched into his private room, a coop with semi-partition of oak and frosted glass, at the back of the office, he reflected how hard it was to find employees who had his own faith that he was going to make sales.

There were nine members of the staff, besides Babbitt and his partner and father-in-law, Henry Thompson, who rarely came to the office. The nine were Stanley Graff, the outside salesman—a youngish man given to cigarettes and the playing of pool; old Mat Penniman, general utility man, collector of rents and salesman of insurance—broken, silent, gray; a mystery, reputed to have been a "crack" real-estate man with a firm of his own in haughty Brooklyn; Chester Kirby Laylock, resident salesman out at the Glen Oriole acreage development—an enthusiastic person with a silky mustache and much family; Miss Theresa McGoun, the swift and rather pretty stenographer; Miss Wilberta Bannigan, the thick, slow, laborious accountant and file-clerk; and four freelance part-time commission salesmen.

As he looked from his own cage into the main room Babbitt mourned, "McGoun's a good stenog, smart's a whip, but Stan Graff and all those bums—" The zest of the spring morning was smothered in the stale office air.

Normally he admired the office, with a pleased surprise that he should have created this sure lovely thing; normally he was stimulated by the clean newness of it and the air of bustle; but to-day it seemed flat—the tiled floor, like a bathroom, the ocher-colored metal ceiling, the faded maps on the hard plaster walls, the chairs of varnished pale oak, the desks and filing-cabinets of steel painted in olive drab. It was a vault, a steel

chapel where loafing and laughter were raw sin.

He hadn't even any satisfaction in the new water-cooler! And it was the very best of water-coolers, up-to-date, scientific, and right-thinking. It had cost a great deal of money (in itself a virtue). It possessed a non-conducting fiber ice-container, a porcelain water-jar (guaranteed hygienic), a dripless non-clogging sanitary faucet, and machine-painted decorations in two tones of gold. He looked down the relentless stretch of tiled floor at the water-cooler, and assured himself that no tenant of the Reeves Building had a more expensive one, but he could not recapture the feeling of social superiority it had given him. He astoundingly grunted, "I'd like to beat it off to the woods right now. And loaf all day. And go to Gunch's again to-night, and play poker, and cuss as much as I feel like, and drink a hundred and nine-thousand bottles of beer."

He sighed; he read through his mail; he shouted "Msgoun," which meant "Miss McGoun"; and began to dictate.

This was his own version of his first letter:

"Omar Gribble, send it to his office, Miss McGoun, yours of twentieth to hand and in reply would say look here, Gribble, I'm awfully afraid if we go on shilly-shallying like this we'll just naturally lose the Allen sale, I had Allen up on carpet day before yesterday and got right down to cases and think I can assure you—uh, uh, no, change that: all my experience indicates he is all right, means to do business, looked into his financial record which is fine—that sentence seems to be a little balled up, Miss McGoun; make a couple sentences out of it if you have to, period, new paragraph.

"He is perfectly willing to pro rate the special assessment and strikes me, am dead sure there will be no difficulty in getting him to pay for title insurance, so now for heaven's sake let's get busy—no, make that: so now let's go to it and get down—no, that's enough—you can tie those sentences up a little better when you type 'em, Miss McGoun—yours sincerely, etcetera."

This is the version of his letter which he received, typed, from Miss McGoun that afternoon:

BABBITT-THOMPSON REALTY CO.
Homes for Folks
Reeves Bldg.
Oberlin Avenue & 3d St., N.E.
Zenith

Omar Gribble, Esq.,
576 North American Building,
Zenith.

Dear Mr. Gribble:
Your letter of the twentieth to hand. I must say I'm awfully afraid that if we go on shilly-shallying like this we'll just naturally lose the Allen sale. I had Allen up on the carpet day before yesterday, and got right down to cases. All my experience indicates that he means to do business. I have also looked into his financial record, which is fine.

He is perfectly willing to pro rate the special assessment and there will be no difficulty in getting him to pay for title insurance.
So let's go!
Yours sincerely,

As he read and signed it, in his correct flowing business-college hand, Babbitt reflected, "Now that's a good, strong letter, and clear's a bell. Now what the— I never told McGoun to make a third paragraph there! Wish she'd quit trying to improve on my dictation! But what I can't understand is: why can't Stan Graff or Chet Laylock write a letter like that? With punch! With a kick!"

The most important thing he dictated that morning was the fortnightly form-letter, to be mimeographed and sent out to a thousand "prospects." It was diligently imitative of the best literary models of the day; of heart-to-heart-talk advertisements, "sales-pulling" letters, discourses on the "development of Will-power," and hand-shaking house-organs, as richly poured forth by the new school of Poets of Business. He had painfully written out a first draft, and he intoned it now like a poet delicate and distrait:

SAY, OLD MAN!
I just want to know can I do you a whaleuva favor? Honest! No kidding! I know you're interested in getting a house, not merely a place where you hang up the old bonnet but a love-nest for the wife and kiddies—and maybe for the flivver out beyant (be sure and spell that b-e-y-a-n-t, Miss McGoun) the spud garden. Say, did you ever stop to think that we're here to save you trouble? That's how we make a living—folks don't pay us for our lovely beauty! Now take a look:
Sit right down at the handsome carved mahogany escritoire and shoot us in a line telling us just what you want, and if we can find it we'll come hopping down your lane with the good tidings, and if we can't we won't bother you. To save your time, just fill out the blank enclosed. On request will also send blank regarding store properties in Floral Heights, Silver Grove, Linton, Bellevue, and all East Side residential districts.
Yours for service,

P.S.—Just a hint of some plums we can pick for you—some genuine bargains that came in to-day:

SILVER GROVE.—Cute four-room California bungalow, a.m.i., garage, dandy shade tree, swell neighborhood, handy car line. $3700, $780 down and balance liberal, Babbitt-Thompson terms, cheaper than rent.

DORCHESTER.—A corker! Artistic two-family house, all oak trim, parquet floors, lovely gas log, big porches, colonial, HEATED ALL-WEATHER GARAGE, a bargain at $11,250.

Dictation over, with its need of sitting and thinking instead of bustling around and making a noise and really doing something, Babbitt sat creakily back in his revolving desk-chair and beamed on Miss McGoun. He was conscious of her as a girl, of black bobbed hair against demure cheeks. A longing which was indistinguishable from loneliness enfeebled him. While she waited, tapping a long, precise pencil-point on the desk-tablet, he half identified her with the fairy girl of his dreams. He imagined their eyes meeting with terrifying recognition; imagined touching her lips with frightened reverence and— She was chirping, "Any more, Mist' Babbitt?" He grunted, "That winds it up, I guess," and turned heavily away.

For all his wandering thoughts, they had never been more intimate than this. He often reflected, "Nev' forget how old Jake Offutt said a wise bird never goes love-making in his own office or his own home. Start trouble. Sure. But—"

In twenty-three years of married life he had peered uneasily at every graceful ankle, every soft shoulder; in thought he had treasured them; but not once had he hazarded respectability by adventuring. Now, as he calculated the cost of re-papering the Styles house, he was restless again, discontented about nothing and everything, ashamed of his discontentment, and lonely for the fairy girl.

CHAPTER 4

It was a morning of artistic creation. Fifteen minutes after the purple prose of Babbitt's form-letter, Chester Kirby Laylock, the resident salesman at Glen Oriole, came in to report a sale and submit an advertisement. Babbitt disap-

proved of Laylock, who sang in choirs and was merry at home over games of Hearts and Old Maid. He had a tenor voice, wavy chestnut hair, and a mustache like a camel's-hair brush. Babbitt considered it excusable in a family-man to growl, "Seen this new picture of the kid—husky little devil, eh?" but Laylock's domestic confidences were as bubbling as a girl's.

"Say, I think I got a peach of an ad for the Glen, Mr. Babbitt. Why don't we try something in poetry? Honest, it'd have wonderful pulling-power. Listen:

'Mid pleasures and palaces,
Wherever you may roam,
You just provide the little bride
And we'll provide the home.

Do you get it? See—like 'Home Sweet Home.' Don't you—"

"Yes, yes, yes, hell yes, of course I get it. But— Oh, I think we'd better use something more dignified and forceful, like 'We lead, others follow,' or 'Eventually, why not now?' Course I believe in using poetry and humor and all that junk when it turns the trick, but with a high-class restricted development like the Glen we better stick to the more dignified approach, see how I mean? Well, I guess that's all, this morning, Chet."

II

By a tragedy familiar to the world of art, the April enthusiasm of Chet Laylock served only to stimulate the talent of the older craftsman, George F. Babbitt. He grumbled to Stanley Graff, "That tan-colored voice of Chet's gets on my nerves," yet he was aroused and in one swoop he wrote:

DO YOU RESPECT
YOUR LOVED ONES?

When the last sad rites of bereavement are over, do you know for certain that you have done your best for the Departed? You haven't unless they lie in the Cemetery Beautiful

LINDEN LANE

the only strictly up-to-date burial place in or near Zenith, where exquisitely gardened plots look from daisy-dotted hill-slopes across the smiling fields of Dorchester.

Sole agents
BABBITT-THOMPSON
REALTY COMPANY
Reeves Building

He rejoiced, "I guess that'll show Chan Mott and his weedy old Wildwood Cemetery something about modern merchandizing!"

III

He sent Mat Penniman to the recorder's office to dig out the names of the owners of houses which were displaying For Rent signs of other brokers; he talked to a man who desired to lease a store-building for a pool-room; he ran over the list of home-leases which were about to expire; he sent Thomas Bywaters, a street-car conductor who played at real estate in spare time, to call on side-street "prospects" who were unworthy the strategies of Stanley Graff. But he had spent his credulous excitement of creation, and these routine details annoyed him. One moment of heroism he had, in discovering a new way of stopping smoking.

He stopped smoking at least once a month. He went through with it like the solid citizen he was: admitted the evils of tobacco, courageously made resolves, laid out plans to check the vice, tapered off his allowance of cigars, and expounded the pleasures of virtuousness to every one he met. He did everything, in fact, except stop smoking.

Two months before, by ruling out a schedule, noting down the hour and minute of each smoke, and ecstatically increasing the intervals between smokes, he

had brought himself down to three cigars a day. Then he had lost the schedule.

A week ago he had invented a system of leaving his cigar-case and cigarette-box in an unused drawer at the bottom of the correspondence-file, in the outer office. "I'll just naturally be ashamed to go poking in there all day long, making a fool of myself before my own employees!" he reasoned. By end of three days he was trained to leave his desk, walk to the file, take out and light a cigar, without knowing that he was doing it.

This morning it was revealed to him that it had been too easy to open the file. Lock it, that was the thing! Inspired, he rushed out and locked up his cigars, his cigarettes, and even his box of safety matches; and the key to the file drawer he hid in his desk. But the crusading passion of it made him so tobacco-hungry that he immediately recovered the key, walked with forbidding dignity to the file, took out a cigar and a match—"but only one match; if ole cigar goes out, it'll by golly have to stay out!" Later, when the cigar did go out, he took one more match from the file, and when a buyer and a seller came in for a conference at eleven-thirty, naturally he had to offer them cigars. His conscience protested, "Why, you're smoking with them!" but he bullied it, "Oh, shut up! I'm busy now. Of course by-and-by—" There was no by-and-by, yet his belief that he had crushed the unclean habit made him feel noble and very happy. When he called up Paul Riesling he was, in his moral splendor, unusually eager.

He was fonder of Paul Riesling than of any one on earth except himself and his daughter Tinka. They had been classmates, roommates, in the State University, but always he thought of Paul Riesling, with his dark slimness, his precisely parted hair, his nose-glasses, his hesitant speech, his moodiness, his love of music, as a younger brother, to be petted and protected. Paul had gone into his father's business, after graduation; he was now a wholesaler and small manufacturer of prepared-paper roofing. But Babbitt strenuously believed and lengthily announced to the world of Good Fellows that Paul could have been a great violinist or painter or writer. "Why say, the letters that boy sent me on his trip to the Canadian Rockies, they just absolutely make you see the place as if you were standing there. Believe me, he could have given any of these bloomin' authors a whale of a run for their money!"

Yet on the telephone they said only:

"South 343. No, no, no! I said *South* —South 343. Say, operator, what the dickens is the trouble? Can't you get me South 343? Why certainly they'll answer. Oh, hello, 343? Wanta speak Mist' Riesling, Mist' Babbitt talking. . . . 'Lo, Paul?"

"Yuh."

" 'S George speaking."

"Yuh.'

"How's old socks?"

"Fair to middlin'. How're you?"

"Fine, Paulibus. Well, what do you know?"

"Oh, nothing much."

"Where you been keepin' yourself?"

"Oh, just stickin' round. What's up, Georgie?"

"How 'bout lil lunch 's noon?"

"Be all right with me, I guess. Club?"

"Yuh. Meet you there twelve-thirty."

"A' right. Twelve-thirty. S' long, Georgie."

IV

His morning was not sharply marked into divisions. Interwoven with correspondence and advertisement-writing were a thousand nervous details: calls from clerks who were incessantly and hopefully seeking five furnished rooms and bath at sixty dollars a month; advice

to Mat Penniman on getting money out of tenants who had no money.

Babbitt's virtues as a real-estate broker —as the servant of society in the department of finding homes for families and shops for distributors of food—were steadiness and diligence. He was conventionally honest, he kept his records of buyers and sellers complete, he had experience with leases and titles and an excellent memory for prices. His shoulders were broad enough, his voice deep enough, his relish of hearty humor strong enough, to establish him as one of the ruling caste of Good Fellows. Yet his eventual importance to mankind was perhaps lessened by his large and complacent ignorance of all architecture save the types of houses turned out by speculative builders; all landscape gardening save the use of curving roads, grass, and six ordinary shrubs; and all the commonest axioms of economics. He serenely believed that the one purpose of the real-estate business was to make money for George F. Babbitt. True, it was a good advertisement at Boosters' Club lunches, and all the varieties of Annual Banquets to which Good Fellows were invited, to speak sonorously of Unselfish Public Service, the Broker's Obligation to Keep Inviolate the Trust of His Clients, and a thing called Ethics, whose nature was confusing but if you had it you were a High-class Realtor and if you hadn't you were a shyster, a piker, and a fly-by-night. These virtues awakened Confidence, and enabled you to handle Bigger Propositions. But they didn't imply that you were to be impractical and refuse to take twice the value of a house if a buyer was such an idiot that he didn't jew you down on the asking-price.

Babbitt spoke well—and often—at these orgies of commercial righteousness about the "realtor's function as a seer of the future development of the community, and as a prophetic engineer clearing the pathway for inevitable changes"—which meant that a real-estate broker could make money by guessing which way the town would grow. This guessing he called Vision.

In an address at the Boosters' Club he had admitted, "It is at once the duty and the privilege of the realtor to know everything about his own city and its environs. Where a surgeon is a specialist on every vein and mysterious cell of the human body, and the engineer upon electricity in all its phases, or every bolt of some great bridge majestically arching o'er a mighty flood, the realtor must know his city, inch by inch, and all its faults and virtues."

Though he did know the market-price, inch by inch, of certain districts of Zenith, he did not know whether the police force was too large or too small, or whether it was in alliance with gambling and prostitution. He knew the means of fire-proofing buildings and the relation of insurance-rates to fire-proofing, but he did not know how many firemen there were in the city, how they were trained and paid, or how complete their apparatus. He sang eloquently the advantages of proximity of school-buildings to rentable homes, but he did not know—he did not know that it was worth while to know—whether the city schoolrooms were properly heated, lighted, ventilated, furnished; he did not know how the teachers were chosen; and though he chanted "One of the boasts of Zenith is that we pay our teachers adequately," that was because he had read the statement in the *Advocate-Times*. Himself, he could not have given the average salary of teachers in Zenith or anywhere else.

He had heard it said that "conditions" in the County Jail and the Zenith City Prison were not very "scientific"; he had, with indignation at the criticism of Zenith, skimmed through a report in which the notorious pessimist Seneca Doane, the radical lawyer, asserted that to throw boys and young girls into a bull-pen crammed with men suffering from syphilis, delirium tremens, and insanity was not the perfect way of educating them. He had controverted the report by growling, "Folks that think a jail ought to be a bloomin' Hotel Thornleigh make me sick. If people don't like a jail, let 'em behave 'emselves and keep out of it. Besides, these reform cranks always exaggerate." That was the beginning and quite completely the end of his investigations into Zenith's charities and corrections; and as to the "vice districts" he brightly expressed it, "Those are things that no decent man monkeys with. Besides, smatter fact, I'll tell you confidentially: it's a protection to our daughters and to decent women to have a district where tough nuts can raise cain. Keeps 'em away from our own homes."

As to industrial conditions, however, Babbitt had thought a great deal, and his opinions may be coördinated as follows:

"A good labor union is of value because it keeps out radical unions, which would destroy property. No one ought to be forced to belong to a union, however. All labor agitators who try to force men to join a union should be hanged. In fact, just between ourselves, there oughtn't to be any unions allowed at all; and as it's the best way of fighting the unions, every business man ought to belong to an employers'-association and to the Chamber of Commerce. In union there is strength. So any selfish hog who doesn't join the Chamber of Commerce ought to be forced to."

In nothing—as the expert on whose advice families moved to new neighborhoods to live there for a generation—was Babbitt more splendidly innocent than in the science of sanitation. He did not know a malaria-bearing mosquito from a bat; he knew nothing about tests of drinking water; and in the matters of plumbing and sewage he was as unlearned as he was voluble. He often referred to the excellence of the bathrooms in the houses he sold. He was fond of explaining why it was that no European ever bathed. Some one had told him, when he was twenty-two, that all cesspools were unhealthy, and he still denounced them. If a client impertinently wanted him to sell a house which had a cesspool, Babbitt always spoke about it—before accepting the house and selling it.

When he laid out the Glen Oriole acreage development, when he ironed woodland and dipping meadow into a glenless, orioleless, sunburnt flat prickly with small boards displaying the names of imaginary streets, he righteously put in a complete sewage-system. It made him feel superior; it enabled him to sneer privily at the Martin Lumsen development, Avonlea, which had a cesspool; and it provided a chorus for the full-page advertisements in which he announced the beauty, convenience, cheapness, and supererogatory healthfulness of Glen Oriole. The only flaw was that the Glen Oriole sewers had insufficient outlet, so that waste remained in them, not very agreeably, while the Avonlea cesspool was a Waring septic tank.

The whole of the Glen Oriole project was a suggestion that Babbitt, though he really did hate men recognized as swindlers, was not too unreasonably honest. Operators and buyers prefer that brokers should not be in competition with them as operators and buyers themselves, but attend to their clients' interests only. It was supposed that the Babbitt-Thompson Company were merely agents for Glen Oriole, serving the real owner, Jake Offutt, but the fact was that Babbitt and Thompson owned sixty-two per cent. of the Glen, the president and purchasing

agent of the Zenith Street Traction Company owned twenty-eight per cent., and Jake Offutt (a gang-politician, a small manufacturer, a tobacco-chewing old farceur who enjoyed dirty politics, business diplomacy, and cheating at poker) had only ten per cent., which Babbitt and the Traction officials had given to him for "fixing" health inspectors and fire inspectors and a member of the State Transportation Commission.

But Babbitt was virtuous. He advocated, though he did not practise, the prohibition of alcohol; he praised, though he did not obey, the laws against motor-speeding; he paid his debts; he contributed to the church, the Red Cross, and the Y.M.C.A.; he followed the custom of his clan and cheated only as it was sanctified by precedent; and he never descended to trickery—though, as he explained to Paul Riesling:

"Course I don't mean to say that every ad I write is literally true or that I always believe everything I say when I give some buyer a good strong selling-spiel. You see—you see it's like this: In the first place, maybe the owner of the property exaggerated when he put it into my hands, and it certainly isn't my place to go proving my principal a liar! And then most folks are so darn crooked themselves that they expect a fellow to do a little lying, so if I was fool enough to never whoop the ante I'd get the credit for lying anyway! In self-defense I got to toot my own horn, like a lawyer defending a client—his bounden duty, ain't it, to bring out the poor dub's good points? Why, the Judge himself would bawl out a lawyer that didn't, even if they both knew the guy was guilty! But even so, I don't pad out the truth like Cecil Rountree or Thayer or the rest of these realtors. Fact, I think a fellow that's willing to deliberately up and profit by lying ought to be shot!"

Babbitt's value to his clients was rarely better shown than this morning, in the conference at eleven-thirty between himself, Conrad Lyte, and Archibald Purdy.

V

Conrad Lyte was a real-estate speculator. He was a nervous speculator. Before he gambled he consulted bankers, lawyers, architects, contracting builders, and all of their clerks and stenographers who were willing to be cornered and give him advice. He was a bold entrepreneur, and he desired nothing more than complete safety in his investments, freedom from attention to details, and the thirty or forty per cent. profit which, according to all authorities, a pioneer deserves for his risks and foresight. He was a stubby man with a cap-like mass of short gray curls and clothes which, no matter how well cut, seemed shaggy. Below his eyes were semicircular hollows, as though silver dollars had been pressed against them and had left an imprint.

Particularly and always Lyte consulted Babbitt, and trusted in his slow cautiousness.

Six months ago Babbitt had learned that one Archibald Purdy, a grocer in the indecisive residential district known as Linton, was talking of opening a butcher shop beside his grocery. Looking up the ownership of adjoining parcels of land, Babbitt found that Purdy owned his present shop but did not own the one available lot adjoining. He advised Conrad Lyte to purchase this lot, for eleven thousand dollars, though an appraisal on a basis of rents did not indicate its value as above nine thousand. The rents, declared Babbitt, were too low; and by waiting they could make Purdy come to their price. (This was Vision.) He had to bully Lyte into buying. His first act as agent for Lyte was to increase the rent of the battered store-building on the lot.

The tenant said a number of rude things, but he paid.

Now, Purdy seemed ready to buy, and his delay was going to cost him ten thousand extra dollars—the reward paid by the community to Mr. Conrad Lyte for the virtue of employing a broker who had Vision and who understood Talking Points, Strategic Values, Key Situations, Underappraisals, and the Psychology of Salesmanship.

Lyte came to the conference exultantly. He was fond of Babbitt, this morning, and called him "old hoss." Purdy, the grocer, a long-nosed man and solemn, seemed to care less for Babbitt and for Vision, but Babbitt met him at the street door of the office and guided him toward the private room with affectionate little cries of "This way, Brother Purdy!" He took from the correspondence-file the entire box of cigars and forced them on his guests. He pushed their chairs two inches forward and three inches back, which gave an hospitable note, then leaned back in his desk-chair and looked plump and jolly. But he spoke to the weakling grocer with firmness.

"Well, Brother Purdy, we been having some pretty tempting offers from butchers and a slew of other folks for that lot next to your store, but I persuaded Brother Lyte that we ought to give you a shot at the property first. I said to Lyte, 'It'd be a rotten shame,' I said, 'if somebody went and opened a combination grocery and meat market right next door and ruined Purdy's nice little business.' Especially—" Babbitt leaned forward, and his voice was harsh, "—it would be hard luck if one of these cash-and-carry chain-stores got in there and started cutting prices below cost till they got rid of competition and forced you to the wall!"

Purdy snatched his thin hands from his pockets, pulled up his trousers, thrust his hands back into his pockets, tilted in the heavy oak chair, and tried to look amused, as he struggled:

"Yes, they're bad competition. But I guess you don't realize the Pulling Power that Personality has in a neighborhood business."

The great Babbitt smiled. "That's so. Just as you feel, old man. We thought we'd give you first chance. All right then—"

"Now look here!" Purdy wailed. "I know f'r a fact that a piece of property 'bout same size, right near, sold for less 'n eighty-five hundred, 'twa'n't two years ago, and here you fellows are asking me twenty-four thousand dollars! Why, I'd have to mortgage— I wouldn't mind so much paying twelve thousand but— Why good God, Mr. Babbitt, you're asking more 'n twice its value! And threatening to ruin me if I don't take it!"

"Purdy, I don't like your way of talking! I don't like it one little bit! Supposing Lyte and I were stinking enough to want to ruin any fellow human, don't you suppose we know it's to our own selfish interest to have everybody in Zenith prosperous? But all this is beside the point. Tell you what we'll do: We'll come down to twenty-three thousand— five thousand down and the rest on mortgage—and if you want to wreck the old shack and rebuild, I guess I can get Lyte here to loosen up for a building-mortgage on good liberal terms. Heavens, man, we'd be glad to oblige you! We don't like these foreign grocery trusts any better 'n you do! But it isn't reasonable to expect us to sacrifice eleven thousand or more just for neighborliness, *is* it! How about it, Lyte? You willing to come down?"

By warmly taking Purdy's part, Babbitt persuaded the benevolent Mr. Lyte to reduce his price to twenty-one thousand dollars. At the right moment Babbitt snatched from a drawer the agreement he had had Miss McGoun type out a week ago and thrust it into Purdy's hands. He genially shook his fountain pen to make certain that it was flowing, handed it to Purdy, and approvingly watched him sign.

The work of the world was being done. Lyte had made something over nine thousand dollars, Babbitt had made a four-hundred-and-fifty dollar commission, Purdy had, by the sensitive mechanism of modern finance, been provided with a business-building, and soon the happy inhabitants of Linton would have meat lavished upon them at prices only a little higher than those down-town.

It had been a manly battle, but after it Babbitt drooped. This was the only really amusing contest he had been planning. There was nothing ahead save details of leases, appraisals, mortgages.

He muttered, "Makes me sick to think of Lyte carrying off most of the profit when I did all the work, the old skinflint! And— What else have I got to do to-day? . . . Like to take a good long vacation. Motor trip. Something."

He sprang up, rekindled by the thought of lunching with Paul Riesling.

CHAPTER 5

Babbitt's preparations for leaving the office to its feeble self during the hour and a half of his lunch-period were somewhat less elaborate than the plans for a general European war.

He fretted to Miss McGoun, "What time you going to lunch? Well, make sure Miss Bannigan is in then. Explain to her that if Wiedenfeldt calls up, she's to tell him I'm already having the title traced. And oh, b' the way, remind me to-morrow to have Penniman trace it. Now if anybody comes in looking for a cheap house, remember we got to shove that

Bangor Road place off onto somebody. If you need me, I'll be at the Athletic Club. And—uh— And—uh— I'll be back by two."

He dusted the cigar-ashes off his vest. He placed a difficult unanswered letter on the pile of unfinished work, that he might not fail to attend to it that afternoon. (For three noons, now, he had placed the same letter on the unfinished pile.) He scrawled on a sheet of yellow backing-paper the memorandum: "See abt apt h drs," which gave him an agreeable feeling of having already seen about the apartment-house doors.

He discovered that he was smoking another cigar. He threw it away, protesting, "Darn it, I thought you'd quit this darn smoking!" He courageously returned the cigar-box to the correspondence-file, locked it up, hid the key in a more difficult place, and raged, "Ought to take care of myself. And need more exercise—walk to the club, every single noon—just what I'll do—every noon—cut out this motoring all the time."

The resolution made him feel exemplary. Immediately after it he decided that this noon it was too late to walk.

It took but little more time to start his car and edge it into the traffic than it would have taken to walk the three and a half blocks to the club.

II

As he drove he glanced with the fondness of familiarity at the buildings.

A stranger suddenly dropped into the business-center of Zenith could not have told whether he was in a city of Oregon or Georgia, Ohio or Maine, Oklahoma or Manitoba. But to Babbitt every inch was individual and stirring. As always he noted that the California Building across the way was three stories lower, therefore three stories less beautiful, than his own Reeves, Building. As always when he

passed the Parthenon Shoe Shine Parlor, a one-story hut which beside the granite and red-brick ponderousness of the old California Building resembled a bath-house under a cliff, he commented, "Gosh, ought to get my shoes shined this afternoon. Keep forgetting it." At the Simplex Office Furniture Shop, the National Cash Register Agency, he yearned for a dictaphone, for a typewriter which would add and multiply, as a poet yearns for quartos or a physician for radium.

At the Nobby Men's Wear Shop he took his left hand off the steering-wheel to touch his scarf, and thought well of himself as one who bought expensive ties "and could pay cash for 'em, too, by golly"; and at the United Cigar Store, with its crimson and gold alertness, he reflected, "Wonder if I need some cigars —idiot—plumb fogot—going t' cut down my fool smoking." He looked at his bank, the Miners' and Drovers' National, and considered how clever and solid he was to bank with so marbled an establishment. His high moment came in the clash of traffic when he was halted at the corner beneath the lofty Second National Tower. His car was banked with four others in a line of steel restless as cavalry, while the cross-town traffic, limousines and enormous moving-vans and insistent motor-cycles, poured by; on the farther corner, pneumatic riveters rang on the sun-plated skeleton of a new building; and out of this tornado flashed the inspiration of a familiar face, and a fellow Booster shouted, "H' are you, George!" Babbitt waved in neighborly affection, and slid on with the traffic as the policeman lifted his hand. He noted how quickly his car picked up. He felt superior and powerful, like a shuttle of polished steel darting in a vast machine.

As always he ignored the next two blocks, decayed blocks not yet reclaimed from the grime and shabbiness of the Zenith of 1885. While he was passing the five-and-ten-cent store, the Dakota Lodging House, Concordia Hall with its lodge-rooms and the offices of fortune-tellers and chiropractors, he thought of how much money he made, and he boasted a little and worried a little and did old familiar sums:

"Four hundred fifty plunks this morning from the Lyte deal. But taxes due. Let's see: I ought to pull out eight thousand net this year, and save fifteen hundred of that—no, not if I put up garage and— Let's see: six hundred and forty clear last month, and twelve times six-forty makes—makes—let see: six times twelve is seventy-two hundred and— Oh rats, anyway, I'll make eight thousand—gee now, that's not so bad; mighty few fellows pulling down eight thousand dollars a year—eight thousand good hard iron dollars—bet there isn't more than five per cent. of the people in the whole United States that make more than Uncle George does, by golly! Right up at the top of the heap! But— Way expenses are— Family wasting gasoline, and always dressed like millionaires, and sending that eighty a month to Mother— And all these stenographers and salesmen gouging me for every cent they can get—"

The effect of his scientific budget-planning was that he felt at once triumphantly wealthy and perilously poor, and in the midst of these dissertations he stopped his car, rushed into a small news-and-miscellany shop, and bought the electric cigar-lighter which he had coveted for a week. He dodged his conscience by being jerky and noisy, and by shouting at the clerk, "Guess this will prett' near pay for itself in matches, eh?"

It was a pretty thing, a nickeled cylinder with an almost silvery socket, to be attached to the dashboard of his car. It was not only, as the placard on the counter observed, "a dandy little refinement, lending the last touch of class to a gentleman's auto," but a priceless time-saver. By freeing him from halting the car to light a match, it would in a month or two easily save ten minutes.

As he drove on he glanced at it. "Pretty nice. Always wanted one," he said wistfully. "The one thing a smoker needs, too."

Then he remembered that he had given up smoking.

"Darn it!" he mourned. "Oh well, I suppose I'll hit a cigar once in a while. And— Be a great convenience for other folks. Might make just the difference in getting chummy with some fellow that would put over a sale. And— Certainly looks nice there. Certainly is a mighty clever little jigger. Gives the last touch of refinement and class. I— By golly, I guess I can afford it if I want to! Not going to be the only member of this family that never has a single doggone luxury!"

Thus, laden with treasure, after three and a half blocks of romantic adventure, he drove up to the club.

III

The Zenith Athletic Club is not athletic and it isn't exactly a club, but it is Zenith in perfection. It has an active and smoke-misted billiard room, it is represented by baseball and football teams, and in the pool and the gymnasium a tenth of the members sporadically try to reduce. But most of its three thousand members use it as a café in which to lunch, play cards, tell stories, meet customers, and entertain out-of-town uncles at dinner. It is the largest club in the city, and its chief hatred is the conservative Union Club, which all sound members of the Athletic call "a rotten, snobbish, dull, expensive old hole—not one Good Mixer in the place—you couldn't hire me to join." Statistics show that no member of the Athletic has ever refused election to the Union, and of those who are elected, sixty-seven per cent. resign from the Athletic and are thereafter heard to say, in the drowsy sanctity of the Union lounge, "The Athletic would be a pretty good hotel, if it were more exclusive."

The Athletic Club building is nine stories high, yellow brick with glassy roof-garden above and portico of huge lime-stone columns below. The lobby, with its thick pillars of porous Caen stone, its pointed vaulting, and a brown glazed-tile floor like well-baked bread-crust, is a combination of cathedral-crypt and rath-skellar. The members rush into the lobby as though they were shopping and hadn't much time for it. Thus did Babbitt enter, and to the group standing by the cigar-counter he whooped, "How's the boys? How's the boys? Well, well, fine day!"

Jovially they whooped back—Vergil Gunch, the coal-dealer, Sidney Finkel-stein, the ladies'-ready-to-wear buyer for Parcher & Stein's department-store, and Professor Joseph K. Pumphrey, owner of the Riteway Business College and in-structor in Public Speaking, Business English, Scenario Writing, and Commercial Law. Though Babbitt admired this savant, and appreciated Sidney Finkel-stein as "a mighty smart buyer and a good liberal spender," it was to Vergil Gunch that he turned with enthusiasm. Mr. Gunch was president of the Boosters' Club, a weekly lunch-club, local chapter of a national organization which promoted sound business and friendliness among Regular Fellows. He was also no less an official than Esteemed Leading Knight in the Benevolent and Protective Order of Elks, and it was rumored that at the next election he would be a candidate for Exalted Ruler. He was a jolly man, given to oratory and to chumminess with the arts. He called on the famous actors and vaudeville artists when they came to town, gave them cigars, addressed them by their first names, and—sometimes—

succeeded in bringing them to the Boosters' lunches to give The Boys a Free Entertainment. He was a large man with hair *en brosse,* and he knew the latest jokes, but he played poker close to the chest. It was at his party that Babbitt had sucked in the virus of to-day's restlessness.

Gunch shouted, "How's the old Bolsheviki? How do you feel, the morning after the night before?"

"Oh, boy! Some head! That was a regular party you threw, Verg! Hope you haven't forgotten I took that last cute little jack-pot!" Babbitt bellowed. (He was three feet from Gunch.)

"That's all right now! What I'll hand you next time, Georgie! Say, juh notice in the paper the way the New York Assembly stood up to the reds?"

"You bet I did. That was fine, eh? Nice day to-day."

"Yes, it's one mighty fine spring day, but nights still cold."

"Yeh, you're right they are! Had to have coupla blankets last night, out on the sleeping-porch. Say, Sid," Babbitt turned to Finkelstein, the buyer, "got something wanta ask you about. I went out and bought me an electric cigar-lighter for the car, this noon, and—"

"Good hunch!" said Finkelstein, while even the learned Professor Pumphrey, a bulbous man with a pepper-and-salt cut-away and a pipe-organ voice, commented, "That makes a dandy accessory. Cigar-lighter gives tone to the dash-board."

"Yep, finally decided I'd buy me one. Got best on the market, the clerk said it was. Paid five bucks for it. Just wondering if I got stuck. What do they charge for 'em at the store, Sid?"

Finkelstein asserted that five dollars was not too great a sum, not for a really high-class lighter which was suitably nickeled and provided with connections of the very best quality. "I always say—

and believe me, I base it on a pretty fairly extensive mercantile experience— the best is the cheapest in the long run. Of course if a fellow wants to be a Jew about it, he can get cheap junk, but in the long *run,* the cheapest thing is—the best you can get! Now you take here just th' other day: I got a new top for my old boat and some upholstery, and I paid out a hundred and twenty-six fifty, and of course a lot of fellows would say that was too much—Lord, if the Old Folks— they live in one of these hick towns up-state and they simply can't get onto the way a city fellow's mind works, and then, of course, they're Jews, and they'd lie right down and die if they knew Sid had anted up a hundred and twenty-six bones. But I don't figure I was stuck, George, not a bit. Machine looks brand new now—not that it's so darned old, of course; had it less 'n three years, but I give it hard service; never drive less 'n a hundred miles on Sunday and, uh— Oh, I don't really think you got stuck, George. In the *long* run, the best is, you might say, it's unquestionably the cheapest."

"That's right," said Vergil Gunch. "That's the way I look at it. If a fellow is keyed up to what you might call intensive living, the way you get it here in Zenith—all the hustle and mental activity that's going on with a bunch of live-wires like the Boosters and here in the Z.A.C., why, he's got to save his nerves by having the best."

Babbitt nodded his head at every fifth word in the roaring rhythm; and by the conclusion, in Gunch's renowned humorous vein, he was enchanted:

"Still, at that, George, don't know's you can afford it. I've heard your business has been kind of under the eye of the gov'ment since you stole the tail of Eathorne Park and sold it!"

"Oh, you're a great little josher, Verg. But when it comes to kidding, how about

this report that you stole the black marble steps off the post-office and sold 'em for high-grade coal!" In delight Babbitt patted Gunch's back, stroked his arm.

"That's all right, but what I want to know is: who's the real-estate shark that bought that coal for his apartment-houses?"

"I guess that'll hold you for a while, George!" said Finkelstein. "I'll tell you, though, boys, what I did hear: George's missus went into the gents' wear department at Parcher's to buy him some collars, and before she could give his neck-size the clerk slips her some thirteens. 'How juh know the size?' says Mrs. Babbitt, and the clerk says, 'Men that let their wives buy collars for 'em always wear thirteen, madam.' How's that! That's pretty good, eh? How's that, eh? I guess that'll about fix you, George!"

"I—I—" Babbitt sought for amiable insults in answer. He stopped, stared at the door. Paul Riesling was coming in. Babbitt cried, "See you later, boys," and hastened across the lobby. He was, just then, neither the sulky child of the sleeping-porch, the domestic tyrant of the breakfast table, the crafty money-changer of the Lyte-Purdy conference, nor the blaring Good Fellow, the Josher and Regular Guy, of the Athletic Club. He was an older brother to Paul Riesling, swift to defend him, admiring him with a proud and credulous love passing the love of women. Paul and he shook hands solemnly; they smiled as shyly as though they had been parted three years, not three days—and they said:

"How's the old horse-thief?"

"All right, I guess. How're you, you poor shrimp?"

"I'm first-rate, you second-hand hunk o' cheese."

Reassured thus of their high fondness, Babbitt grunted, "You're a fine guy, you are! Ten minutes late!" Riesling snapped,

"Well, you're lucky to have a chance to lunch with a gentleman!" They grinned and went into the Neronian washroom, where a line of men bent over the bowls inset along a prodigious slab of marble as in religious prostration before their own images in the massy mirror. Voices thick, satisfied, authoritative, hurtled along the marble walls, bounded from the ceiling of lavender-bordered milky tiles, while the lords of the city, the barons of insurance and law and fertilizers and motor tires, laid down the law for Zenith; announced that the day was warm—indeed, indisputably of spring; that wages were too high and the interest on mortgages too low; that Babe Ruth, the eminent player of baseball, was a noble man; and that "those two nuts at the Climax Vaudeville Theater this week certainly are a slick pair of actors." Babbitt, though ordinarily his voice was the surest and most episcopal of all, was silent. In the presence of the slight dark reticence of Paul Riesling, he was awkward, he desired to be quiet and firm and deft.

The entrance lobby of the Athletic Club was Gothic, the washroom Roman Imperial, the lounge Spanish Mission, and the reading-room in Chinese Chippendale, but the gem of the club was the dining-room, the masterpiece of Ferdinand Reitman, Zenith's busiest architect. It was lofty and half-timbered, with Tudor leaded casements, an oriel, a somewhat musicianless musicians' gallery, and tapestries believed to illustrate the granting of Magna Charta. The open beams had been hand-adzed at Jake Offutt's car-body works, the hinges were of hand-wrought iron, the wainscot studded with handmade wooden pegs, and at one end of the room was a heraldic and hooded stone fireplace which the club's advertising-pamphlet asserted to be not only larger than any of the fireplaces in European castles but of a draught incomparably more scientific.

It was also much cleaner, as no fire had ever been built in it.

Half of the tables were mammoth slabs which seated twenty or thirty men. Babbitt usually sat at the one near the door, with a group including Gunch, Finkelstein, Professor Pumphrey, Howard Littlefield, his neighbor, T. Cholmondeley Frink, the poet and advertising-agent, and Orville Jones, whose laundry was in many ways the best in Zenith. They composed a club within the club, and merrily called themselves "The Roughnecks." To-day as he passed their table the Roughnecks greeted him, "Come on, sit in! You 'n' Paul too proud to feed with poor folks? Afraid somebody might stick you for a bottle of Bevo, George? Strikes me you swells are getting awful darn exclusive!"

He thundered, "You bet! We can't afford to have our reps ruined by being seen with you tightwads!" and guided Paul to one of the small tables beneath the musicians'-gallery. He felt guilty. At the Zenith Athletic Club, privacy was very bad form. But he wanted Paul to himself.

That morning he had advocated lighter lunches and now he ordered nothing but English mutton chops, radishes, peas, deep-dish apple pie, a bit of cheese, and a pot of coffee with cream, adding, as he did invariably, "And uh— Oh, and you might give me an order of French fried potatoes." When the chop came he vigorously peppered it and salted it. He always peppered and salted his meat, and vigorously, before tasting it.

Paul and he took up the spring-like quality of the spring, the virtues of the electric cigar-lighter, and the action of the New York State Assembly. It was not till Babbitt was thick and disconsolate with mutton grease that he flung out:

"I wound up a nice little deal with Conrad Lyte this morning that put five hundred good round plunks in my

pocket. Pretty nice—pretty nice! And yet
— I don't know what's the matter with
me to-day. Maybe it's an attack of spring
fever, or staying up too late at Verg
Gunch's, or maybe it's just the winter's
work piling up, but I've felt kind of down
in the mouth all day long. Course I
wouldn't beef about it to the fellows at
the Roughnecks' Table there, but you—
Ever feel that way, Paul? Kind of comes
over me: here I've pretty much done all
the things I ought to; supported my family, and got a good house and a six-
cylinder car, and built up a nice little
business, and I haven't any vices 'specially, except smoking—and I'm practically cutting that out, by the way. And I
belong to the church, and play enough
golf to keep in trim, and I only associate
with good decent fellows. And yet, even
so, I don't know that I'm entirely satisfied!"

It was drawled out, broken by shouts
from the neighboring tables, by mechanical love-making to the waitress, by
stertorous grunts as the coffee filled him
with dizziness and indigestion. He was
apologetic and doubtful, and it was Paul,
with his thin voice, who pierced the fog:

"Good Lord, George, you don't suppose it's any novelty to me to find that
we hustlers, that think we're so all-fired
successful, aren't getting much out of it?
You look as if you expected me to report
you as seditious! You know what my
own life's been."

"I know, old man."

"I ought to have been a fiddler, and
I'm a pedler of tar-roofing! And Zilla—
Oh, I don't want to squeal, but you know
as well as I do about how inspiring a wife
she is. . . . Typical instance last evening: We went to the movies. There was
a big crowd waiting in the lobby, us at
the tail-end. She began to push right
through it with her 'Sir, how dare you?'
manner— Honestly, sometimes when I
look at her and see how she's always so

made up and stinking of perfume and
looking for trouble and kind of always
yelping, 'I tell yuh I'm a lady, damn
yuh!'—why, I want to kill her! Well, she
keeps elbowing through the crowd, me
after her, feeling good and ashamed, till
she's almost up to the velvet rope and
ready to be the next let in. But there was
a little squirt of a man there—probably
been waiting half an hour—I kind of
admired the little cuss—and he turns on
Zilla and says, perfectly polite, 'Madam,
why are you trying to push past me?'
And she simply—God, I was so
ashamed!—she rips out at him, 'You're
no gentleman,' and she drags me into it
and hollers, 'Paul this person insulted
me!' and the poor skate he got ready to
fight.

"I made out I hadn't heard them—
sure! same as you wouldn't hear a boiler-
factory!—and I tried to look away—I
can tell you exactly how every tile looks
in the ceiling of that lobby; there's one
with brown spots on it like the face of
the devil—and all the time the people
there—they were packed in like sardines
—they kept making remarks about us,
and Zilla went right on talking about the
little chap, and screeching that 'folks like
him oughtn't to be admitted in a place
that's *supposed* to be for ladies and
gentlemen,' and 'Paul, will you kindly
call the manager, so I can report this
dirty rat?' and— Oof! Maybe I wasn't
glad when I could sneak inside and hide
in the dark!

"After twenty-four years of that kind
of thing, you don't expect me to fall
down and foam at the mouth when you
hint that this sweet, clean, respectable,
moral life isn't all it's cracked up to be,
do you? I can't even talk about it, except
to you, because anybody else would
think I was yellow. Maybe I am. Don't
care any longer. . . . Gosh, you've had
to stand a lot of whining from me, first
and last, Georgie!"

"Rats, now, Paul, you've never really what you could call whined. Sometimes — I'm always blowing to Myra and the kids about what a whale of a realtor I am, and yet sometimes I get a sneaking idea I'm not such a Pierpont Morgan as I let on to be. But if I ever do help by jollying you along, old Paulski, I guess maybe Saint Pete may let me in after all!"

"Yuh, you're an old blow-hard, Georgie, you cheerful cut-throat, but you've certainly kept me going."

"Why don't you divorce Zilla?"

"Why don't I! If I only could! If she'd just give me the chance! You couldn't hire her to divorce me, no, nor desert me. She's too fond of her three squares and a few pounds of nut-center chocolates in between. If she'd only be what they call unfaithful to me! George, I don't want to be too much of a stinker; back in college I'd 've thought a man who could say that ought to be shot at sunrise. But honestly, I'd be tickled to death if she'd really go making love with somebody. Fat chance! Of course she'll flirt with anything—you know how she holds hands and laughs— that laugh—that horrible brassy laugh— the way she yaps, 'You naughty man, you better be careful or my big husband will be after you!'—and the guy looking me over and thinking, 'Why, you cute little thing, you run away now or I'll spank you!' And she'll let him go just far enough so she gets some excitement out of it and then she'll begin to do the injured innocent and have a beautiful time wailing, 'I didn't think you were that kind of a person.' They talk about these *demi-vierges* in stories—"

"These *whats?*"

"—but the wise, hard, corseted, old married women like Zilla are worse than any bobbed-haired girl that ever went boldly out into this-here storm of life— and kept her umbrella slid up her sleeve! But rats, you know what Zilla is. How

she nags—nags—nags. How she wants everything I can buy her, and a lot that I can't, and how absolutely unreasonable she is, and when I get sore and try to have it out with her she plays the Perfect Lady so well that even I get fooled and get all tangled up in a lot of 'Why did you say's' and 'I didn't mean's.' I'll tell you, Georgie: You know my tastes are pretty fairly simple—in the matter of food, at least. Course, as you're always complaining, I do like decent cigars—not those Flor de Cabagos you're smoking—"

"That's all right now! That's a good two-for. By the way, Paul, did I tell you I decided to practically cut out smok—"

"Yes you— At the same time, if I can't get what I like, why, I can do without it. I don't mind sitting down to burnt steak, with canned peaches and store cake for a thrilling little dessert afterwards, but I do draw the line at having to sympathize with Zilla because she's so rotten bad-tempered that the cook has quit, and she's been so busy sitting in a dirty lace negligée all afternoon, reading about some brave manly Western hero, that she hasn't had time to do any cooking. You're always talking about 'morals' —meaning monogamy, I suppose. You've been the rock of ages to me, all right, but you're essentially a simp. You—"

"Where d' you get that 'simp,' little man? Let me tell you—"

"—love to look earnest and inform the world that it's the 'duty of responsible business men to be strictly moral, as an example to the community.' In fact you're so earnest about morality, old Georgie, that I hate to think how essentially immoral you must be underneath. All right, you can—"

"Wait, wait now! What's—"

"—talk about morals all you want to, old thing, but believe me, if it hadn't been for you and an occasional evening playing the violin to Terrill O'Farrell's 'cello, and three or four darling girls that let me forget this beastly joke they call 'respectable life,' I'd 've killed myself years ago.

"And business! The roofing business! Roofs for cowsheds! Oh, I don't mean I haven't had a lot of fun out of the Game; out of putting it over on the labor unions, and seeing a big check coming in, and the business increasing. But what's the use of it? You know, my business isn't distributing roofing—it's principally keeping my competitors from distributing roofing. Same with you. All we do is cut each other's throats and make the public pay for it!"

"Look here now, Paul! You're pretty darn near talking socialism!"

"Oh yes, of course I don't really exactly mean that—I s'pose. Course—competition—brings out the best—survival of the fittest—but— But I mean: Take all these fellows we know, the kind right here in the club now, that seem to be perfectly content with their home-life and their businesses, and that boost Zenith and the Chamber of Commerce and holler for a million population. I bet if you could cut into their heads you'd find that one-third of 'em are sure-enough satisfied with their wives and kids and friends and their offices; and one-third feel kind of restless but won't admit it; and one-third are miserable and know it. They hate the whole peppy, boosting, go-ahead game, and they're bored by their wives and think their families are fools—at least when they come to forty or forty-five they're bored—and they hate business, and they'd go— Why do you suppose there's so many 'mysterious' suicides? Why do you suppose so many Substantial Citizens jumped right into the war? Think it was all patriotism?"

Babbitt snorted, "What do you expect? Think we were sent into the world to have a soft time and—what is it?—'float

on flowery beds of ease'? Think Man was just made to be happy?"

"Why not? Though I've never discovered anybody that knew what the deuce Man really was made for!"

"Well we know—not just in the Bible alone, but it stands to reason—a man who doesn't buckle down and do his duty, even if it does bore him sometimes, is nothing but a—well, he's simply a weakling. Mollycoddle, in fact! And what do you advocate? Come down to cases! If a man is bored by his wife, do you seriously mean he has a right to chuck her and take a sneak, or even kill himself?"

"Good Lord, I don't know what 'rights' a man has! And I don't know the solution of boredom. If I did, I'd be the one philosopher that had the cure for living. But I do know that about ten times as many people find their lives dull, and unnecessarily dull, as ever admit it; and I do believe that if we busted out and admitted it sometimes, instead of being nice and patient and loyal for sixty years, and then nice and patient and dead for the rest of eternity, why, maybe, possibly, we might make life more fun."

They drifted into a maze of speculation. Babbitt was elephantishly uneasy. Paul was bold, but not quite sure about what he was being bold. Now and then Babbitt suddenly agreed with Paul in an admission which contradicted all his defense of duty and Christian patience, and at each admission he had a curious reckless joy. He said at last:

"Look here, old Paul, you do a lot of talking about kicking things in the face, but you never kick. Why don't you?"

"Nobody does. Habit too strong. But— Georgie, I've been thinking of one mild bat—oh, don't worry, old pillar of monogamy; it's highly proper. It seems to be settled now, isn't it—though of course Zilla keeps rooting for a nice expensive vacation in New York and Atlantic City, with the bright lights and the bootlegged cocktails and a bunch of lounge-lizards to dance with—but the Babbitts and the Rieslings are sure-enough going to Lake Sunasquam, aren't we? Why couldn't you and I make some excuse—say business in New York—and get up to Maine four or five days before they do, and just loaf by ourselves and smoke and cuss and be natural?"

"Great! Great idea!" Babbitt admired.

Not for fourteen years had he taken a holiday without his wife, and neither of them quite believed they could commit this audacity. Many members of the Athletic Club did go camping without their wives, but they were officially dedicated to fishing and hunting, whereas the sacred and unchangeable sports of Babbitt and Paul Riesling were golfing, motoring, and bridge. For either the fishermen or the golfers to have changed their habits would have been an infraction of their self-imposed discipline which would have shocked all right-thinking and regularized citizens.

Babbitt blustered, "Why don't we just put our foot down and say, 'We're going on ahead of you, and that's all there is to it! Nothing criminal in it. Simply say to Zilla—"

"You don't say anything to Zilla simply. Why, Georgie, she's almost as much of a moralist as you are, and if I told her the truth she'd believe we were going to meet some dames in New York. And even Myra—she never nags you, the way Zilla does, but she'd worry. She'd say, 'Don't you *want* me to go to Maine with you? I shouldn't dream of going unless you wanted me'; and you'd give in to save her feelings. Oh, the devil! Let's have a shot at duck-pins."

During the game of duck-pins, a juvenile form of bowling, Paul was silent. As they came down the steps of the club,

not more than half an hour after the time at which Babbitt had sternly told Miss McGoun he would be back, Paul sighed, "Look here, old man, oughtn't to talk about Zilla way I did."

"Rats, old man, it lets off steam."

"Oh, I know! After spending all noon sneering at the conventional stuff, I'm conventional enough to be ashamed of saving my life by busting out with my fool troubles!"

"Old Paul, your nerves are kind of on the bum. I'm going to take you away. I'm going to rig this thing. I'm going to have an important deal in New York and—and sure, of course!—I'll need you to advise me on the roof of the building! And the ole deal will fall through, and there'll be nothing for us but to go on ahead to Maine. I—Paul, when it comes right down to it, I don't care whether you bust loose or not. I do like having a rep for being one of the Bunch, but if you ever needed me I'd chuck it and come out for you every time! Not of course but what you're—course I don't mean you'd ever do anything that would put—that would put a decent position on the fritz but—See how I mean? I'm kind of a clumsy old codger, and I need your fine Eye-talian hand. We— Oh, hell, I can't stand here gassing all day! On the job! S' long! Don't take any wooden money, Paulibus! See you soon! S' long!"

CHAPTER 6

He forgot Paul Riesling in an afternoon of not unagreeable details. After a return to his office, which seemed to have staggered on without him, he drove a "prospect" out to view a four-flat tenement in the Linton district. He was inspired by the customer's admiration of the new cigar-lighter. Thrice its novelty made him use it, and thrice he hurled half-smoked cigarettes from the car, protesting, "I *got* to quit smoking so blame much!"

Their ample discussion of every detail of the cigar-lighter led them to speak of electric flat-irons and bed-warmers. Babbitt apologized for being so shabbily old-fashioned as still to use a hot-water bottle, and he announced that he would have the sleeping-porch wired at once. He had enormous and poetic admiration, though very little understanding, of all mechanical devices. They were his symbols of truth and beauty. Regarding each new intricate mechanism—metal lathe, two-jet carburetor, machine gun, oxy-acetylene welder—he learned one good realistic-sounding phrase, and used it over and over, with a delightful feeling of being technical and initiated.

The customer joined him in the worship of machinery, and they came buoyantly up to the tenement and began that examination of plastic slate roof, kalamein doors, and seven-eighths-inch blind-nailed flooring, began those diplomacies of hurt surprise and readiness to be persuaded to do something they had already decided to do, which would some day result in a sale.

On the way back Babbitt picked up his partner and father-in-law, Henry T. Thompson, at his kitchen-cabinet works, and they drove through South Zenith, a high-colored, banging, exciting region: new factories of hollow tile with gigantic wire-glass windows, surly old red-brick factories stained with tar, high-perched water-tanks, big red trucks like locomotives, and, on a score of hectic sidetracks, far-wandering freight-cars from the New York Central and apple orchards, the Great Northern and wheat-plateaus, the Southern Pacific and orange groves.

They talked to the secretary of the Zenith Foundry Company about an interesting artistic project—a cast-iron fence for Linden Lane Cemetery. They drove on to the Zeeco Motor Company and interviewed the sales-manager, Noël Ryland, about a discount on a Zeeco car for Thompson. Babbitt and Ryland were fellow-members of the Boosters' Club, and no Booster felt right if he bought anything from another Booster without receiving a discount. But Henry Thompson growled, "Oh, t' hell with 'em! I'm not going to crawl around mooching discounts, not from nobody." It was one of the differences between Thompson, the old-fashioned, lean Yankee, rugged, traditional, stage type of American business man, and Babbitt, the plump, smooth, efficient, up-to-the-minute and otherwise perfected modern. Whenever Thompson twanged, "Put your John Hancock on that line," Babbitt was as much amused by the antiquated provincialism as any proper Englishman by any American. He knew himself to be of a breeding altogether more esthetic and sensitive than Thompson's. He was a college graduate, he played golf, he often smoked cigarettes instead of cigars, and when he went to Chicago he took a room with a private bath. "The whole thing is," he explained to Paul Riesling, "these old codgers lack the subtlety that you got to have today."

This advance in civilization could be carried too far, Babbitt perceived. Noël Ryland, sales-manager of the Zeeco, was a frivolous graduate of Princeton, while Babbitt was a sound and standard ware from that great department-store, the State University. Ryland wore spats, he wrote long letters about City Planning and Community Singing, and, though he was a Booster, he was known to carry in his pocket small volumes of poetry in a foreign language. All this was going too far. Henry Thompson was the extreme of insularity, and Noël Ryland the extreme of frothiness, while between them, supporting the state, defending the evangelical churches and domestic brightness and sound business, were Babbitt and his friends.

With this just estimate of himself— and with the promise of a discount on Thompson's car—he returned to his office in triumph.

But as he went through the corridor of the Reeves Building he sighed, "Poor old Paul! I got to— Oh, damn Noël Ryland! Damn Charley McKelvey! Just because they make more money than I do, they think they're so superior. I wouldn't be found dead in their stuffy old Union Club! I—Somehow, to-day, I don't feel like going back to work. Oh well—"

II

He answered telephone calls, he read the four o'clock mail, he signed his morning's letters, he talked to a tenant about repairs, he fought with Stanley Graff.

Young Graff, the outside salesman, was always hinting that he deserved an increase of commission, and to-day he complained, "I think I ought to get a bonus if I put through the Heiler sale. I'm chasing around and working on it every single evening, almost."

Babbitt frequently remarked to his wife that it was better to "con your office-help along and keep 'em happy 'stead of jumping on 'em and poking 'em up—get more work out of 'em that way," but this unexampled lack of appreciation hurt him, and he turned on Graff:

"Look here, Stan; let's get this clear. You've got an idea somehow that it's you that do all the selling. Where d' you get that stuff? Where d' you think you'd be if it wasn't for our capital behind you, and our lists of properties, and all the prospects we find for you? All you got to do is follow up our tips and close the deal. The hall-porter could sell Babbitt-Thompson listings! You say you're en-gaged to a girl, but have to put in your evenings chasing after buyers. Well, why the devil shouldn't you? What do you want to do? Sit around holding her hand? Let me tell you, Stan, if your girl is worth her salt, she'll be glad to know you're out hustling, making some money to furnish the home-nest, instead of doing the lovey-dovey. The kind of fellow that kicks about working overtime, that wants to spend his evenings reading trashy novels or spooning and exchanging a lot of nonsense and foolishness with some girl, he ain't the kind of upstanding, energetic young man, with a future—and with Vision!—that we want here. How about it? What's your Ideal, anyway? Do you want to make money and be a responsible member of the community, or do you want to be a loafer, with no Inspiration or Pep?"

Graff was not so amenable to Vision and Ideals as usual. "You bet I want to make money! That's why I want that bonus! Honest, Mr. Babbitt, I don't want to get fresh, but this Heiler house is a terror. Nobody'll fall for it. The flooring is rotten and the walls are full of cracks."

"That's exactly what I mean! To a salesman with a love for his profession, it's hard problems like that that inspire him to do his best. Besides, Stan— Matter o' fact, Thompson and I are against bonuses, as a matter of principle. We like you, and we want to help you so you can get married, but we can't be unfair to the others on the staff. If we start giving you bonuses, don't you see we're going to hurt the feelings and be unjust to Penniman and Laylock? Right's right, and discrimination is unfair, and there ain't going to be any of it in this office! Don't get the idea, Stan, that because during the war salesmen were hard to hire, now, when there's a lot of men out of work, there aren't a slew of bright young fellows that would be glad to step in and enjoy your opportunities, and not act as if Thompson and I were his enemies and not do any work except for bonuses. How about it, heh? How about it?"

"Oh—well—gee—of course—" sighed Graff, as he went out, crabwise.

Babbitt did not often squabble with his employees. He liked to like the people about him; he was dismayed when they did not like him. It was only when they attacked the sacred purse that he was frightened into fury, but then, being a man given to oratory and high principles, he enjoyed the sound of his own vocabulary and the warmth of his own virtue. Today he had so passionately indulged in self-approval that he wondered whether he had been entirely just:

"After all, Stan isn't a boy any more. Oughtn't to call him so hard. But rats, got to haul folks over the coals now and then for their own good. Unpleasant duty, but— I wonder if Stan is sore? What's he saying to McGoun out there?"

So chill a wind of hatred blew from the outer office that the normal comfort of his evening home-going was ruined. He was distressed by losing that approval of his employees to which an executive is always slave. Ordinarily he left the office with a thousand enjoyable fussy directions to the effect that there would undoubtedly be important tasks to-morrow, and Miss McGoun and Miss Bannigan would do well to be there early, and for heaven's sake remind him to call up Conrad Lyte soon's he came in. To-night he departed with feigned and apologetic liveliness. He was as afraid of his still-faced clerks—of the eyes focused on him, Miss McGoun staring with head lifted from her typing, Miss Bannigan looking over her ledger, Mat Penniman craning around at his desk in the dark alcove, Stanley Graff sullenly expressionless—as a parvenu before the bleak propriety of his butler. He hated to expose his back to their laughter, and in his effort to be casually merry he stammered and was raucously friendly and oozed wretchedly out of the door.

But he forgot his misery when he saw from Smith Street the charms of Floral Heights; the roofs of red tile and green slate, the shining new sun-parlors, and the stainless walls.

III

He stopped to inform Howard Littlefield, his scholarly neighbor, that though the day had been springlike the evening might be cold. He went in to shout "Where are you?" at his wife, with no very definite desire to know where she was. He examined the lawn to see whether the furnace-man had raked it properly. With some satisfaction and a good deal of discussion of the matter with Mrs. Babbitt, Ted, and Howard Littlefield, he concluded that the furnace-man had not raked it properly. He cut two tufts of wild grass with his wife's largest dressmaking-scissors; he informed Ted that it was all nonsense having a furnace-man—"big husky fellow like you ought to do all the work around the house"; and privately he meditated that it was agreeable to have it known throughout the neighborhood that he was so prosperous that his son never worked around the house.

He stood on the sleeping-porch and did his day's exercises: arms out sidewise for two minutes, up for two minutes, while he muttered, "Ought to take more exercise; keep in shape"; then went in to see whether his collar needed changing before dinner. As usual it apparently did not.

The Lettish-Croat maid, a powerful woman, beat the dinner-gong.

The roast of beef, roasted potatoes, and string beans were excellent this evening and, after an adequate sketch of the day's progressive weather-states, his four-hundred-and-fifty-dollar fee, his lunch with Paul Riesling, and the proven merits of the new cigar-lighter, he was moved to a benign, "Sort o' thinking about buying a new car. Don't believe we'll get one till next year, but still, we might."

Verona, the older daughter, cried, "Oh, Dad, if you do, why don't you get a sedan? That would be perfectly slick! A closed car is so much more comfy than an open one."

"Well now, I don't know about that. I kind of like an open car. You get more fresh air that way."

"Oh, shoot, that's just because you never tried a sedan. Let's get one. It's got a lot more class," said Ted.

"A closed car does keep the clothes nicer," from Mrs. Babbitt; "You don't get your hair blown all to pieces," from Verona; "It's a lot sportier," from Ted; and from Tinka, the youngest, "Oh, let's have a sedan! Mary Ellen's father has got one." Ted wound up, "Oh, everybody's got a closed car now, except us!"

Babbitt faced them: "I guess you got nothing very terrible to complain about! Anyway, I don't keep a car just to enable you children to look like millionaires! And I like an open car, so you can put the top down on summer evenings and go out for a drive and get some good fresh air. Besides— A closed car costs more money."

"Aw, gee whiz, if the Doppelbraus can afford a closed car, I guess we can!" prodded Ted.

"Humph! I make eight thousand a year to his seven! But I don't blow it all in and waste it and throw it around, the way he does! Don't believe in this business of going and spending a whole lot of money to show off and—"

They went, with ardor and some thoroughness, into the matters of streamline bodies, hill-climbing power, wire wheels, chrome steel, ignition systems, and body colors. It was much more than a study of transportation. It was an aspiration for knightly rank. In the city of Zenith, in the barbarous twentieth century, a family's motor indicated its social rank as precisely as the grades of the peerage determined the rank of an English family —indeed, more precisely, considering the opinion of old county families upon newly created brewery barons and woolen-mill viscounts. The details of precedence we never officially determined. There was no court to decide whether the second son of a Pierce Arrow limousine should go in to dinner before the first son of a Buick roadster, but of their respective social importance there was no doubt; and where Babbitt as a boy had aspired to the presidency, his son Ted aspired to a Packard twin-six and an established position in the motored gentry.

The favor which Babbitt had won from his family by speaking of a new car evaporated as they realized that he didn't intend to buy one this year. Ted lamented, "Oh, punk! The old boat looks as if it'd had fleas and been scratching its varnish off." Mrs. Babbitt said abstractedly, "Snoway talkcher father." Babbitt raged, "If you're too much of a high-class gentleman, and you belong to the *bon ton* and so on, why, you needn't take the car out this evening." Ted explained, "I didn't mean—" and dinner dragged on with normal domestic delight to the inevitable point at which Babbitt protested, "Come, come now, we can't sit here all evening. Give the girl a chance to clear away the table."

He was fretting, "What a family! I don't know how we all get to scrapping this way. Like to go off some place and be able to hear myself think. . . . Paul . . . Maine . . . Wear old pants, and loaf, and cuss." He said cautiously to his wife, "I've been in correspondence with a man in New York—wants me to see him about a real-estate trade—may not come off till summer. Hope it doesn't break just when we and the Rieslings get ready to go to Maine. Be a shame if we couldn't make the trip there together. Well, no use worrying now."

Verona escaped, immediately after dinner, with no discussion save an automatic "Why don't you ever stay home?" from Babbitt.

In the living-room, in a corner of the davenport, Ted settled down to his Home Study; plain geometry, Cicero, and the agonizing metaphors of Comus.

"I don't see why they give us this old-fashioned junk by Milton and Shakespeare and Wordsworth and all these has-beens," he protested. "Oh, I guess I could stand it to see a show by Shakespeare, if they had swell scenery and put on a lot of dog, but to sit down in cold blood and *read* 'em— These teachers—how do they get that way?"

Mrs. Babbitt, darning socks, speculated, "Yes, I wonder why. Of course I don't want to fly in the face of the professors and everybody, but I do think there's things in Shakespeare—not that I read him much, but when I was young the girls used to show me passages that weren't, really, they weren't at all nice."

Babbitt looked up irritably from the comic strips in the *Evening Advocate*. They composed his favorite literature and art, these illustrated chronicles in which Mr. Mutt hit Mr. Jeff with a rotten egg, and Mother corrected Father's vulgarisms by means of a rolling-pin. With the solemn face of a devotee, breathing heavily through his open mouth, he plodded nightly through every picture, and during the rite he detested interruptions. Furthermore, he felt that on the subject of Shakespeare he wasn't really an authority. Neither the *Advocate-Times,* the *Evening Advocate,* nor the *Bulletin of the Zenith Chamber of Commerce* had ever had an editorial on the matter, and until one of them had spoken

he found it hard to form an original opinion. But even at risk of floundering in strange bogs, he could not keep out of an open controversy.

"I'll tell you why you have to study Shakespeare and those. It's because they're required for college entrance, and that's all there is to it! Personally, I don't see myself why they stuck 'em into an up-to-date high-school system like we have in this state. Be a good deal better if you took Business English, and learned how to write an ad, or letters that would pull. But there it is, and there's no talk, argument, or discussion about it! Trouble with you, Ted, is you always want to do something different! If you're going to law-school—and you are!—I never had a chance to, but I'll see that you do—why, you'll want to lay in all the English and Latin you can get."

"Oh punk. I don't see what's the use of law-school—or even finishing high school. I don't want to go to college 'specially. Honest, there's lot of fellows that have graduated from colleges that don't begin to make as much money as fellows that went to work ᴇarly. Old Shimmy Peters, that teaches Latin in the High, he's a what-is-it from Columbia and he sits up all night reading a lot of greasy books and he's always spieling about the 'value of languages,' and the poor soak doesn't make but eighteen hundred a year, and no traveling salesman would think of working for that. I know what I'd like to do. I'd like to be an aviator, or own a corking big garage, or else—a fellow was telling me about it yesterday—I'd like to be one of these fellows that the Standard Oil Company sends out to China, and you live in a compound and don't have to do any work, and you get to see the world and pagodas and the ocean and everything! And then I could take up correspondence-courses. That's the real stuff! You don't have to recite to some frosty-faced old dame that's trying to show off to the principal, and you can study any subject you want to. Just listen to these! I clipped out the ads of some swell courses."

He snatched from the back of his geometry half a hundred advertisements of those home-study courses which the energy and foresight of American commerce have contributed to the science of education. The first displayed the portrait of a young man with a pure brow, an iron jaw, silk socks, and hair like patent leather. Standing with one hand in his trousers-pocket and the other extended with chiding forefinger, he was bewitching an audience of men with gray beards, paunches, bald heads, and every other sign of wisdom and prosperity. Above the picture was an inspiring educational symbol—no antiquated lamp or torch or owl of Minerva, but a row of dollar signs. The text ran:

$ $ $ $ $ $ $ $ $

POWER AND PROSPERITY IN
PUBLIC SPEAKING

A Yarn Told at the Club

Who do you think I ran into the other evening at the De Luxe Restaurant? Why, old Freddy Durkee, that used to be a dead-or-alive shipping clerk in my old place—Mr. Mouse-Man we used to laughingly call the

---

PROF. W. F. PEET

author of the Shortcut Course in Public-Speaking, is easily the foremost figure in practical literature, psychology & oratory. A graduate of some of our leading universities, lecturer, extensive traveler, author of books, poetry, etc., a man with the unique PERSONALITY OF THE MASTER MINDS, he is ready to give *YOU* all the secrets of his culture and hammering Force, in a few easy lessons that will not interfere with other occupations.

---

dear fellow. One time he was so timid he was plumb scared of the Super, and never got credit for the dandy work he did. Him at the De Luxe! And if he wasn't ordering a tony feed with all the "fixings" from celery to nuts! And instead of being embarrassed by the waiters, like he used to be at the little dump where we lunched in Old Lang Syne, he was bossing them around like he was a millionaire!

I cautiously asked him what he was doing. Freddy laughed and said, "Say, old chum, I guess you're wondering what's come over me. You'll be glad to know I'm now Assistant Super at the old shop, and right on the High Road to Prosperity and Domination, and I look forward with confidence to a twelve-cylinder car, and the wife is making things hum in the best society and the kiddies getting a first-class education.

"Here's how it happened. I ran across an ad of a course that claimed to teach people how to talk easily and on their feet, how to answer complaints, how to lay a proposition before the Boss, how to hit a bank for a loan, how to hold a big audience spellbound with wit, humor, anecdote, inspiration, etc. It was compiled by the Master Orator, Prof. Waldo F. Peet. I was skeptical, too, but I wrote (just *on a postcard,* with name and address) to the publisher for the lessons— sent On Trial, money back if you are not absolutely satisfied. There were eight simple lessons in plain language anybody could understand, and I studied them just a few

---

WHAT WE TEACH YOU!

How to address your lodge.
How to give toasts.
How to tell dialect stories.
How to propose to a lady.
How to entertain banquets.
How to make convincing selling-talks.
How to build big vocabulary.
How to create a strong personality.
How to become a rational, powerful and original thinker.
How to be a MASTER MAN!

SINCLAIR LEWIS

hours a night, then started practising on the wife. Soon found I could talk right up to the Super and get due credit for all the good work I did. They began to appreciate me and advance me fast, and say, old doggo, what do you think they're paying me now? $6,500 per year! And say, I find I can keep a big audience fascinated, speaking on any topic. As a friend, old boy, I advise you to send for circular (no obligation) and valuable free Art Picture to:—

SHORTCUT EDUCATIONAL PUB. CO.
Desk WA   Sandpit, Iowa

ARE YOU A 100 PERCENTER
OR A 10 PERCENTER?

Babbitt was again without a canon which would enable him to speak with authority. Nothing in motoring or real estate had indicated what a Solid Citizen and Regular Fellow ought to think about culture by mail. He began with hesitation:'

"Well—sounds as if it covered the ground. It certainly is a fine thing to be able to orate. I've sometimes thought I had a little talent that way myself, and I know darn well that one reason why a fourflushing old back-number like Chan Mott can get away with it in real estate is just because he can make a good talk, even when he hasn't got a doggone thing to say! And it certainly is pretty cute the way they get out all these courses on various topics and subjects nowadays. I'll tell you, though: No need to blow in a lot of good money on this stuff when you can get a first-rate course in eloquence and English and all that right in your own school—and one of the biggest school buildings in the entire country!"

"That's so," said Mrs. Babbitt comfortably, while Ted complained:

"Yuh, but Dad, they just teach a lot of old junk that isn't any practical use—except the manual training and typewriting and basketball and dancing—and in these correspondence-courses, gee, you

can get all kinds of stuff that would come in handy. Say, listen to this one:

CAN YOU PLAY A MAN'S PART?

If you are walking with your mother, sister or best girl and some one passes a slighting remark or uses improper language, won't you be ashamed if you can't take her part? Well, can you?

We teach boxing and self-defense by mail. Many pupils have written saying that after a few lessons they've outboxed bigger and heavier opponents. The lessons start with simple movements practised before your mirror—holding out your hand for a coin, the breast-stroke in swimming, etc. Before you realize it you are striking scientifically, ducking, guarding and feinting, just as if you had a real opponent before you.

"Oh, baby, maybe I wouldn't like that!" Ted chanted. "I'll tell the world! Gosh, I'd like to take one fellow I know in school that's always shooting off his mouth, and catch him alone—"

"Nonsense! The idea! Most useless thing I ever heard of!" Babbitt fulminated.

"Well, just suppose I was walking with Mama or Rone, and somebody passed a slighting remark or used improper language. What would I do?"

"Why, you'd probably bust the record for the hundred-yard dash!"

"I would not! I'd stand right up to any mucker that passed a slighting remark on my sister and I'd show him—"

"Look here, young Dempsey! If I ever catch you fighting I'll whale the everlasting daylights out of you—and I'll do it without practicing holding out my hand for a coin before the mirror, too!"

"Why, Ted dear," Mrs. Babbitt said placidly, "it's not at all nice, your talking of fighting this way!"

"Well, gosh almighty, that's a fine way to appreciate— And then suppose I was walking with you, Ma, and somebody passed a slighting remark—"

"Nobody's going to pass no slighting remarks on nobody," Babbitt observed, "not if they stay home and study their geometry and mind their own affairs instead of hanging around a lot of pool-rooms and soda-fountains and places where nobody's got any business to be!"

"But goooooooosh, Dad, if they DID!"

Mrs. Babbitt chirped, "Well, if they did, I wouldn't do them the honor of paying any attention to them! Besides, they never do. You always hear about these women that get followed and insulted and all, but I don't believe a word of it, or it's their own fault, the way some women look at a person. I certainly never 've been insulted by—"

"Aw shoot. Mother, just suppose you *were* sometime! Just *suppose!* Can't you suppose something? Can't you imagine things?"

"Certainly I can imagine things! The idea!"

"Certainly your mother can imagine things—and suppose things! Think you're the only member of this household that's got an imagination?" Babbitt demanded. "But what's the use of a lot of supposing? Supposing never gets you anywhere. No sense supposing when there's a lot of real facts to take into considera—"

"Look here, Dad. Suppose—I mean, just—just suppose you were in your office and some rival real-estate man—"

"Realtor!"

"—some realtor that you hated came in—"

"I don't hate any realtor."

"But suppose you *did!*"

"I don't intend to suppose anything of the kind! There's plenty of fellows in my profession that stoop and hate their competitors, but if you were a little older and understood business, instead of always going to the movies and running around with a lot of fool girls with their dresses up to their knees and powdered and painted and rouged and God knows what all as if they were chorus-girls, then you'd know—and you'd suppose—that if there's any one thing that I stand for in the real-estate circles of Zenith, it is that we ought to always speak of each other only in the friendliest terms and institute a spirit of brotherhood and coöperation, and so I certainly can't suppose and I can't imagine my hating any realtor, not even that dirty, fourflushing society sneak, Cecil Rountree!"

"But—"

"And there's no If, And or But about it! But if I *were* going to lambaste somebody, I wouldn't require any fancy ducks or swimming-strokes before a mirror, or any of these doodads and flipflops! Suppose you were out some place and a fellow called you vile names. Think you'd want to box and jump around like a dancing-master? You'd just lay him out cold (at least I certainly hope any son of mine would!) and then you'd dust off your hands and go on about your business, and that's all there is to it, and you aren't going to have any boxing-lessons by mail, either!"

"Well but— Yes— I just wanted to show how many different kinds of correspondence-courses there are, instead of all the camembert they teach us in the High."

"But I thought they taught boxing in the school gymnasium."

"That's different. They stick you up there and some big stiff amuses himself pounding the stuffin's out of you before you have a chance to learn. Hunka! Not any! But anyway— Listen to some of these others."

The advertisements were truly philanthropic. One of them bore the rousing headline: "Money! Money!! Money!!!" The second announced that "Mr. P. R., formerly making only eighteen a week in a barber shop, writes to us that since taking our course he is now pulling down $5,000 as an Osteo-vitalic Physician"; and the third that "Miss J. L., recently a wrapper in a store, is now getting Ten Real Dollars a day teaching our Hindu System of Vibratory Breathing and Mental Control."

Ted had collected fifty or sixty announcements, from annual reference-books, from Sunday School periodicals, fiction-magazines, and journals of discussion. One benefactor implored, "Don't be a Wallflower—Be More Popular and Make More Money—*You* Can Ukulele or Sing Yourself into Society! By the secret principles of a Newly Discovered System of Music Teaching, any one—man, lady or child—can, without tiresome exercises, special training or long drawn out study, and without waste of time, money or energy, learn to play by note, piano, banjo, cornet, clarinet, saxophone, violin or drum, and learn sight-singing."

The next, under the wistful appeal "Finger Print Detectives Wanted—Big Incomes!" confided: "YOU red-blooded men and women—this is the PROFESSION you have been looking for. There's MONEY in it, BIG money, and that rapid change of scene, that entrancing and compelling interest and fascination, which your active mind and adventurous spirit crave. Think of being the chief figure and directing factor in solving strange mysteries and baffling crimes. This wonderful profession brings you into contact with influential men on the basis of equality, and often calls upon you to travel everywhere, maybe to distant lands—all expenses paid. NO SPECIAL EDUCATION REQUIRED."

"Oh, boy! I guess that wins the fire-brick necklace! Wouldn't it be swell to travel everywhere and nab some famous crook!" whooped Ted.

"Well, I don't think much of that.

Doggone likely to get hurt. Still, that music-study stunt might be pretty fair, though. There's no reason why, if efficiency-experts put their minds to it the way they have to routing products in a factory, they couldn't figure out some scheme so a person wouldn't have to monkey with all this practicing and exercises that you get in music." Babbitt was impressed, and he had a delightful parental feeling that they two, the men of the family, understood each other.

He listened to the notices of mail-box universities which taught Short-story Writing and Improving the Memory, Motion-picture-acting and Developing the Soul-power, Banking and Spanish, Chiropody and Photography, Electrical Engineering and Window-trimming, Poultry-raising and Chemistry.

"Well—well—" Babbitt sought for adequate expression of his admiration. "I'm a son of a gun! I knew this correspondence-school business had become a mighty profitable game—makes suburban real-estate look like two cents!—but I didn't realize it'd got to be such a reg'lar key-industry! Must rank right up with groceries and movies. Always figured somebody'd come along with the brains to not leave education to a lot of bookworms and impractical theorists but make a big thing out of it. Yes, I can see how a lot of these courses might interest you. I must ask the fellows at the Athletic if they ever realized— But same time, Ted, you know how advertisers, I means some advertisers, exaggerate. I don't know as they'd be able to jam you through these courses as fast as they claim they can."

"Oh sure, Dad; of course." Ted had the immense and joyful maturity of a boy who is respectfully listened to by his elders. Babbitt concentrated on him with grateful affection:

"I can see what an influence these courses might have on the whole educational works. Course I'd never admit it publicly—fellow like myself, a State U. graduate, it's only decent and patriotic for him to blow his horn and boost the Alma Mater—but 'smatter of fact, there's a whole lot of valuable time lost even at the U., studying poetry and French and subjects that never brought in anybody a cent. I don't know but what maybe these correspondence-courses might prove to be one of the most important American inventions.

"Trouble with a lot of folks is: they're so blame material; they don't see the spiritual and mental side of American supremacy; they think that inventions like the telephone and the areoplane and wireless—no, that was a Wop invention, but anyway: they think these mechanical improvements are all that we stand for; whereas to a real thinker, he sees that spiritual and, uh, dominating movements like Efficiency, and Rotarianism, and Prohibition, and Democracy are what compose our deepest and truest wealth. And maybe this new principle in education-at-home may be another—may be another factor. I tell you, Ted, we've got to have Vision—"

"I think those correspondence-courses are terrible!"

The philosophers gasped. It was Mrs. Babbitt who had made this discord in their spiritual harmony, and one of Mrs. Babbitt's virtues was that, except during dinner-parties, when she was transformed into a raging hostess, she took care of the house and didn't bother the males by thinking. She went on firmly:

"It sounds awful to me, the way they coax those poor young folks to think they're learning something, and nobody 'round to help them and— You two learn so quick, but me, I always was slow. But just the same—"

Babbitt attended to her: "Nonsense! Get just as much, studying at home. You

don't think a fellow learns any more because he blows in his father's hard-earned money and sits around in Morris chairs in a swell Harvard dormitory with pictures and shields and table-covers and those doodads, do you? I tell you, I'm a college man—I *know!* There is one objection you might make though. I certainly do protest against any effort to get a lot of fellows out of barber shops and factories into the professions. They're too crowded already, and what'll we do for workmen if all those fellows go and get educated?"

Ted was leaning back, smoking a cigarette without reproof. He was, for the moment, sharing the high thin air of Babbitt's speculation as though he were Paul Riesling or even Dr. Howard Littlefield. He hinted:

"Well, what do you think then, Dad? Wouldn't it be a good idea if I could go off to China or some peppy place, and study engineering or something by mail?"

"No, and I'll tell you why, son. I've found out it's a mighty nice thing to be able to say you're a B.A. Some client that doesn't know what you are and thinks you're just a plug business man, he gets to shooting off his mouth about economics or literature or foreign trade conditions, and you just ease in something like, 'When I was in college—course I got my B.A. in sociology and all that junk—' Oh, it puts an awful crimp in their style! But there wouldn't be any class to saying 'I got the degree of Stamplicker from the Bezuzus Mail-order University!' You see— My dad was a pretty good old coot, but he never had much style to him, and I had to work darn hard to earn my way through college. Well, it's been worth it, to be able to associate with the finest gentlemen in Zenith, at the clubs and so on, and I wouldn't want you to drop out of the gentlemen class—the class that are just as red-blooded as the Common People but still have power and personality. It would kind of hurt me if you did that, old man!"

"I know, Dad! Sure! All right. I'll stick to it. Say! Gosh! Gee whiz! I forgot all about those kids I was going to take to the chorus rehearsal. I'll have to duck!"

"But you haven't done all your homework."

"Do it first thing in the morning."

"Well—"

Six times in the past sixty days Babbitt had stormed, "You will not 'do it first thing in the morning'! You'll do it right now!" but to-night he said, "Well, better hustle," and his smile was the rare shy radiance he kept for Paul Riesling.

IV

"Ted's a good boy," he said to Mrs. Babbitt.

"Oh, he is!"

"Who's these girls he's going to pick up? Are they nice decent girls?"

"I don't know. Oh dear, Ted never tells me anything any more. I don't understand what's come over the children of this generation. I used to have to tell Papa and Mama everything, but seems like the children to-day have just slipped away from all control."

"I hope they're decent girls. Course Ted's no longer a kid, and I wouldn't want him to, uh, get mixed up and everything."

"George: I wonder if you oughtn't to take him aside and tell him about— Things!" She blushed and lowered her eyes.

"Well, I don't know. Way I figure it, Myra, no sense suggesting a lot of Things to a boy's mind. Think up enough devilment by himself. But I wonder— It's kind of a hard question. Wonder what Littlefield thinks about it?"

"Course Papa agrees with you. He says all this—Instruction—is— He says 'tisn't decent."

"Oh, he does, does he! Well, let me tell you that whatever Henry T. Thompson thinks—about morals, I mean, though course you can't beat the old duffer—"

"Why, what a way to talk of Papa!"

"—simply can't beat him at getting in on the ground floor of a deal, but let me tell you whenever he springs any ideas about higher things and education, then I know I think just the opposite. You may not regard me as any great brainshark, but believe me, I'm a regular college president, compared with Henry T.! Yes sir, by golly, I'm going to take Ted aside and tell him why I lead a strictly moral life."

"Oh, will you? When?"

"When? When? What's the use of trying to pin me down to When and Why and Where and How and When? That's the trouble with women, that's why they don't make high-class executives; they haven't any sense of diplomacy. When the proper opportunity and occasion arises so it just comes in natural, why then I'll have a friendly little talk with him and—and— Was that Tinka hollering up-stairs? She ought to been asleep, long ago."

He prowled through the living-room, and stood in the sun-parlor, that glass-walled room of wicker chairs and swinging couch in which they loafed on Sunday afternoons. Outside, only the lights of Doppelbrau's house and the dim presence of Babbitt's favorite elm broke the softness of April night.

"Good visit with the boy. Getting over feeling cranky, way I did this morning. And restless. Though, by golly, I will have a few days alone with Paul in Maine! . . . That devil Zilla! . . . But . . . Ted's all right. Whole family all right. And good business. Not many fellows make four hundred and fifty bucks, practically half of a thousand dollars, easy as I did to-day! Maybe when we all get to rowing it's just as much my fault as it is theirs. Oughtn't to get grouchy like I do. But— Wish I'd been a pioneer, same as my grand-dad. But then, wouldn't have a house like this. I— Oh, gosh, *I don't know!*"

He thought moodily of Paul Riesling, of their youth together, of the girls they had known.

When Babbitt had graduated from the State University, twenty-four years ago, he had intended to be a lawyer. He had been a ponderous debater in college; he felt that he was an orator; he saw himself becoming governor of the state. While he read law he worked as a real-estate salesman. He saved money, lived in a boarding-house, supped on poached egg on hash. The lively Paul Riesling (who was certainly going off to Europe to study violin, next month or next year) was his refuge till Paul was bespelled by Zilla Colbeck, who laughed and danced and drew men after her plump and gaily wagging finger.

Babbitt's evenings were barren then, and he found comfort only in Paul's second cousin, Myra Thompson, a sleek and gentle girl who showed her capacity by agreeing with the ardent young Babbitt that of course he was going to be governor some day. Where Zilla mocked him as a country boy, Myra said indignantly that he was ever so much solider than the young dandies who had been born in the great city of Zenith—an ancient settlement in 1897, one hundred and five years old, with two hundred thousand population, the queen and wonder of all the state and, to the Catawba boy, George Babbitt, so vast and thunderous and luxurious that he was flattered to know a girl ennobled by birth in Zenith.

Of love there was no talk between them. He knew that if he was to study law he could not marry for years; and Myra was distinctly a Nice Girl—one didn't kiss her, one didn't "think about her that way at all" unless one was going to marry her. But she was a dependable companion. She was always ready to go skating, walking; always content to hear his discourses on the great things he was going to do, the distressed poor whom he would defend against the Unjust Rich, the speeches he would make at Banquets, the inexactitudes of popular thought which he would correct.

One evening when he was weary and soft-minded, he saw that she had been weeping. She had been left out of a party given by Zilla. Somehow her head was on his shoulder and he was kissing away the tears—and she raised her head to say trustingly, "Now that we're engaged, shall we be married soon or shall we wait?"

Engaged? It was his first hint of it. His affection for this brown tender woman thing went cold and fearful, but he could not hurt her, could not abuse her trust. He mumbled something about waiting, and escaped. He walked for an hour, trying to find a way of telling her that it was a mistake. Often, in the month after, he got near to telling her, but it was pleasant to have a girl in his arms, and less and less could he insult her by blurting that he didn't love her. He himself had no doubt. The evening before his marriage was an agony, and the morning wild with the desire to flee.

She made him what is known as a Good Wife. She was loyal, industrious, and at rare times merry. She passed from a feeble disgust at their closer relations into what promised to be ardent affection, but it drooped into bored routine. Yet she existed only for him and for the children, and she was as sorry, as worried as himself, when he gave up the law and trudged on in a rut of listing real estate.

"Poor kid, she hasn't had much better time than I have," Babbitt reflected, standing in the dark sun-parlor. "But— I wish I could've had a whirl at law and

politics. Seen what I could do. Well—
Maybe I've made more money as it is."

He returned to the living-room but
before he settled down he smoothed his
wife's hair, and she glanced up, happy
and somewhat surprised.

CHAPTER 7

He solemnly finished the last copy of the
American Magazine, while his wife
sighed, laid away her darning, and
looked enviously at the lingerie designs in
a women's magazine. The room was very
still.

It was a room which observed the best
Floral Heights standards. The gray walls
were divided into artificial paneling by
strips of white-enameled pine. From the
Babbitts' former house had come two
much-carved rocking-chairs, but the
other chairs were new, very deep and
restful, upholstered in blue and gold-
striped velvet. A blue velvet davenport
faced the fireplace, and behind it was a
cherrywood table and a tall piano-lamp
with a shade of golden silk. (Two out of
every three houses in Floral Heights had
before the fireplace a davenport, a mahogany table real or imitation, and a
piano-lamp or a reading-lamp with a
shade of yellow or rose silk.)

On the table was a runner of gold-
threaded Chinese fabric, four magazines,
a silver box containing cigarette-crumbs,
and three "gift-books"—large, expensive
editions of fairy-tales illustrated by English artists and as yet unread by any
Babbitt save Tinka.

In a corner by the front windows was
a large cabinet Victrola. (Eight out of
every nine Floral Heights houses had a
cabinet phonograph.)

Among the pictures, hung in the exact
center of each gray panel, were a red and
black imitation English hunting-print, an
anemic imitation boudoir-print with a
French caption of whose morality Babbitt had always been rather suspicious,
and a "hand-colored" photograph of a
Colonial room—rag rug, maiden spinning, cat demure before a white fireplace.
(Nineteen out of every twenty houses in
Floral Heights had either a hunting-print,
a *Madame Fait la Toilette* print, a colored photograph of a New England
house, a photograph of a Rocky Mountain, or all four.)

It was a room as superior in comfort
to the "parlor" of Babbitt's boyhood as
his motor was superior to his father's
buggy. Though there was nothing in the
room that was interesting, there was
nothing that was offensive. It was as
neat, and as negative, as a block of artificial ice. The fireplace was unsoftened by
downy ashes or by sooty brick; the brass
fire-irons were of immaculate polish; and
the grenadier andirons were like samples
in a shop, desolate, unwanted, lifeless
things of commerce.

Against the wall was a piano, with
another piano-lamp, but no one used it
save Tinka. The hard briskness of the
phonograph contented them; their store
of jazz records made them feel wealthy
and cultured; and all they knew of creating music was the nice adjustment of a
bamboo needle. The books on the table
were unspotted and laid in rigid parallels;
not one corner of the carpet-rug was
curled; and nowhere was there a hockey-
stick, a torn picture-book, an old cap, or
a gregarious and disorganizing dog.

II

At home, Babbitt never read with absorption. He was concentrated enough at
the office but here he crossed his legs and
fidgeted. When his story was interesting
he read the best, that is the funniest,
paragraphs to his wife; when it did not
hold him he coughed, scratched his
ankles and his right ear, thrust his left

thumb into his vest pocket, jingled his silver, whirled the cigar-cutter and the keys on one end of his watch-chain, yawned, rubbed his nose, and found errands to do. He went upstairs to put on his slippers—his elegant slippers of seal-brown, shaped like medieval shoes. He brought up an apple from the barrel which stood by the trunk-closet in the basement.

"An apple a day keeps the doctor away," he enlightened Mrs. Babbitt, for quite the first time in fourteen hours.

"That's so."

"An apple is Nature's best regulator."

"Yes, it——"

"Trouble with women is, they never have sense enough to form regular habits."

"Well, I—"

"Always nibbling and eating between meals."

"George!" She looked up from her reading. "Did you have a light lunch to-day, like you were going to? I did!"

This malicious and unprovoked attack astounded him. "Well, maybe it wasn't as light as— Went to lunch with Paul and didn't have much chance to diet. Oh, you needn't to grin like a chessy cat! If it wasn't for me watching out and keeping an eye on our diet— I'm the only member of this family that appreciates the value of oatmeal for breakfast. I—"

She stooped over her story while he piously sliced and gulped down the apple, discoursing:

"One thing I've done: cut down my smoking.

"Had kind of a run-in with Graff in the office. He's getting too darn fresh. I'll stand for a good deal, but once in a while I got to assert my authority, and I jumped him. 'Stan,' I said— Well, I told him just exactly where he got off.

"Funny kind of a day. Makes you feel restless.

"Welllllllll, uh—" That sleepiest

sound in the world, the terminal yawn. Mrs. Babbitt yawned with it, and looked grateful as he droned, "How about going to bed, eh? Don't suppose Rone and Ted will be in till all hours. Yep, funny kind of a day; not terribly warm but yet— Gosh, I'd like— Some day I'm going to take a long motor trip."

"Yes, we'd enjoy that," she yawned.

He looked away from her as he realized that he did not wish to have her go with him. As he locked doors and tried windows and set the heat regulator so that the furnace-drafts would open automatically in the morning, he sighed a little, heavy with a lonely feeling which perplexed and frightened him. So absent-minded was he that he could not remember which window-catches he had inspected, and through the darkness, fumbling at unseen perilous chairs, he crept back to try them all over again. His feet were loud on the steps as he clumped upstairs at the end of this great and treacherous day of veiled rebellions.

III

Before breakfast he always reverted to up-state village boyhood, and shrank from the complex urban demands of shaving, bathing, deciding whether the current shirt was clean enough for another day. Whenever he stayed home in the evening he went to bed early, and thriftily got ahead in those dismal duties. It was his luxurious custom to shave while sitting snugly in a tubful of hot water. He may be viewed tonight as a plump, smooth, pink, baldish, podgy goodman, robbed of the importance of spectacles, squatting in breast-high water, scraping his lather-smeared cheeks with a safety-razor like a tiny lawn-mower, and with melancholy dignity clawing through the water to recover a slippery and active piece of soap.

He was lulled to dreaming by the caressing warmth. The light fell on the inner surface of the tub in a pattern of delicate wrinkled lines which slipped with a green sparkle over the curving porcelain as the clear water trembled. Babbitt lazily watched it; noted that along the silhouette of his legs against the radiance on the bottom of the tub, the shadows of the air-bubbles clinging to the hairs were reproduced as strange jungle mosses. He patted the water, and the reflected light capsized and leaped and volleyed. He was content and childish. He played. He shaved a swath down the calf of one plump leg.

The drain-pipe was dripping, a dulcet and lively song: drippety drip drip dribble, drippety drip drip drip. He was enchanted by it. He looked at the solid tub, the beautiful nickel taps, the tiled walls of the room, and felt virtuous in the possession of this splendor.

He roused himself and spoke gruffly to his bath-things. "Come here! You've done enough fooling!" he reproved the treacherous soap, and defied the scratchy nail-brush with "Oh, you would, would you!" He soaped himself, and rinsed himself, and austerely rubbed himself; he noted a hole in the Turkish towel, and meditatively thrust a finger through it, and marched back to the bedroom, a grave and unbending citizen.

There was a moment of gorgeous abandon, a flash of melodrama such as he found in traffic-driving, when he laid out a clean collar, discovered that it was frayed in front, and tore it up with a magnificent yeeeeeing sound.

Most important of all was the preparation of his bed and the sleeping-porch.

It is not known whether he enjoyed his sleeping-porch because of the fresh air or because it was the standard thing to have a sleeping-porch.

Just as he was an Elk, a Booster, and a member of the Chamber of Commerce, just as the priests of the Presbyterian Church determined his every religious belief and the senators who controlled the Republican Party decided in little smoky rooms in Washington what he should think about disarmament, tariff, and Germany, so did the large national advertisers fix the surface of his life, fix what he believed to be his individuality. These standard advertised wares—toothpastes, socks, tires, cameras, instantaneous hot-water heaters—were his symbols and proofs of excellence; at first the signs, then the substitutes, for joy and passion and wisdom.

But none of these advertised tokens of financial and social success was more significant than a sleeping-porch with a sun-parlor below.

The rites of preparing for bed were elaborate and unchanging. The blankets had to be tucked in at the foot of his cot. (Also, the reason why the maid hadn't tucked in the blankets had to be discussed with Mrs. Babbitt.) The rag rug was adjusted so that his bare feet would strike it when he arose in the morning. The alarm clock was wound. The hot-water bottle was filled and placed precisely two feet from the bottom of the cot.

These tremendous undertakings yielded to his determination; one by one they were announced to Mrs. Babbitt and smashed through to accomplishment. At last his brow cleared, and in his "Gnight!" rang virile power. But there was yet need of courage. As he sank into sleep, just at the first exquisite relaxation, the Doppelbrau car came home. He bounced into wakefulness, lamenting, "Why the devil can't some people ever get to bed at a reasonable hour?" So familiar was he with the process of putting up his own car that he awaited each step like an able executioner condemned to his own rack.

The car insultingly cheerful on the driveway. The car door opened and banged shut, then the garage door slid open, grating on the sill, and the car door again. The motor raced for the climb up into the garage and raced once more, explosively, before it was shut off. A final opening and slamming of the car door. Silence then, a horrible silence filled with waiting, till the leisurely Mr. Doppelbrau had examined the state of his tires and had at last shut the garage door. Instantly, for Babbitt, a blessed state of oblivion.

IV

At that moment in the city of Zenith, Horace Updike was making love to Lucile McKelvey in her mauve drawing-room on Royal Ridge, after their return from a lecture by an eminent English novelist. Updike was Zenith's professional bachelor; a slim-waisted man of forty-six with an effeminate voice and taste in flowers, cretonnes, and flappers. Mrs. McKelvey was red-haired, creamy, discontented, exquisite, rude, and honest. Updike tried his invariable first maneuver —touching her nervous wrist.

"Don't be an idiot!" she said.

"Do you mind awfully?"

"No! That's what I mind!"

He changed to conversation. He was famous at conversation. He spoke reasonably of psychoanalysis, Long Island polo, and the Ming platter he had found in Vancouver. She promised to meet him in Deauville, the coming summer, "though," she sighed, "it's becoming too dreadfully banal; nothing but Americans and frowsy English baronesses."

And at that moment in Zenith, a cocaine-runner and a prostitute were drinking cocktails in Healey Hanson's saloon on Front Street. Since national prohibition was now in force, and since Zenith was notoriously law-abiding, they were compelled to keep the cocktails innocent by drinking them out of tea-cups. The lady threw her cup at the cocaine-runner's head. He worked his revolver out of the pocket in his sleeve, and casually murdered her.

At that moment in Zenith, two men sat in a laboratory. For thirty-seven hours now they had been working on a report of their investigations of synthetic rubber.

At that moment in Zenith, there was a conference of four union officials as to whether the twelve thousand coal-miners within a hundred miles of the city should strike. Of these men one resembled a testy and prosperous grocer, one a Yankee carpenter, one a soda-clerk, and one a Russian Jewish actor. The Russian Jew quoted Kautsky, Gene Debs, and Abraham Lincoln.

At that moment a G. A. R. veteran was dying. He had come from the Civil War straight to a farm which, though it was officially within the city-limits of Zenith, was primitive as the backwoods. He had never ridden in a motor car, never seen a bath-tub, never read any book save the Bible, McGuffey's readers, and religious tracts; and he believed that the earth is flat, that the English are the Lost Ten Tribes of Israel, and that the United States is a democracy.

At that moment the steel and cement town which composed the factory of the Pullmore Tractor Company of Zenith was running on night shift to fill an order of tractors for the Polish army. It hummed like a million bees, glared through its wide windows like a volcano. Along the high wire fences, searchlights played on cinder-lined yards, switch-tracks, and armed guards on patrol.

At that moment Mike Monday was finishing a meeting. Mr. Monday, the distinguished evangelist, the best-known Protestant pontiff in America, had once been a prize-fighter. Satan had not dealt justly with him. As a prize-fighter he gained nothing but his crooked nose, his celebrated vocabulary, and his stage-presence. The service of the Lord had been more profitable. He was about to retire with a fortune. It had been well earned, for, to quote his last report, "Rev. Mr. Monday, the Prophet with a Punch, has shown that he is the world's greatest salesman of salvation, and that by efficient organization the overhead of spiritual regeneration may be kept down to an unprecedented rock-bottom basis. He has converted over two hundred thousand lost and priceless souls at an average cost of less than ten dollars a head."

Of the larger cities of the land, only Zenith had hesitated to submit its vices to Mike Monday and his expert reclamation corps. The more enterprising organizations of the city had voted to invite him—Mr. George F. Babbitt had once praised him in a speech at the Boosters' Club. But there was opposition from certain Episcopalian and Congregationalist ministers, those renegades whom Mr. Monday so finely called "a bunch of gospel-pushers with dish-water instead of blood, a gang of squealers that need more dust on the knees of their pants and more hair on their skinny old chests." This opposition had been crushed when the secretary of the Chamber of Commerce had reported to a committee of manufacturers that in every city where he had appeared, Mr. Monday had turned the minds of workmen from wages and hours to higher things, and thus averted strikes. He was immediately invited.

An expense fund of forty thousand dollars had been underwritten; out on the County Fair Grounds a Mike Monday Tabernacle had been erected, to seat fifteen thousand people. In it the prophet was at this moment concluding his message:

"There's a lot of smart college professors and tea-guzzling slobs in this burg that say I'm a roughneck and a never-wuzzer and my knowledge of history is not-yet. Oh, there's a gang of woolly-whiskered book-lice that think they know more than Almighty God, and prefer a lot of Hun science and smutty German criticism to the straight and simple Word of God. Oh, there's a swell bunch of Lizzie boys and lemon-suckers and pie-faces and infidels and beer-bloated scribblers that love to fire off their filthy mouths and yip that Mike Monday is vulgar and full of mush. Those pups are saying now that I hog the gospel-show, that I'm in it for the coin. Well, now listen, folks! I'm going to give those birds a chance! They can stand right up here and tell me to my face that I'm a galoot and a liar and a hick! Only if they do—if they do!—don't faint with surprise if some of those rum-dumm liars get one good swift poke from Mike, with all the kick of God's Flaming Righteousness behind the wallop! Well, come on, folks! Who says it? Who says Mike Monday is a four-flush and a yahoo? Huh? Don't I see anybody standing up? Well, there you are! Now I guess the folks in this man's town will quit listening to all this kyooding from behind the fence; I guess you'll quit listening to the guys that pan and roast and kick and beef, and vomit out filthy atheism; and all of you 'll come in, with every grain of pep and reverence you got, and boost all together for Jesus Christ and his everlasting mercy and tenderness!"

v

At that moment Seneca Doane, the radical lawyer, and Dr. Kurt Yavitch, the histologist (whose report on the destruction of epithelial cells under radium had made the name of Zenith known in Munich, Prague, and Rome), were talking in Doane's library.

"Zenith's a city with gigantic power—gigantic buildings, gigantic machines, gigantic transportation," meditated Doane.

"I hate your city. It has standardized all the beauty out of life. It is one big railroad station—with all the people taking tickets for the best cemeteries," Dr. Yavitch said placidly.

Doane roused. "I'm hanged if it is! You make me sick, Kurt, with your perpetual whine about 'standardization.' Don't you suppose any other nation is 'standardized?' Is anything more standardized than England, with every house that can afford it having the same muffins at the same tea-hour, and every retired general going to exactly the same evensong at the same gray stone church with a square tower, and every golfing prig in Harris tweeds saying 'Right you are!' to every other prosperous ass? Yet I love England. And for standardization—just look at the sidewalk cafés in France and the love-making in Italy!

"Standardization is excellent, *per se*. When I buy an Ingersoll watch or a Ford, I get a better tool for less money, and I know precisely what I'm getting, and that leaves me more time and energy to be individual in. And— I remember once in London I saw a picture of an American suburb, in a toothpaste ad on the back of the *Saturday Evening Post*—an elm-lined snowy street of these new houses, Georgian some of 'em, or with low raking roofs and— The kind of street you'd find here in Zenith, say in Floral Heights. Open. Trees. Grass. And I was homesick! There's no other country in the world that has such pleasant houses. And I don't care if they *are* standardized. It's a corking standard!

"No, what I fight in Zenith is standardization of thought, and, of course, the traditions of competition. The real villains of the piece are the clean, kind, industrious Family Men who use every known brand of trickery and cruelty to insure the prosperity of their cubs. The worst thing about these fellows is that they're so good and, in their work at least, so intelligent. You can't hate them properly, and yet their standardized minds are the enemy.

"Then this boosting— Sneakingly I have a notion that Zenith is a better place to live in than Manchester or Glasgow or Lyons or Berlin or Turin—"

"It is not, and I have lift in most of them," murmured Dr. Yavitch.

"Well, matter of taste. Personally, I prefer a city with a future so unknown that it excites my imagination. But what I particularly want—"

"You," said Dr. Yavitch, "are a middle-road liberal, and you haven't the slightest idea what you want. I, being a revolutionist, know exactly what I want—and what I want now is a drink."

VI

At that moment in Zenith, Jake Offutt, the politician, and Henry T. Thompson were in conference. Offutt suggested, "The thing to do is to get your fool son-in-law, Babbitt, to put it over. He's one of these patriotic guys. When he grabs a piece of property for the gang, he makes it look like we were dyin' of love for the dear peepul, and I do love to buy respectability—reasonable. Wonder how long we can keep it up, Hank? We're safe as long as the good little boys like George Babbitt and all the nice respectable labor-leaders think you and me are rugged patriots. There's swell pickings for an honest politician here, Hank: a whole city working to provide cigars and fried chicken and dry martinis for us, and rallying to our banner with indignation, oh, fierce indignation, whenever some squealer like this fellow Seneca Doane comes along! Honest, Hank, a smart codger like me ought to be ashamed of himself if he didn't milk cattle like them, when they come around mooing for it! But the Traction gang can't get away with grand larceny like it used to. I wonder when— Hank, I wish we could fix some way to run this fellow Seneca Doane out of town. It's him or us!"

At that moment in Zenith, three hundred and forty or fifty thousand Ordinary People were asleep, a vast unpenetrated shadow. In the slum beyond the railroad tracks, a young man who for six months had sought work turned on the gas and killed himself and his wife.

At that moment Lloyd Mallam, the poet, owner of the Hafiz Book Shop, was finishing a rondeau to show how diverting was life amid the feuds of medieval Florence, but how dull it was in so obvious a place as Zenith.

And at that moment George F. Babbitt turned ponderously in bed—the last turn, signifying that he'd had enough of this worried business of falling asleep and was about it in earnest.

Instantly he was in the magic dream. He was somewhere among unknown people who laughed at him. He slipped away, ran down the paths of a midnight garden, and at the gate the fairy child was waiting. Her dear and tranquil hand caressed his cheek. He was gallant and wise and well-beloved; warm ivory were her arms; and beyond perilous moors the brave sea glittered.

CHAPTER 8

The great events of Babbitt's spring were the secret buying of real-estate options in Linton for certain street-traction officials, before the public announcement that the Linton Avenue Car Line would be extended, and a dinner which was, as he rejoiced to his wife, not only "a regular

society spread but a real sure-enough highbrow affair, with some of the keenest intellects and the brightest bunch of little women in town." It was so absorbing an occasion that he almost forgot his desire to run off to Maine with Paul Riesling.

Though he had been born in the village of Catawba, Babbitt had risen to that metropolitan social plane on which hosts have as many as four people at dinner without planning it for more than an evening or two. But a dinner of twelve, with flowers from the florist's and all the cut-glass out, staggered even the Babbitts.

For two weeks they studied, debated, and arbitrated the list of guests.

Babbitt marveled, "Of course we're up-to-date ourselves, but still, think of us entertaining a famous poet like Chum Frink, a fellow that on nothing but a poem or so every day and just writing a few advertisements pulls down fifteen thousand berries a year!"

"Yes, and Howard Littlefield. Do you know, the other evening Eunice told me her papa speaks three languages!" said Mrs. Babbitt.

"Huh! That's nothing! So do I—American, baseball, and poker!"

"I don't think it's nice to be funny about a matter like that. Think how wonderful it must be to speak three languages, and so useful and— And with people like that, I don't see why we invite the Orville Joneses."

"Well now, Orville is a mighty up-and-coming fellow!"

"Yes, I know, but— A laundry!"

"I'll admit a laundry hasn't got the class of poetry or real estate, but just the same, Orvy is mighty deep. Ever start him spieling about gardening? Say, that fellow can tell you the name of every kind of tree, and some of their Greek and Latin names too! Besides, we owe the Joneses a dinner. Besides, gosh, we got to have some boob for audience, when a bunch of hot-air artists like Frink and Littlefield get going."

"Well, dear—I meant to speak of this —I do think that as host you ought to sit back and listen, and let your guests have a chance to talk once in a while!"

"Oh, you do, do you! Sure! I talk all the time! And I'm just a business man— oh sure!—I'm no Ph.D. like Littlefield, and no poet, and I haven't anything to spring! Well, let me tell you, just the other day your darn Chum Frink comes up to me at the club begging to know what I thought about the Springfield school-bond issue. And who told him? I did! You bet your life I told him! Little me! I certainly did! He came up and asked me, and I told him all about it! You bet! And he was darn glad to listen to me and— Duty as a host! I guess I know my duty as a host and let me tell you—"

In fact, the Orville Joneses were invited.

II

On the morning of the dinner, Mrs. Babbitt was restive.

"Now, George, I want you to be sure and be home early tonight. Remember, you have to dress."

"Uh-huh. I see by the *Advocate* that the Presbyterian General Assembly has voted to quit the Interchurch World Movement. That—"

"George! Did you hear what I said? You must be home in time to dress tonight."

"Dress? Hell! I'm dressed now! Think I'm going down to the office in my B.V.D.'s?"

"I will not have you talking indecently before the children! And you do have to put on your dinner-jacket!"

"I guess you mean my Tux. I tell you, of all the doggone nonsensical nuisances that was ever invented—"

Three minutes later, after Babbitt had wailed, "Well, I don't know whether I'm going to dress or *not*" in a manner which showed that he was going to dress, the discussion moved on.

"Now, George, you mustn't forget to call in at Vecchia's on the way home and get the ice cream. Their delivery-wagon is broken down, and I don't want to trust them to send it by—"

"All right! You told me that before breakfast!"

"Well, I don't want you to forget. I'll be working my head off all day long, training the girl that's to help with the dinner—"

"All nonsense, anyway, hiring an extra girl for the feed. Matilda could perfectly well—"

"—and I have to go out and buy the flowers, and fix them, and set the table, and order the salted almonds, and look at the chickens, and arrange for the children to have their supper upstairs and— And I simply must depend on you to go to Vecchia's for the ice cream."

"All riiiiight! Gosh, I'm going to get it!"

"All you have to do is to go in and say you want the ice cream that Mrs. Babbitt ordered yesterday by 'phone, and it will be all ready for you."

At ten-thirty she telephoned to him not to forget the ice cream from Vecchia's.

He was surprised and blasted then by a thought. He wondered whether Floral Heights dinners were worth the hideous toil involved. But he repented the sacrilege in the excitement of buying the materials for cocktails.

Now this was the manner of obtaining alcohol under the reign of righteousness and prohibition:

He drove from the severe rectangular streets of the modern business center into the tangled byways of Old Town—jagged blocks filled with sooty warehouses and lofts; on into The Arbor, once a pleasant orchard but now a morass of lodging-houses, tenements, and brothels. Exquisite shivers chilled his spine and stomach, and he looked at every policeman with intense innocence, as one who loved the law, and admired the Force, and longed to stop and play with them. He parked his car a block from Healey Hanson's saloon, worrying, "Well, rats, if anybody did see me, they'd think I was here on business."

He entered a place curiously like the saloons of ante-prohibition days, with a long greasy bar with sawdust in front and streaky mirror behind, a pine table at which a dirty old man dreamed over a glass of something which resembled whisky, and with two men at the bar, drinking something which resembled beer, and giving that impression of forming a large crowd which two men always give in a saloon. The bartender, a tall pale Swede with a diamond in his lilac scarf, stared at Babbitt as he stalked plumply up to the bar and whispered, "I'd, uh— Friend of Hanson's sent me here. Like to get some gin."

The bartender gazed down on him in the manner of an outraged bishop. "I guess you got the wrong place, my friend. We sell nothing but soft drinks here." He cleaned the bar with a rag which would itself have done with a little cleaning, and glared across his mechanically moving elbow.

The old dreamer at the table petitioned the bartender, "Say, Oscar, listen."

Oscar did not listen.

"Aw, say, Oscar, listen, will yuh? Say, lis-sen!"

The decayed and drowsy voice of the loafer, the agreeable stink of beer-dregs, threw a spell of inanition over Babbitt. The bartender moved grimly toward the crowd of two men. Babbitt followed him as delicately as a cat, and wheedled, "Say, Oscar, I want to speak to Mr. Hanson."

"Whajuh wanta see him for?"

"I just want to talk to him. Here's my card."

It was a beautiful card, an engraved card, a card in the blackest black and the sharpest red, announcing that Mr. George F. Babbitt was Estates, Insurance, Rents. The bartender held it as though it weighed ten pounds, and read it as though it were a hundred words long. He did not bend from his episcopal dignity, but he growled, "I'll see if he's around."

From the back room he brought an immensely old young man, a quiet sharp-eyed man, in tan silk shirt, checked vest hanging open, and burning brown trousers—Mr. Healey Hanson. Mr. Hanson said only "Yuh?" but his implacable and contemptuous eyes queried Babbitt's soul, and he seemed not at all impressed by the new dark-gray suit for which (as he had admitted to every acquaintance at the Athletic Club) Babbitt had paid a hundred and twenty-five dollars.

"Glad to meet you, Mr. Hanson. Say, uh— I'm George Babbitt of the Babbitt-Thompson Realty Company. I'm a great friend of Jake Offutt's."

"Well, what of it?"

"Say, uh, I'm going to have a party, and Jake told me you'd be able to fix me up with a little gin." In alarm, in obsequiousness, as Hanson's eyes grew more bored, "You telephone to Jake about me, if you want to."

Hanson answered by jerking his head to indicate the entrance to the back room, and strolled away. Babbitt melodramatically crept into an apartment containing four round tables, eleven chairs, a brewery calendar, and a smell. He waited. Thrice he saw Healey Hanson saunter through, humming, hands in pockets, ignoring him.

By this time Babbitt had modified his valiant morning vow, "I won't pay one cent over seven dollars a quart" to "I might pay ten." On Hanson's next weary entrance he besought, "Could you fix that up?" Hanson scowled, and grated, "Just a minute—Pete's sake—just a minute!" In growing meekness Babbitt went on waiting till Hanson casually reappeared with a quart of gin—what is euphemistically known as a quart—in his disdainful long white hands.

"Twelve bucks," he snapped.

"Say, uh, but say, cap'n, Jake thought you'd be able to fix me up for eight or nine a bottle."

"Nup. Twelve. This is the real stuff, smuggled from Canada. This is none o' your neutral spirits with a drop of juniper extract," the honest merchant said virtuously. "Twelve bones—if you want it. Course y' understand I'm just doing this anyway as a friend of Jake's."

"Sure! Sure! I understand!" Babbitt gratefully held out twelve dollars. He felt honored by contact with greatness as Hanson yawned, stuffed the bills, uncounted, into his radiant vest, and swaggered away.

He had a number of titillations out of concealing the gin-bottle under his coat and out of hiding it in his desk. All afternoon he snorted and chuckled and gurgled over his ability to "give the Boys a real shot in the arm to-night." He was, in fact, so exhilarated that he was within a block of his house before he remembered that there was a certain matter, mentioned by his wife, of fetching ice cream from Vecchia's. He explained, "Well, darn it—" and drove back.

Vecchia was not a caterer, he was The Caterer of Zenith. Most coming-out parties were held in the white and gold ballroom of the Maison Vecchia; at all nice teas the guests recognized the five kinds of Vecchia sandwiches and the seven kinds of Vecchia cakes; and all really smart dinners ended, as on a resolving chord, in Vecchia Neapolitan ice cream in one of the three reliable molds—the

melon mold, the round mold like a layer cake, and the long brick.

Vecchia's shop had pale blue woodwork, tracery of plaster roses, attendants in frilled aprons, and glass shelves of "kisses" with all the refinement that inheres in whites of eggs. Babbitt felt heavy and thick amid this professional daintiness, and as he waited for the ice cream he decided, with hot prickles at the back of his neck, that a girl customer was giggling at him. He went home in a touchy temper. The first thing he heard was his wife's agitated:

"George! *Did* you remember to go to Vecchia's and get the ice cream?"

"Say! Look here! Do I ever forget to do things?"

"Yes! Often!"

"Well now, it's darn seldom I do, and it certainly makes me tired, after going into a pink-tea joint like Vecchia's and having to stand around looking at a lot of half-naked young girls, all rouged up like they were sixty and eating a lot of stuff that simply ruins their stomachs—"

"Oh, it's too bad about you! I've noticed how you hate to look at pretty girls!"

With a jar Babbitt realized that his wife was too busy to be impressed by that moral indignation with which males rule the world, and he went humbly upstairs to dress. He had an impression of a glorified dining-room, of cut-glass, candles, polished wood, lace, silver, roses. With the awed swelling of the heart suitable to so grave a business as giving a dinner, he slew the temptation to wear his plaited dress-shirt for a fourth time, took out an entirely fresh one, tightened his black bow, and rubbed his patent-leather pumps with a handkerchief. He glanced with pleasure at his garnet and silver studs. He smoothed and patted his ankles, transformed by silk socks from the sturdy shanks of George Babbitt to the elegant limbs of what is called a Clubman. He stood before the pier-glass, viewing his trim dinner-coat, his beautiful triple-braided trousers; and murmured in lyric beatitude, "By golly, I don't look so bad. I certainly don't look like Catawba. If the hicks back home could see me in this rig, they'd have a fit!"

He moved majestically down to mix the cocktails. As he chipped ice, as he squeezed oranges, as he collected vast stores of bottles, glasses, and spoons at the sink in the pantry, he felt as authoritative as the bartender at Healey Hanson's saloon. True, Mrs. Babbitt said he was under foot, and Matilda and the maid hired for the evening brushed by him, elbowed him, shrieked "Pleasopn door," as they tottered through with trays, but in this high moment he ignored them.

Besides the new bottle of gin, his cellar consisted of one half-bottle of Bourbon whisky, a quarter of a bottle of Italian vermouth, and approximately one hundred drops of orange bitters. He did not possess a cocktail-shaker. A shaker was proof of dissipation, the symbol of a Drinker, and Babbitt disliked being known as a Drinker even more than he liked a Drink. He mixed by pouring from an ancient gravy-boat into a handleless pitcher; he poured with a noble dignity, holding his alembics high beneath the powerful Mazda globe, his face hot, his shirt-front a glaring white, the copper sink a scoured red-gold.

He tasted the sacred essence. "Now, by golly, if that isn't pretty near one fine old cocktail! Kind of a Bronx, and yet like a Manhattan. Ummmmmm! Hey, Myra, want a little nip before the folks come?"

Bustling into the dining-room, moving each glass a quarter of an inch, rushing back with resolution implacable on her face, her gray and silver-lace party frock protected by a denim towel, Mrs. Babbitt glared at him, and rebuked him, "Certainly not!"

"Well," in a loose, jocose manner, "I think the old man will!"

The cocktail filled him with a whirling exhilaration behind which he was aware of devastating desires—to rush places in fast motors, to kiss girls, to sing, to be witty. He sought to regain his lost dignity by announcing to Matilda:

"I'm going to stick this pitcher of cocktails in the refrigerator. Be sure you don't upset any of 'em."

"Yeh."

"Well, be sure now. Don't go putting anything on this top shelf."

"Yeh."

"Well, be—" He was dizzy. His voice was thin and distant. "Whee!" With enormous impressiveness he commanded, "Well, be sure now," and minced into the safety of the living-room. He wondered whether he could persuade "as slow a bunch as Myra and the Littlefields to go some place aft' dinner and raise Cain and maybe dig up smore booze." He perceived that he had gifts of profligacy which had been neglected.

By the time the guests had come, including the inevitable late couple for whom the others waited with painful amiability, a great gray emptiness had replaced the purple swirling in Babbitt's head, and he had to force the tumultuous greetings suitable to a host on Floral Heights.

The guests were Howard Littlefield, the doctor of philosophy who furnished publicity and comforting economics to the Street Traction Company; Vergil Gunch, the coal-dealer, equally powerful in the Elks and in the Boosters' Club; Eddie Swanson, the agent for the Javelin Motor Car, who lived across the street; and Orville Jones, owner of the Lily White Laundry, which justly announced itself "the biggest, busiest, bulliest cleanerie shoppe in Zenith." But, naturally, the most distinguished of all was T. Cholmondeley Frink, who was not only the author of "Poemulations," which, syndicated daily in sixty-seven leading newspapers, gave him one of the largest audiences of any poet in the world, but also an optimistic lecturer and the creator of "Ads that Add." Despite the searching philosophy and high morality of his verses, they were humorous and easily understood by any child of twelve; and it added a neat air of pleasantry to them that they were set not as verse but as prose. Mr. Frink was known from Coast to Coast as "Chum."

With them were six wives, more or less—it was hard to tell, so early in the evening, as at first glance they all looked alike, and as they all said, "Oh, *isn't* this nice!" in the same tone of determined liveliness. To the eye, the men were less similar: Littlefield, a hedge-scholar, tall and horse-faced; Chum Frink, a trifle of a man with soft and mouse-like hair, advertising his profession as poet by a silk cord on his eye-glasses; Vergil Gunch, broad, with coarse black hair *en brosse;* Eddie Swanson, a bald and bouncing young man who showed his taste for elegance by an evening waist-coat of figured black silk with glass buttons; Orville Jones, a steady-looking, stubby, not very memorable person, with a hemp-colored toothbrush mustache. Yet they were all so well fed and clean, they all shouted " 'Evenin', Georgie!" with such robustness, that they seemed to be cousins, and the strange thing is that the longer one knew the women, the less alike they seemed; while the longer one knew the men, the more alike their bold patterns appeared.

The drinking of the cocktails was as canonical a rite as the mixing. The company waited, uneasily, hopefully, agreeing in a strained manner that the weather had been rather warm and slightly cold, but still Babbitt said nothing about drinks. They became despondent. But when the late couple (the Swansons) had arrived, Babbitt hinted, "Well, folks, do you think you could stand breaking the law a little?"

They looked at Chum Frink, the recognized lord of language. Frink pulled at his eye-glass cord as at a bell-rope, he cleared his throat and said that which was the custom:

"I'll tell you, George: I'm a law-abiding man, but they do say Verg Gunch is a regular yegg, and of course he's bigger 'n I am, and I just can't figure out what I'd do if he tried to force me into anything criminal!"

Gunch was roaring, "Well, I'll take a chance—" when Frink held up his hand and went on, "So if Verg and you insist, Georgie, I'll park my car on the wrong side of the street, because I take it for granted that's the crime you're hinting at!"

There was a great deal of laughter. Mrs. Jones asserted, "Mr. Frink is simply too killing! You'd think he was so innocent!"

Babbitt clamored, "How did you guess it, Chum? Well, you-all just wait a moment while I go out and get the—keys to your cars!" Through a froth of merriment he brought the shining promise, the mighty tray of glasses with the cloudy yellow cocktails in the glass pitcher in the center. The men babbled, "Oh, gosh, have a look!" and "This gets me right where I live!" and "Let me at it!" But Chum Frink, a traveled man and not unused to woes, was stricken by the thought that the potion might be merely fruit-juice with a little neutral spirits. He looked timorous as Babbitt, a moist and ecstatic almoner, held out a glass, but as he tasted it he piped, "Oh, man, let me dream on! It ain't true, but don't waken me! Jus' lemme slumber!"

Two hours before, Frink had completed a newspaper lyric beginning:

I sat alone and groused and thunk, and scratched my head and sighed and wunk, and groaned, "There still are boobs, alack, who'd like the old-time gin-mill back; that den that makes a sage a loon, the vile and smelly old saloon!" I'll never miss their poison booze, whilst I the bubbling spring can use, that leaves my head at merry morn as clear as any babe new-born!

Babbitt drank with the others; his moment's depression was gone; he perceived that these were the best fellows in the world; he wanted to give them a thousand cocktails. "Think you could stand another?" he cried. The wives refused, with giggles, but the men, speaking in a wide, elaborate, enjoyable manner, gloated, "Well, sooner than have you get sore at me, Georgie—"

"You got a little dividend coming," said Babbitt to each of them, and each intoned, "Squeeze it, Georgie, squeeze it!"

When, beyond hope, the pitcher was empty, they stood and talked about prohibition. The men leaned back on their heels, put their hands in their trousers-pockets, and proclaimed their views with the booming profundity of a prosperous male repeating a thoroughly hackneyed statement about a matter of which he knows nothing whatever.

"Now, I'll tell you," said Vergil Gunch; "way I figure it is this, and I can speak by the book, because I've talked to a lot of doctors and fellows that ought to know, and the way I see it is that it's a good thing to get rid of the saloon, but they ought to let a fellow have beer and light wines."

Howard Littlefield observed, "What isn't generally realized is that it's a dangerous prop'sition to invade the rights of personal liberty. Now, take this for instance: The King of—Bavaria? I think it was Bavaria—yes, Bavaria, it was—in 1862, March, 1862, he issued a proclamation against public grazing of live-

stock. The peasantry had stood for over-taxation without the slightest complaint, but when this proclamation came out, they rebelled. Or it may have been Saxony. But it just goes to show the dangers of invading the rights of personal liberty."

"That's it—no one got a right to invade personal liberty," said Orville Jones.

"Just the same, you don't want to forget prohibition is a mighty good thing for the working-classes. Keeps 'em from wasting their money and lowering their productiveness," said Vergil Gunch.

"Yes, that's so. But the trouble is the manner of enforcement," insisted Howard Littlefield. "Congress didn't understand the right system. Now, if I'd been running the thing, I'd have arranged it so that the drinker himself was licensed, and then we could have taken care of the shiftless workman—kept him from drinking—and yet not 've interfered with the rights—with the personal liberty—of fellows like ourselves."

They bobbed their heads, looked admiringly at one another, and stated, "That's so, that would be the stunt."

"The thing that worries me is that a lot of these guys will take to cocaine," sighed Eddie Swanson.

They bobbed more violently, and groaned, "That's so, there is a danger of that."

Chum Frink chanted, "Oh, say, I got hold of a swell new receipt for home-made beer the other day. You take—"

Gunch interrupted, "Wait! Let me tell you mine!" Littlefield snorted, "Beer! Rats! Thing to do is to ferment cider!" Jones insisted, "I've got the receipt that does the business!" Swanson begged, "Oh, say, lemme tell you the story—" But Frink went on resolutely, "You take and save the shells from peas, and pour six gallons of water on a bushel of shells and boil the mixture till—"

Mrs. Babbitt turned toward them with

yearning sweetness; Frink hastened to finish even his best beer-recipe; and she said gaily, "Dinner is served."

There was a good deal of friendly argument among the men as to which should go in last, and while they were crossing the hall from the living-room to the dining-room Vergil Gunch made them laugh by thundering, "If I can't sit next to Myra Babbitt and hold her hand under the table, I won't play—I'm goin' home." In the dining-room they stood embarrassed while Mrs. Babbitt fluttered, "Now, let me see— Oh, I was going to have some nice hand-painted place-cards for you but— Oh, let me see; Mr. Frink, you sit there."

The dinner was in the best style of women's-magazine art, whereby the salad was served in hollowed apples, and everything but the invincible fried chicken resembled something else.

Ordinarily the men found it hard to talk to the women; flirtation was an art unknown on Floral Heights, and the realms of offices and of kitchens had no alliances. But under the inspiration of the cocktails, conversation was violent. Each of the men still had a number of important things to say about prohibition, and now that each had a loyal listener in his dinner-partner he burst out:

"I found a place where I can get all the hootch I want at eight a quart—"

"Did you read about this fellow that went and paid a thousand dollars for ten cases of red-eye that proved to be nothing but water? Seems this fellow was standing on the corner and fellow comes up to him—"

"They say there's a whole raft of stuff being smuggled across at Detroit—"

"What I always say is—what a lot of folks don't realize about prohibition—"

"And then you get all this awful poison stuff—wood alcohol and everything—"

"Course I believe in it on principle, but I don't propose to have anybody telling me what I got to think and do. No American 'll ever stand for that!"

But they all felt that it was rather in bad taste for Orville Jones—and he not recognized as one of the wits of the occasion anyway—to say, "In fact, the whole thing about prohibition is this: it isn't the initial cost, it's the humidity."

Not till the one required topic had been dealt with did the conversation become general.

It was often and admiringly said of Vergil Gunch, "Gee, that fellow can get away with murder! Why, he can pull a Raw One in mixed company and all the ladies 'll laugh their heads off, but me, gosh, if I crack anything that's just the least bit off color I get the razz for fair!" Now Gunch delighted them by crying to Mrs. Eddie Swanson, youngest of the women, "Louetta! I managed to pinch Eddie's doorkey out of his pocket, and what say you and me sneak across the street when the folks aren't looking? Got something," with a gorgeous leer, "awful important to tell you!"

The women wriggled, and Babbitt was stirred to like naughtiness. "Say, folks, I wished I dared show you a book I borrowed from Doc Patten!"

"Now, George! The idea!" Mrs. Babbitt warned him.

"This book—racy isn't the word! It's some kind of an anthropological report about—about Customs, in the South Seas, and what it doesn't say! It's a book you can't buy. Verg, I'll lend it to you."

"Me first!" insisted Eddie Swanson. "Sounds spicy!"

Orville Jones announced, "Say, I heard a Good One the other day about a coupla Swedes and their wives," and, in the best Jewish accent, he resolutely carried the Good One to a slightly disinfected ending. Gunch capped it. But the cocktails waned, the seekers dropped back into cautious reality.

Chum Frink had recently been on a lecture-tour among the small towns, and he chuckled, "Awful good to get back to civilization! I certainly been seeing some hick towns! I mean—Course the folks there are the best on earth, but, gee whiz, those Main Street burgs are slow, and you fellows can't hardly appreciate what it means to be here with a bunch of live ones!"

"You bet!" exulted Orville Jones. "They're the best folks on earth, those small-town folks, but, oh, mama! what conversation! Why, say, they can't talk about anything but the weather and the ne-oo Ford, by heckalorum!"

"That's right. They all talk about just the same things," said Eddie Swanson.

"Don't they, though! They just say the same things over and over," said Vergil Gunch.

"Yes, it's really remarkable. They seem to lack all power of looking at things impersonally. They simply go over and over the same talk about Fords and the weather and so on," said Howard Littlefield.

"Still, at that, you can't blame 'em. They haven't got any intellectual stimulus such as you get up here in the city," said Chum Frink.

"Gosh, that's right," said Babbitt. "I don't want you high-brows to get stuck on yourselves but I must say it keeps a fellow right up on his toes to sit in with a poet and with Howard, the guy that put the con in economics! But these small-town boobs, with nobody but each other to talk to, no wonder they get so sloppy and uncultured in their speech, and so balled-up in their thinking!"

Orville Jones commented, "And, then take our other advantages—the movies, frinstance. These Yapville sports think they're all-get-out if they have one change of bill a week, where here in the city you got your choice of a dozen diff'rent movies any evening you want to name!"

"Sure, and the inspiration we get from rubbing up against high-class hustlers every day and getting jam full of ginger," said Eddie Swanson.

"Same time," said Babbitt, "no sense excusing these rube burgs too easy. Fellow's own fault if he doesn't show the initiative to up and beat it to the city, like we done—did. And, just speaking in confidence among friends, they're jealous as the devil of a city man. Every time I go up to Catawba I have to go around apologizing to the fellows I was brought up with because I've more or less succeeded and they haven't. And if you talk natural to 'em, way we do here, and show finesse and what you might call a broad point of view, why, they think you're putting on side. There's my own half-brother Martin—runs the little ole general store my Dad used to keep. Say, I'll bet he don't know there is such a thing as a Tux—as a dinner-jacket. If he was to come in here now, he'd think we were a bunch of—of— Why, gosh, I swear, he wouldn't know what to think! Yes, sir, they're jealous!"

Chum Frink agreed, "That's so. But what I mind is their lack of culture and appreciation of the Beautiful—if you'll excuse me for being highbrow. Now, I like to give a high-class lecture, and read some of my best poetry—not the newspaper stuff but the magazine things. But say, when I get out in the tall grass, there's nothing will take but a lot of cheesy old stories and slang and junk that if any of us were to indulge in it here, he'd get the gate so fast it would make his head swim."

Vergil Gunch summed it up: "Fact is, we're mighty lucky to be living among a bunch of city-folks, that recognize artistic things and business-punch equally. We'd feel pretty glum if we got stuck in

some Main Street burg and tried to wise
up the old codgers to the kind of life
we're used to here. But, by golly, there's
this you got to say for 'em: Every small
American town is trying to get population and modern ideals. And darn if a lot
of 'em don't put it across! Somebody
starts panning a rube crossroads, telling
how he was there in 1900 and it consisted of one muddy street, count 'em,
one, and nine hundred human clams.
Well, you go back there in 1920, and you
find pavements and a swell little hotel
and a first-class ladies' ready-to-wear
shop—real perfection, in fact! You don't
want to just look at what these small
towns are, you want to look at what
they're aiming to become, and they all
got an ambition that in the long run is
going to make 'em the finest spots on
earth—they all want to be just like
Zenith!"

III

However intimate they might be with
T. Cholmondeley Frink as a neighbor, as
a borrower of lawn-mowers and monkey-
wrenches, they knew that he was also a
Famous Poet and a distinguished advertising-agent; that behind his easiness were
sultry literary mysteries which they could
not penetrate. But to-night, in the gin-
evolved confidence, he admitted them to
the arcanum:

"I've got a literary problem that's worrying me to death. I'm doing a series of
ads for the Zeeco Car and I want to
make each of 'em a real little gem—
reg'lar stylistic stuff. I'm all for this
theory that perfection is the stunt, or
nothing at all and these are as tough
things as I ever tackled. You might think
it'd be harder to do my poems—all these
Heart Topics: home and fireside and
happiness—but they're cinches. You
can't go wrong on 'em; you know what
sentiments any decent go-ahead fellow

must have if he plays the game, and you
stick right to 'em. But the poetry of
industrialism, now there's a literary line
where you got to open up new territory.
Do you know the fellow who's really *the*
American genius? The fellow who you
don't know his name and I don't either,
but his work ought to be preserved so's
future generations can judge our American thought and originality to-day? Why,
the fellow that writes the Prince Albert
Tobacco ads! Just listen to this:

It's P.A. that jams such joy in jimmy pipes.
Say—bet you've often bent-an-ear to that
spill-of-speech about hopping from five to
f-i-f-t-y p-e-r by "stepping on her a bit!"
Guess that's going some, all right—BUT—
just among ourselves, you better start a
rapidwhiz system to keep tabs as to how fast
you'll buzz from low smoke spirits to *tip-top-
high*—once you line up behind a jimmy pipe
that's all aglow with that peach-of-a-pal,
Prince Albert.

Prince Albert is john-on-the-job—always
joy'usly more-*ish* in flavor; always delight-
fully cool and fragrant! For a fact, you never
hooked such double-decked, copper-riveted,
two-fisted smoke enjoyment!

Go to a pipe—speed-o-quick like you light on
a good thing! Why—packed with Prince Albert you can play a joy'us jimmy straight
across the boards! *And you know what that
means!*"

"Now that," caroled the motor agent,
Eddie Swanson, "that's what I call he-
literature! That Prince Albert fellow—
though, gosh, there can't be just one fellow that writes 'em; must be a big board
of classy ink-slingers in conference, but
anyway: now, him, he doesn't write for
long-haired pikers, he writes for Regular
Guys, he writes for *me*, and I tip my
benny to him! The only thing is: I wonder
if it sells the goods? Course, like all
these poets, this Prince Albert fellow lets
his idea run away with him. It makes

SINCLAIR LEWIS

elegant reading, but it don't say nothing. I'd never go out and buy Prince Albert Tobacco after reading it, because it doesn't tell me anything about the stuff. It's just a bunch of fluff."

Frink faced him: "Oh, you're crazy! Have I got to sell you the idea of Style? Anyway, that's the kind of stuff I'd like to do for the Zeeco. But I simply can't. So I decided to stick to the straight poetic, and I took a shot at a highbrow ad for the Zeeco. How do you like this:

The long white trail is calling—calling—and it's over the hills and far away for every man or woman that has red blood in his veins and on his lips the ancient song of the buccaneers. It's away with dull drudging, and a fig for care. Speed—glorious Speed—it's more than just a moment's exhilaration—it's Life for you and me! This great new truth the makers of the Zeeco Car have considered as much as price and style. It's fleet as the antelope, smooth as the glide of a swallow, yet powerful as the charge of a bull-elephant. Class breathes in every line. Listen, brother! You'll never know what the high art of hiking is till you TRY LIFE'S ZIPPINGEST ZEST—THE ZEECO!

"Yes," Frink mused, "that's got an elegant color to it, if I do say so, but it ain't got the originality of 'spill-of-speech!'"

The whole company sighed with sympathy and admiration.

CHAPTER 9

Babbitt was fond of his friends, he loved the importance of being host and shouting, "Certainly, you're going to have smore chicken—the idea!" and he appreciated the genius of T. Cholmondeley Frink, but the vigor of the cocktails was gone, and the more he ate the less joyful he felt. Then the amity of the dinner was destroyed by the nagging of the Swansons.

In Floral Heights and the other prosperous sections of Zenith, especially in the "young married set," there were many women who had nothing to do. Though they had few servants, yet with gas stoves, electric ranges and dishwashers and vacuum cleaners, and tiled kitchen walls, their houses were so convenient that they had little housework, and much of their food came from bakeries and delicatessens. They had but two, one, or no children; and despite the myth that the Great War had made work respectable, their husbands objected to their "wasting time and getting a lot of crank ideas" in unpaid social work, and still more to their causing a rumor, by earning money, that they were not adequately supported. They worked perhaps two hours a day, and the rest of the time they ate chocolates, went to the motion-pictures, went window-shopping, went in gossiping twos and threes to card-parties, read magazines, thought timorously of the lovers who never appeared, and accumulated a splendid restlessness which they got rid of by nagging their husbands. The husbands nagged back.

Of these naggers the Swansons were perfect specimens.

Throughout the dinner Eddie Swanson had been complaining, publicly, about his wife's new frock. It was, he submitted, too short, too low, too immodestly thin, and much too expensive. He appealed to Babbitt:

"Honest, George, what do you think of that rag Louetta went and bought? Don't you think it's the limit?"

"What's eating you, Eddie? I call it a swell little dress."

"Oh, it is, Mr. Swanson. It's a sweet frock," Mrs. Babbitt protested.

"There now, do you see, smarty! You're such an authority on clothes!" Louetta raged, while the guests ruminated and peeped at her shoulders.

"That's all right now," said Swanson.

[344]

"I'm authority enough so I know it was a waste of money, and it makes me tired to see you not wearing out a whole closetful of clothes you got already. I've expressed my idea about this before, and you know good and well you didn't pay the least bit of attention. I have to camp on your trail to get you to do anything—"

There was much more of it, and they all assisted, all but Babbitt. Everything about him was dim except his stomach, and that was a bright scarlet disturbance. "Had too much grub; oughtn't to eat this stuff," he groaned—while he went on eating, while he gulped down a chill and glutinous slice of the ice-cream brick, and cocoanut cake as oozy as shaving-cream. He felt as though he had been stuffed with clay; his body was bursting, his throat was bursting, his brain was hot mud; and only with agony did he continue to smile and shout as became a host on Floral Heights.

He would, except for his guests, have fled outdoors and walked off the intoxication of food, but in the haze which filled the room they sat forever, talking, talking, while he agonized, "Darn fool to be eating all this—not 'nother mouthful," and discovered that he was again tasting the sickly welter of melted ice cream on his plate. There was no magic in his friends; he was not uplifted when Howard Littlefield produced from his treasure-house of scholarship the information that the chemical symbol for raw rubber is $C_{10}H_{16}$, which turns into isoprene, or $2C_5H_8$. Suddenly, without precedent, Babbitt was not merely bored but admitting that he was bored. It was ecstasy to escape from the table, from the torture of a straight chair, and loll on the davenport in the living-room.

The others, from their fitful unconvincing talk, their expressions of being slowly and painfully smothered, seemed to be suffering from the toil of social life and the horror of good food as much as

himself. All of them accepted with relief the suggestion of bridge.

Babbitt recovered from the feeling of being boiled. He won at bridge. He was again able to endure Vergil Gunch's inexorable heartiness. But he pictured loafing with Paul Riesling beside a lake in Maine. It was as overpowering and imaginative as homesickness. He had never seen Maine, yet he beheld the shrouded mountains, the tranquil lake of evening. "That boy Paul's worth all these bally-hooing highbrows put together," he muttered; and, "I'd like to get away from—everything."

Even Louetta Swanson did not rouse him.

Mrs. Swanson was pretty and pliant. Babbitt was not an analyst of women, except as to their tastes in Furnished Houses to Rent. He divided them into Real Ladies, Working Women, Old Cranks, and Fly Chickens. He mooned over their charms but he was of opinion that all of them (save the women of his own family) were "different" and "mysterious." Yet he had known by instinct that Louetta Swanson could be approached. Her eyes and lips were moist. Her face tapered from a broad forehead to a pointed chin, her mouth was thin but strong and avid, and between her brows were two outcurving and passionate wrinkles. She was thirty, perhaps, or younger. Gossip had never touched her, but every man naturally and instantly rose to flirtatiousness when he spoke to her, and every woman watched her with stilled blankness.

Between games, sitting on the davenport, Babbitt spoke to her with the requisite gallantry, that sonorous Floral Heights gallantry which is not flirtation but a terrified flight from it:

"You're looking like a new soda-fountain to-night, Louetta."

"Am I?"

"Ole Eddie kind of on the rampage."

"Yes. I get so sick of it."

"Well, when you get tired of hubby, you can run off with Uncle George."

"If I ran away— Oh, well—"

"Anybody ever tell you your hands are awful pretty?"

She looked down at them, she pulled the lace of her sleeves over them, but otherwise she did not heed him. She was lost in unexpressed imaginings.

Babbitt was too languid this evening to pursue his duty of being a captivating (though strictly moral) male. He ambled back to the bridge-tables. He was not much thrilled when Mrs. Frink, a small twittering woman, proposed that they "try and do some spiritualism and table-tipping—you know Chum can make the spirits come—honest, he just scares me!"

The ladies of the party had not emerged all evening, but now, as the sex given to things of the spirit while the men warred against base things material, they took command and cried, "Oh, let's!" In the dimness the men were rather solemn and foolish, but the goodwives quivered and adored as they sat about the table. They laughed, "Now, you be good or I'll tell!" when the men took their hands in the circle.

Babbitt tingled with a slight return of interest in life as Louetta Swanson's hand closed on his with quiet firmness.

All of them hunched over, intent. They startled as some one drew a strained breath. In the dusty light from the hall they looked unreal, they felt dis-embodied. Mrs. Gunch squeaked, and they jumped with unnatural jocularity, but at Frink's hiss they sank into sub-dued awe. Suddenly, incredibly, they heard a knocking. They stared at Frink's half-revealed hands and found them lying still. They wriggled, and pretended not to be impressed.

Frink spoke with gravity: "Is some one there?" A thud. "Is one knock to be

the sign for 'yes'?" A thud. "And two for 'no'?" A thud.

"Now, ladies and gentlemen, shall we ask the guide to put us into communica-tion with the spirit of some great one passed over?" Frink mumbled.

Mrs. Orville Jones begged, "Oh, let's talk to Dante! We studied him at the Reading Circle. You know who he was, Orvy."

"Certainly I know who he was! The Wop poet. Where do you think I was raised?" from her insulted husband.

"Sure—the fellow that took the Cook's Tour to Hell. I've never waded through his po'try, but we learned about him in the U.," said Babbitt.

"Page Mr. Dannnnnty!" intoned Eddie Swanson.

"You ought to get him easy, Mr. Frink, you and he being fellow-poets," said Louetta Swanson.

"Fellow-poets, rats! Where d' you get that stuff?" protested Vergil Gunch. "I suppose Dante showed a lot of speed for an old-timer—not that I've actually read him, of course—but to come right down to hard facts, he wouldn't stand one-two-three if he had to buckle down to practi-cal literature and turn out a poem for the newspaper-syndicate every day, like Chum does!"

"That's so," from Eddie Swanson. "Those old birds could take their time. Judas Priest, I could write poetry myself if I had a whole year for it, and just wrote about that old-fashioned junk like Dante wrote about."

Frink demanded, "Hush, now! I'll call him. . . . O, Laughing Eyes, emerge forth into the, uh, the ultimates and bring hither the spirit of Dante, that we mortals may list to his words of wisdom."

"You forgot to give um the address: 1658 Brimstone Avenue. Fiery Heights, Hell," Gunch chuckled, but the others felt that this was irreligious. And be-sides—"problably it was just Chum mak-ing the knocks, but still, if there did happen to be something to all this, be exciting to talk to an old fellow belong-ing to—way back in early times—"

A thud. The spirit of Dante had come to the parlor of George F. Babbitt.

He was, it seemed, quite ready to an-swer their questions. He was "glad to be with them, this evening."

Frink spelled out the messages by run-ning through the alphabet till the spirit interpreter knocked at the right letter.

Littlefield asked, in a learned tone, "Do you like it in the Paradiso, Messire?"

"We are very happy on the higher plane, Signor. We are glad that you are studying this great truth of spiritualism," Dante replied.

The circle moved with an awed creak-ing of stays and shirtfronts. "Suppose—suppose there were something to this?"

Babbitt had a different worry. "Sup-pose Chum Frink was really one of these spiritualists! Chum had, for a literary fellow, always seemed to be a Regular Guy; he belonged to the Chatham Road Presbyterian Church and went to the Boosters' lunches and liked cigars and motors and racy stories. But suppose that secretly— After all, you never could tell about these darn highbrows; and to be an out-and-out spiritualist would be almost like being a socialist!"

No one could long be serious in the presence of Vergil Gunch. "Ask Dant' how Jack Shakespeare and old Verg'— the guy they named after me—are gettin' along, and don't they wish they could get into the movie game!" he blared, and in-stantly all was mirth. Mrs. Jones shrieked, and Eddie Swanson desired to know whether Dante didn't catch cold with nothing on but his wreath.

The pleased Dante made humble answer.

But Babbitt—the curst discontent was

torturing him again, and heavily, in the impersonal darkness, he pondered, "I don't— We're all so flip and think we're so smart. There'd be— A fellow like Dante— I wish I'd read some of his pieces. I don't suppose I ever will, now."

He had, without explanation, the im-pression of a slaggy cliff and on it, in silhouette against menacing clouds, a lone and austere figure. He was dismayed by a sudden contempt for his surest friends. He grasped Louetta Swanson's hand, and found the comfort of human warmth. Habit came, a veteran warrior; and he shook himself. "What the deuce is the matter with me, this evening?"

He patted Louetta's hand, to indicate that he hadn't meant anything improper by squeezing it, and demanded of Frink, "Say, see if you can get old Dant' to spiel us some of his poetry. Talk up to him. Tell him, 'Buena giorna, señor, com sa va, wie geht's? Keskersaykersa a little pome, señor?'"

II

The lights were switched on; the women sat on the fronts of their chairs in that determined suspense whereby a wife indicates that as soon as the present speaker has finished, she is going to re-mark brightly to her husband, "Well, dear, I think per-haps it's about time for us to be saying good-night." For once Babbitt did not break out in blustering efforts to keep the party going. He had— there was something he wished to think out— But the psychical research had started them off again. ("Why didn't they go home! Why didn't they go home!") Though he was impressed by the profun-dity of the statement, he was only half-enthusiastic when Howard Littlefield lec-tured, "The United States is the only nation in which the government is a Moral Ideal and not just a social ar-rangement." ("True—true—weren't they ever going home?") He was usually delighted to have an "inside view" of the momentous world of motors but to-night he scarcely listened to Eddie Swanson's revelation: "If you want to go above the Javelin class, the Zeeco is a mighty good buy. Couple weeks ago, and mind you, this was a fair, square test, they took a Zeeco stock touring-car and they slid up the Tonawanda hill on high, and fellow told me—" ("Zeeco—good boat but— Were they planning to stay all night?")

They really were going, with a flutter of "We did have the best time!"

Most aggressively friendly of all was Babbitt, yet as he burbled he was reflecting, "I got through it, but for a while there I didn't hardly think I'd last out." He prepared to taste that most delicate pleasure of the host: making fun of his guests in the relaxation of midnight. As the door closed he yawned voluptuously, chest out, shoulders wriggling, and turned cynically to his wife.

She was beaming. "Oh, it was nice, wasn't it! I know they enjoyed every minute of it. Don't you think so?"

He couldn't do it. He couldn't mock. It would have been like sneering at a happy child. He lied ponderously: "You bet! Best party this year, by a long shot."

"Wasn't the dinner good! And honestly I thought the fried chicken was delicious!"

"You bet! Fried to the Queen's taste. Best fried chicken I've tasted for a coon's age."

"Didn't Matilda fry it beautifully! And don't you think the soup was simply delicious?"

"It certainly was! It was corking! Best soup I've tasted since Heck was a pup!" But his voice was seeping away. They stood in the hall, under the electric light in its square box-like shade of red glass bound with nickel. She stared at him.

"Why, George, you don't sound—you sound as if you hadn't really enjoyed it."

"Sure I did! Course I did!"

"George! What is it?"

"Oh, I'm kind of tired, I guess. Been pounding pretty hard at the office. Need to get away and rest up a little."

"Well, we're going to Maine in just a few weeks now, dear."

"Yuh—" Then he was pouring it out nakedly, robbed of reticence. "Myra: I think it'd be a good thing for me to get up there early."

"But you have this man you have to meet in New York about business."

"What man? Oh, sure. Him. Oh, that's all off. But I want to hit Maine early— get in a little fishing, catch me a big trout, by golly!" A nervous, artificial laugh.

"Well, why don't we do it? Verona and Matilda can run the house between them, and you and I can go any time, if you think we can afford it."

"But that's—I've been feeling so jumpy lately, I thought maybe it might be a good thing if I kind of got off by myself and sweat it out of me."

"George! Don't you *want* me to go along?" She was too wretchedly in earnest to be tragic, or gloriously insulted, or anything save dumpy and defenseless and flushed to the red steaminess of a boiled beet.

"Of course I do! I just meant—" Remembering that Paul Riesling had predicted this, he was as desperate as she. "I mean, sometimes it's a good thing for an old grouch like me to go off and get it out of his system." He tried to sound paternal. "Then when you and the kids arrive—I figured maybe I might skip up to Maine just a few days ahead of you— I'd be ready for a real bat, see how I mean?" He coaxed her with large booming sounds, with affable smiles, like a popular preacher blessing an Easter congregation, like a humorous lecturer completing his stint of eloquence, like all perpetrators of masculine wiles.

She stared at him, the joy of festival drained from her face. "Do I bother you when we go on vacations? Don't I add anything to your fun?"

He broke. Suddenly, dreadfully, he was hysterical, he was a yelping baby. "Yes, yes, yes! Hell, yes! But can't you understand I'm shot to pieces? I'm all in! I got to take care of myself! I tell you, I got to— I'm sick of everything and everybody! I got to—"

It was she who was mature and protective now. "Why, of course! You shall run off by yourself! Why don't you get Paul to go along, and you boys just fish and have a good time?" She patted his shoulder—reaching up to it—while he shook with palsied helplessness, and in that moment was not merely by habit fond of her but clung to her strength.

She cried cheerily, "Now up-stairs you go, and pop into bed. We'll fix it all up. I'll see to the doors. Now skip!"

For many minutes, for many hours, for a bleak eternity, he lay awake, shivering, reduced to primitive terror, comprehending that he had won freedom, and wondering what he could do with anything so unknown and so embarrassing as freedom.

CHAPTER 10

No apartment-house in Zenith had more resolutely experimented in condensation than the Revelstoke Arms, in which Paul and Zilla Riesling had a flat. By sliding the beds into low closets the bedrooms were converted into living-rooms. The kitchens were cupboards each containing an electric range, a copper sink, a glass refrigerator, and, very intermittently, a Balkan maid. Everything about the arms was excessively modern, and everything was compressed—except the garages.

The Babbitts were calling on the Rieslings at the Arms. It was a speculative venture to call on the Rieslings; interesting and sometimes disconcerting. Zilla was an active, strident, full-blown, high-bosomed blonde. When she condescended to be good-humored she was nervously amusing. Her comments on people were saltily satiric and penetrative of accepted hypocrisies. "That's so!" you said, and looked sheepish. She danced wildly, and called on the world to be merry, but in the midst of it she would turn indignant. She was always becoming indignant. Life was a plot against her, and she exposed it furiously.

She was affable to-night. She merely hinted that Orville Jones wore a toupé, that Mrs. T. Cholmondeley Frink's singing resembled a Ford going into high, and that the Hon. Otis Deeble, mayor of Zenith and candidate for Congress, was a flatulent fool (which was quite true). The Babbitts and Rieslings sat doubtfully on stone-hard brocade chairs in the small living-room of the flat, with its mantel unprovided with a fireplace, and its strip of heavy gilt fabric upon a glaring new player-piano, till Mrs. Riesling shrieked, "Come on! Let's put some pep in it! Get out your fiddle, Paul, and I'll try to make Georgie dance decently."

The Babbitts were in earnest. They were plotting for the escape to Maine. But when Mrs. Babbitt hinted with plump smilingness, "Does Paul get as tired after the winter's work as Georgie does?" then Zilla remembered an injury; and when Zilla Riesling remembered an injury the world stopped till something had been done about it.

"Does he get tired? No, he doesn't get tired, he just goes crazy, that's all! You think Paul is so reasonable, oh, yes, and he loves to make out he's a little lamb, but he's stubborn as a mule. Oh, if you had to live with him—! You'd find out how sweet he is! He just pretends to be meek so he can have his own way. And me, I get the credit for being a terrible old crank, but if I didn't blow up once in a while and get something started, we'd die of dry-rot. He never wants to go any place and— Why, last evening, just because the car was out of order—and that was his fault, too, because he ought to have taken it to the service-station and had the battery looked at—and he didn't want to go down to the movies on the trolley. But we went, and then there was one of those impudent conductors, and Paul wouldn't do a thing.

"I was standing on the platform waiting for the people to let me into the car, and this beast, this conductor, hollered at me, 'Come on, you, move up!' Why, I've never had anybody speak to me that way in all my life! I was so astonished I just turned to him and said—I thought there must be some mistake, and so I said to him, perfectly pleasant, 'Were you speaking to me?' and he went on and bellowed at me, 'Yes, I was! You're keeping the whole car from starting!' he said, and then I saw he was one of these dirty ill-bred hogs that kindness is wasted on, and so I stopped and looked right at him, and I said, 'I—beg—your—pardon, I am not doing anything of the kind,' I said, 'it's the people ahead of me, who won't move up,' I said, 'and furthermore, let me tell you, young man, that you're a low-down, foul-mouthed, impertinent skunk,' I said, 'and you're no gentleman! I certainly intend to report you, and we'll see,' I said, 'whether a lady is to be insulted by any drunken bum that chooses to put on a ragged uniform, and I'd thank you,' I said, 'to keep your filthy abuse to yourself.' And then I waited for Paul to show he was half a man and come to my defense, and he just stood there and pretended he hadn't heard a word, and so I said to him, 'Well,' I said—"

"Oh, cut it, cut it, Zill!" Paul groaned. "We all know I'm a mollycoddle, and you're a tender bud, and let's let it go at that."

"Let it go?" Zilla's face was wrinkled like the Medusa, her voice was a dagger of corroded brass. She was full of the joy of righteousness and bad temper. She was a crusader and, like every crusader, she exulted in the opportunity to be vicious in the name of virtue. "Let it go? If people knew how many things I've let go—"

"Oh, quit being such a bully."

"Yes, a fine figure you'd cut if I didn't bully you! You'd lie abed till noon and play your idiotic fiddle till midnight! You're born lazy, and you're born shiftless, and you're born cowardly, Paul Riesling—"

"Oh, now, don't say that, Zilla; you don't mean a word of it!" protested Mrs. Babbitt.

"I will say that, and I mean every single last word of it!"

"Oh, now, Zilla, the idea!" Mrs. Babbitt was maternal and fussy. She was no older than Zilla, but she seemed so—at first. She was placid and puffy and mature, where Zilla, at forty-five, was so bleached and tight-corseted that you knew only that she was older than she looked. "The idea of talking to poor Paul like that!"

"Poor Paul is right! We'd both be poor, we'd be in the poorhouse, if I didn't jazz him up!"

"Why, now, Zilla, Georgie and I were just saying how hard Paul's been working all year, and we were thinking it would be lovely if the Boys could run off by themselves. I've been coaxing George to go up to Maine ahead of the rest of us and get the tired out of his system before we come, and I think it would be lovely if Paul could manage to get away and join him."

At this exposure of his plot to escape, Paul was startled out of impassivity. He rubbed his fingers. His hands twitched.

Zilla bayed, "Yes! You're lucky! You can let George go, and not have to watch him. Fat old Georgie! Never peeps at another woman! Hasn't got the spunk!"

BABBITT

"The hell I haven't!" Babbitt was fervently defending his priceless immorality when Paul interrupted him—and Paul looked dangerous. He rose quickly; he said gently to Zilla:

"I suppose you imply I have a lot of sweethearts."

"Yes, I do!"

"Well, then, my dear, since you ask for it— There hasn't been a time in the last ten years when I haven't found some nice little girl to comfort me, and as long as you continue your amiability I shall probably continue to deceive you. It isn't hard. You're so stupid."

Zilla gibbered; she howled; words could not be distinguished in her slaver of abuse.

Then the bland George F. Babbitt was transformed. If Paul was dangerous, if Zilla was a snake-locked fury, if the neat emotions suitable to the Revelstoke Arms had been slashed into raw hatreds, it was Babbitt who was the most formidable. He leaped up. He seemed very large. He seized Zilla's shoulder. The cautions of the broker were wiped from his face, and his voice was cruel:

"I've had enough of all this damn nonsense! I've known you for twenty-five years, Zil, and I never knew you to miss a chance to take your disappointments out on Paul. You're not wicked. You're worse. You're a fool. And let me tell you that Paul is the finest boy God ever made. Every decent person is sick and tired of your taking advantage of being a woman and springing every mean innuendo you can think of. Who the hell are you that a person like Paul should have to ask your *permission* to go with me? You act like you were a combination of Queen Victoria and Cleopatra. You fool, can't you see how people snicker at you, and sneer at you?"

Zilla was sobbing, "I've never—I've never—nobody ever talked to me like this in all my life!"

"No, but that's the way they talk behind your back! Always! They say you're a scolding old woman. Old, by God!"

That cowardly attack broke her. Her eyes were blank. She wept. But Babbitt glared stolidly. He felt that he was the all-powerful official in charge; that Paul and Mrs. Babbitt looked on him with awe; that he alone could handle this case.

Zilla writhed. She begged, "Oh, they don't!"

"They certainly do!"

"I've been a bad woman! I'm terribly sorry! I'll kill myself! I'll do anything. Oh, I'll— What do you want?"

She abased herself completely. Also, she enjoyed it. To the connoisseur of scenes, nothing is more enjoyable than a thorough, melodramatic, egoistic humility.

"I want you to let Paul beat it off to Maine with me," Babbitt demanded.

"How can I help his going? You've just said I was an idiot and nobody paid any attention to me."

"Oh, you can help it, all right, all right! What you got to do is to cut out hinting that the minute he gets out of your sight, he'll go chasing after some petticoat. Matter fact, that's the way you start the boy off wrong. You ought to have more sense—"

"Oh, I will, honestly, I will, George. I know I was bad. Oh, forgive me, all of you, forgive me—"

She enjoyed it.

So did Babbitt. He condemned magnificently and forgave piously, and as he went parading out with his wife he was grandly explanatory to her:

"Kind of a shame to bully Zilla, but course it was the only way to handle her. Gosh, I certainly did have her crawling!"

She said calmly, "Yes. You were horrid. You were showing off. You were having a lovely time thinking what a great fine person you were!"

"Well, by golly! Can you beat it! Of

[351]

course I might of expected you to not stand by me! I might of expected you'd stick up for your own sex!"

"Yes. Poor Zilla, she's so unhappy. She takes it out on Paul. She hasn't a single thing to do, in that little flat. And she broods too much. And she used to be so pretty and gay, and she resents losing it. And you were just as nasty and mean as you could be. I'm not a bit proud of you—or of Paul, boasting about his horrid love-affairs!"

He was sulkily silent; he maintained his bad temper at a high level of outraged nobility all the four blocks home. At the door he left her, in self-approving haughtiness, and tramped the lawn.

With a shock it was revealed to him: "Gosh, I wonder if she was right—if she was partly right?" Overwork must have flayed him to abnormal sensitiveness; it was one of the few times in his life when he had queried his eternal excellence; and he perceived the summer night, smelled the wet grass. Then: "I don't care! I've pulled it off. We're going to have our spree. And for Paul, I'd do anything."

II

They were buying their Maine tackle at Ijams Brothers', the Sporting Goods Mart, with the help of Willis Ijams, fellow member of the Boosters' Club. Babbitt was completely mad. He trumpeted and danced. He muttered to Paul, "Say, this is pretty good, eh? To be buying the stuff, eh? And good old Willis Ijams himself coming down on the floor to wait on us! Say, if those fellows that are getting their kit for the North Lakes knew we were going clear up to Maine, they'd have a fit, eh? . . . Well, come on, Brother Ijams—Willis, I mean. Here's your chance! We're a couple of easy marks! Whee! Let me at it! I'm going to buy out the store!"

He gloated on fly-rods and gorgeous rubber hip-boots, on tents with celluloid windows and folding chairs and iceboxes. He simple-heartedly wanted to buy all of them. It was the Paul whom he was always vaguely protecting who kept him from his drunken desires.

But even Paul lightened when Willis Ijams, a salesman with poetry and diplomacy, discussed flies. "Now, of course, you boys know," he said, "the great scrap is between dry flies and wet flies. Personally, I'm for dry flies. More sporting."

"That's so. Lots more sporting," fulminated Babbitt, who knew very little about flies either wet or dry.

"Now if you'll take my advice, Georgie, you'll stock up well on these pale evening dims, and silver sedges, and red ants. Oh, boy, there's a fly, that red ant!"

"You bet! That's what it is—a fly!" rejoiced Babbitt.

"Yes, sir, that red ant," said Ijams, "is a real honest-to-God *fly!*"

"Oh, I guess ole Mr. Trout won't come a-hustling when I drop one of those red ants on the water!" asserted Babbitt, and his thick wrists made a rapturous motion of casting.

"Yes, and the landlocked salmon will take it, too," said Ijams, who had never seen a landlocked salmon.

"Salmon! Trout! Say, Paul, can you see Uncle George with his khaki pants on haulin' 'em in, some morning 'bout seven? Whee!"

III

They were on the New York express, incredibly bound for Maine, incredibly without their families. They were free, in a man's world, in the smoking-compartment of the Pullman.

Outside the car window was a glaze of darkness stippled with the gold of infrequent mysterious lights. Babbitt was immensely conscious, in the sway and authoritative clatter of the train, of going, of going on. Leaning toward Paul he grunted, "Gosh, pretty nice to be hiking, eh?"

The small room, with its walls of ocher-colored steel, was filled mostly with the sort of men he classified as the Best Fellows You'll Ever Meet—Real Good Mixers. There were four of them on the long seat; a fat man with a shrewd fat face, a knife-edged man in a green velour hat, a very young young man with an imitation amber cigarette-holder, and Babbitt. Facing them, on two movable leather chairs, were Paul and a lanky, old-fashioned man, very cunning, with wrinkles bracketing his mouth. They all read newspapers or trade journals, boot-and-shoe journals, crockery journals, and waited for the joys of conversation. It was the very young man, now making his first journey by Pullman, who began it.

"Say, gee, I had a wild old time in Zenith!" he gloried. "Say, if a fellow knows the ropes there he can have as wild a time as he can in New York!"

"Yuh, I bet you simply raised the old Ned. I figured you were a bad man when I saw you get on the train!" chuckled the fat one.

The others delightedly laid down their papers.

"Well, that's all right now! I guess I seen some things in the Arbor you never seen!" complained the boy.

"Oh, I'll bet you did! I bet you lapped up the malted milk like a reg'lar little devil!"

Then, the boy having served as introduction, they ignored him and charged into real talk. Only Paul, sitting by himself, reading at a serial story in a newspaper, failed to join them, and all but Babbitt regarded him as a snob, an eccentric, a person of no spirit.

Which of them said which has never been determined, and does not matter, since they all had the same ideas and expressed them always with the same ponderous and brassy assurance. If it was

not Babbitt who was delivering any given verdict, at least he was beaming on the chancellor who did deliver it.

"At that, though," announced the first, "they're selling quite some booze in Zenith. Guess they are everywhere. I don't know how you fellows feel about prohibition, but the way it strikes me is that it's a mighty beneficial thing for the poor zob that hasn't got any will-power but for fellows like us, it's an infringement of personal liberty."

"That's a fact. Congress has got no right to interfere with a fellow's personal liberty," contended the second.

A man came in from the car, but as all the seats were full he stood up while he smoked his cigarette. He was an Outsider; he was not one of the Old Families of the smoking-compartment. They looked upon him bleakly and, after trying to appear at ease by examining his chin in the mirror, he gave it up and went out in silence.

"Just been making a trip through the South. Business conditions not very good down there," said one of the council.

"Is that a fact! Not very good, eh?"

"No, didn't strike me they were up to normal."

"Not up to normal, eh?"

"No, I wouldn't hardly say they were."

The whole council nodded sagely and decided, "Yump, not hardly up to snuff."

"Well, business conditions ain't what they ought to be out West, neither, not by a long shot."

"That's a fact. And I guess the hotel business feels it. That's one good thing, though: These hotels that've been charging five bucks a day—yes, and maybe six-seven!—for a rotten room are going to be darn glad to get four, and maybe give you a little service."

"That's a fact. Say, uh, speaknubout hotels, I hit the St. Francis at San Francisco for the first time, the other day, and, say, it certainly is a first-class place."

SINCLAIR LEWIS

"You're right, brother! The St. Francis is a swell place—absolutely A1."

"That's a fact. I'm right with you. It's a first-class place."

"Yuh, but say, any of you fellows ever stay at the Rippleton, in Chicago? I don't want to knock—I believe in boosting wherever you can—but say, of all the rotten dumps that pass 'emselves off as first-class hotels, that's the worst. I'm going to *get* those guys, one of these days, and I told 'em so. You know how I am—well, maybe you don't know, but I'm accustomed to first-class accommodations, and I'm perfectly willing to pay a reasonable price. I got into Chicago late the other night, and the Rippleton's near the station—I'd never been there before, but I says to the taxi-driver—I always believe in taking a taxi when you get in late; may cost a little more money, but, gosh, it's worth it when you got to be up early next morning and out selling a lot of crabs—and I said to him, 'Oh, just drive me over to the Rippleton.'

"Well, we got there, and I breezed up to the desk and said to the clerk, 'Well, brother, got a nice room with bath for Cousin Bill?' Saaaay! You'd 'a' thought I'd sold him a second, or asked him to work on Yom Kippur! He hands me the cold-boiled stare and yaps, 'I dunno, friend, I'll see,' and he ducks behind the rigamajig they keep track of the rooms on. Well, I guess he called up the Credit Association and the American Security League to see if I was all right—he certainly took long enough—or maybe he just went to sleep; but finally he comes out and looks at me like it hurts him, and croaks, 'I think I can let you have a room with bath.' 'Well, that's awful nice of you—sorry to trouble you—how much 'll it set me back?' I says, real sweet. 'It'll cost you seven bucks a day, friend,' he says.

"Well, it was late, and anyway, it went down on my expense-account—gosh, if

I'd been paying it instead of the firm, I'd 'a' tramped the streets all night before I'd 'a' let any hick tavern stick me seven great big round dollars, believe me! So I lets it go at that. Well, the clerk wakes a nice young bell-hop—fine lad—not a day over seventy-nine years old—fought at the Battle of Gettysburg and doesn't know it's over yet—thought I was one of the Confederates, I guess, from the way he looked at me—and Rip van Winkle took me up to something—I found out afterwards they called it a room, but first I thought there'd been some mistake—I thought they were putting me in the Salvation Army collection-box! At seven *per* each and every *diem!* Gosh!"

"Yuh, I've heard the Rippleton was pretty cheesy. Now, when I go to Chicago I always stay at the Blackstone or the La Salle—first-class places."

"Say, any of you fellows ever stay at the Birchdale at Terre Haute? How is it?"

"Oh, the Birchdale is a first-class hotel."

(Twelve minutes of conference on the state of hotels in South Bend, Flint, Dayton, Tulsa, Wichita, Fort Worth, Winona, Erie, Fargo, and Moose Jaw.)

"Speaknubout prices," the man in the velour hat observed, fingering the elk-tooth on his heavy watch-chain, "I'd like to know where they get this stuff about clothes coming down. Now, you take this suit I got on." He pinched his trousers-leg. "Four years ago I paid forty-two fifty for it, and it was real sure-'nough value. Well, here the other day I went into a store back home and asked to see a suit, and the fellow yanks out some hand-me-downs that, honest, I wouldn't put on a hired man. Just out of curiosity I asks him, 'What you charging for that junk?' 'Junk,' he says, 'what d' you mean junk? That's a swell piece of goods, all wool—' Like hell! It was nice vegetable wool, right off the Ole Plantation! 'It's all wool,' he says, 'and we get sixty-seven ninety for it.' 'Oh, you do, do you!' I says. 'Not from me you don't,' I says, and I walks right out on him. You bet! I says to the wife, 'Well,' I said, 'as long as your strength holds out and you can go on putting a few more patches on papa's pants, we'll just pass up buying clothes.' "

"That's right, brother. And just look at collars, frinstance—"

"Hey! Wait!" the fat man protested. "What's the matter with collars? I'm selling collars! D' you realize the cost of labor on collars is still two hundred and seven per cent. above—"

They voted that if their old friend the fat man sold collars, then the price of collars was exactly what it should be; but all other clothing was tragically too expensive. They admired and loved one another now. They went profoundly into the science of business, and indicated that the purpose of manufacturing a plow or a brick was so that it might be sold. To them, the Romantic Hero was no longer the knight, the wandering poet, the cowpuncher, the aviator, nor the brave young district attorney, but the great sales-manager, who had an Analysis of Merchandising Problems on his glass-topped desk, whose title of nobility was "Go-getter," and who devoted himself and all his young samurai to the cosmic purpose of Selling—not of selling anything in particular, for or to anybody in particular, but pure Selling.

The shop-talk roused Paul Riesling. Though he was a player of violins and an interestingly unhappy husband, he was also a very able salesman of tar-roofing. He listened to the fat man's remarks on "the value of house-organs and bulletins as a method of jazzing-up the Boys out on the road"; and he himself offered one or two excellent thoughts on the use of two-cent stamps on circulars. Then he committed an offense against the holy law of the Clan of Good Fellows. He became highbrow.

They were entering a city. On the outskirts they passed a steel-mill which flared in scarlet and orange flame that licked at the cadaverous stacks, at the iron-sheathed walls and sullen converters.

"My Lord, look at that—beautiful!" said Paul.

"You bet it's beautiful, friend. That's the Shelling-Horton Steel Plant, and they tell me old John Shelling made a good three million bones out of munitions during the war!" the man with the velour hat said reverently.

"I didn't mean—I mean it's lovely the way the light pulls that picturesque yard, all littered with junk, right out of the darkness," said Paul.

They stared at him, while Babbitt crowed, "Paul there has certainly got one great little eye for picturesque places and quaint sights and all that stuff. 'D of been an author or something if he hadn't gone into the roofing line."

Paul looked annoyed. (Babbitt sometimes wondered if Paul appreciated his loyal boosting.) The man in the velour hat grunted, "Well, personally, I think Shelling-Horton keep their works awful dirty. Bum routing. But I don't suppose there's any law against calling 'em 'picturesque' if it gets you that way!"

Paul sulkily returned to his newspaper and the conversation logically moved on to trains.

"What time do we get into Pittsburg?" asked Babbitt.

"Pittsburg? I think we get in at—no, that was last year's schedule—wait a minute—let's see—got a time-table right here."

"I wonder if we're on time?"

"Yuh, sure, we must be just about on time."

"No, we aren't—we were seven minutes late, last station."

"Were we? Straight? Why, gosh, I thought we were right on time."

"No, we're about seven minutes late."

"Yuh, that's right; seven minutes late."

The porter entered—a negro in white jacket with brass buttons.

"How late are we, George?" growled the fat man.

" 'Deed, I don't know, sir. I think we're about on time," said the porter, folding towels and deftly tossing them up on the rack above the washbowls. The council stared at him gloomily and when he was gone they wailed:

"I don't know what's come over these niggers, nowadays. They never give you a civil answer."

"That's a fact. They're getting so they don't have a single bit of respect for you. The old-fashioned coon was a fine old cuss—he knew his place—but these young dinges don't want to be porters or cotton-pickers. Oh, no! They got to be lawyers and professors and Lord knows what all! I tell you, it's becoming a pretty serious problem. We ought to get together and show the black man, yes, and the yellow man, his place. Now, I haven't got one particle of race-prejudice. I'm the first to be glad when a nigger succeeds—so long as he stays where he belongs and doesn't try to usurp the rightful authority and business ability of the white man."

"That's the i.! And another thing we got to do," said the man with the velour hat (whose name was Koplinsky), "is to keep these damn foreigners out of the country. Thank the Lord, we're putting a limit on immigration. These Dagoes and Hunkies have got to learn that this is a white man's country, and they ain't wanted here. When we've assimilated the foreigners we got here now and learned 'em the principles of Americanism and turned 'em into regular folks, why then maybe we'll let in a few more."

"You bet. That's a fact," they observed, and passed on to lighter topics. They rapidly reviewed motor-car prices, tire-mileage, oil-stocks, fishing, and the prospects for the wheat-crop in Dakota.

But the fat man was impatient at this waste of time. He was a veteran traveler and free of illusions. Already he had asserted that he was "an old he-one." He leaned forward, gathered in their attention by his expression of sly humor, and grumbled, "Oh, hell, boys, let's cut out the formality and get down to the stories!"

They became very lively and intimate.

Paul and the boy vanished. The others slid forward on the long seat, unbuttoned their vests, thrust their feet up on the chairs, pulled the stately brass cuspidors nearer, and ran the green window-shade down on its little trolley, to shut them in from the uncomfortable strangeness of night. After each bark of laughter they cried, "Say, jever hear the one about—" Babbitt was expansive and virile. When the train stopped at an important station, the four men walked up and down the cement platform, under the vast smoky train-shed roof, like a stormy sky, under the elevated footways, beside crates of ducks and sides of beef, in the mystery of an unknown city. They strolled abreast, old friends and well content. At the long-drawn "Alllll aboarrrrrd"—like a mountain call at dusk—they hastened back into the smoking-compartment, and till two of the morning continued the droll tales, their eyes damp with cigar-smoke and laughter. When they parted they shook hands, and chuckled, "Well, sir, it's been a great session. Sorry to bust it up. Mighty glad to met you."

Babbitt lay awake in the close hot tomb of his Pullman berth, shaking with remembrance of the fat man's limerick about the lady who wished to be wild. He raised the shade; he lay with a puffy arm tucked between his head and the skimpy pillow, looking out on the sliding silhouettes of trees, and village lamps like exclamation-points. He was very happy.

THE LIFE AND WORKS OF
SINCLAIR LEWIS

By *MARK SCHORER*

SINCLAIR LEWIS was the first American to win the Nobel Prize for Literature. Nothing in his beginnings, either domestic or literary, suggests that this international honor would one day fall to him.

Lewis was born on February 7, 1885, in the bleak little Minnesota town of Sauk Centre. The town was then less than thirty years old, and its character was in many ways still that of the American frontier town. Lewis was the third son of a rather flinty, parsimonious country doctor who had come to Sauk Centre from Wisconsin only a few years before the boy's birth. He was named Harry Sinclair Lewis. His older brothers satisfied the father's conventional expectations but Harry never did. Badly coordinated, he was inept at boys' games and sports and at the hunting and fishing that his father and brothers enjoyed. He was homely, red haired (he was later known to his friends as "Red" Lewis), his face scarred by acne, and the girls he pursued only laughed at him. The town regarded him as an odd boy, and he was the butt of cruel jokes, lonely, and an outsider from the start. It was a miserable boyhood and early in his adolescence he determined that when the time came for his university education, he would seek it far from home.

He chose Yale College, and his father agreed, but before he could be admitted he had to spend six months in preparation at the Oberlin Academy in Ohio. That experience behind him, he thought that everything would be different, but at Yale, then an exclusive college chiefly for the sons of the rich, the ill-dressed and awkward midwestern country boy was more the friendless outsider than ever. Some of his professors recognized his intelligence and encouraged his literary ambitions. Soon writing became his refuge. In high school he had written sentimental verses; now he continued to write poetry and also began to write fiction. His early poems were mannered imitations of Tennyson and Kipling, and his prose was equally artificial. Still, many of these pieces were good enough to be accepted by the college literary magazines, and presently he was sure that he was going to be a writer.

Both to broaden his experience and to avoid summers in Sauk Centre, he spent two of his vacations working his way to England on cattleboats. During the one summer that he spent at home, he was so bored that he began to plan a novel built around the town. But he was not yet prepared to undertake such an ambitious project.

At the beginning of his fourth and final year at Yale he found life there so exasperating that he left suddenly to become a janitor at Helicon Hall, Upton Sinclair's experiment in communal living in New Jersey. After about a month there, he went to New York, determined to become a free-lance writer. Living in genuine poverty, without any help from his father, he managed to place a few of his pieces in obscure periodicals and for a time he found employment as a translator of French and German on a magazine called *Transatlantic Tales.* But at best it was a precarious existence and in the summer of 1907 he went to Panama to find work on the Canal, then under construction. Those efforts failing, he turned once more to his father for help, returned to New Haven, was readmitted to Yale, and was graduated in 1908, a year behind his class.

There followed about eight years of miscellaneous employment and adventure that took him all over the United States. He worked as a reporter-editorialist for a Waterloo, Iowa, newspaper; he was a case worker for a Manhattan philanthropic organization; then, after the sudden sale of a short story for seventy-five dollars, he went to the newly developing artists' colony at Carmel, California, where he met Jack London, to whom he sold story plots for prices ranging from five to fifteen dollars. At this time he also planned a novel about American labor, but he did not write it. For two months he was employed by the San Francisco *Bulletin,* and for two more in the San Francisco offices of the Associated Press. Then suddenly he left for the East again, this time Washington, D.C., where he worked on a periodical, *The Volta Review,* which was dedicated to teaching speech to the deaf. His chief publications now were in an absurd magazine of new thought called *Nautilus;* however, he was also beginning his first novel, *Our Mr.*

Wrenn, and, in the interests of his publishing career, he felt he should be in New York. To that end he found a job as a publisher's reader in the firm of Frederick A. Stokes Company.

From 1910 to 1915, New York editorial employment of one kind or another was the chief source of his income, with a miniscule supplement from his own literary efforts. For one month's salary he wrote a boys' adventure story called *Hike and the Aeroplane* for Stokes, which they published under the pseudonym "Tom Graham." When he finished his more serious novel, *Our Mr. Wrenn,* Stokes declined it, but it was finally accepted by Harper and Brothers and published in February of 1914. Two months later Lewis was married to Grace Livingstone Hegger, a staff member of *Vogue,* and they settled into a little house at Port Washington, Long Island. His first novel was moderately well received but it had small sales. Written in the manner of the H. G. Wells of *Kipps* and *Mr. Polly,* the story of the rebellion of a plain and humble clerk who relives Lewis's cattleboat experiences, it combined a fairly realistic treatment with a note of comic optimism, but hardly presaged a great satirist.

A second novel, *The Trail of the Hawk,* published in 1915, had much the same kind of reception. Although the subject of this book, the recently invented airplane, had the kind of topicality that was more and more to characterize Lewis's work, this novel did not free him from other employment and he continued to do his own writing before and after office hours at home and on commuting trains.

Then suddenly everything changed. The sale at high rates of a series of short stories to *The Saturday Evening Post* abruptly freed him to pursue only his own writing. He resigned his editorial position at the George A. Doran Company and set off with his wife on a tour of the United States that marked the continuation of what had already been and would always be a restless, wandering life. They went first to Florida, then north to Chicago and Sauk Centre. In Minnesota they bought a Ford touring car and drove west to Seattle, down to California, east to New Orleans, and back to New York where Lewis's first son, Wells, was born in 1917. In the winter of 1918 they lived in St. Paul, Minnesota, and in 1919, in Minneapolis. From 1919 to 1921 they established residence in Washington, D.C.

During all this moving about, Lewis wrote many short stories for the slick magazines of large circulation and also a number of books. The first book, *The Innocents* (1917), was in fact a magazine serial—and one of the very worst novels he ever perpetrated, a silly melodrama about old people. In the same year appeared *The Job,* the best of his early novels and probably the first American novel to concern itself with the career woman in competition with men in a commercial world. *Free Air* (1919) is a sentimentalized fictional account of the Lewis motor trip across the United States. While finishing *Free Air,* he was also working on *Main Street.* That novel, completed in Washington in 1920 and published in the autumn of that year, was the book he had first conceived during the summer college vacation he spent in Sauk Centre. With it, Lewis's long apprenticeship was abruptly finished, and finished to almost as much shocked abuse as ringing applause. He was suddenly famous and infamous.

It is not easy today to imagine the noisy literary commotion that *Main Street* caused back then, and we must remind ourselves that to readers who knew Lewis's earlier works, it seemed like a nearly savage break from them, and that to most of his new readers, it seemed

like a radical break from the picture of small-town life that American fiction had until then presented. Neither impression was quite accurate.

What Lewis had done in his sixth novel was to consolidate and intensify the preoccupations of his first five by applying them to an area of experience that had a more pressing reality for him than any of his previous scenes. In each of those earlier works one can detect the same essential pattern of a person struggling against some constrictive circumstances (of status or environment or routine), breaking into flight from them, succeeding in part but finally lapsing into compromise. And that is the story of Carol Kennicott. In each of those earlier novels, too, there had been a strain of satire, although less consistently present, yet satire directed at much the same shortcomings in American life, its conventionality, provincialism, narrowness of view, and materialistic motivation. The success of his earlier novels lay largely in the closely observed details of conduct and speech within that life, and of its physical realities. *Main Street* eliminated much of the sentimental optimism that had suffused the details of the earlier work and had diffused the satire, while the observed details were more massively assembled than before.

As for the traditional picture of American village life in fiction, it is true enough that the most popular view presented, for example, by the so-called Hoosier school, Meredith Nicholson, Booth Tarkington and others, was of innocence, goodness, sweetness, noble suffering, and fulfillment, as opposed to the cruelties and frustrations and brutalities of city life. But there was another tradition of village life as mean and raw and cruel in its own way, a tradition that includes the work of Edward Eggleston, E. W. Howe, Joseph Kirkland, Hamlin Garland, and the early Sherwood Anderson. It was upon this less popular tradition that Sinclair Lewis had drawn in *Main Street,* and which, with his own rather strident emphasis, he had brought to its climax. The picture of small-town America was changed once and for all, and for the first time literally thousands and thousands of Americans were made to face it.

Most readers sympathized with Carol Kennicott. Very few of them observed that she was in fact a rather foolish young woman, or, at any rate, that her notions about improving the quality of life in Gopher Prairie were silly and utterly incapable of realization. Few observed either that the author's final sympathies seemed to lie not with her but with her husband, "Doc" Kennicott, the good, commonsensical, hard-working, plodding village doctor who performed his duties faithfully and without complaint. The distinction is significant in the basic quality of Sinclair Lewis as a novelist. If his satire is directed at the worst qualities of the American middle class, his values are not in the impossibly romantic antitheses to them as represented by Carol but in the best qualities of that class as represented by Kennicott. This would always be the situation in his numerous novels.

But the satiric impulse in him was stronger than any impulse to assert positive values. So having drawn his picture of small-town meanness, he moved on to the area where middle-class grossness was even more apparent, the commercial world of the medium-sized midwestern city. With the publication of *Babbitt* in 1922, he became the undisputed master of American satire. With *Babbitt,* too, he consolidated what was to become his characteristic method of work. Instead of beginning with a character, situation, or a theme, he would start with a subject *area*—a profession, a special section of the middle class, or a special problem in

such a section. Then he would "research" it by himself, living in that area and mingling as intimately as possible with its representatives, keeping elaborate notebooks in which he listed characteristic names, habits of speech, details of the environment, and social conduct. Gradually, from the people he observed, he would draw up a list of characters, and for each important character he would write out a detailed biography. By now a general situation would have come into focus, and he would make maps of the settings he planned to use, detailed maps of houses and rooms and streets. Then he would write out a kind of scenario, and from that, a fuller "plan," and at last expand the "plan" into his first draft, after which there usually came a number of revisions, chiefly cutting. For *Babbitt,* he visited many American cities while this process went on, but if the city he called Zenith had any one near counterpart, it was apparently Cincinnati, Ohio, where he made the Queen City Club his *pied-à-terre.*

The appearance of *Babbitt* was an even greater sensation in the publishing world than *Main Street* had been, and again Lewis was both enthusiastically praised for the comic sharpness of his satire of American provinciality and roundly abused for his treachery to American enterprise and virtue. Various as its reception was, from the point of view of sales it was an enormous and unqualified success. Its title character not only brought a new word into the language but defined once and for all a familiar type which until then had been without a name. The small American businessman, formed by and confined within the clichés of a suffocating because exclusively commercial culture, was henceforth to be known as "a Babbitt."

Ever since the Civil War, American novelists had been concerned with the economic expansion of the United States and with the role of the businessman in that development. But generally speaking, the businessman who interested the novelists was the *big* man, not the little one. Some writers, like Howells and Tarkington after him, treated this figure sympathetically, as the embodiment of an admirable spirit of enterprise and independence. But more and more novelists, with Theodore Dreiser at the forefront, dealt with the tycoon, the ruthless titan, and the picture of the business community became characterized by brutal aggression and savage competition dominated by archindividualists powerful and corrupt to such a spectacular degree that they seemed to exist quite beyond the bounds of any merely ethical considerations.

After World War I, the powerful and autocratic individualist, the "robber barron" in the American economy, gradually gave way more and more to the even vaster but also anonymous corporate power, and the characteristic individual figure became the small businessman, even the middle man, the entrepreneur no longer productive himself but exploiting, in much smaller ways than his predecessor, the productiveness of others. *Babbitt* was the first novel to mark this historic change. If the new man was hardly moral, he was pompously moralistic and hypocritical in his own frequent lapses from morality. Lacking individuality himself and suspicious of individuality in others, he was, all of his talk of individual enterprise to the contrary, first of all a conformist. Without self-confidence, he found his security in the group. He was the great "joiner," the faceless man who had no identity apart from his "service" clubs, his lodges, or the Chamber of Commerce. For friendship he substituted fraternal orders; for human relations he substituted public relations. Innocent of ideas, his mind swarmed

with "projects." An enemy of art, he had endless respect for gadgets, for manufactured things, and money.

All this and a good deal more *Babbitt* gave back to a culture that was just discovering that it did not really like what it had become. And *Babbitt* did it with a difference. Whereas the older novels had a certain grandeur and sweep, often enough melodramatic to be sure, *Babbitt* was raucously satirical, poking fun at a throng of oafs and buffoons who, if they were malicious and mean and even on occasion frightening, were also absurd. And yet, along with all that, George Babbitt himself was pathetic.

The pathos lay in the by now familiar Lewis narrative pattern of a person trapped in a self-defeating environment, having some sense of more desirable conditions beyond it, striving to grasp them, succeeding or failing. Because Babbitt himself failed, or nearly did, the comic-satiric element here was both heightened and broadened over that of the earlier novels, and this fact, together with the novel's much heavier social documentation, tended to conceal the essential pathos. Most contemporary readers saw in *Babbitt* only H. L. Mencken's pessimism (the novel was enthusiastically praised by him), American middle-class life as a dehumanized jungle.

But Lewis meant to suggest at least some hope in characters such as Paul Riesling and Seneca Doane, the one with a rudimentary but nevertheless real sensitivity to beauty, the other with the dissenter's belief in the possibility of justice. There was even hope in George Babbitt's own bumbling capacity and need for friendship, his awareness that the beauties of external nature could enrich the lives of others if not his own, his awkward attempt to find some fuller emotional life than his domestic situation permitted, and his dim sense in his period of rebellion that conformity was death.

In short, Lewis's *Babbit* tried to suggest, through its very picture of a gross, even a debased middle class, the means whereby the middle class could move beyond the lash of his own satire.

Seneca Doane was a radical labor lawyer, and in creating that character, Lewis's old interest in writing a novel about the labor movement in the United States was renewed. After an extended journey in Europe, he returned to the Middle West with the idea of beginning his researches for that novel. He was deflected from this project (as he would be again and again) by an almost accidental meeting in Chicago with Paul de Kruif, a young medical research scientist recently associated with the Rockefeller Institute in New York. De Kruif persuaded Lewis that a great subject for fiction lay in the corruptions of the medical profession, and now Lewis extended his "research" methods by actually employing de Kruif as his assistant. Lewis's own family background in the practice of backwoods medicine was adequate for his account of the early stages of Martin Arrowsmith's career, but for his participation in the more sophisticated world of medical research, de Kruif's experience was essential. Together they traveled in the Caribbean, where much of the action of *Arrowsmith* (1925) was to take place, and then moved on to London, where, with his assistant at his elbow, Lewis finished the work.

Arrowsmith differs from Lewis's earlier novels in that here we find not one or two but many idealists—Gottlieb, Sondelius, Terry Wickett, Arrowsmith himself, and others, the dedicated truth seekers and pure scientists who will not compromise with commercial standards or yield to institutional pressures. There is also an admirable heroine, Leora, Martin's wife. Even though Leora dies and the "good" scientists finally have to detach themselves entirely from institutions, it is their values that dominate the novel, and the old objects of satire—provincialism, hypocrisy, complacency, the commercial spirit, the anonymity of organizational activity—are more than balanced by Lewis's explicit idealistic avowals. Not surprisingly, this book was awarded the Pulitzer Prize. It was not surprising, either, that Sinclair Lewis, whose public conduct over the years had become considerably eccentric and who was disgruntled that *Babbit* had not won that prize, declined the award in an explosion of publicity much greater than any he would have received had he accepted it. With this gesture and his next two novels Lewis quickly dispelled the new reputation *Arrowsmith* had briefly won him as a novelist who knew how fine America was at heart.

The first of these next books was a piece of inexplicable hack work called *Mantrap* (1926). It was an absurd melodrama set in the Canadian wilderness, taking off, perhaps, from Babbitt's frustrated vacation in the Maine woods or Arrowsmith's final retreat to a Vermont camp, but made possible by a fiasco of an actual excursion into the wilds of Saskatchewan arranged for Lewis by his older brother, a true outdoorsman as Lewis certainly was not. The second, *Elmer Gantry* (1927), was the most scandalous of all Lewis's novels, the cause of the greatest uproar, and the most unqualified assault on American pieties, in this instance as embodied in the excesses and hypocrisies of religious practice.

For this novel Lewis returned to his familiar methods of "research": he set himself up for an extended stay in Kansas City, found a cooperative clerical assistant, read hundreds of books and pamphlets on his subject, met weekly with a group of clergymen for discussion and debate, attended all possible religious services, and himself took the pulpit in a number of churches, once to give God fifteen minutes to strike him down if He existed. From all this emerged the chronicle of Elmer Gantry.

Like *Babbitt,* it is loosely organized, breaking into three large parts, each almost independent of the others except for the constant presence of the hero. In each part, Elmer's progress is colored and in two of them threatened by his relation with a woman, but from each he emerges triumphant. The first part takes us through his humble backwoods beginnings, his Baptist education, his ordination, his first pulpit, and his escape, through a double-cross, from Lulu; the second takes us through his career as an evangelist with the extraordinary Sharon Falconer and ends with her death by fire; the third takes us through his experience of New Thought and his rise in Methodism, together with the decline of his marriage to Cleo and his escape from Hettie, who threatens to bring him to public ruin but who is herself routed as, in the final sentence, Elmer promises that "We shall yet make these United States a moral nation"—while studying a new choir singer's ankle.

Such a bare outline of the novel may suggest either a farce or a melodramatic cartoon, but the fact is that the revulsion of feeling at its root keeps it from being the first and the extraordinarily substantial body of detail from the second. While the novel's criticism is directed at a smaller area of American life than that of *Babbitt,* it is conceivable that it slashes deeper as certainly it slashes harder. While a few good, honest clergymen of sincere religious conviction lurk on the fringes of the plot, these are defeated characters who are allowed no real part in the action. The central action involves an amazingly full account of every form of religious decay in American life, an account in which nothing is missing ex-

cept religion and humanity. Undilutedly brutish, it creates a cloacal world.

That it should have been denounced from nearly every pulpit in the United States and from many another quarter came as no surprise to Sinclair Lewis; that such denunciations only increased its vast sales was no surprise either. I can think of no other American novel which has caused its author to be invited to his own lynching; and certainly it was the only novel to bring the announcement from H. L. Mencken, to whom the book was dedicated, that here was another Voltaire!

In the summer of 1926, when Lewis wrote most of *Elmer Gantry,* his father died, and when he returned to Washington, where his wife had once more set up their residence, he found that he could no longer endure his marriage. Once the novel was finished he fled to Europe. Searching for new subject matter, he found it when he met Dorothy Thompson, the best-known American newspaperwoman in Europe, who presently became his second wife. After meeting her he went to work at once on *Dodsworth* (1929). While Samuel Dodsworth, the hero, is a millionaire automobile manufacturer and not a best-selling novelist, the story is *au fond* an account of the deterioration of Lewis's first marriage and his courtship of the woman who would become his second.

He interrupted the writing of *Dodsworth* to expand a short story he had recently published in *The American Mercury* into a novel—*The Man Who Knew Coolidge* (1928). This series of monologues by a mindless, sub-Babbitt type named Lowell Schmaltz added little to Lewis's stature as a novelist but it is the climactic example, probably going even beyond *Babbitt,* of his remarkable gift for imitating the cliché-ridden, middle-class American dialogue, with all its clotted argot.

After his marriage in London in 1928, he returned to the United States and finished *Dodsworth*. On its publication readers were once more assured that Sinclair Lewis was a good American. The terms of this novel are much the same as always, and, except for *Elmer Gantry*, the pattern is the same—the man who glimpses a richer life beyond the stifling routines he knows and who, now, for the first time, can realize it. But here the terms of his satire have been drastically reversed. Whereas in earlier novels he satirized the provincial midwest citizenry and approved of the rebels in their midst, he now satirizes the rather poor critic of Babbittry that he presents in Fran Dodsworth, while giving full sympathy to Sam, a somewhat more dignified representation of the midwestern citizenry than those he had earlier presented. Attacking pretentious "Europeanized" snobberies, he praises American self-reliance, candor, and self-respecting modesty. More than that, beginning with a faceless American businessman, he lets him discover a way of life in which he can live as a man with a face. There was no cause at all for controversy.

This novel marked a greater change than any other in the career of Sinclair Lewis. The 1920s had come to an end and America was abruptly plunged into the Great Depression. A revolution had overtaken American life in manners and morals and nearly all intellectual assumptions, and Lewis's four important iconoclastic novels no doubt played a major literary part in that transformation. But with the beginning of the 1930s, that kind of iconoclasm had come to an end, and writers now confronted two extremes: on one hand, the somewhat jaded aristocratic attitude implied by novels like those of F. Scott Fitzgerald and reinforced by the school of criticism known as the New Humanism (although these two had, to be sure, little else in common), and on the other hand, the revolutionary "working-class" attitude exemplified by any number of radical and "proletarian" writers. In *Dodsworth*, Sinclair Lewis refused both these extremes: he chose instead the view of the middle class, the Middle West, and the middlebrow; to those values he remained faithful, and, whatever commercial success he continued to have, he henceforth seemed among the most old-fashioned of American novelists.

Dodsworth appeared just before that alteration in the climate occurred, but it was the Lewis of *Babbitt* rather than the Lewis of *Dodsworth* that led the Swedish Academy, at the end of 1930, to award him with the Nobel Prize for Literature. News of that award came to him shortly after the birth of his second son, Michael, and it came as a great surprise. For while it had been rumored in American publishing circles for some time that this year's award would go to an American and that the two possibilities were Lewis and Theodore Dreiser, Lewis's publishers and friends tried to keep this rumor from him lest he think up some characteristically outlandish response. Instead, he accepted the award quietly. It was clear to him, however, when reporters asked him how he could accept this Prize after he had turned down the Pulitzer, that his motives were suspect and that many writers and critics did not think that he deserved the Nobel. And it is true enough that, in the words of Ludwig Lewissohn, "Something very like a groan went up."

On the afternoon of December 12, 1930, he delivered a lecture in Stockholm, in which he attempted to answer his critics, and the whole speech was aimed at those forces of conservative gentility in American culture that tried to restrain any bold impulse of honesty in our literature. Lewis's attack was a bit late. Whatever the preferences of "official" custodians of American culture might be, Lewis's own fantastically successful books in the past decade seemed to demonstrate that American readers in general were eager for such stronger fare. Yet his account of the status of the artist in America had much to commend it, and his argument that our material culture had far outstripped our intellectual culture was axiomatic. Naming our major writers in the United States, with Anderson and Dreiser at their head, and some of the best younger writers who were just emerging to European audiences, he called attention to the fact that America had indeed come of age. If his reception of the Nobel Prize was an historic event, its import did not lie merely in its elevation of American literature to a par with other world literature, but also in its acknowledgment that America was a world power, a fact that Europe had been reluctant to concede. Sinclair Lewis may have been a lesser writer than he thought, but he was a larger symbol, and on December 13th the *New York Times* quite accurately reported, "Sinclair Lewis became the hero of all Stockholm today."

The Nobel Prize came at precisely the right moment, because after that everything was downhill. The descent began in London early in 1931 when, in a fit of pique that climaxed long brooding, Lewis broke with Harcourt, Brace & Company, the publishers who had seen him through his long decade of triumph. There were to be other publishers and other commercial triumphs, but never again a really serious literary achievement. He was forty-six years old now and the author of twelve novels. There were to be twenty more years and ten more novels. The allurements of alcohol, which, for some time, had been a problem for him, became increasingly acute as those twenty years wore away. His second marriage soon came to its frazzled end, even more rapidly than his first. His first

son was killed in World War II. His second son became an actor, relatively successful in that world that would presently enchant the father but in which Lewis was never really able to make his mark.

Lewis became an increasingly restless man, moving from one establishment to another, from one city to another, briefly occupying great houses which, after a few months or a year or two at most, he would sell at great loss, to drift on again in the hope of finding a more congenial place. In those fine establishments he had moved far from his humble origins, yet there was always something hotel-like and impersonal, even in his most lavish houses, suggesting that the bleakness of Sauk Centre clung to and lived on in him. With his international reputation, he had removed himself far from the taunts and jibes that had plagued his youth, and yet he felt himself still the victim of taunts and jibes, never really taken seriously as an artist by other artists. In a kind of menopausal frenzy he sought out the comforts of women younger than he. During the period when without success he tried to write for the theater and himself took to acting, he sought the company of young actresses. Finally, at the end of the 1930s and for a while during the 1940s, he did find a young woman who was willing to try to comfort him. But he was really beyond consolation, and when she abandoned him to marry a man more nearly her own age, Lewis took to restless wanderings in Europe. It was in Rome where finally, in January of 1951, he was to die alone, among strangers. And yet, through all those maddening years of decline in powers and reputation, he continued, with nearly mechanical compulsiveness, to produce novels. Most of them, it need hardly be said, deserve scant attention.

The first of these was *Ann Vickers* (1933), the story of an American career woman that spans the whole period of American social history from before World War I into the Great Depression. Drawing on his own experiences in New York earlier in the century but more especially on the life of his second wife, the novel is chiefly interesting in that it reveals his ambiguous feelings about his new marriage, especially his first resentments aroused by her busy and involved life as a woman with a career quite independent of his own. The next novel, *Work of Art* (1934), a stolidly solemn story about the hotel industry, indicates nothing about the decline of that marriage. But his next, *It Can't Happen Here* (1935), would not have been written at all if he had not been intimately exposed to his wife's intense interest in international affairs, a subject whose discussion he continually complained, would drive him out of his wits. Instead, it seems to have driven him into conceiving this novel which took as its subject the rise of a Fascist dictatorship in the United States.

At least one of Lewis's novels after *It Can't Happen Here* had greater sales, but no other was to cause such excitement. The horror of Fascism in Europe and the threat of its local imitations were enough to persuade many readers that Lewis had written a bold and impressively prophetic work. Yet to have seen the novel as committing Sinclair Lewis to what was then called the Popular Front, the collaborative effort of all liberal and radical parties against Fascism, was an error; for Sinclair Lewis, while a liberal of sorts, was certainly not a political radical. Almost as if to make the fact quite clear he published *The Prodigal Parents* (1938), another story of Middle America, in which Fred and Hazel Cornplow reject their foolishly radical and irresponsible children, and in which Cornplow, the "good" American, a stodgy bundle of re-

ceived opinions, the perfect middle class stereotype, is approved.

With the United States about to plunge into World War II, Sinclair Lewis retreated into the absorbing life of the theater, and he turned, not surprisingly, to frivolous subject matter. *Bethel Merriday* (1940), less embarrassing than its predecessor but hardly more impressive, is the story of a young actress and her education in summer stock and touring theatrical companies. Next, with his aberrant stage career behind him, he seemed to promise something of a return to the old Lewis in *Gideon Planish* (1943), a satiric attack on organized philanthropy and the activities of liberal "do-gooders"; but the satire deteriorates very quickly into simplistic and essentially anti-intellectual farce. It is almost a relief to turn to the next, less ambitious novel, *Cass Timberlane* (1945), a half-splenetic, half-sentimental account of American marriages.

He made his last really serious effort in *Kingsblood Royal* (1947), where he addressed himself to the problem of the black minority in the United States. The book aroused some excitement as a social document but none as a literary performance; even its social usefulness, it is now all too clear, is minimized by Lewis's mechanical oversimplification of what is perhaps the most complex as well as the most pressing problem in our national life. After this attempt to deal with the immediate present, Lewis retreated into the historical past of Minnesota. *The God-Seeker* (1949) is the first part of what was projected as a trilogy about labor, Lewis's final hope to realize that old ambition. But the ambition was not fulfilled, and his last novel, *World So Wide*, published posthumously in 1951, was a thin attempt to write another, later *Dodsworth* (and indeed, Samuel Dodsworth reappeared in this novel as a resident of Florence). It is the final self-parody.

Just as he had gone through a long and undistinguished apprenticeship before his phenomenal ten-year triumph with its succession of five smashing titles, so Lewis now suffered a long and dispirited decline. This beginning and this end do not make easy the problem of delivering any final literary judgment on Sinclair Lewis. But a few conclusions can be safely asserted.

All his novels, good and bad, were directed toward one discovery, the "reality" of America. This aim was his inheritance as a writer formed before World War I—a time when the discovery of the "real" America, an America beyond chauvinistic nonsense and merely sentimental optimism, became the aim of nearly every writer who took himself seriously. It was an era that trusted in the democratic promise of American life. For Sinclair Lewis, to the very end, America was always promises.

Promises of what? Promises of a society that would not only have tolerated but also *treasured* him. That was the personal basis. Generalized, it became an idealization of an older America, the America of the mid-nineteenth century, a vast and formless America overflowing with the potentialities of a wide, casually human freedom, the individual life lived in honest and perhaps eccentric effort (all the better for that), and the social life lived in a spirit that tolerates first of all difference and variety. It was the ideal America of Thoreau, of Whitman, of the early Mark Twain, of the cracker barrel in the village store, and of the village atheist on a wooden sidewalk. Like Thoreau, Whitman, and Twain, Lewis could see the disparity between the idealization and the actuality. When Lewis claimed Thoreau as the major influence on his work, it could only have been this

basic element, Thoreau's ideal of individual freedom, that he had in mind.

The source of Lewis's satire lies in the American defection from the potential for individual freedom. When he lacerated America, it was because Americans would not be free, and he attacked all the sources by which they bound themselves: the economic system and materialism, intellectual rigidity, theological dogma, legal repression, class convention, social timidity, hypocrisy, affectation, complacency.

These two, the individual impulse to freedom and the social impulse to restrict it, provide the bases of his plots in novel after novel. Even when he used Europe as his counter, the conflict was not so much between America and Europe as between the true America (that is, individual Americans true to themselves) and the false America (that is, Americans who submit to values not their own or to values less expansive than their own should be). The result in his novels is often an apparent praise of provincialism, even of philistinism, but in its impulse the praise is of something much larger.

If he had no influence on younger writers, that was because he spoke for an older American experience than theirs. Yet he was probably the major figure in what is called the "liberation" of American literature.

He created a gallery of characters who have independent life outside the novels, characters that live now in the American tradition itself. One or two of them have become nearly mythological figures that embody the major traits of their class. His novels, as a result, are perhaps the last important American novels that are primarily concerned with social class. If they often depended too exclusively on the report of social minutiae and the recording of the American lingo and too often failed to realize that material imaginatively, they nevertheless reproduced a scene of grotesque vulgarity that no other novelist has ever captured.

He performed a function that has nearly gone out of American fiction, and American fiction is thinner for the loss. He could tell Americans little or nothing about their subjective lives, he had no sense of the tragic dimension in human experience, he could not feel or give expression to sensuous ecstasy or lyric emotion. But he could give Americans their first shuddering glimpse into a kind of frightening reality of which perhaps even he himself was not aware. He made thousands of commonplace Americans cognizant of the horrors of the commonplace, and thus, finally, fulfilled the ultimate, supreme artistic function: he helped Americans into the imagination of themselves.

Mark Schorer, professor of literature at the University of California at Berkley, is one of America's most distinguished literary critics and author of numerous books and articles on Sinclair Lewis.

THE 1930 PRIZE

By GUNNAR AHLSTRÖM

By 1930, it was the turn of the United States to be honored by a Nobel Prize for Literature. The event marks a turning point not only in the annals of the Nobel Committee but also in the evolution of European attitudes toward North American writers. Through this award they became respectable on the conventional level of the literary academies. It had taken years to reach this point. Surely it is to the honor of the nation charged with selecting the winners of the Prize that it was not tardy in showing its admiration for the literature of the New World and in selecting as the object of its tribute the American novelist Sinclair Lewis.

For many years the United States had seemed to Europeans as a land of adventure, the goal of emigrants and gold prospectors, or as the chosen land of voluble business types and the gold-toothed parvenus of Wall Street. The Statue of Liberty, Edison's phonograph, Henry Ford's automobiles, and the film comedies of Mack Sennett—these were the best-known representatives of what was thought to be a civilization untouched by true culture. From the literary point of view, there was little to detain the traveler. An occasional Longfellow or Emerson at best offered some pallid literary virtues which, however, were already things of the past.

Fenimore Cooper, with his *The Last Mohican* or Mark Twain with his *Huckleberry Finn* were classified as writers of "juvenile books." The new names that began to be heard shortly before the Great War had not yet been approved for mention in sophisticated salons. Jack London and Upton Sinclair found their audience among the working classes. To the academicians they seemed pretty rough hewn and not quite within the confines of proper literature, and the Socialist ideas which they expounded in their books reinforced the impression of robust naiveté which they made upon their European critics.

Then America entered the war, and through Woodrow Wilson its voice became heard in the deliberations of the Old World. The resulting curiosity was quite natural, and people began to wonder what the Star Spangled Banner might have concealed in its folds. People began to suspect powerful forces behind the deceptive image which had prevailed until then. During the years which followed the Treaty of Versailles, the impulses reaching Europe from overseas became progressively stronger, and American literature, as a reflection of how people lived in the land of skyscrapers, obviously began to take on a certain importance.

To its great relief, Europe was able to

see that the new emissaries from beyond the Atlantic were far from being one with that vulgarity which was traditionally ascribed to American civilization. They were the first to attack the blustering and phony pretensions of their countrymen. An H. L. Mencken, a Theodore Dreiser, a Sinclair Lewis apparently made common cause with their counterparts in Europe. They unmasked, they ridiculed, they stoned their targets, and their denunciations, their refusal to be snared were in keeping with the antipathies felt by intellectuals in Paris and in London. Thus their works awakened great interest in Europe, making their force felt even in circles which otherwise would have been quite impervious to any form of Americanism. The reticences which their more or less outspoken radicalism might inspire were outweighed by the sympathy awakened by their critical attitude, which was welcomed by the Europeans.

America became a fad, and the name of the United States was heard regularly each year in the discussions of the Nobel Committee. In 1930, press forecasts were leaning in that direction from the very beginning. It was of course well known that the favored French candidate was Paul Valéry, but the Prize had gone to Henri Bergson in 1927, too recently to make it likely that a French writer could again be chosen. Maxim Gorki of Russia was a strong candidate, but it was hard to imagine the Swedish Academy crowning one of the USSR's party stalwarts. Dreiser's own outspoken enthusiasm for the Soviets did his cause harm, and the reading of his massive novels was not likely to excite the Academicians to any great degree.

The case of Sinclair Lewis was quite different. Several influential members of the Swedish Academy had already noted his production, and their comments, both oral and in the press, had given a certain prestige to his name. *Main Street, Babbitt, Arrowsmith* had all been best sellers in Sweden. Lewis's candidacy was ripe, and when *Dodsworth* proved successful in 1929, the moment seemed to have come. Within the Swedish Academy the first shot in the Lewis campaign was fired by Heinrik Schück, the perspicacious promoter of several fine choices in the past. He hailed the book as a new masterpiece, and on November 5, the nomination of Lewis rallied majority support. The result, which was generally expected, was greeted with satisfaction throughout the world.

Equally satisfying to the Swedish was the news that Sinclair Lewis was planning to travel to Stockholm in person to receive his award. The weight of years—the usual excuse for not showing up for the awards—was not applicable in Lewis's case. Only forty-five at the time, he succeeded Rudyard Kipling as the youngest literature laureate. His entry into the arena also satisfied the widespread desire to see a relaxed Yankee, one who would not mince words and an easy subject to interview. Personally, the distinguished guest had certain traits in common with his hosts. He had been born in Minnesota, which since the nineteenth century had been heavily populated by Swedish immigrants. There are several Swedish characters in his novels, chief among them the admirable Sondelius in *Arrowsmith*. During the Atlantic crossing Lewis and his wife, the journalist Dorothy Thompson, had prepared for the event by studying Swedish "in ten easy lessons," using a grammar keyed to a set of phonograph records.

"Where is the doctor? A whisky for everybody!" These were Lewis's welcoming words when, shortly before dawn, he received the newsmen who had come aboard off the coast of Sweden. "My idea of a Nobel laureate is a pontificating, solemn fellow—not a guy like me. This is the first time they have given the prize to a reporter. I'm a reporter, my whole life has been a job of reporting. When the King offers me the Prize, I feel I ought to say, 'Your Majesty, are you sure you don't have the wrong guy?'"

Mark Twain wrote a burlesque fantasy describing the adventures of a Yankee at King Arthur's court. Lewis's visit did not lend itself in any way to this kind of situation comedy. The laureate played his role to the end with a sovereign ease, his russet face blazing with a charming spontaneity and simplicity. He sat through the long ceremony with dignity and listened attentively to the fine speech delivered in a foreign tongue by Erik Axel Karlfeldt, the eminent permanent secretary of the Swedish Academy (who, incidentally, was taking part in his last public ceremony before his death a year later).

Mr. Lewis bowed to the King in the European manner and later, at the traditional banquet, he expressed his gratitude in a short address which was very well received. The following day at the traditional dinner offered in the laureates' honor by the King at the Royal Palace, Lewis explained to Prince Charles, the King's brother, in fine Swedish that "the sparrow is a small bird with a stiff tail which hops about and eats worms." This was one of the sentences from the manual for learning Swedish in ten easy lessons. The Prince continued the conversation in English.

The outstanding event of Lewis's stay in Stockholm was his lecture, delivered in the ancient hall of the Swedish Academy. The title of his lecture was "The American Fear of Literature." His listeners were struck by the simplicity and freedom of his presentation. Recalling his personal experience, especially the way in which *Elmer Gantry* had been received, he painted a rather frightening picture of the working conditions met with by a liberal writer in a narrow-minded cultural environment infested with carica-

tures of university professors. American officials, he explained, feared all literature which did not flatter them and which did not describe their superiority. In contrast to the eloquent examples which he marshaled to illustrate this fact, he presented another image, the image of a country undergoing a literary renewal and producing works in protest against mediocrity. Generously he sketched profiles of several colleagues who were deserving of the Nobel Prize—Upton Sinclair, Theodore Dreiser, Eugene O'Neill, Sherwood Anderson. In the same spirit he cited the authors of the younger generation—Thomas Wolfe, Thornton Wilder, Ernest Hemingway. All of this constituted a splendid demonstration of freedom of thought, of breadth of spirit, of perspicacity; it takes on a prophetic aspect when one thinks of the role which American literature was eventually to play in world culture and in the future deliberations of the Nobel judges.

How did all this strike George Babbitt and his fellow Americans? The news that Lewis had been chosen for the award called forth a storm of bitter protest. In New York people complained that Sweden had chosen a rather unsavory critic of his native land. Lewis's address at Stockholm inspired an outpouring of severe reprimands, based largely on recommendations in favor of washing one's dirty linen at home rather than in a foreign capital.

The hullaballoo inspired a slender volume entitled *Why Sinclair Lewis Won the Nobel Prize,* which reprinted the famous Stockholm speech together with a translation of Karlfeldt's address. Lewis issued one correction to Karlfeldt's text. The Swedish academician had written a brief sketch of Sauk Centre (Gopher Prairie in *Main Street*), where Lewis had been born. He wrote that the summer heat and the absence of sewers caused the town to smell. "Here Dr. Karlfeldt is quite wrong," Lewis wrote. "Although in my day the small towns in the Middle West had neither sewers nor garbage collection services, each family could dispose of its own rubbish. In spite of the summer heat, the prevailing smell was the fragrance of wild roses and the wheatfields covering thousands of acres—that indescribable smell of intensely cultivated regions."

On this pastoral note Sinclair Lewis took leave of his Nobel experience.

Translated by Dale McAdoo.

NOBEL PRIZE
LIBRARY

*is published by Grolier Enterprises with
text printed on 55-pound Lockhaven paper
specifically prepared for this edition by the
Hammermill Paper Company. Printed and
bound by R.R. Donnelley and Sons. End-
leaf design is reproduced from an original
marbled pattern created for this edition by
Faith Harrison. Cover stampings and
design by Daniel B. Bianchi and Selma
Ordewer.*